THE GENERAL
PROPERTIES OF MATTER

Ian B. White,
13, Lammerton Terrace,
Dundee.

Feb. 1952.

THE GENERAL PROPERTIES OF MATTER

BY

F. H. NEWMAN

D.Sc. (Lond.), A.R.C.S., F.Inst.P.

PROFESSOR OF PHYSICS IN THE UNIVERSITY COLLEGE OF THE
SOUTH-WEST OF ENGLAND, EXETER

AND

V. H. L. SEARLE

M.Sc. (Lond.)

LECTURER IN PHYSICS, UNIVERSITY COLLEGE OF THE
SOUTH-WEST OF ENGLAND, EXETER

FOURTH EDITION

LONDON
EDWARD ARNOLD & CO.

Printed in Great Britain by
Butler & Tanner Ltd., Frome and London

PREFACE TO THE FOURTH EDITION

An understanding of the quantitative principles of physical science is required not only by the physicist, but also by students of engineering and chemistry. Very frequently no attempt is made in books to correlate one scientific subject with another, and even when such correlation is attempted it is done, very often, too briefly and in a manner which does not encourage the reader to study more closely the related subjects.

This book, which was first published in 1929, is intended primarily for the physicist. It embodies the results of much practical experience in the teaching of physics, and presents a fairly complete survey of the fundamental properties of matter, with the special aim of developing those branches of the subject, such as surface tension, osmosis, and viscosity which verge towards chemistry, and hydrodynamics and vibrations which are of importance and interest more particularly to the mathematician and engineer. By this development, and throughout the book, the aim has been to emphasise the essential unity of scientific knowledge.

The necessary mathematics are explained, step by step, and there are no gaps in the reasoning for expert readers to fill and the less experienced to neglect; but the assumption has been made that students who use the book will be equipped with a sufficient mastery of the fundamental processes of the calculus to make its methods familiar and its advantages appreciated. Although it is suggested that some parts may be omitted by the less advanced students, no indication of such possible omissions has been made. They will depend upon individual ability, requirements, and initial equipment.

Modern theories of surface tension and lubrication, depending, as they do, on the orientation of surface molecules, have received liberal consideration. The study of the molecular structure and the kinetics of surfaces has advanced with great rapidity through the pioneer work of Rayleigh, Hardy, and Langmuir, whose researches indicate how widely molecular orientation enters into natural phenomena.

Elasticity and gravitation—the former of fundamental importance to engineers—have been treated as fully as possible, with special emphasis on experimental investigations, while the Eötvös gravity balance and the gyro-compass are described at some length. The provision of numerical examples, with answers, adds to the usefulness of the book as an aid to students reading for Degrees.

One of the minor consequences of the war was the destruction by enemy action of the blocks, diagrams, and remaining stock of

v

the third edition of this book in 1940. The stringency of material and labour prevented the immediate replacement, but owing to the co-operation of Messrs. Arnold & Co. it has been possible to produce a fourth and entirely revised edition of the book. The most important new matter is a chapter on the production and measurement of low pressures. Every chapter has been revised and brought up to date, and, in addition to the provision of new material, some portions of the book have been re-arranged. In place of the bibliographies previously appended to each chapter, additional footnote references have been given as these, by their direct indication of the subject-matter, have proved more useful.

F. H. N.
V. H. L. S.

1946.

CONTENTS

CHAPTER XIII

CHAPTER XIV

CHAPTER XV

LIST OF TABLES

xi

THE GENERAL PROPERTIES OF MATTER

CHAPTER I

GENERAL PRINCIPLES

1. Weight and Mass.—The mass of a body, usually described as the quantity of matter in it, is one of the fundamental entities which are more easily understood than adequately defined. To call it a particular aggregation of substance is no more than a restatement of the previous definition in parallel terms, but from this description the constancy of the mass of a body can be recognised more easily, since one of the basic hypotheses of science is the indestructibility of substance. The definition, however, is not of great practical importance, as we are more concerned with the effects of mass than with its exact formulation. The most important of these effects, or qualities, is that of *weight*, and this is attributable to the attraction which the earth exercises on bodies near its surface. Since this weight is due to the earth's existence, as well as that of the body, it must be fundamentally different from the mass, which is evidently a property peculiar to the body itself, and is independent of any neighbouring bodies. The difference between weight and mass is illustrated in another way by the consideration that, while the effect of the former is to cause the body to move, the mass of the body gives it the characteristic quality of inertia, or reluctance to movement. At the same time common experience shows that there is some essential connection between weight and mass, since, with bodies of the same material, the effort necessary to move them against the earth's attraction is greatest in the case of the largest body, while exact experiment shows that this connection is one of direct proportionality.

To prove this it is necessary to show that all bodies, moving under the sole action of their weights, have a common acceleration at the same place. Experimental evidence of this fact was first obtained by Galileo in 1590 by simultaneously releasing two bodies of different masses from the top of the leaning tower at Pisa. They reached the ground together, thus showing, at least approximately, equal accelerations. Cases of apparent disagreement, such as the slow fall of fine rain, the ascent of a balloon, the almost imperceptible vertical drift of thistledown, can be explained by the forces opposing downward motion which reduce, or even reverse, the downward acceleration. As these counter-forces are continually reduced, the downward acceleration increases to that constant value denoted by g.

A more exact confirmation of the proportionality of mass and

weight is given by pendulum experiments, in which the acceleration
of free fall is measured. If two pendulums of different masses are
used, then different values for g should be deduced from their times
of vibration, unless the weight of each is exactly proportional to
its mass. Newton, and later Bessel, using pendulums with cavities
in the bobs for the insertion of materials having different densities,
showed that no variation greater than the possible limit of accuracy
could be detected. In some cases experimenters have detected an
apparent small difference in the weight of equal masses of different
substances, but these results lack confirmation.

The most precise experiments proving the proportionality of
weight and mass are those of Eötvös,[1] who, by an ingenious application of the torsion balance, succeeded in raising the precision to
6 parts in 10^9. In these experiments two masses, of different materials
but equal weights, were suspended from the arms of a torsion balance.
They were acted upon by the gravitational attraction of the earth,
i.e. their weights, and by a centrifugal force, due to the rotation
of the earth, which was proportional to each mass. If the masses
were unequal the centrifugal forces on the two bodies would have
been different and a torque, supplied by the suspension thread,
would have been necessary to hold the beam in an east-west position. This torque would have been reversed when the balance was
turned through 180°. In practice, as described in Art. 25, the
whole apparatus, including an observing telescope and scale, was
rotated. Thus the effect sought would have been disclosed by a
change in the equilibrium reading.

If λ is the latitude of an observing station then the horizontal components of the centrifugal forces are $mR\omega^2 \cos \lambda \sin \lambda$ and
$m_1 R\omega^2 \cos \lambda \sin \lambda$, respectively, where m and m_1 are the two masses,
R is the radius of the earth and ω its angular velocity about the
polar axis. These forces act in a southerly direction in the northern
hemisphere and the resultant torque on the beam, when E-W, is

$$lR\omega^2 \cos \lambda \sin \lambda \, (m-m_1)$$

where $2l$ is the length of the torsion beam. If the balance is turned
through 180° the direction of this torque is reversed and the equilibrium position, relative to a telescope and scale moving with the
instrument, is changed by an amount θ. Thus

$$\tau\theta = 2lR\omega^2 \cos \lambda \sin \lambda \, (m-m_1)$$

where τ is the torsional rigidity of the suspension thread. If T is the
periodic time of vibration of the torsion balance and I the moment
of inertia of the suspended system, $\tau = 4\pi^2 I/T^2$ and thus

$$\theta = lRT^2 \sin 2\lambda (m-m_1)/It^2,$$

in which t is the periodic time of rotation of the earth. Thus a zero
value of θ indicates the equality of masses having equal weights.

The constants and sensitivity of Eötvös' balance were such that

[1] Eötvös, *Ann. d. Physik*, **68**, 1, 11 (1922).

a value of $(m-m_1)/m$, exceeding 6 parts in 10^9, could have been detected.

The unit of mass is chosen arbitrarily. We might select any piece of matter and state that it contains one, or any number of units. If, then, care is taken to preserve the selected specimen from damage and disintegration, the unit would remain definite and consistent. This is the actual procedure. In England the selected unit of mass for commercial purposes, called the Imperial Standard Pound, is a piece of platinum, housed at the Board of Trade Standards Office. The scientific unit, the gramme, is defined as having one-thousandth of the mass of the International Kilogramme. Replicas of these standard masses are widely distributed, and are more or less accurately represented in the multiples and submultiples contained in a box of " weights."

2. The Balance.—The mass of a body in terms of standard units is obtained by " weighing " the body. This term has obtained

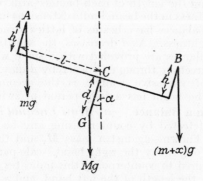

FIG. 1.—THEORY OF THE BALANCE.

universal sanction, and arose from the fact that if, at one place, two bodies have the same weight, they must have the same mass also. It must be remembered, however, that the ordinary beam-balance merely indicates equality of weights and does not give an absolute measure of them.

As a rule the beam-balance has the same sensitiveness over a considerable range of loads, the sensitiveness for any particular load being defined as the deflection, in scale divisions, produced when an excess weight of 1 milligramme is added to a scale-pan. The factors which influence the sensitiveness may be seen from the following considerations. Suppose a vertical section is taken through the centre of the beam, cutting the knife-edges at A, B, C (Fig. 1). Let l be the length of each arm, d the depth of the centre of gravity G below C, and h the height of A and B above C when the balance is at rest with the beam horizontal. Let the mass of the beam be M, and the masses of the scale-pans with their loads m and $m+x$, where x is very small. Finally, let the beam come to rest inclined at an angle α to the horizontal.

Taking moments about C,

$$(m+x)g(l \cos \alpha+h \sin \alpha)=Mgd \sin \alpha+mg(l \cos \alpha-h \sin \alpha),$$

i.e. $$x(l \cos \alpha+h \sin \alpha)=Md \sin \alpha-2mh \sin \alpha.$$

If α is sufficiently small, $\sin \alpha=\alpha$ and $\cos \alpha=1$, and, neglecting the small term $xh.\sin \alpha$,

$$xl=(Md-2mh)\alpha,$$

or $$\frac{\alpha}{x}=\frac{l}{Md-2mh}.$$

If the knife-edges are coplanar the sensitiveness is independent of the load, but if A and B are above the central knife-edge the sensitiveness increases with the load; if below, it decreases. Greater sensitiveness may be obtained by decreasing the mass of the beam and by increasing the length of each balance-arm, but the necessity for sufficient stiffness in the beam limits extensions in these directions. Very sensitive balances have beams of lattice structure to combine stiffness with lightness. As d decreases, the sensitiveness increases, and accurate balances are provided with a small weight, adjustable in a vertical direction through C, whereby d may be varied. The disadvantage of excessive control is the accompanying loss of stability, and the beam has a long period of swing.

3. Faults in a Balance.—(*a*) *Arms Unequal in Length.*—This error may be detected by counterpoising any body of mass M— not necessarily known—against a mass M_1 and then changing the mass M to the other, say the right hand, scale-pan. If a different mass M_2 is required to counterpoise, this indicates inequality in the arms. Let l be the length of the left hand, and r that of the right hand, balance-arm. Taking moments in each case,

$$Mg.l=M_1g.r, \quad \text{and} \quad Mg.r=M_2g.l,$$

i.e.

$$\frac{l}{r}=\frac{M_1}{M_2}.\frac{r}{l}, \quad \text{or} \quad \frac{l}{r}=\sqrt{\frac{M_1}{M_2}},$$

and

$$M^2=M_1M_2, \quad \text{or} \quad M=\sqrt{M_1M_2}.$$

Thus the ratio of the arm lengths and the true mass are determined.

(*b*) *Weights Inaccurate.*—A set of weights may be tested to a limited extent by comparison with one another. It is usual to assume one, generally that of the highest denomination, to be correct, and, by comparing, say, the 50 gm. with the $20+10+10+5+2+2+1$, and then recomparing the 20 against $10+5+2+2+1$, *etc.*, the errors in the lower denominations are determined. Finally, the assumed standard should be tested against a mass whose value in terms of the International Kilogramme is known.

(c) *Knife-edges.*—In the course of time these become rounded, and the line of contact with the support plane changes, as the beam tilts from the horizontal. This is equivalent to a small change in the length of the balance-arms.

4. The Laws of Motion.—In his monumental *Principia* Newton postulated a number of definitions of quantity of matter, inertia, centripetal force, *etc.*, and then stated the three fundamental laws of motion which have been used as the foundations of dynamics. These laws may be enunciated as follows :—

Law I.—Every body perseveres in its state of rest, or uniform motion in a straight line, except in so far as it is compelled to change that state by forces impressed on it.

Law II.—Change of motion is proportional to the moving force impressed, and takes place in the straight line in which that force acts.

Law III.—An action is always opposed by an equal reaction, or the mutual actions of two bodies are always equal and act in opposite directions.

The first law may be regarded as a definition of *force—i.e.* force is the agency by which a body's state of motion is changed.

To understand the implications of the second law, it is necessary to consider what Newton meant by the " motion " of a body. In his definition he states : " The quantity of motion of a body is the measure of it arising from its velocity and the quantity of matter conjointly." Thus the motion referred to is *momentum*, and the law may be expressed thus :—The rate of change of momentum is proportional to the impressed force. It should be realised, however, that even this definition can be regarded only as formulating a suitable way by which forces may be measured, that is, by the accelerations they produce, *i.e.*

$$\text{Force} \propto \frac{d}{dt}(mv).$$

If the mass of the body remains constant,

$$\text{Force} \propto m\frac{d}{dt}(v), \quad \propto ma.$$

The third law contains a principle of great importance, which may be illustrated by the following examples. When a body falls towards the earth the latter moves to meet the body, and a shell fired from a gun projects the gun backwards. The sun attracts the earth, and consequently is itself attracted by the earth with a precisely equal force, so that, as in an action confined to a given system of bodies, the forces generate movements reciprocally proportional to the masses acted upon, the centre of mass of the whole system remains stationary.

From these laws of motion the unit of force is defined as that force which, acting on unit mass, produces unit acceleration. In the C.G.S. system such a unit is called a *dyne,* and in the F.P.S. system a *poundal.* They are the fundamental units of force.

The weight of a body is a conveniently available force, so that in most practical cases such forces are used as units; but these are only secondary units, and must be capable of expression in terms of dynes, or poundals. The weight of a body is given by

$$W = mg,$$

where m is its mass and g is the acceleration due to gravity. Thus one *pound weight* is equivalent to g poundals, and one *kilogramme weight* is equal to $1000g$ dynes, the actual value of g being that appropriate to the system of units employed.

5. Motion of a Massive Particle.—Consider a particle acted upon by a constant force P, so that its velocity changes from u to v in time t while a distance x is traversed, then

$$v - u = at,$$

and

$$v^2 - u^2 = 2ax,$$

or

$$mv - mu = mat = Pt \qquad . \qquad . \qquad . \qquad (1)$$

$$\tfrac{1}{2}mv^2 - \tfrac{1}{2}mu^2 = max = Px, \qquad . \qquad . \qquad . \qquad (2)$$

where Pt is called the *impulse.* Thus impulse is equivalent to change of momentum, and (2) expresses the fact that the change in the kinetic energy of a particle is equal to the work done by the force. The work expended by a force is not always transferred into kinetic energy, since the force may be opposed by a practically equal one, resulting in no acceleration. In this case the work done raises the potential energy. Thus the total energy of a body is partly kinetic and partly potential, and is measured relative to a chosen arbitrary zero of velocity and of position. The chief units in the British and Metric systems are as follows:—

TABLE I.—UNITS

Quantity.	Metric Unit.	British Unit.
Length . .	Centimetre	Foot
Time . . .	Mean solar second	Mean solar second
Mass . . .	Gramme	Pound
Force . . .	Dyne	Poundal
Momentum . .	Dyne-second	Poundal-second
Energy . .	Erg	Foot-poundal

6. Rotational Movements of Massive Bodies.—When a body revolves about a fixed axis, there is no progressive linear motion of the body as a whole, and new terms of description are required in discussing such a motion. The change from the familiar terms of the rectilinear movement of a massive particle is, however, easily made, since, in rotational motion, it is the angle between the instantaneous position of any line in the body, passing through the axis and in the plane of rotation, and its initial position, which varies continuously with time. Thus this angular displacement is analogous to the linear displacement in the previous case. Before a complete analogy can be made, it is necessary to find expressions for those characteristics of rotational motion that correspond to force, mass, momentum, *etc.*, of rectilinear motion.

If OP is the position at time t of any line through the axis of rotation at O and OA is the position of the line at $t=0$ the angle $AOP=\theta$ is the angular displacement in time t while $\dfrac{d\theta}{dt}$, usually denoted by ω, is called the angular velocity. Any point, such as P, on the line has linear velocity and acceleration and, since the arc AP, the linear displacement of P in time t, is $r\theta$, where r is the length of OP, the linear velocity of P is $\dfrac{d}{dt}(r\theta)$, *i.e.* $r\omega$ if the body is rigid, and its linear acceleration is $\dfrac{d}{dt}(r\omega)$ or $r\dfrac{d^2\theta}{dt^2}$. Hence the linear motion of any point in the body may be correlated with the angular motion of the body as a whole.

The total kinetic energy of a rotating body is the sum of the separate kinetic energies associated with each of its parts, *i.e.* the summation over the whole body of these contributive elements. If a particle of mass m occupies the position P then the kinetic energy of this massive particle is $\frac{1}{2}mr^2\omega^2$, and, since ω is constant for all parts of the body at a given instant, the kinetic energy of the whole body is $\frac{1}{2}\omega^2\Sigma mr^2$, or $\frac{1}{2}I\omega^2$, where I represents the summation Σmr^2 over the whole body, and is termed the *Moment of Inertia* of the body about the given axis of rotation. Comparing this with the expression for the kinetic energy in translational motion, $\frac{1}{2}Mv^2$, and remembering that ω is the rotational analogue of v, I corresponds to M, and represents the effect of the mass and its space distribution in rotational dynamics.

7. Calculation of Moments of Inertia.—The value of I in many particular cases may be found by simple integration. Thus, if dm represents an infinitesimal part of the whole mass and is situated at a distance r from the axis of rotation, then

$$I=\int r^2 . dm,$$

the limits of the integral being chosen to cover the whole of the body concerned.

Consider a rod having a uniform linear distribution of mass m. The moment of inertia of an element of length dx, situated at a distance x from an axis, passing through the centre of gravity and perpendicular to its length, is $mx^2.dx$, and I is given by

$$I=2\int_0^{\frac{l}{2}} mx^2.dx=\frac{Ml^2}{12}, \qquad . \qquad . \qquad . \qquad (3)$$

where M is the mass of the rod.

The moment of inertia about a parallel axis through the end of the rod is

$$I=\int_0^l mx^2.dx=\frac{Ml^2}{3}.$$

The moment of inertia of a circular disc about an axis through its centre, and perpendicular to its plane, is obtained by dividing the disc into thin circular rings. Consider one of these rings of radius x and width dx. Then, if m is the mass per unit volume and t the thickness of the disc, the moment of inertia of this elementary ring is $2\pi x.mt.x^2.dx$, and

$$I=\int_0^r 2\pi x^3 mt.dx=\frac{Mr^2}{2},$$

M being the mass of the disc.

For an annular disc of inner and outer radii r_1 and r_2,

$$I=\int_{r_1}^{r_2} 2\pi x^3 mt.dx=\frac{2\pi mt(r_2^4-r_1^4)}{4},$$

but M, the mass of the disc, is $\pi mt(r_2^2-r_1^2)$, and hence

$$I=\frac{M}{2}(r_2^2+r_1^2).$$

In many cases the evaluation of moments of inertia is simplified by applying the following general theorems :—

(a) *Parallel Axes Theorem.*—Let I_z be the moment of inertia of a body about a given axis QZ (Fig. 2) (a), I_g that about a parallel

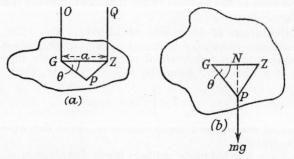

FIG. 2.—MOMENTS OF INERTIA. PARALLEL AXES THEOREM.

axis OG through the centre of gravity of the body, and a the distance between these axes. Then, if m is the mass of a particle situated at P, such that the angle PGZ *is* θ,

$$I_z = \Sigma m . PZ^2 = \Sigma m(PG^2 + GZ^2 - 2PG.GZ.\cos\theta)$$
$$= I_g + Ma^2 - 2a.\Sigma m PG.\cos\theta.$$

If the body is suspended at G (Fig. 2) (*b*), with the triangle PGZ vertical and GZ horizontal, it will be, by the properties of the centre of gravity, in equilibrium. Thus the sum of the turning moments of its individual particle weights about G will be zero. The turning moment of mg, acting vertically downwards through P, is $mg.GN$, *i.e.* $mg.PG.\cos\theta$. Hence $\Sigma mg.PG.\cos\theta$ is zero, and

$$I_z = I_g + Ma^2 \qquad . \qquad . \qquad . \qquad . \qquad (4)$$

(b) Perpendicular Axes Theorem. Laminar Body.—Let I_x, I_y, I_z be the moments of inertia of a laminar body about three

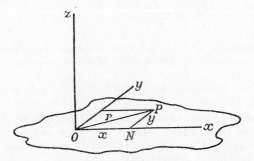

FIG. 3.—MOMENTS OF INERTIA. PERPENDICULAR AXES THEOREM FOR TWO DIMENSIONS.

mutually perpendicular axes Ox, Oy, Oz—Ox and Oy being in the plane of the lamina—and let a particle of mass m be placed at P (x, y) (Fig. 3). Then

$$I_x + I_y = \Sigma m(x^2 + y^2) = \Sigma m r^2 = I_z . \qquad . \qquad . \qquad (5)$$

(c) Perpendicular Axes Theorem. Three-dimensional Body.—Let I_x, I_y, I_z be the moments of inertia about any three mutually perpendicular axes Ox, Oy, Oz (Fig. 4), and let a particle of mass m be situated at P (x, y, z) so that $PM = z$, $MN = y$, $NO = x$. Draw PR, PN, and PQ perpendicular to Oz, Ox, and Oy, respectively. Then

$$I_x = \Sigma m . PN^2 = \Sigma m(y^2 + z^2),$$
$$I_y = \Sigma m . PQ^2 = \Sigma m(z^2 + x^2),$$
$$I_z = \Sigma m . PR^2 = \Sigma m . MO^2 = \Sigma m(x^2 + y^2),$$
$$I_0 = \Sigma m . PO^2 = \Sigma m(x^2 + y^2 + z^2),$$

Hence

$$I_x+I_y+I_z=2\Sigma m(x^2+y^2+z^2)=2I_0, \qquad . \qquad . \quad (6)$$

where I_0 is the summation Σmr^2 about the origin O.

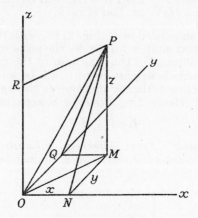

FIG. 4.—MOMENTS OF INERTIA. PERPENDICULAR AXES THEOREM FOR THREE DIMENSIONS.

These three theorems can be applied in the following examples, where M in all cases denotes the mass of the body.

Rectangular Plate about an Axis through its Centre and Perpendicular to its Plane.—Let O be the centre of the plate and Oz the given axis. Draw Ox and Oy parallel to the length a and the width b of the plate, respectively. From (3)

$$I_x=\frac{Mb^2}{12}, \quad \text{and} \quad I_y=\frac{Ma^2}{12}.$$

Hence

$$I_z=I_x+I_y=\frac{M}{12}(a^2+b^2) \qquad . \qquad . \qquad . \quad (7)$$

Circular, or Annular, Disc about a Diameter.—If Oz be an axis through the centre of the disc, or annulus, perpendicular to its plane, and Ox, Oy perpendicular axes in the plane of the disc, or annulus, then, since for a disc $I_z=\dfrac{Mr^2}{2}$, for an annulus $I_z=\dfrac{M}{2}(r_2{}^2+r_1{}^2)$ and $I_x=I_y$, from (5),

$$\left.\begin{aligned} I_x\ (\text{disc}) &=\frac{Mr^2}{4}, \\[2mm] I_x\ (\text{annulus}) &=\frac{M}{4}(r_2{}^2+r_1{}^2). \end{aligned}\right\} \qquad . \qquad . \qquad . \quad (8)$$

and

Circular Disc, or Annulus, about a Tangent.—In this case the axis is at a distance r from the centre for the disc and r_2 for the annulus. Thus, from (4),

$$I_T \text{ (disc)} \quad = \frac{Mr^2}{4} + Mr^2 = \tfrac{5}{4}Mr^2,$$

and

$$I_T \text{ (annulus)} = \frac{M}{4}(r_2{}^2 + r_1{}^2) + Mr_2{}^2$$

$$= \frac{M}{4}(5r_2{}^2 + r_1{}^2) \qquad . \quad . \quad . \quad (9)$$

Thin Spherical Shell.—All parts of a thin spherical shell being equidistant from the centre O, $I_0 = Mr^2$. If $I_x = I_y = I_z$ is the moment of inertia about a diameter, then, from (6),

$$3I_x = 2I_0 = 2Mr^2,$$

and

$$I_x = \tfrac{2}{3}Mr^2 \quad . \qquad . \qquad . \qquad . \qquad (10)$$

For a spherical shell about a tangent,

$$I_T = I_x + Mr^2 = \tfrac{5}{3}Mr^2 \qquad . \quad . \quad . \quad (11)$$

Solid Sphere about a Diameter.—In this case it is convenient first to find I_0. Divide the sphere into thin concentric shells of which a typical one has a radius x and thickness dx. If m is the mass per unit volume, the mass of the shell is $4\pi x^2 . m . dx$. Hence for the whole sphere

$$I_0 = \int_0^r 4\pi x^2 m x^2 . dx = \tfrac{3}{5}Mr^2 \quad . \qquad . \qquad . \quad (12)$$

If $I_x = I_y = I_z$ is the moment of inertia about a diameter, then, by (6),

$$3I_x = 2I_0 = \tfrac{6}{5}Mr^2$$

and

$$I_x = \tfrac{2}{5}Mr^2 \quad . \qquad . \qquad . \qquad . \qquad (13)$$

For a solid sphere about a tangent,

$$I_T = I_x + Mr^2 = \tfrac{7}{5}Mr^2. \qquad . \quad . \quad (14)$$

If part of a body is removed, the moment of inertia about any axis is reduced in value by that of the portion taken away. Hence the moment of inertia of a body containing a cavity is determined by the difference between the moment of inertia of the complete body and of the part which would completely fill the cavity.

In all the examples quoted above the moment of inertia is expressed in the form Mk^2, where k is a quantity depending on the size and shape of the body, and is called the *radius of gyration* of the body about the given axis. Its significance may be understood by assuming that the mass is distributed uniformly in a ring of radius k, whose centre lies on the axis, the plane of the ring being perpendicular to this axis. This ring, revolving about the axis, has the same inertial properties as the rotating body. In other words, the radius of gyration indicates the influence of the mass distribution in space on the moment of inertia.

8. Uniform Angular Acceleration.—Uniformly accelerated angular motion is produced by a *couple*—two equal, parallel, and oppositely directed forces, not in the same straight line. Such a system has no tendency to change the mean position of the body on which it acts, but merely produces a rotation. The magnitude of this turning effort is called the moment, or *torque*, and is given by Px, where each force is of magnitude P, and x is the perpendicular distance between them. If one point in a body is fixed, then a single force not passing through this point will, together with the reaction at the pivot, constitute a couple, whose moment is the product of the magnitude of the force and the perpendicular distance between the pivot and the line of action of the force. This product is the moment of the force about the point.

The general equations (1), (2) of uniform linear acceleration may be adapted to the case of angular motion, or rotation, by identifying v and u, the final and initial linear velocities, with ω and ω_0, the final and initial angular velocities, a with $\dfrac{d\omega}{dt}$, the angular acceleration, x with θ, the angular displacement, and P with the torque $\varGamma$. Hence

$$I\omega - I\omega_0 = I\frac{d\omega}{dt}t, \qquad . \qquad . \qquad . \quad (15)$$

$$\tfrac{1}{2}I\omega^2 - \tfrac{1}{2}I\omega_0{}^2 = I\frac{d\omega}{dt}\theta. \qquad . \qquad . \qquad (16)$$

$I\omega$ is called the *angular momentum* and $\tfrac{1}{2}I\omega^2$ the angular kinetic energy.

If a point P in the body has linear acceleration $r\dfrac{d\omega}{dt}$, and if at this point a force p acts perpendicularly to OP, the radius passing through P, then p is given by $mr\dfrac{d\omega}{dt}$, where m is the mass of the particle at P. This force has a moment $mr^2\dfrac{d\omega}{dt}$ about O, and the sum of the moments about O of all the unbalanced forces acting on the body is $\varGamma$, the torque. Hence

$$\Sigma mr^2\frac{d\omega}{dt} = I\frac{d\omega}{dt} = \varGamma, \qquad . \qquad . \qquad (17)$$

so that, from (15), $\varGamma t$ is equal to the change of angular momentum, and is termed the *angular impulse*, or impulsive moment. Similarly, from (16), the change of angular kinetic energy is $\varGamma\theta$, and is the work done by a couple of moment $\varGamma$ in moving through an angle θ.

The similarities between rectilinear and rotational dynamical units are given in Table II.

TABLE II.—UNITS IN RECTILINEAR AND ROTATIONAL DYNAMICS

Rectilinear Motion.	Rotational Motion.
Displacement, x.	Displacement, θ.
Velocity, $\dfrac{dx}{dt}$, v, u.	Velocity, $\dfrac{d\theta}{dt}$, ω, ω_0.
Acceleration, $\dfrac{d^2x}{dt^2}$, $\dfrac{dv}{dt}$, a.	Acceleration, $\dfrac{d^2\theta}{dt^2}$, $\dfrac{d\omega}{dt}$.
Mass, M.	Moment of inertia, I, Mk^2.
Force, $P=ma$.	Torque, $\Gamma=I\dfrac{d\omega}{dt}$.
Momentum, mv	Momentum, $I\omega$.
Impulse, $Pt=m(v-u)$.	Impulsive moment, $\Gamma t=I(\omega-\omega_0)$.
Kinetic energy, $\frac{1}{2}mv^2$.	Kinetic energy, $\frac{1}{2}I\omega^2$.
Work, Px.	Work, $\Gamma\theta$.

9. Torsional Oscillations.—A simple but important example of angular motion occurs in torsional oscillations. If a body is suspended in such a way that its displacement about a given axis produces a couple tending to prevent further displacement in the same direction, then, in many cases, this couple is proportional to the displacement, and an equilibrium position is reached when the opposing torque is equal in magnitude to the displacing torque. If, now, the latter is removed, the restoring couple is unbalanced and generates an angular acceleration given by $\Gamma=I\dfrac{d\omega}{dt}$, Γ being the torque externally applied. Since the restoring couple is proportional to the angular displacement, $\Gamma=\tau\theta$, where τ is a constant for the given type of suspension. Hence

$$I\frac{d\omega}{dt}=I\frac{d^2\theta}{dt^2}=-\tau\theta,$$

the negative sign indicating that the displacing and restoring torques act in opposite directions. Thus the equation of motion of such a body is

$$\frac{d^2\theta}{dt^2}+\frac{\tau}{I}\cdot\theta=0 \quad . \quad . \quad . \quad . \quad (18)$$

The angular acceleration is proportional to the angular displacement, and thus the motion is simple harmonic and may be represented by

$$\theta=\theta_0 \, sin \, \frac{2\pi t}{t_0},$$

where θ_0 is the amplitude and t_0 is the periodic time of oscillation. If this value of θ is substituted in (18), we obtain

$$\frac{\tau}{I} \cdot \theta_0 \sin \frac{2\pi t}{t_0} = \theta_0 \left(\frac{2\pi}{t_0}\right)^2 \sin \frac{2\pi t}{t_0},$$

or
$$t_0 = 2\pi \sqrt{\frac{I}{\tau}} \qquad . \qquad . \qquad . \qquad . \qquad (19)$$

10. Vectors and their Graphical Representation.—The total moment of inertia of any number of bodies about a given axis is the direct sum of their separate moments, and, similarly, the combined mass of a series of bodies is the sum total of their separate masses. Physical quantities such as these, which may be compounded by direct algebraic addition, are called *scalar* quantities. There are other quantities which cannot be added in this manner. Thus the resultant of two individual displacements, d_1 and d_2, is not necessarily $d_1 + d_2$. This is the resultant displacement only if d_1 and d_2 both lie in the same straight line. Similarly, if two forces P_1 and P_2 act on a body, their resultant is again $P_1 + P_2$ only if they act in the same direction. Quantities such as displacement, velocity, acceleration, force, and momentum which require, for their complete description and compounding, a statement of direction as well as magnitude, are called *vector* quantities. They are most conveniently added by a graphical method, in which the vector is represented by a straight line, whose length is proportional to the magnitude of the quantity, and whose direction, relative to any convenient reference line, represents its direction.

Any quantity which is derived from a vector, or which is obtained by a combination of vectors and scalars, remains vectorial. Thus linear velocity, depending on linear displacement (vector) and time (scalar), is a vector.

In rotational dynamics some quantities are directional, in the sense that they are confined to a plane, and are called plane vectors. By means of a simple convention the rule for the addition of linear vectors may be applied also to these plane vectors. The two-dimensional vector is represented by a straight line drawn *normal* to its plane, and of length proportional to the magnitude of the vector, the sense of the latter being given by the side of the plane from which the normal is drawn.

It must be remembered that a change of direction, without change in magnitude, is a variation of velocity, *etc.* For example, a body moving in a circular orbit with constant speed has a velocity at any instant along the tangent, and the body is maintained in its circular path only because of an acceleration towards the centre of the circle. This acceleration constantly changes the direction of the velocity but does not alter the speed. Thus we may have uniform acceleration at constant speed. In a similar manner it is possible to have angular acceleration at constant angular speed. In this case the plane of rotation changes direction at a given rate, without any variation in the rate of rotation about the rotation axis. Such a change in the plane of rotation is called *precession*, and is caused by the action of a torque, whose plane is always perpendicular to the instantaneous plane of rotation. If the torque remains constant in magnitude, the result will be a constant precessional motion.

EXAMPLES

1. Define the sensitivity of a balance and obtain a formula connecting the sensitivity with other constants of the balance. In using such a balance it is found that the sensitivity for no load is 3·00 scale divisions per mg. and for a load of 100 gm. is 2·70 scale divisions per mg. Find the sensitivity for a load of 200 gm. assuming the beam to be rigid ; indicate the relation between the knife-edge positions.
[2·45 ; end knife edges below centre.]

2. Show how the rest point of a balance may be deduced while the pointer is still swinging over the scale. If successive turning points on a scale with its zero at one end are 10, 2 and 8 divisions deduce the rest point. [5·43.]

3. A glass sphere of density 2·50 gm. per c.c. is being weighed, and is counterpoised by brass weights of density 8·60 gm. per c.c. The counterpoising weights are 25·138 and 25·206 gm. when in the right- and left-hand scale pans respectively. Find (a) the ratio of the balance arm lengths, (b) the apparent weight of the sphere in air, (c) the true mass of the sphere if the density of air is 0·00129 gm. per c.c.
[(a) 1·0011 ; (b) 25·172 gm. ; (c) 25·181 gm.]

4. A catherine wheel when burning has its initial moment of inertia, I, reduced at a uniform rate, k. If the couple, G, acting on it is constant, find the connection between the time, t, and (a) its angular velocity, ω, (b) its angular acceleration $d\omega/dt$.
[(a) $Gt = \omega(I - kt)$; (b) $(I - kt)^2 . d\omega/dt = GI$.]

5. A stream of water issues horizontally from an orifice of cross-sectional area 0·03 sq. cm. at the rate of 20 c.c. per sec., and impinges perpendicularly upon a flat plate. Calculate approximately the mean pressure which is exerted on the plate. [$4·4 \times 10^5$ dynes per sq. cm.]

6. A sphere of radius $2r$ and density d has an internal spherical cavity, of radius r, the diameter of which is a radius of the sphere. Find the moment of inertia, I, of the body about an axis perpendicular to the common diameter of sphere and cavity and at a distance x from the centre of the sphere. [$15I = 4\pi r^3 d(57r^2 + 35x^2 \pm 10rx)$.]

7. A cylinder has a mass M, length l, and radius r. Find the ratio of l to r if the moment of inertia about an axis through the centre and perpendicular to the length is a minimum. [$\sqrt{3} : \sqrt{2}$.]

CHAPTER II

THE ACCELERATION OF GRAVITY

11. The Acceleration of Gravity.—The acceleration of gravity, g, is the acceleration produced in any body by the earth's attractive force, and, as actually measured, is the acceleration due to the earth's attraction, less the centrifugal acceleration of the earth's rotation. The importance of this physical quantity has been stressed in dealing with the relation between mass and weight, and its value may be found experimentally by various methods.

12. Atwood's Machine.—The most direct method for the measurement of g is by means of Atwood's machine. In the ribbon form, which is shown in Fig. 5, equal intervals of time are given by the transverse vibrations of a steel strip S. A light pulley A runs on ball-bearings and carries, over its flat rim, a strip of paper C, to which are attached two equal weights M. The strip S is rigidly clamped at one end, and carries at the other a brush B, which is impregnated with ink and which just touches the surface of the paper band stretched over the pulley. The two weights M carry a similar paper strip below, so that in the motion no additional excess weight is transferred from one side of the pulley to the other. Resting on M is a small rider m, while premature movement is prevented by the platform P. Before the system is set into motion the brush B is moved across the paper to indicate the starting-point, and then, by means of trigger releases, P is allowed to fall, and the spring is simultaneously set into oscillation. Owing to the acceleration produced, the inked line traced on the paper is a gradually lengthening wave, for which one wavelength represents the distance moved by any point on C in the periodic time of the spring. Thus, by measuring the distances occupied by each complete wave, the successive distances covered by the system in the 1st, 2nd, *etc.*, periods of the spring are known.

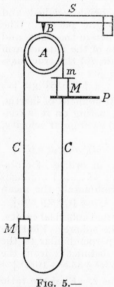

Fig. 5.—
Ribbon form of
Atwood's Machine.

Then, if a is the acceleration of the falling weight, t_0 the period

16

of the spring, and x_1, x_2, etc., are the distances covered in successive periods,

$$x_1 = \tfrac{1}{2}at_0{}^2,$$
$$x_2 = at_0{}^2 + \tfrac{1}{2}at_0{}^2 = \tfrac{3}{2}at_0{}^2,$$
$$x_3 = 2at_0{}^2 + \tfrac{1}{2}at_0{}^2 = \tfrac{5}{2}at_0{}^2,$$

or
$$(x_2 - x_1) = (x_3 - x_2) = etc. = at_0{}^2.$$

Thus, t_0 being known, a is determined.

If v is the velocity acquired after a distance x, the kinetic energy gained must be equal to the potential energy lost. Hence

$$\tfrac{1}{2}I\omega^2 + \tfrac{1}{2}[2M+m]v^2 = mgx,$$

where I and ω are the moment of inertia and instantaneous angular velocity of the pulley. But, since $v = r\omega$, where r is the radius of the pulley,

$$\tfrac{1}{2}\left(\frac{I}{r^2}\right)v^2 + \tfrac{1}{2}[2M+m]v^2 = mgx,$$

or
$$v^2 = 2x \cdot \frac{mg}{W+2M+m},$$

W, written for $\dfrac{I}{r^2}$, being the equivalent mass of the pulley wheel.

If we compare this with the expression for uniform acceleration, $v^2 = 2ax$, it is evident that

$$a = \left[\frac{m}{W+2M+m}\right]g.$$

W may be eliminated by carrying out experiments with two different masses M_1 and M_2, in which case

$$g = \frac{2[M_1 - M_2]}{m\left[\dfrac{1}{a_1} - \dfrac{1}{a_2}\right]}.$$

It has been assumed that the pulley is not retarded by friction. To ensure this, the weight M, carrying the rider, is loaded by means of a small auxiliary rider until, if the main rider m is removed and the system is given an initial velocity, there is neither acceleration nor retardation. The weight of this rider then just neutralises the friction, and both may be ignored in the subsequent experiment.

13. Body Rolling down an Inclined Plane.—If a body rolls, without slipping, down an inclined plane, a value may be obtained for g by timing the motion between two points whose distance apart is known. Suppose the body commences from rest at a position A, and has acquired a translational velocity v after rolling a distance x, measured along the plane and reaching a point B. Then the kinetic energy at B is equal to the potential energy lost from A to B. The former is partly translational and partly rotational, and if ω is the angular velocity at B, then, since the point of contact with the plane is momentarily at rest, $v=r\omega$, where r is the radius of the body. Thus the kinetic energy at B is

$$\tfrac{1}{2}mv^2+\tfrac{1}{2}mk^2\omega^2,$$

k being the radius of gyration about the axis of the body. The potential energy lost from A to B is $mgx \sin \theta$, and, therefore,

$$\tfrac{1}{2}mv^2+\tfrac{1}{2}mk^2\frac{v^2}{r^2}=mgx \sin \theta,$$

where θ is the inclination to the horizontal. Thus,

$$v^2=2x\frac{g \sin \theta}{1+\dfrac{k^2}{r^2}}.$$

But, since $v^2=2ax$, the acceleration of the body rolling down the plane is given by

$$a=\frac{g \sin \theta}{1+\dfrac{k^2}{r^2}}\qquad \cdot \quad \cdot \quad \cdot \quad \cdot \quad (20)$$

The following cases are important :—

(a) Solid sphere :

$$k^2=\tfrac{2}{5}r^2, \qquad a=\tfrac{5}{7}g \sin \theta.$$

(b) Solid cylinder or solid disc :

$$k^2=\tfrac{1}{2}r^2, \qquad a=\tfrac{2}{3}g \sin \theta.$$

(c) Hollow cylinder or hoop :

$$k^2=r^2, \qquad a=\tfrac{1}{2}g \sin \theta.$$

14. Body Rolling on a Concave Surface.—If a ball is made to roll down the line of maximum slope of a spherical surface, placed with its concavity upwards, the oscillation about the lowest point in the surface will be simple harmonic. Suppose that the ball is released from rest at A (Fig. 6). Then, by the conservation of energy principle,

$$\tfrac{1}{2}mv^2+\tfrac{1}{2}mk^2\frac{v^2}{r^2}=mgh,$$

or

$$v^2=\frac{2gh}{1+\dfrac{k^2}{r^2}}.$$

But h, the vertical distance between A and B, is related to the amplitude, a_1, of the motion by $a_1{}^2=h[2R-h]$, where R is the

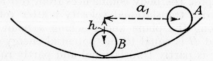

FIG. 6.—MOTION ON A CONCAVE SURFACE.

difference in the radii of curvature of the surface and sphere. If r is very small compared with R, the latter is then approximately equal to the radius of the surface. Hence $a_1{}^2=2Rh$ if h is small, and

$$v^2 = \frac{2g}{1+\dfrac{k^2}{r^2}} \cdot \frac{a_1{}^2}{2R},$$

i.e. v is proportional to a_1. This is the case in simple harmonic motion where

$$v^2 = a_1{}^2\left(\frac{2\pi}{t_0}\right)^2,$$

and thus we have, equating these values of v^2,

$$t_0 = 2\pi \sqrt{\frac{R\left(1+\dfrac{k^2}{r^2}\right)}{g}} \qquad . \qquad . \qquad . \quad (21)$$

15. Simple Pendulum.—The simple pendulum consists of a light string supporting a small massive body, usually a sphere, and fixed firmly at its upper end. If such a pendulum is given a small displacement, and then oscillates in a vertical plane it describes a simple harmonic motion, for, if l is its length and θ its instantaneous displacement (Fig. 7) (*a*), the restoring force on the bob is $mg\ sin\ \theta$, where mg is the weight of the bob. This generates an acceleration, towards the centre, of $g\ sin\ \theta$, or, if θ is small, of $g\theta$. But, since the velocity of the bob in this position is $l\dfrac{d\theta}{dt}$, the acceleration towards the centre is $-l\dfrac{d^2\theta}{dt^2}$, so that

$$\frac{d^2\theta}{dt^2} + \frac{g}{l}\theta = 0.$$

This, again, represents a simple harmonic motion of period t_0 given by

$$t_0 = 2\pi\sqrt{\frac{l}{g}} \qquad . \qquad . \qquad . \qquad . \quad (22)$$

16. Conical Pendulum.—If the bob of the simple pendulum is projected so as to describe a horizontal circle, then its periodic time may be used to measure g. Let v be the uniform speed of the bob (Fig. 7) (*b*), and let r be the radius of its circular path. The inclination, θ, of the string to the vertical is given by $r=l\ sin\ \theta$. The three forces which maintain equilibrium are the weight of the bob acting vertically down, the centrifugal force $\dfrac{mv^2}{r}$ acting horizontally, and F, the tension in the string, acting at an angle θ to the vertical. For vertical equilibrium $F\ cos\ \theta=mg$, while horizontally $F\ sin\ \theta=\dfrac{mv^2}{r}$.

Hence $tan\ \theta = \dfrac{v^2}{gr}$. But if t_0 is the period, $t_0 = \dfrac{2\pi r}{v}$, and thus

$$tan\ \theta = \left(\frac{2\pi}{t_0}\right)^2 \frac{r}{g} = \left(\frac{2\pi}{t_0}\right)^2 \frac{l\ sin\ \theta}{g},$$

or

$$t_0 = 2\pi \sqrt{\frac{l\ cos\ \theta}{g}}, \quad \cdots \quad (23)$$

and, if θ is small,

$$t_0 = 2\pi \sqrt{\frac{l}{g}} \quad \cdots \quad (24)$$

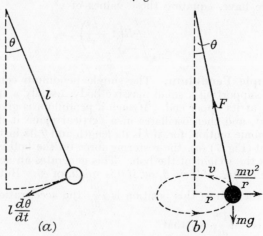

FIG. 7.—SIMPLE AND CONICAL PENDULUMS.

17. Bifilar Suspension.—In the bifilar experiment a heavy uniform rod is suspended in a horizontal position by two equal vertical threads of length l and distance $2d$ apart. The rod is then displaced, about a vertical axis, through an angle θ. Let $A'C'$ (Fig. 8) be the equilibrium position of the rod—whose weight is mg —and let DB be its position when displaced through the angle $A'OB = \theta$, where θ is sufficiently small for $sin\ \theta = \theta$, and $cos\ \theta = 1$, within the errors of experiment. The suspension threads AB, CD are inclined at an angle ϕ to the vertical when in the displaced position.

For vertical equilibrium $2F\ cos\ \phi = mg$, but since

$$l\phi = d\theta, \qquad cos\ \phi = cos\left(\frac{d}{l}\theta\right) = 1,$$

and $$F = \frac{mg}{2}, \text{ approximately.}$$

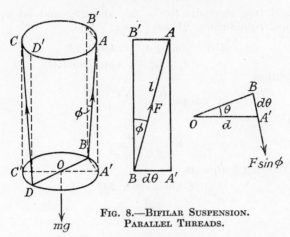

FIG. 8.—BIFILAR SUSPENSION.
PARALLEL THREADS.

The horizontal component of the tension F, acting along BA', is

$$F \sin \phi = F\phi = \frac{mgd}{2l}\theta,$$

and, as BA' is sensibly at right angles to OB, the restoring torque is $\frac{mgd}{2l}\theta \cdot 2d$.

Hence the restoring torque for unit twist is $\frac{mgd^2}{l}$, and

$$t_0 = 2\pi\frac{k}{d}\sqrt{\frac{l}{g}} \qquad . \qquad . \qquad . \qquad . \qquad (25)$$

Fig. 9 represents the arrangement of the bifilar suspension with non-parallel threads. Let the distance between the threads at the

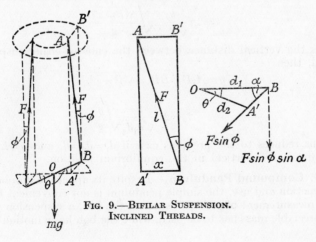

FIG. 9.—BIFILAR SUSPENSION.
INCLINED THREADS.

bottom and top, respectively, be $2d_1$ and $2d_2$, and let $d_1-d_2=x$. For vertical equilibrium, $2F \cos \phi=mg$. Also,

$$A'B=\sqrt{d_1{}^2+d_2{}^2-2d_1d_2 \cos \theta}$$
$$=[d_1-d_2]=x, \text{ approximately.}$$

In addition

$$\cos \phi=\frac{BB'}{l}=\frac{\sqrt{l^2-x^2}}{l},$$

and thus

$$F=\frac{mgl}{2\sqrt{l^2-x^2}}.$$

The restoring torque is

$$F \sin \phi \sin \alpha . 2d_1$$
$$=2d_1\frac{mgl}{2\sqrt{l^2-x^2}}.\frac{x}{l} \sin \alpha.$$

But

$$\frac{d_2}{\sin \alpha}=\frac{A'B}{\sin \theta}=\frac{x}{\theta},$$

and thus

$$\sin \alpha=\frac{d_2}{x}\theta,$$

so that the restoring torque for unit twist is

$$\frac{mgd_1d_2}{\sqrt{l^2-x^2}}.$$

Hence,

$$t_0=2\pi\sqrt{\frac{mk^2\sqrt{l^2-x^2}}{mgd_1d_2}}$$
$$=2\pi\frac{k}{\sqrt{d_1d_2}}\sqrt{\frac{\sqrt{l^2-x^2}}{g}}.$$

If y is the vertical distance between the ends of either suspension thread, then

$$y=AA'=BB'=\sqrt{l^2-x^2},$$

and

$$t_0=2\pi\frac{k}{\sqrt{d_1d_2}}\sqrt{\frac{y}{g}} \qquad . \qquad . \qquad . \quad (26)$$

This reduces to the previous case if $d_1=d_2=d$, and $y=l$, i.e. if the threads are vertical in the equilibrium position.

18. Compound Pendulum.—Despite its apparent simplicity in construction and use, the simple pendulum is not convenient for the exact measurement of g, for, to support the bob, a suspension thread of appreciable mass has to be used, while the bob has a motion which is not merely one of translation, since it turns about the point of suspension. It is therefore necessary to evaluate the moment of inertia of the whole system to take these factors into account. Additionally, the suspension thread slackens when approaching the limits of swing, and introduces a complication into the motion which limits the accuracy of the experiment, unless complex corrections are made to eliminate the effect of flexure. The last defect is absent from the compound pendulum, a rigid body swinging in a vertical plane about any horizontal axis passing through the body.

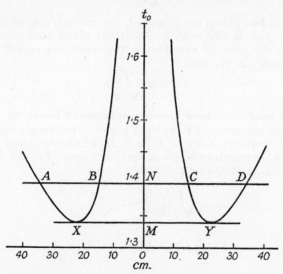

FIG. 10.—COMPOUND PENDULUM. VARIATION OF PERIOD WITH DISTANCE OF AXIS FROM THE CENTRE OF GRAVITY.

Let O be a point on this axis, G the centre of gravity of the body, and θ the angular displacement, at time t, from the equilibrium position OA. Let $OG=l$. The restoring torque is $mgl \sin \theta$, or, if θ is small, $mgl\theta$. Thus the restoring torque for unit displacement is mgl, and the period t_0 is given by

$$t_0 = 2\pi \sqrt{\frac{I}{mgl}},$$

where I is the moment of inertia of the body about the axis of suspension.

If k is the radius of gyration about a parallel axis through G, then, by equation (4),

$$I = mk^2 + ml^2,$$

and
$$t_0 = 2\pi \sqrt{\frac{k^2 + l^2}{lg}} \qquad . \qquad . \qquad . \qquad . \qquad (27)$$

If different values of l are taken, and the corresponding values of t_0 found and plotted, then the result is as shown in Fig. 10, and the following conclusions may be drawn :—

(a) The minimum time of vibration is obtained when the body is suspended from points, represented by X and Y, situated at equal distances $l_0 = MX = MY$ from the centre of gravity. This may also be deduced by differentiating equation (27) with respect to l and equating the result to zero. This gives

$$l_0 = k,$$

and thus, if two points are identified, one on each side of the centre of gravity and in line with it, such that about each as centre of oscillation the time of vibration is the minimum period t_0', their distance apart is $2k$, and

$$t_0' = 2\pi \sqrt{\frac{2k}{g}}.$$

The body now acts like a simple pendulum of length $2k$, i.e. XY.

(b) Any line above XY, at right angles to the time axis, cuts the curve in four points, such as A, B, C, D, which are placed by pairs, AD and BC, symmetrically about the centre line. Let $AN = ND = l_1$, $BN = NC = l_2$, and $ON = t_1$. Then,

$$t_1 = 2\pi \sqrt{\frac{k^2 + l_1^2}{l_1 g}} = 2\pi \sqrt{\frac{k^2 + l_2^2}{l_2 g}},$$

or

$$\frac{g}{4\pi^2} t_1^2 [l_1 - l_2] = l_1^2 - l_2^2,$$

and

$$t_1 = 2\pi \sqrt{\frac{l_1 + l_2}{g}} \qquad . \qquad . \qquad . \qquad . \qquad (28)$$

Thus the length of the simple equivalent pendulum in this case is $(l_1 + l_2)$, which is given by AC or BD.

The bar form of compound pendulum consists of a heavy uniform rectangular bar along the length of which a regular series of holes has been bored. The bar is supported by a horizontal knife-edge, placed in turn in each of these holes, and the various periods of vibration for these suspensions are measured. The distance from one end of the bar to each of these axes is measured, and the relation between the period and distance is similar to that shown in Fig. 10. In using this graph to measure g, lines such as $ABCD$ are drawn, and an average of the distances AC and BD is substituted in equation (28). Thus a mean value of g may be obtained.

19. Kater's Reversible Pendulum.—The compound pendulum, used in 1817 by Kater [1] in his celebrated measurement of the value

[1] Kater, *Phil. Trans.*, **108** (1818).

of g at London, is represented in Fig. 11. The rod carried three weights—the bob W and two adjustable weights A and B. It could be pivoted at either of the knife-edges K_1 and K_2. The larger weight A was moved until the times of swing about the two knife-edges were nearly equal, and was then fixed in position. The smaller weight B was moved by means of a screw until the number of swings made in twenty-four hours about the two knife-edges differed only by a small fraction of one vibration. Within the limits of experimental error K_1 and K_2 were then reciprocal points of oscillation and suspension, and their distance apart was carefully measured. This distance gives the length of an ideal simple pendulum of the same period, and thus could be used to calculate g accurately.

The adjustment of the pendulum to exact equality of period is extremely tedious, and, as was pointed out by Bessel, is not absolutely necessary, for, if the two times, t_1 and t_2, are very nearly equal, and l_1, l_2 are the distances of K_1, K_2 from the centre of gravity,

$$\frac{g}{4\pi^2}t_1{}^2 = \frac{k^2+l_1{}^2}{l_1}, \quad \text{and} \quad \frac{g}{4\pi^2}t_2{}^2 = \frac{k^2+l_2{}^2}{l_2},$$

so that

$$\frac{g}{4\pi^2}[t_1{}^2l_1 - t_2{}^2l_2] = l_1{}^2 - l_2{}^2,$$

or

$$\frac{4\pi^2}{g} = \frac{t_1{}^2l_1 - t_2{}^2l_2}{l_1{}^2 - l_2{}^2} = \tfrac{1}{2}\left[\frac{t_1{}^2+t_2{}^2}{l_1+l_2} + \frac{t_1{}^2-t_2{}^2}{l_1-l_2}\right] \quad . \quad . \quad (29)$$

Since $t_1{}^2$ is very nearly equal to $t_2{}^2$, the term $\dfrac{t_1{}^2-t_2{}^2}{l_1-l_2}$ is small compared with $\dfrac{t_1{}^2+t_2{}^2}{l_1+l_2}$, and thus does not require such exact evaluation. The length (l_1+l_2) is given by the distance between the knife-edges, while (l_1-l_2) is obtained with sufficient accuracy by balancing the pendulum horizontally on a knife-edge to locate the centre of gravity.

To determine the period a method of coincidences, such as that described by Horton [1] and suggested by Poynting, may be used. Two mirrors are observed through a telescope, one being fixed and the other attached to the vibrating body, so that, when parallel, they both reflect the 1-second flashes of light produced by a standard clock. Thus one flash always occurs at a fixed point in the field of view, while the other may have any position. As an example of the method, assume that the period is known to be approximately

FIG. 11.—
KATER'S
REVERSIBLE
PENDULUM.

[1] Horton, *Phil. Trans.*, A, **204**, 1 (1904).

4·116 seconds, and suppose also that an exact coincidence has just occurred. Calling this moment 0, then after 4 seconds the mirrors will not be exactly parallel again, since the moving one has lagged slightly behind. If, however, we wait for such a number of seconds, n, as is very nearly an exact multiple of the time of vibration, then at the nth fixed flash the mirrors will be very nearly parallel, and an approximate coincidence occurs. For example, $9 \times 4 \cdot 116 = 37 \cdot 044$, so that after 37 seconds the time-lag of the moving flash is only 0·044 second. After this 37th second count one, two, three, *etc.*, up to 37 again, then restart counting again, and so on. Every 37th flash will appear to have lost on the preceding one—*i.e.* the lag increases —until after say N sets of 37 seconds one second has been lost, and the 1st second of the next set will be a time of exact coincidence. Then the vibrator has made $9N$ vibrations in $37N+1$ seconds, so that the period t_0 is given by

$$9Nt_0 = 37N+1, \quad \text{or} \quad t_0 = \tfrac{37}{9} + \frac{1}{9N}.$$

In general an exact coincidence is very rare, and that nearest to coincidence is taken. Thus suppose that at one 37th flash the separation of the images is a lead of x scale divisions in the telescope, and at the next 37th flash it is a lag of y divisions. The exact coincidence must then have occurred at the fraction $\dfrac{x}{x+y}$ of an interval after the first observation, and we have

$$t_0 = \tfrac{37}{9} + \frac{1}{9(N+\alpha)},$$

where α has been written for $\dfrac{x}{x+y}$.

To estimate the accuracy of the method, suppose N is 20. The maximum error which can arise in α is $\dfrac{\alpha}{10}$, and

$$\frac{1}{9(N+\alpha)} = \frac{1}{9N} - \frac{\alpha}{9N^2}, \quad \text{approximately,}$$

so that the error cannot exceed $\dfrac{1}{90 \times 400}$ or 0·000027 second.

20. Corrections Applicable to the Use of the Compound Pendulum.

—For very accurate measurements with the compound pendulum a number of corrections are necessary.

(*a*) *Finite Arc of Swing.*—The formula given in equation (27) was obtained on the assumption of a vanishingly small angular amplitude, and only in these circumstances will the motion be truly simple harmonic. It is therefore necessary to investigate the effect on the period of the finite magnitude of the amplitude. The energy equation of motion may be written in the form :—

$$(k^2+l^2)\left(\frac{d\theta}{dt}\right)^2 = 2gl \, (cos \, \theta - cos \, \alpha),$$

where α is the amplitude and θ is the displacement at time t. On integrating this we have

$$\sqrt{\frac{2gl}{k^2+l^2}} \int_0^{\frac{t_0}{4}} dt = \int_0^\alpha \frac{d\theta}{\sqrt{cos \, \theta - cos \, \alpha}},$$

where t_0 is the period. Thus,

$$\frac{t_0}{2}\sqrt{\frac{gl}{k^2+l^2}} = \int_0^\alpha \frac{d\theta}{\sqrt{sin^2 \, \frac{\alpha}{2} - sin^2 \, \frac{\theta}{2}}}.$$

If we put $sin \, \frac{\theta}{2} = sin \, \frac{\alpha}{2} \, sin \, \phi,$

$$\frac{t_0}{2}\sqrt{\frac{gl}{k^2+l^2}} = \int_0^{\frac{\pi}{2}} \frac{2 \, sin \, \frac{\alpha}{2} \, cos \, \phi \, . \, d\phi}{cos \, \frac{\theta}{2} \, sin \, \frac{\alpha}{2} \, cos \, \phi},$$

or

$$t_0 = 4\sqrt{\frac{k^2+l^2}{lg}} \int_0^{\frac{\pi}{2}} \frac{d\phi}{\sqrt{1 - sin^2 \, \frac{\alpha}{2} \, sin^2 \, \phi}}$$

$$= 4\sqrt{\frac{k^2+l^2}{lg}} \int_0^{\frac{\pi}{2}} \left[1 + \tfrac{1}{2} \, sin^2 \, \frac{\alpha}{2} \, sin^2 \, \phi + \frac{1.3}{2.4} \, sin^4 \, \frac{\alpha}{2} \, sin^4 \, \phi + \ldots \right] d\phi$$

$$= 4\sqrt{\frac{k^2+l^2}{lg}} \cdot \frac{\pi}{2}\left[1 + (\tfrac{1}{2})^2 \, sin^2 \, \frac{\alpha}{2} + \left(\frac{1.3}{2.4}\right)^2 \, sin^4 \, \frac{\alpha}{2} + \ldots \right],$$

or

$$t_0 = t_1\left(1 + \tfrac{1}{4} \, sin^2 \, \frac{\alpha}{2}\right),$$

where t_1 is the period for an infinitely small amplitude, and t_0 is the observed period for an amplitude α.

If, during an experiment, the amplitude falls from α_1 to α_2, where each is small, we may put $sin \, \frac{\alpha_1}{2} = \frac{\alpha_1}{2}$, $sin \, \frac{\alpha_2}{2} = \frac{\alpha_2}{2}$, and thus obtain

$$t_1 = t_0\left(1 - \frac{\alpha_1\alpha_2}{16}\right) \qquad . \qquad . \qquad . \qquad . \quad (30)$$

where t_1 is the " corrected " period.

(b) *Air Correction.*—Since the pendulum swings in air and not *in vacuo*, it is necessary to investigate the corrections arising from

the reaction of the medium. The formula given above assumes that
the pendulum itself is a conservative system, but actually the energy
conservation applies to the pendulum and its associated medium.
Kater, following Newton, took into consideration only the *buoyancy
effect* which produces a virtual diminution in the weight of the pendulum, and he assumed that the air effect was completely represented
by the equation

$$m[k^2+l^2]\frac{d^2\theta}{dt^2}=(m-m')gl\ sin\ \theta,$$

in which m' is the mass of air displaced by the pendulum. From
this we should have, as the length of the simple equivalent pendulum,

$$\sqrt{\frac{k^2+l^2}{lg\left(1-\frac{m'}{m}\right)}},$$

and m' may be calculated from the volume of the pendulum and
the density of air at the time of the experiment.

Bessel, however, showed that the effect is more complicated, for
the resultant accelerating force acts not only on the pendulum, but
also on the associated parts of the medium, and produces an effect
on each part of the energy equation:

$$m(k^2+l^2)\left(\frac{d\theta}{dt}\right)^2-2mgl\ cos\ \theta=C_1.$$

In the first place there will be a loss in accelerating force due to motion
communicated to the fluid. This loss will depend on the velocity
and external shape of the body, and may be expressed as $f\left(\frac{d\theta}{dt}\right)$. In
a time dt the diminution in C_1 will be $d\theta.f\left(\frac{d\theta}{dt}\right)$, and after a time t,
C_1 becomes

$$C_1-\int f\left(\frac{d\theta}{dt}\right)d\theta.$$

Secondly, kinetic energy is generated in each moving particle, and
if dm' and v are the mass and velocity of one such particle, the first
term must be increased by an amount $\int v^2dm'$, where the integral
includes all the affected portion of the medium. Finally, the remaining term must be increased by $2m'gs\ cos\ \theta$, where m' is the mass of
air displaced, and s is the distance between the centre of gravity
of the displaced fluid and the rotation axis.

Thus the equation of motion becomes

$$m(k^2+l^2)\left(\frac{d\theta}{dt}\right)^2+\int v^2dm'-2g(ml-m's)\ cos\ \theta=C_1-\int f\left(\frac{d\theta}{dt}\right)d\theta.$$

The quantity diminishing C_1 is merely a damping factor which, in the case of a pendulum moving in air, has negligible effect on the period.[1]

The integral $\int v^2 dm'$, which should be taken throughout the affected medium, has not been completely investigated, but if it is assumed that each particle is in motion only while the body is moving, the velocity v will be proportional to $\left(\dfrac{d\theta}{dt}\right)$, and will depend on the shape of the body and the position of the particle. Thus

$$\int v^2 dm' = m' K_0 \left(\frac{d\theta}{dt}\right)^2,$$

where K_0 is a constant. The modified equation of motion then becomes

$$C_1 = m\left(k^2 + l^2 + \frac{m'}{m} K_0\right)\left(\frac{d\theta}{dt}\right)^2 - 2g(ml - m's)\cos\theta,$$

and the equivalent simple pendulum length is

$$\frac{k^2 + l^2 + \dfrac{m'}{m} K_0}{l - \dfrac{m'}{m} s} \qquad . \qquad . \qquad . \qquad . \qquad (31)$$

The previously neglected effect is thus a virtual addition to the moment of inertia, and may be realised by assuming that the pendulum carries with it an adherent mass of the medium. The quantity K_0 is constant, or variable, according as the motion of the fluid is, or is not, proportional to the amplitude, and an experiment is necessary to test this. It is found that, very approximately, K_0 is constant.

For a reversible pendulum let t_1 and t_2 be the periods about the two knife-edges, and l_1, l_2 the corresponding distances of the centre of gravity. Then from expression (31),

$$\frac{g}{4\pi^2} t_1{}^2 = \frac{k^2 + l_1{}^2 + K_1}{l_1\left(1 - \dfrac{m'}{m} \cdot \dfrac{s_1}{l_1}\right)}$$

$$= \frac{k^2 + l_1{}^2}{l_1} + \frac{k^2 + l_1{}^2}{l_1} \cdot \frac{m'}{m} \cdot \frac{s_1}{l_1} + \frac{K_1}{l_1} +,$$

where products of small quantities are neglected. Also,

$$\frac{g}{4\pi^2} t_2{}^2 = \frac{k^2 + l_2{}^2}{l_2} + \frac{k^2 + l_2{}^2}{l_2} \cdot \frac{m'}{m} \cdot \frac{s_2}{l_2} + \frac{K_2}{l_2} + \cdots$$

[1] See Chapter XII, Article 187.

Hence,

$$\frac{g}{4\pi^2}[t_1{}^2l_1-t_2{}^2l_2]=l_1{}^2-l_2{}^2+(k^2+l_1{}^2)\frac{m'}{m}\cdot\frac{s_1}{l_1}-(k^2+l_2{}^2)\frac{m'}{m}\cdot\frac{s_2}{l_2}+(K_1-K_2).$$

Approximately,

$$\frac{k^2+l_1{}^2}{l_1}=\frac{k^2+l_2{}^2}{l_2}=l,$$

where l is the length of the simple equivalent pendulum. Thus, substituting l for these quantities and dividing through by (l_1-l_2), we have

$$\frac{g}{4\pi^2}\cdot\frac{t_1{}^2l_1-t_2{}^2l_2}{l_1-l_2}=(l_1+l_2)+\frac{m'l}{m}\cdot\frac{s_1-s_2}{l_1-l_2}+\frac{K_1-K_2}{l_1-l_2}.$$

Both quantities on the right are small corrective terms and so need merely approximate evaluation. Also (s_1-s_2) may be obtained, with sufficient accuracy, by calculation. The last factor is obtained by the use of two pendulums of the same size and shape, but of different masses. The quantity $m(K_1-K_2)$ will be the same for both pendulums, and thus the two equations may be solved to find the value of this factor. It will be noticed that, if the pendulum is symmetrical in form about the middle point, $s_1=s_2$, $K_1=K_2$, and the correction due to air effect is eliminated. A pendulum fulfilling this condition was constructed by Repsold, and is shown in Fig. 12. A bar L is fixed into two rings R_1 and R_2, into which, in turn, are screwed two short rods, terminating in knife-edges K_1, K_2, and carrying the two bobs A and B, of which one is solid and the other hollow. These bobs are adjusted by screwing them up or down on the supporting stem, and thus the periods about K_1 and K_2 can be brought to practical equality.

FIG. 12.—
REPSOLD'S
PENDULUM.

The whole of the air effect may be made negligible by swinging the pendulum in a reduced pressure, and this is now the usual procedure. At low pressures the residual effect is a linear function of the pressure, and thus measurements may be made at two or three different pressures and the graph extrapolated to find the period at zero pressure.[1]

(c) *Curvature of the Knife-edges.*—The effect of knife-edge curvature may be avoided by having plane bearings on the pendulum and a fixed knife-edge on the support.[2] This is now the accepted practice, the knife-edge being ground to a fairly sharp edge, and the plane bearings being accurately flat and always replaced in the same position on the knife-edge.

[1] Heyl and Cook, *Bur. Stds. J. Res.*, 17, 805 (1936).
[2] Heyl and Cook, *loc. cit.*; Clark, *Phil. Trans.*, 238A, 65 (1939).

(d) *Yielding of the Support.*—Unless the support is very rigidly fixed, it will be forced to oscillate coperiodically with the pendulum. This motion may be resolved into vertical and horizontal components. Of these, the latter has much greater effect on the period, and may become an extremely disturbing factor. It is thus necessary to arrange that the support is fixed rigidly, particularly in a lateral direction, and to ensure that no cumulative resonance effect is permitted.

Let O be the point of support of the knife-edge on the plane, and A the centre of gravity, where $OA = l_1$. Suppose that the support yields in a horizontal direction by an amount α per unit force. The acceleration horizontally is $l_1 \dfrac{d^2\theta}{dt^2}$, and thus the force is $ml_1 \dfrac{d^2\theta}{dt^2}$. But

$$\frac{d^2\theta}{dt^2} = -\frac{gl_1\theta}{k^2 + l_1{}^2},$$

and so the force P on the support is given by

$$P = \frac{mgl_1{}^2\theta}{k^2 + l_1{}^2} = \frac{mgl_1\theta}{l_1 + l_2},$$

since $k^2 = l_1 l_2$. Hence the yield, OO', for an angular displacement θ is given by

$$OO' = \alpha mg \frac{l_1}{l_1 + l_2}\theta.$$

Thus the centre of oscillation is raised to C where $OC = \delta_1$ and $OO' = \delta_1\theta$, so that

$$\delta_1 = \frac{mg\alpha l_1}{l_1 + l_2}.$$

The period is therefore given by

$$\frac{g}{4\pi^2}t_1{}^2 = \frac{(l_1 + \delta_1)^2 + k^2}{(l_1 + \delta_1)} = l_1 + \delta_1 + \frac{k^2}{l_1 + \delta_1}.$$

For the other knife-edge we have

$$\frac{g}{4\pi^2}t_2{}^2 = l_2 + \delta_2 + \frac{k^2}{l_2 + \delta_2},$$

and so

$$\frac{g}{4\pi^2}\left[\frac{t_1{}^2 l_1 - t_2{}^2 l_2}{l_1 - l_2}\right] = \frac{1}{l_1 - l_2}\left[l_1{}^2 + \delta_1 l_1 + \frac{k^2 l_1}{l_1 + \delta_1} - l_2{}^2 - l_2\delta_2 - \frac{k^2 l_2}{l_2 + \delta_2}\right]$$

$$= (l_1 + l_2) + \frac{1}{l_1 - l_2}(\delta_1 l_1 - \delta_2 l_2)$$

$$= l_1 + l_2 + mga,$$

since

$$l_1\delta_2 = l_2\delta_1.$$

There is also a varying vertical force on the support, but since the pendulum's vertical acceleration, due to oscillation, is of the second order of smallness in θ, this force will have only a small effect, compared with that due to the horizontal yield.

It will be observed that the correction factor $mg\alpha$ is the movement of the support, produced by a horizontal force equal to the weight of the pendulum, and this may be found by hanging the pendulum over a pulley by a string which is attached horizontally to the support. Then the quantity $mg\alpha$ is measured by means of a microscope.

An additional possible source of error was investigated in the Potsdam measurements made, under the supervision of Helmert, by Kuhnen and Furtwangler.[1] This is the effect of the elasticity of the pendulum in causing a periodic extension due to varying longitudinal tension, and flexure due to changing bending moment. The latter is, in general, the more important,[2] and has the effect of reducing the effective length of the pendulum.

Until recently, the Potsdam value was accepted as a standard of reference, but the work of Clark and of Heyl and Cook [3] has shown it to be about 17 parts in a million too high. Reference to this work will show how the various measurements are made, and how accuracy to about one part in a million is attainable. The American experiments utilised fused silica pendulums in simple rod form with attached flats, one at an end and the other about two-thirds along the rod, the periods being adjusted to practical equality by grinding away one end of the pendulum.

21. Variations of Gravity.—Measurements of g at widely separated localities establish that this quantity is a constant only for a given place, and changes decidedly from place to place, particularly if the alteration in locality involves a marked difference in latitude, or altitude. The acceleration of gravity is intimately connected with distance from the centre of the earth, and thus the variations observed in g are due, in the main, to those two changes in position —latitude and altitude—which produce correspondingly different distances from the centre of the earth. It must be remembered, however, that the value of g, measured by the pendulum, is really the resultant acceleration due to (a) the attraction of the earth, and (b) the tendency of the body to move in a straight line. In other words, the attraction of the earth produces two effects : (i) it supplies the necessary centripetal force, $\dfrac{mv^2}{R}$, to maintain constant the distance, R, of the body from the centre of the earth ; and (ii) the remainder of the attraction generates the acceleration which the pendulum measures. Thus, to deduce the value of the acceleration produced in the body by the earth's attraction acting alone, it is

[1] Kuhnen and Furtwangler, *Veroff. Preuss. geodat. Inst. N.F.*, No. **27** (1906).
[2] See Clark, *loc. cit.*   [3] *loc. cit.*

necessary to make allowance for the radial acceleration due to rotation about the earth's polar axis.

22. Shape of the Earth.—The pendulum experiments of Richer, in 1672, established the difference in g at Paris and Cayenne, and this was explained by Newton by assuming that the earth acted as a uniformly gravitating fluid globe which would, by reason of its rotation, necessarily have an equatorial protuberance. Taking into account both the variation in attraction and in centrifugal action, he calculated the ratio of the axes of the spheroid to be 230 to 229.

Later Clairaut, in his *Theory of the Figure of the Earth*, deduced the result of supposing that the earth's surface is a spheroid of equilibrium, *i.e.* such that a layer of water would spread evenly over it, and he further assumed that the internal density was such that layers of uniform density were concentric and similar spheroids. This latter assumption was shown by Laplace,[1] and later by Stokes,[2] to be unnecessary, the latter proving that no special law of density is required, if the external surface is a spheroid of equilibrium. Clairaut's result may be expressed in the following way : Let g_e and g_λ be the values of gravity at the equator and latitude λ, respectively ; let r_1 and r_2 be the equatorial and polar radii, and m, the ratio of the centrifugal acceleration to gravity at the equator. Then

$$g_\lambda = g_e[1 + (\tfrac{5}{2}m - \varepsilon)\sin^2\lambda],$$

where ε, the ellipticity, $= \dfrac{r_1 - r_2}{r_1}.$

It follows from this that if the earth is an oblate spheroid, two determinations of gravity at stations of widely differing latitude should be sufficient to determine its ellipticity. Actually, local variations interfere, and it is necessary to compare a large number of determinations made at scattered stations. As a result of considering data obtained in experiments, ranging over all inhabited latitudes, Helmert[3] gave as the value of gravity :

$$g_\lambda = 978 \cdot 00[1 + 0 \cdot 005310 \sin^2\lambda] \qquad . \qquad . \qquad (32)$$

and $$\varepsilon = \tfrac{1}{299}.$$

More recently the International Geodetic Association adopted the value :—

$$g_\lambda = 978 \cdot 049[1 + 0 \cdot 0052884\ sin^2\lambda - 0 \cdot 0000059\ sin^2 2\lambda]$$

which agrees very closely with the value suggested by Jeffreys[4] from which the ellipticity of the Earth became $1 : (296 \cdot 4 \pm 0 \cdot 5)$.

23. Divergences from Clairaut's Theorem.—Although to a first approximation the spheroid of equilibrium—ellipticity $\tfrac{1}{300}$—represents the figure of the earth, the result of numerous pendulum

---

[1] Laplace, *Mécanique Celeste*, Bk. 3.
[2] Stokes, *Math. and Phys. Papers*, 2, 104.
[3] Helmert, *Berl. Ber.*, p. 329 (1901) ; p. 843 (1902) ; p. 650 (1903).
[4] Jeffreys, *Roy. Astron. Soc. M.N.*, 97, 3 (1936).

experiments indicated the large variation produced by local effects. Of these, altitude is most important, as was first pointed out by Bouguer. If there were no matter above sea-level, the correction for altitude would be simple, since the decrease should be $\dfrac{2h}{R}$ of the sea-level value, where h is the altitude. The centrifugal force would act in an opposite manner, though to a negligible extent. When tested, this formula gave a greater decrease with altitude than that actually observed, and the difference must be due to the attractive action of elevated masses. Bouguer suggested as the correct expression,

$$g_h = g\left[1 - \frac{2h}{R} + \frac{3hd}{2RD}\right],$$

where g is the sea-level value, d is the density of the earth's surface constituents in the locality of the station, and D is its mean density. This formula—known as *Bouguer's Rule*—was once widely used, but better results are obtained by the application of *Faye's Rule*, which replaces the $\dfrac{3hd}{2RD}$ term of Bouguer's rule, by one taking into account the attraction of the excess of matter under the station and above the average level of the district.

24. Gravity Surveys.—In order to obtain data applying to a more detailed examination than is possible using the full technique of an absolute determination of gravity, it is more usual to combine with such widely separated, but accurate absolute measurements, some form of comparative readings. The means adopted will vary with circumstances but include the following :—

(a) Invariable Pendulums for place-to-place comparisons in regions where no marked local abnormalities exist.

(b) Gravity Balances for use as prospecting instruments for the moderately accurate surveying of abnormal conditions due, for example, to high- or low-density surface constituents.

(c) The Eötvös Balance for the most sensitive small-scale measurements of gravity variations.

The Invariable Pendulum.—This usually takes the form of a rigid pendulum of invar steel oscillating in a partially evacuated vessel from the support provided by a substantial tripod. If such a pendulum vibrates in two different places then, if no other change than a variation in g affects the motion, the ratio of the g values is the inverse ratio of the squares of the times for a given number of vibrations. By standardising the air pressure the various air corrections are made constant, and the only variable condition which may affect the simple relation stated above is that of temperature. In addition to making this small by the use of invar steel, the change of period with temperature may be directly determined and thus corrected for, and in this way the accuracy of the gravity ratio is that of a timing operation which, with frequent and precise broadcast time signals, is of a high order. Since the original period and the correction terms are obtained at a base station where g is known, this makes the dependent determination of the same order of accuracy as that of the absolute measurement.

The use of time signals at the field station may be eliminated by the technique adopted by Bullard[1] in accurate determinations of g in East Africa. Two pendulums are necessary, one at the base, in this case Cambridge, and the other at the field station. An agreed wireless signal, *e.g.* the Rugby weather forecast, in Morse is recorded alongside the pendulum vibrations on a photographic trace, and about an hour later this is repeated. The Morse signals give equal time intervals with which to compare the pendulum periods.

Gravity Balance or Meter.—Next in order of sensitivity and closeness of investigation come the gravity meters, of which several

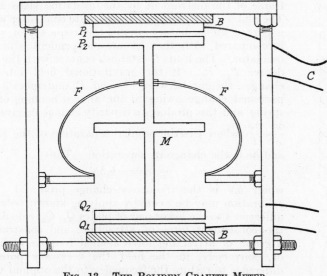

FIG. 13.—THE BOLIDEN GRAVITY METER.

different forms are now in commercial employment. One of the earliest was that described by Threlfall and Pollock[2] in 1899. A fine quartz thread, anchored at one end, can be twisted at the other end by means of a pointer which moves over a circular scale. Fused athwart the thread near the centre is a short metal rod which is weighted so that its centre of gravity is on one side of the thread. Thus to pull it into a horizontal position it is necessary to twist the thread by means of the pointer. This position is only just

[1] Bullard, *Roy. Soc. Proc.*, **141A**, 233 (1933) ; *Phil. Trans.*, **235A**, 445 (1936).
[2] Threlfall and Pollock, *Phil. Trans.*, **193A**, 215 (1900).

stable, since a slight additional movement causes the rod to rotate completely. An arrester prevents this excessive movement, but its tendency to occur makes the position of approaching instability readily determinable. The instrument is calibrated by means of pointer readings at two places where g is accurately known and the linear calibration curve makes it available at other places. The readings may be made rapidly and, when correction is made for temperature effects, they have considerable accuracy.

A more recent form of instrument in which the controlling element is a thin spring under flexure is the Boliden [1] gravity meter which is shown diagrammatically in Fig. 13. The mass M is sustained by the supporting springs F, F and ends in two flat plates P_2, Q_2 which are parallel to, and a short distance from, the plates P_1, Q_1. These are insulated from the main frame of the instrument by the insulating slabs B, B. The plates P_1, P_2 form a parallel plate condenser which is part of an oscillatory circuit, the frequency of which is compared with that of an independent standard oscillator. The leads C establish contact with the condenser P_1, P_2. If the gravitational field intensity changes, the gap between P_1 and P_2 undergoes a proportional change owing to the altered bending of the spring, and this produces a capacity change δc given by $\dfrac{\delta c}{c} = \dfrac{\delta x}{t}$, where t is the original separation of the plates and δx is the change in separation. Thus

$$\delta g = k\delta x = k_1\delta N,$$

where δN is the frequency change produced. The calibration may be made by applying known potential differences to the lower pair of plates Q_1, Q_2, calculating the consequent force of attraction, and constructing a graph of attracting force against frequency change or, conversely, in the field the necessary potential difference to restore the frequency to the original value may be measured as applied to the plates P_1, P_2 or Q_1, Q_2.

FIG. 14.—
GULF
GRAVITY
METER.

Another form of gravity meter is shown in Fig. 14. This instrument, which is known as the Gulf Gravity Meter,[2] makes use of the fact that a spiral spring, constructed from a flat ribbon of metal, tends to unwind, or wind up, when the load it sustains is increased, or decreased. The spiral, fastened to a torsion head at the top,

[1] See Sundberg, K., *Bull. Instr. Min. Met.*, *London*, 402 (1938).
[2] Wyckoff, R. D., *Geophys.*, **6**, 13 (1941). See also *Reports on Progress in Physics*, Vol. IX, 198 (1942–3).

sustains a load, including the mirror M, at the bottom and the constants are such that the load produces an untwisting of about 8 revolutions. Thus any alteration in the weight of the attached mass will produce a proportional rotation of M. A beam of light is then reflected to and fro between M and a fixed reflector so producing a magnified deviation, and after four such reflections, the illuminated slit image is observed by means of a microscope with a micrometer scale in the focal plane of the eyepiece. The operation of the optical system can be understood by reference to Fig. 15 in which M, a plano-convex lens, faces a similar lens N through which passes the light from a slit at S. Each of the plane faces of the lenses has a thin aluminium film, the density of which is arranged to produce maximum intensity in light which has made two transmissions and four reflections. A series of such images is seen, as indicated by A, B, C, D, in which A is the direct image, B that seen after 2 reflections, *etc.*

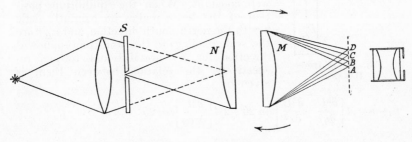

Fig. 15.

In both these instruments the effect of temperature change, though small, is appreciable and control to about $0 \cdot 02°$ C. is necessary. The Boliden instrument is sensitive to about 1×10^{-3} cm. per sec. per sec. and the Gulf Meter to about 5×10^{-5} cm. per sec. per sec., or 5×10^{-2} *milligals*. The last-named unit is now commonly used for small changes in g and is defined by the relation

$$1 \text{ cm. per sec. per sec.} = 1000 \ milligals.$$

25. Eötvös Balance.—The accuracy of the pendulum is insufficient to permit its use for the measurement of small variations in gravity, caused by such neighbouring masses as buildings or comparatively small geological deposits. For this purpose some instrument much more sensitive to changes in g must be used. The Eötvös [1] balance has the necessary sensitiveness. It aims at measuring the gravity gradient, so that it is only comparative.

The essential parts of the balance are shown in Fig. 16. A torsion head T is connected to a platinum iridium suspension

[1] Eötvös, *Wied. Ann.*, **59**, 385 (1896).

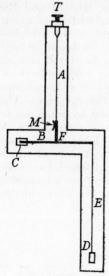

FIG. 16.—EÖTVÖS
BALANCE.

thread A, 60 cm. long, which supports the torsion beam B of length 40 cm. At one end of B a fine platinum wire E, 65 cm. long, supports a small platinum weight D about 25 gm., while at the other end is a counterpoise weight C. A light aluminium rod F, joined to the beam at its centre of gravity, carries a circular mirror M, which is used, in conjunction with a telescope and scale, to measure the deflections of the beam.

If the value of g varies from point to point in the neighbourhood of the instrument, a couple will act on the suspended system and will produce some twist in the wire, deflecting the beam from that (unknown) position which it would occupy if gravity were constant. When the equilibrium position of the beam makes an azimuth angle θ with the north–south direction, and n_1, n are the scale readings in this and the (unknown) direction for no gravitational torque, respectively, the relation between them is given by

$$n_1-n=A\left[\frac{\partial^2 U}{\partial y^2}-\frac{\partial^2 U}{\partial x^2}\right] sin\ 2\theta+2A\left[\frac{\partial^2 U}{\partial x\partial y}\right] cos\ 2\theta$$

$$-C\left[\frac{\partial^2 U}{\partial z\partial x}\right] sin\ \theta+C\left[\frac{\partial^2 U}{\partial y\partial z}\right] cos\ \theta, \qquad . \quad (33)$$

where A and C are instrumental constants, U is the gravity potential, and

$X=\dfrac{\partial U}{\partial x}$ is the value of the gravitational attraction along the
        north direction,

$Y=\dfrac{\partial U}{\partial y}$ is that along the east direction,

$Z=\dfrac{\partial U}{\partial z}$ is that in the vertical direction.

This formula may be deduced as follows [1] :—

The beam is in equilibrium under the opposite actions of the force systems due to

(a) The force of gravity, and
(b) Torsion in the suspension.

[1] See Shaw and Lancaster Jones, *Phys. Soc. Proc.*, 35, 151 (1923) ; 35, 204 (1923) ; Lancaster Jones, *Reports on Progress in Physics*, Vol. II, 97 (1935).

With respect to (a) it is assumed that the complete system has a potential function U, which is uniform in the neighbourhood of any point external to the earth, and of which the derivatives $\dfrac{\partial U}{\partial x}$, $\dfrac{\partial U}{\partial y}$, $\dfrac{\partial U}{\partial z}$, $\dfrac{\partial^2 U}{\partial x^2}$, $\dfrac{\partial^2 U}{\partial x \partial y}$, etc., are also uniform at such points for any system of rectangular axes.

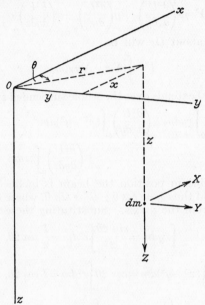

FIG. 17.

In Fig. 17, axes Ox, Oy, Oz are chosen so that Oz is vertical, while Ox and Oy are horizontal. Let X, Y, Z be the forces along these axes on unit mass at a point (xyz). At O we have $X=Y=0$ and $Z=g_0$, if we assume that the resultant force at O is along Oz. At the point xyz,

$$X = X_0 + x\left(\frac{\partial X}{\partial x}\right)_0 + y\left(\frac{\partial X}{\partial y}\right)_0 + z\left(\frac{\partial X}{\partial z}\right)_0 + \cdots$$

$$Y = Y_0 + x\left(\frac{\partial Y}{\partial x}\right)_0 + y\left(\frac{\partial Y}{\partial y}\right)_0 + z\left(\frac{\partial Y}{\partial z}\right)_0 + \cdots$$

$$Z = Z_0 + x\left(\frac{\partial Z}{\partial x}\right)_0 + y\left(\frac{\partial Z}{\partial y}\right)_0 + z\left(\frac{\partial Z}{\partial z}\right)_0 + \cdots$$

and if we assume that, in the region covered by the balance, the forces X, Y, Z are so nearly uniform that we can neglect terms involving x^2, y^2, etc., and the second derivatives of X, Y, Z, then

$$X = x\left(\frac{\partial X}{\partial x}\right)_0 + y\left(\frac{\partial X}{\partial y}\right)_0 + z\left(\frac{\partial X}{\partial z}\right)_0$$

$$= x\left(\frac{\partial^2 U}{\partial x^2}\right)_0 + y\left(\frac{\partial^2 U}{\partial x \partial y}\right)_0 + z\left(\frac{\partial^2 U}{\partial z \partial x}\right)_0,$$

$$Y = x\left(\frac{\partial^2 U}{\partial x \partial y}\right)_0 + y\left(\frac{\partial^2 U}{\partial y^2}\right)_0 + z\left(\frac{\partial^2 U}{\partial y \partial z}\right)_0,$$

and the torque about Oz will be

$$\Gamma = \int (Yx - Xy) dm,$$

where the integral extends over the whole suspended system. Hence,

$$\Gamma = \left(\frac{\partial^2 U}{\partial y^2} - \frac{\partial^2 U}{\partial x^2}\right)_0 \int xy\, dm + \left(\frac{\partial^2 U}{\partial x \partial y}\right)_0 \int (x^2 - y^2) dm$$

$$+ \left(\frac{\partial^2 U}{\partial y \partial z}\right)_0 \int zx\, dm - \left(\frac{\partial^2 U}{\partial z \partial x}\right)_0 \int yz\, dm.$$

In the equilibrium position the beam is inclined at an angle θ to the Ox axis and thus $x = r\cos\theta$; $y = r\sin\theta$, where r is the distance of the particle from the z axis. Substituting these values we have

$$\int xy\, dm = \frac{\sin 2\theta}{2} \int r^2 dm = \frac{I}{2} \sin 2\theta,$$

$$\int (x^2 - y^2) dm = \cos 2\theta \int r^2 dm = I \cos 2\theta,$$

$$\int zx\, dm = \cos\theta \int zr\, dm = mhl \cos\theta,$$

$$\int yz\, dm = \sin\theta \int rz\, dm = mhl \sin\theta$$

in which I is the moment of inertia about the z axis. The latter results follow from the symmetry which exists about the axis of the beam. Thus

$$\Gamma = \frac{I}{2} \sin 2\theta \left(\frac{\partial^2 U}{\partial y^2} - \frac{\partial^2 U}{\partial x^2}\right) + I \cos 2\theta \left(\frac{\partial^2 U}{\partial x \partial y}\right)$$

$$+ mhl\left(\frac{\partial^2 U}{\partial y \partial z} \cos\theta - \frac{\partial^2 U}{\partial z \partial x} \sin\theta\right),$$

where the quantities $\frac{\partial^2 U}{\partial x \partial y}$, etc., are supposed to have the values at the origin. For equilibrium $\Gamma = \tau\phi$, where ϕ is the angle of twist. Let n_1 be the scale reading corresponding to the θ position, and let

n be the reading for the true zero when $\Gamma=0$. Then if d is the distance from the mirror to the scale,

$$n_1-n=2d.\phi,$$

and

$$n_1-n=\frac{2d.I}{\tau}\left[\left(\frac{\partial^2 U}{\partial y^2}-\frac{\partial^2 U}{\partial x^2}\right)\frac{\sin 2\theta}{2}+\frac{\partial^2 U}{\partial x\partial y}\cos 2\theta\right]$$
$$+\frac{2d.mhl}{\tau}\left[\frac{\partial^2 U}{\partial y\partial z}\cos\theta-\frac{\partial^2 U}{\partial z\partial x}\sin\theta\right].$$

If, now, we write

$$A=\frac{d.I}{\tau}, \quad \text{and} \quad C=\frac{2d.mhl}{\tau},$$

we have

$$n_1-n=A\sin 2\theta\left(\frac{\partial^2 U}{\partial y^2}-\frac{\partial^2 U}{\partial x^2}\right)+2A\cos 2\theta\left(\frac{\partial^2 U}{\partial x\partial y}\right)$$
$$-C\sin\theta\left(\frac{\partial^2 U}{\partial z\partial x}\right)+C\cos\theta\left(\frac{\partial^2 U}{\partial y\partial z}\right),$$

which is equation (33).

The quantities I and τ are instrumental constants, and are evaluated as follows :—

(a) **Determination of τ.**—An accurately turned lead sphere—placed alternately on the left and right sides of m in a line perpendicular to the beam and at a measured distance from m—is used to produce a deflection of the beam. Then

$$\tau\frac{n-n'}{2d}=G\frac{Mm}{s^2}\cdot\frac{l}{\sqrt{1+\dfrac{b^2}{4s^2}}},$$

where $(n-n')$ is the displacement of the zero, M, the mass of the sphere, s, the mean distance of the centre of the sphere from the axis of the suspended cylinder, b, the length of the cylinder, and G is the constant of gravitation.

(b) **Determination of I.**—The quantity I is most conveniently determined by hanging the suspended system from a shorter and thicker suspension—in its usual form the period is very long—and finding the time of vibration first alone, and then with added masses on the beam. This is the usual torsion balance method of measuring moments of inertia.

By these preliminary experiments and measurements of d, m, h, and l, the quantities A and C are determined, and thus observations of n_1 in five different azimuths are sufficient to determine n and the quantities

$$\left(\frac{\partial^2 U}{\partial y^2}-\frac{\partial^2 U}{\partial x^2}\right), \quad \left(\frac{\partial^2 U}{\partial x\partial y}\right), \quad \left(\frac{\partial^2 U}{\partial y\partial z}\right), \quad \left(\frac{\partial^2 U}{\partial z\partial x}\right)$$

at the point O.

It is convenient to take readings of n_1 for six different azimuths at intervals of $60°$; the one superfluous reading then affords a check on the observations and enables the readings to be immediately repeated, if any discrepancy of unusual magnitude is disclosed.

Equation (33) may be rewritten

$$n_1-n=A' \sin 2\theta+B' \cos 2\theta+C' \sin \theta+D' \cos \theta \ \dots \quad (34)$$

where

$$A'=A\left[\frac{\partial^2 U}{\partial y^2}-\frac{\partial^2 U}{\partial x^2}\right], \quad B'=2A\left[\frac{\partial^2 U}{\partial x\partial y}\right],$$

$$C'=-C\left[\frac{\partial^2 U}{\partial z\partial x}\right], \quad D'=C\left[\frac{\partial^2 U}{\partial y\partial z}\right].$$

If we put $\theta=0°$, $60°$, $120°$, $180°$, $240°$, $300°$ in (34), and the corresponding values of n_1 are n_1, n_2, n_3, n_4, n_5, n_6 we have

$$n_1+n_3+n_5=n_2+n_4+n_6=3n,$$

$$2\sqrt{3}A'=2(n_2-n_3)-(n_1-n_4),$$

$$2B'=n_1+n_4-2n, \quad 2D'=n_1-n_4,$$

$$2\sqrt{3}C'=2(n_2-n_5)-(n_1-n_4).$$

Thus all the derivatives in equation (33) are determined. In particular the rate of change of g northwards is given by $-C'/C$ and that eastwards by D'/C.

To estimate their magnitude, and thus to obtain an idea of the necessary sensitiveness, we may apply Helmert's formula [1] to the latitude of London, viz. $51° 30'$. At London $g=981\cdot1806$, and thus

$$\frac{\partial g}{\partial x}=\frac{\partial^2 U}{\partial z\partial x}=7\cdot9376\times 10^{-9},$$

$$\frac{\partial g}{\partial y}=0, \quad \frac{\partial^2 U}{\partial x\partial y}=0,$$

$$\left(\frac{\partial^2 U}{\partial y^2}-\frac{\partial^2 U}{\partial x^2}\right)=4\cdot005\times 10^{-9}.$$

In one of Eötvös' instruments the constants A and C were $0\cdot05162\times10^9$ and $0\cdot14087\times10^9$, respectively. Thus for $\theta=90°$,

$$n_1-n=-(4\cdot005\times0\cdot05162)-(0\cdot14087\times7\cdot9376)$$
$$=-1\cdot3, \text{ approximately.}$$

This difference in reading would be easily noted. If there are large local masses, the differences in reading may be as much as ten times the above quantity.[2] The limit of accuracy with pendulum experiments is about 1×10^{-4} C.G.S. units, while that of the Eötvös balance is of the order 1×10^{-9} C.G.S. units, and because of its great sensitiveness the balance has been used commercially in the survey of oil fields, while Shaw and Lancaster Jones used it to map the local gravitational field in a laboratory.

---

[1] Equation (32).   [2] See Shaw and Lancaster Jones, *loc. cit.*

26. Geophysical Prospecting.—Geophysical prospecting is the location of mineral deposits by means of measurements of gravitational, electrical, magnetic, and seismic magnitudes, which have been modified from the normal values by the nature and position of the deposit. There are peculiar difficulties associated with the work, owing to the extreme smallness of the magnitudes measured, the exigencies of field work, and the aggregation of effects, since it is impossible to isolate the deposit from its surroundings.

The gravitational method, with which we are concerned, depends upon the fact that local anomalies of density affect to a measurable extent the space variations of the gravity force which operates upon some type of balance or *gradiometer*, as it is now commonly termed. There are many types of such instruments, *e.g.* Eötvös balance, Oertling and Cambridge gradiometers, but in all cases the readings obtained by means of the instrument are reduced to provide the desired values of the gravity gradients, $\dfrac{\partial^2 U}{\partial x \partial y}$ *etc.*, relating to subterranean anomalies. The procedure is then as follows :—

These subterranean gravity gradients are combined into gradient and curvature vectors, *e.g.*

$$\frac{\partial^2 U}{\partial x \partial z} = \frac{\partial}{\partial x}\left(\frac{\partial U}{\partial z}\right) = \frac{\partial g}{\partial x},$$

where $\dfrac{\partial g}{\partial x}$ is the gradient of g at a point O in the direction Ox, the axis of z being taken as vertical. In a similar manner $\dfrac{\partial^2 U}{\partial y \partial z} = \dfrac{\partial g}{\partial y}$ *i.e.* the gradient of g in the direction Oy. Thus the resultant horizontal gradient, G, is known in magnitude and direction.

Putting $U_\Delta = \dfrac{\partial^2 U}{\partial y^2} - \dfrac{\partial^2 U}{\partial x^2}$ and remembering that the magnitudes of $\dfrac{\partial^2 U}{\partial x \partial y}$ and of U_Δ are fixed in space, and depend only upon the field of gravity at the point considered, we can combine these quantities to form a vector, specified by a magnitude R in a direction making an angle λ with Ox, where $tan\ 2\lambda = \dfrac{2}{U_\Delta} \cdot \dfrac{\partial^2 U}{\partial x \partial y}$. The two solutions λ_1 and λ_2 differ by $\pi/2$, and give the directions of the two principal axes of curvature of the level surface, or as it is called, the equipotential surface at O.

The values of the gradients G and curvature vectors R at the various observing stations in a gravity survey are plotted, the direction of λ_2 being such that *secant* $2\lambda_2$ is of opposite sign to U_Δ. In this manner a representation of the gravity variations over the region is obtained, and from the gradients a series of closed lines, called *isogams*, can be drawn on the plan. These isogams resemble contour lines on an ordnance map, and are everywhere perpendicular to the gradients.

Such an isogam chart is an effective visual guide to the interpretation of the subterranean anomalies which give rise to the gravity variations. If the isogams are parallel and equally spaced, it can be assumed that the structure below the surface is uniformly monoclinic in type, whereas dome-like subterranean structures give rise to isogams resembling the contour of a surface dome.

The variations of the magnitude of the gravity gradient, along a section line of the area, is also used as a means of the interpretation of structures, a type of profile chart being constructed for selected sections. For success in geophysical prospecting, considerable experience, both in the use of instruments and in the interpretation of their indications, is necessary.

27. Acceleration of Gravity at Sea.—The measurement of gravity at sea presents many difficulties, but Duffield [1] carried out a series of experiments during a visit of the British Association to Australia in 1914. The underlying principle was to compare the atmospheric pressure, given by a special marine barometer, with that found by an aneroid barometer. The reading of the former, only, varies with gravity. The value of g is found from

$$g = g_1 \frac{p}{B}, \quad \text{or} \quad \delta g = \frac{g_1}{B} \delta p,$$

where g_1 is the value of gravity in latitude 45°, and p, B are the pressures given by the aneroid and mercury barometers, respectively.

In addition to the temperature correction, the ship's motion involves a correction for the change in centrifugal effect. This amounts to about 0·05 millibar per knot at latitude 50°. A vertical acceleration of the barometer is produced by the rolling and pitching of the ship, or by its rise and fall as a whole. When the mercury is oscillating from this cause, it is necessary to take a mean of successive maxima and minima readings.

The results show that the general deviation of gravity from the theoretical value, over oceans of 6000 metres depth, is not greater than 0·3 cm. per sec. per sec. There appears to be a defect of gravity over very deep oceans and on the edge of a continental mass, especially if there is a coastal mountain range. Higher values are obtained over island stations than over deep seas.

In a gravity expedition, undertaken by the U.S. Navy,[2] measurements of g were made in a submarine at forty-nine stations in the Gulf of Mexico, the Caribbean Sea, and on the way to and from the Hampton Roads. At the same time echo soundings of the depth were made. The results showed a generally high value of g over almost the whole of the Gulf of Mexico, but over very deep water the expected decrease in gravity was observed.

[1] Duffield, *Proc. Roy. Soc.*, **92**, 505 (1916).
[2] Meinesz, *K. Akad. Amsterdam*, **32**, 2, 94 (1929).

A further survey from Curacao to the Azores has been made and discussed by Meinesz,[1] using a more robust form of apparatus.

EXAMPLES

1. Two masses 90 gm. and 100 gm. respectively are supported vertically by a weightless inextensible string passing over a light frictionless pulley. If the pulley is pulled upwards by a force of 200 gm. weight find the acceleration of each of the masses relative to the ground.
$$[g/9 \text{ upwards}; \quad 0.]$$

2. If, in the above question, the mass, radius, and moment of inertia of the pulley were 100 gm., 2 cm., and 200 C.G.S. units respectively, find the linear accelerations of the suspended masses and of the pulley relative to the ground. $\quad [0.280 \ g; \ 0.338 \ g; \ 0.309 \ g.]$

3. Two cylinders of equal size, one solid, the other hollow but with closed ends, roll without slipping down an inclined plane. If the wall thickness of the hollow cylinder is half the external radius while each end thickness is one-eighth of the external length, compare the times for equal distances down the plane and the distances for equal times of travel assuming that each cylinder starts from rest.
$$[0.972; \quad 1.058.]$$

4. A uniform horizontal circular disc is suspended by three equidistant vertical threads of length l attached to the rim of the disc. The disc is now given a small angular horizontal displacement and released. Find the time of one complete oscillation and show that it is independent of the number of supporting threads. $\quad [2\pi\sqrt{(l/2g)}.]$

5. A magnet of moment M is suspended in the magnetic meridian by a bifilar support with inclined threads each of length l, their distance apart being $2a$ and $2b$ at the top and bottom respectively. In order to bring the magnet, whose mass is m, into a position perpendicular to the meridian it is found necessary to revolve the upper points of attachment of the threads through 180 degrees about the vertical symmetrical line. If the horizontal component of the earth's magnetic field is H show that $MH = abmg/\sqrt{(l^2 - a^2 - b^2)}$.

6. A pendulum consists of a metal sphere of radius 1 cm. and mass 35 gm., and a metal thread of mass 2 gm. and length 100 cm. Calculate the periodic time of swing (a) neglecting rotational energy about the centre of mass, (b) taking account of this energy. Take g as 981 cm. per sec. per sec. $\quad [1.986 \text{ sec.}; \quad 2.007 \text{ sec.}]$

7. A uniform square lamina of side 30 cm. oscillates in a vertical plane about an axis perpendicular to the lamina and within its boundary. Find (a) the minimum periodic time of oscillation and (b) the locus of points of suspension about each of which the periodic time is a minimum.
$$[0.993 \text{ sec.}; \quad \text{circle radius } 12.25 \text{ cm.}]$$

8. A thin metal rod is supported by parallel bifilar supports connected to its ends, each thread being equal to the length of the rod. Compare the periodic time of oscillation in a horizontal plane with that when the rod swings as a rigid pendulum about a horizontal axis through one end. $\quad [1 : \sqrt{2}.]$

[1] Meinesz, K. Ned. Akad. Wet. Proc., 43, 278 (1940).

9. In an experiment with a Kater pendulum the mean periodic time about the first knife edge was 1·6248 sec., while the arc of swing of the other knife edge decreased from 8·5 to 6·1 cm. On reversal the mean periodic time about the second knife edge was 1·6232 sec., while the arc of swing of the first knife edge decreased from 8·4 to 5·8 cm. If the distance between the knife edges was 65·77 cm., and the first and second knife-edge distances from the centre of gravity were 42·8 and 23·0 cm. (to the nearest mm.) calculate the value of g.   [981·6.]

10. If the value of gravity in latitude λ at sea level is given in cm. per sec. per sec. by

$$g = 978\cdot00[1 + 0\cdot005310\ sin^2\ \lambda]$$

and the equatorial radius of the earth is 3985 miles, show that the earth is a spheroid produced by the rotation about its minor axis of an ellipse of eccentricity 0·0819 and calculate the value of the polar radius.

[3972 miles.]

11. A simple pendulum, with spherical bob of mass 1 kg., has a length of 100 cm. and hangs from the end of a metal rod which is fixed horizontally into a wall. If the rod is pulled sideways by 1 cm. when a horizontal force of 1 kg. acts parallel to the wall, estimate the per-centage error in a measurement of g when this yielding of the support is neglected.   [0·99.]

12. A common hydrometer has its 1·00 and 0·90 specific gravity divisions 1 cm. apart. When it floats in water its vertical oscillations are found to have a periodic time of 0·7 sec. Calculate its periodic time on the assumption that gravity ($g = 981$) is the only controlling force and explain the difference between the calculated and observed values.

[0·6 sec.]

13. A wheel and axle rotates about a horizontal axis without appre-ciable friction. The motion is caused by the descent of a mass m sup-ported at the end of a thread which is wound around the axle of radius r. If the descending mass falls a distance x from rest in t sec. find the moment of inertia of the wheel and axle. $[I = mr^2(gt^2 - 2x)/2x.]$

14. A massive hoop oscillates in its own plane about a horizontal axis at a distance x above the centre of the hoop. Find the value of x if the periodic time is to be a minimum. Hence, or otherwise, show that when x equals the radius of the hoop the addition of a massive particle at the lowest point of the hoop makes no difference in the periodic time.

$[x = a.]$

15. A double inclined plane in the form of an inverted V has a light frictionless pulley of radius 2 cm. at its apex and, passing over this pulley, is a light inextensible string which is connected at one end to the axis of a solid cylinder of mass 400 gm. and radius 4 cm. and, at the other, to the axis of a thin hollow cylinder of mass 100 gm. and radius 4 cm. These cylinders run freely along the directions of greatest slope of the inclined planes each of which is at 30° to the horizontal. Find (a) the acceleration of the system if the plane is rough enough to prevent sliding, (b) the tension in the string.

[3g/16 ; 87·5 gm. wt.]

16. A heavy uniform rod of length l swings in a vertical plane about a horizontal knife edge passing through one end. Find at what point a

concentrated mass may be placed so that the time of swing may be unaltered. [2*l*/3.]

17. A balance has arms of 10 cm. each and all three knife edges in the same plane. Each scale pan is 8 cm. below its supporting knife edge and the periodic time of oscillation with no load is 4 sec. When each scale pan carries a concentrated load of 100 gm. the time of swing becomes 5 sec. What will be the time of swing for concentrated loads of 200 gm. in each scale pan ? *g*=981. [5·83 sec.]

CHAPTER III

GRAVITATION

28. Newton's Law of Gravitation.—Experiment shows that the attraction exerted by any portion of matter on another depends only on their masses and distance apart. Each body may be regarded as an aggregation of massive particles, and the total gravitational action is the resultant of the individual actions of these constituent elements. The law of gravitational attraction which Newton discovered may be enunciated thus : " Any particle of mass m_1 attracts another of mass m_2, distant d away, with a force, in the line joining them, proportional to the product of the masses divided by the square of the distance of separation." In symbols this becomes

$$F = G \cdot \frac{m_1 m_2}{d^2},$$

where G is a universal constant whose value depends only on the chosen units of mass, distance, and force.

This law has been regarded as the most perfect generalisation of experience in the whole of Physics, because, on the one hand, its range is so wide and, on the other, there is such a vast amount of confirmatory evidence—the divergences, indeed, being so few that until recently it was thought that they were due to undiscovered perturbing influences, rather than to a want of exactness in the law. It is now realised, however, that serious objections may be raised to the above enunciation as a complete description of gravitational force, although these cannot, of course, destroy the harmony between the overwhelming majority of experimental facts and the predictions arising from the Newtonian formula. We shall later discuss the evidence in favour of this law, and review briefly the considerations for the modern view introduced by Einstein.

29. Gravitational Attraction and Potential.—At any point in the space surrounding a gravitating particle, there will be a definite attracting action on another particle placed at that point. Thus the whole of this space may be regarded as permeated by the gravitative influence of the original mass, and we may speak of the *attraction at a point*, when we mean the force which would act on a particle of unit mass placed at that point. Also, to move this unit mass, from one point to another in the gravitational field, would require an expenditure of work against the attraction. The amount of this work—which may be positive or negative according to the direction of movement—is called the *difference in gravitational potential* at the points. The absolute measure of the potential at either point

48

will be indeterminate, until some arbitrary choice of *zero potential* is made. This zero is conventionally taken to be that at a point at an indefinitely large distance from all attracting matter, or, as it is usually expressed, at infinity. We then have the definition : "The (negative) gravitational potential at a given point, due to any system of attracting masses, is the work done in bringing unit mass from infinity up to the point."

It will be realised that the attraction at a point is a vector quantity, while the potential is scalar. If the potential had direction, it would be possible to accumulate energy by bringing the unit mass up to the point along the potential direction, and removing it to a very large distance away in some other direction. It would then be possible to regain the original (infinitely distant) starting-point through a path each point of which is at zero potential, and this would require no expenditure of work. Thus there would be a net gain of energy without a compensating loss at another point, and this is contrary to the principle of energy conservation.

30. Connection between Attraction and Potential.—If at any point in a gravitational field the attraction component in a specified direction is F, then the work done in moving unit mass an infinitesimal distance ds, against the attraction, is Fds. But this is the difference in potential dV between the points at a distance apart ds. Thus

$$dV = Fds, \quad \text{or} \quad F = \frac{dV}{ds} \quad . \quad . \quad . \quad (35)$$

To find the difference in potential at two points, separated by a finite difference, we have $V = \int Fds$, where the limits for s apply to the two points considered.

31. Special Cases of Attractions.—The following cases of attraction are important :—

(*i*) **Thin Spherical Shell.**—In Fig. 18 P is a point placed at a distance a from the centre O of a thin spherical shell of radius r, mass M, and wall thickness t. By symmetry the attraction at P

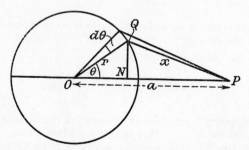

Fig. 18.—Attraction of a Spherical Shell.

will be along OP. Divide the shell into thin circular rings, with centres on OP, of which the typical one has radius $QN = r \sin \theta$ and width $rd\theta$. Each element of this ring is at the same distance, $QP = x$, from P. Its attraction at P along PO is given by

$$dF = G\frac{2\pi r \sin \theta . rd\theta . t . m}{x^2} \cos QPO,$$

where m is the mass per unit volume of the shell. Thus

$$dF = G\frac{2\pi r^2 tm \sin \theta d\theta}{x^2} . \frac{a - r \cos \theta}{x}.$$

This equation contains two variables, θ and x. To eliminate one we may utilise the relation

$$x^2 = r^2 + a^2 - 2ar \cos \theta,$$

or

$$xdx = ar \sin \theta d\theta,$$

and

$$a - r \cos \theta = \frac{a^2 + x^2 - r^2}{2a},$$

so that

$$dF = G\frac{2\pi mtr^2 xdx}{x^2 ar} . \frac{a^2 + x^2 - r^2}{2ax},$$

and

$$F = G\frac{\pi mrt}{a^2} \int \left[1 + \frac{a^2 - r^2}{x^2}\right] dx,$$

where the limits of the integral are given by the position of P.

(a) *P External to the Shell.*

$$F = G\frac{\pi mrt}{a^2} \int_{a-r}^{a+r} \left[1 + \frac{a^2 - r^2}{x^2}\right] dx$$

$$= G\frac{4\pi r^2 mt}{a^2} = G\frac{M}{a^2} \qquad . \qquad . \qquad . \qquad . \qquad (36)$$

Thus the shell attracts an external particle as if its mass were concentrated at its centre.

(b) *P on the Surface of the Shell.*

$$F = G\frac{\pi mrt}{a^2} \int_{0}^{2r} \left[1 + \frac{a^2 - r^2}{x^2}\right] dx.$$

A difficulty appears here, since it seems that the second term of the integral is zero for $a = r$. This is not so when $x = 0$. To find the true value of the integral, we may suppose P to be very near the surface, and thus $a = r + \delta$, where δ is very small, and find its value when δ becomes indefinitely small. Then

$$F = G\frac{\pi mrt}{a^2}\int_\delta^{2r+\delta}\left[1 + \frac{a^2 - r^2}{x^2}\right]dx$$

$$= G\frac{\pi mrt}{a^2}\int_\delta^{2r+\delta}\left[1 + \frac{2r\delta}{x^2}\right]dx$$

$$= G\frac{4\pi mr^2t}{a^2}, \text{ when } \delta \text{ vanishes,}$$

$$\left.\begin{array}{l} = G\dfrac{M}{r^2} \\[2mm] = 4\pi Gmt \end{array}\right\} \qquad . \qquad . \qquad . \qquad . \qquad . \qquad (37)$$

(c) *P Inside the Shell.*

$$F = G\frac{\pi mrt}{a^2}\int_{r-a}^{r+a}\left[1 + \frac{a^2 - r^2}{x^2}\right]dx$$

$$= 0 \qquad . \qquad . \qquad . \qquad . \qquad . \qquad . \qquad (38)$$

There is thus no resultant attraction, due to the shell itself, at any internal point.

(**ii**) *Solid Sphere and Thick Shell.*—A thick shell and a solid sphere may be supposed to consist of concentric thin shells, and thus the results proved above may be utilised in determining their force of attraction.

(a) *P External to Shell or Solid Sphere.*—The whole mass may be supposed to be concentrated at the centre, and thus the field is given, over the range $a = \infty$ to $a = r$, by

$$F = G\frac{M}{a^2} \qquad . \qquad . \qquad . \qquad . \qquad (39)$$

(b) *P in the Thick Shell Cavity.*—The point now considered is within all the constituent thin shells, and thus there is no resultant attraction.

(c) *P in the Material of the Shell.*—Those constituent shells external to P will exercise no attraction, while those inside will act as if their masses were all at their common centre. Thus, if a is the distance of P from the centre, and it has a value intermediate between the external and internal radii of the shell,

$$F = \frac{G}{a^2} \cdot \frac{4}{3}\pi[a^3 - r_1^3]\rho$$

$$= \frac{GM}{a^2}\left[\frac{a^3 - r_1^3}{r^3 - r_1^3}\right], \qquad . \qquad . \qquad . \qquad (40)$$

where r_1 is the internal radius and ρ the density of the material of the shell.

(d) **P in the Material of the Solid Sphere.**—In this case $r_1 = 0$, and

$$F = \frac{G}{a^2} \cdot \tfrac{4}{3}\pi a^3 \rho$$

$$= \tfrac{4}{3}\pi\rho G a = G\frac{Ma}{r^3} \quad . \quad . \quad . \quad . \quad (41)$$

Thus the attraction, which, of course, is directed towards the centre, is directly proportional to the distance from the centre.

32. Special Cases of Potential.—As potential is of the greatest importance in the theory of gravitation, the value of the function, due to a given mass system, will be determined in a few cases from the fundamental definition.

(i) **Potential due to a " Massive Particle."**—Consider the potential at a distance a from the particle of mass M. The attraction at a distance x is $\frac{GM}{x^2}$ towards the particle, and the work done in moving unit mass away from the point by the small amount dx, is $\frac{GM}{x^2}dx$. The total work done in moving the unit mass from a distance a to infinity is

$$-V_a = \int_a^\infty \frac{GM}{x^2}dx = \frac{GM}{a}.$$

The work performed in bringing unit mass from infinity to the distance a from the particle is

$$V_a = -\frac{GM}{a} \quad . \quad . \quad . \quad . \quad (42)$$

(ii) **Potential due to a Thin Spherical Shell.**—Let the shell be divided into rings, such that each element of a particular ring is at a distance x from P (Fig. 18), and thus the potential dV at P due to this ring is, from equation (42),

$$dV = -G\frac{2\pi r \sin\theta . rd\theta . mt}{x}$$

$$= -G\frac{2\pi rmt}{a}dx,$$

$$V_P = \int -G\frac{2\pi rmt}{a}dx,$$

and, again, the limits of integration depend on the position of P.

(a) **P External to the Shell.**

$$V_P = -G\frac{2\pi mrt}{a}\int_{a-r}^{a+r} dx$$

$$= -G\frac{4\pi r^2 mt}{a} = -G\frac{M}{a}, \quad . \quad . \quad . \quad (43)$$

and this would be the result, if all the mass of the shell were placed at O.

(b) *P on the Shell.*—In this case $a=r$, and

$$V_P=-G\frac{2\pi rmt}{a}\int_0^{2r}dx$$

$$=-G\frac{M}{a}=-G\frac{M}{r}, \qquad . \qquad . \qquad . \qquad (44)$$

so that the whole mass of the shell may still be supposed situated at its centre.

(c) *P Inside the Shell.*

$$V_P=-G\frac{2\pi rmt}{a}\int_{r-a}^{r+a}dx$$

$$=-G.4\pi rmt=-G\frac{M}{r}, \qquad . \qquad . \qquad . \qquad (45)$$

i.e. the potential inside the shell is constant and equal to its surface value.

(iii) Thick Spherical Shell and Solid Sphere.—(*a*) *P External to Shell, or Sphere.*—A constituent thin shell of mass M_1 produces a potential dV at P, given by equation (43), *i.e.*

$$dV=-G\frac{M_1}{a},$$

$$V_P=-\frac{G}{a}\Sigma M_1=-G\frac{M}{a} \qquad . \qquad . \qquad . \qquad (46)$$

(*b*) *P in Cavity of Thick Shell.*—A constituent thin shell of radius x and thickness dx produces, at an internal point, a potential dV given by

$$dV=-G\frac{4\pi x^2 dx.\rho}{x}.$$

Thus, for a shell of radii r and r_1,

$$V_P=-G.4\pi\rho\int_{r_1}^r xdx$$

$$=-G.2\pi\rho[r^2-r_1{}^2]$$

$$=-\tfrac{3}{2}GM\left[\frac{r+r_1}{r^2+rr_1+r_1{}^2}\right] \qquad . \qquad . \qquad (47)$$

(*c*) *P in the Material of the Thick Shell.*—The part of the shell exterior to P produces a potential V_1 given by

$$V_1=-G.2\pi\rho[r^2-a^2].$$

The remainder, to which P is external, produces a potential V_2, where

$$V_2=-\tfrac{4}{3}G.\frac{\pi\rho}{a}[a^3-r_1{}^3].$$

Hence

$$V_P = V_1 + V_2 = -G.2\pi\rho\left[r^2 - a^2 + \frac{2}{3a}(a^3 - r_1{}^3)\right]$$

$$= -\tfrac{2}{3}G.\frac{\pi\rho}{a}[-a^3 + 3ar^2 - 2r_1{}^3]$$

$$= -G\frac{M}{a}\cdot\frac{3ar^2 - 2r_1{}^3 - a^3}{2[r^3 - r_1{}^3]} \qquad . \qquad . \qquad . \qquad (48)$$

(d) *P in the Material of the Solid Sphere.*—In this case P is external to a solid sphere of radius a, and internal to a thick shell of radii r and a. The potentials, V_1 and V_2, at P due to these two parts are :—

$$V_1 = -G.\tfrac{4}{3}\pi\rho a^2,$$
$$V_2 = -G.2\pi\rho[r^2 - a^2],$$

and
$$V_P = V_1 + V_2 = -G.2\pi\rho[r^2 - a^2 + \tfrac{2}{3}a^2]$$

$$= -GM\frac{3r^2 - a^2}{2r^3} \qquad . \qquad . \qquad . \qquad . \qquad (49)$$

This result is also given by putting $r_1 = 0$ in (48). It is left to the student, as an interesting exercise, to represent these potentials graphically, and to deduce the attractive forces from the potentials by means of the relation $F = \dfrac{dV}{da}$. As an example, consider equation (48) :—

$$V = -G\frac{M}{2a}\left[\frac{3ar^2 - 2r_1{}^3 - a^3}{r^3 - r_1{}^3}\right],$$

$$F = \frac{dV}{da} = G\frac{M}{a^2}\cdot\frac{a^3 - r_1{}^3}{r^3 - r_1{}^3},$$

and this is the attraction given by (40).

33. Constant of Gravitation—Mass and Density of the Earth.—The attraction exerted by the earth on a body near its surface is merely a special case—although an important one—of universal gravitation, and thus follows the same law. If M is the mass of the earth and R is its radius, while m is the mass of a body on the earth's surface, the gravitational force F is given by $F = G\dfrac{Mm}{R^2}$, since the earth is so nearly spherical that its mass may be supposed to be concentrated at its centre. The acceleration generated, if the body is able to fall freely, is

$$g = G\frac{Mm}{mR^2} = \frac{GM}{R^2} \qquad . \qquad . \qquad . \qquad (50)$$

The radius of the earth is known, and thus, since the acceleration due to gravity is also known, a measurement of either G, or M, suffices to determine the other. An experiment which aims at the measurement of M is sometimes called " weighing the earth," but such a term is used only in the inaccurate sense in which we speak of weighing a body by means of a beam-balance. The earth cannot properly be said to have any weight, if we restrict the latter term to the attraction which the earth exerts on a body near its surface. Experiments on the constant of gravitation arrange themselves naturally into two classes. In the first, the primary measurement is that of M, and then G is deduced from (50), while, in the other, the direct measurement is of G. A knowledge of M and R gives a value for the mean density D of the earth, since

$$M = \tfrac{4}{3}\pi R^3 D \quad . \quad . \quad . \quad . \quad (51)$$

34. The Measurement of M.—(a) *The Mountain Experiment.*—In his experiments in the Andes, Bouguer attempted to demonstrate the presence and the magnitude of a plumb-line's local deflection, due to the neighbouring large mass of Chimborazo. If an instrument is set by means of a plumb-line, it will observe in a vertical plane, only if the line is accurately vertical. If the bob is drawn aside towards the north, the axis of the observing telescope will intersect the celestial sphere to the south of the meridian, and a star in the meridian will appear to have been displaced in a northerly direction, the angular displacement being equal to the divergence of the plumb-line from the vertical. At a second station in the same latitude, some miles to the east or west of the first, the attraction of the mountain is inappreciable, and thus the star has no apparent displacement. These two observations determine the ratio of the two attractions—the mountain's and the earth's—this ratio being the tangent of the star's angular displacement. From the dimensions and structure of the mountain its local attractive action may be calculated, and thus the mass of the mountain is compared with that of the earth. Bouguer's experiment was carried out in very difficult circumstances, and, although successful in detecting the expected effect, his result, which attributed to the earth a mean density of about twelve times that of the mountain, was too high.

The experiment was repeated under the direction of Maskelyne, who was then the Astronomer Royal. The mountain selected was Schiehallion in Perthshire, and it was elaborately surveyed to obtain, with the greatest possible accuracy, both the mountain's mass and the position of its centre of gravity. The plumb-line deflection was determined by means of a zenith sector, the two stations being at equal distances from the centre of gravity and in a north-south line. The apparent shift of a star gave a value double that of the plumb-line deflection produced by the mountain. The estimated average density of the mountain was 2·5 gm. per c.c., while the total relative deflection of the plumb-lines was 12 sec. of arc. From these results the earth's mean density was calculated to be 4·5 gm. per c.c. This value was increased to 5·0 gm. per c.c. after a resurvey of the mountain.

(b) Airy's Mine Experiment.—In this experiment Airy compared the earth's mean density, D, with that, d, of the surface constituents, by determining the values of g at the top and bottom of a coal-mine shaft. If g_1 and g_2 are these two values as measured by means of a pendulum, then, from (50) and (51),

$$g_1 = \frac{GM}{R^2} = \tfrac{4}{3}\pi RDG,$$

$$g_2 = \frac{G}{(R-h)^2}[\tfrac{4}{3}\pi R^3 D - 4\pi R^2 hd],$$

where h is the depth of the shaft; or

$$\frac{g_1}{g_2} = \frac{[R-h]^2}{R} \cdot \frac{D}{RD - 3hd}$$

$$= 1 - \frac{2h}{R} + \frac{3hd}{RD}, \text{ (approximately)}$$

i.e.
$$\frac{g_2 - g_1}{g_2} = \frac{h}{R}\left[2 - \frac{3d}{D}\right] \cdot \text{ (approximately)} \qquad . \qquad . \qquad (52)$$

After two failures through accident, Airy performed the experiment at the Harton coal-pit. The pendulum readings were taken with the greatest care, and this part of the experiment extended over three weeks. Samples of the rocks through which the shaft was bored were assayed, and the value of d was found to be 2·5 gm. per c.c., and the mean density of the earth was calculated to be 6·5 gm. per c.c.

In these and other attempts to utilise large natural masses in the measurement of D, the source of greatest error lies in the calculation of the comparative mass, and the divergence of Maskelyne's and Airy's values for D must be attributed to this difficulty.

35. The Measurement of G.—(a) *The Cavendish Experiment.*—As an alternative to using large masses and comparing their attractions with that due to the earth—which, as we have seen, does not yield results of high accuracy—it is possible to deal directly with the mutual attraction between bodies of comparatively small size. In this case the gravitational forces are so small that refined methods of observation are needed, and all other forces affecting the body must be negligibly small, or accurately measurable. Mitchell suggested that a torsion-balance might be used, but he was prevented from carrying out the experiment, and his apparatus and suggestion passed to Cavendish,[1] giving rise to the famous Cavendish experiment.

A long light rod carried at each end a small massive sphere m, and the whole was supported by a suspension wire attached to a torsion head. Two large spheres M were brought near to the ends of the rod, so that the line of centres was horizontal and at right angles to the rod. In this way the attraction between the spheres

[1] Cavendish, *Phil. Trans.*, **83**, 388 (1798).

produced a couple which tended to twist the suspension thread, and the beam was deflected until the restoring torque, due to the twist in the fibre, equalled the displacing couple. If θ is the deflection, d the distance between the centres of the interacting spheres in that position, and l the length of the beam, then the deflecting couple Γ is

$$\Gamma = G\frac{Mm}{d^2}l.$$

The restoring couple is proportional to the relative twist between the ends of the thread, and so, for equilibrium,

$$G = \frac{\tau\theta d^2}{Mml}, \qquad \cdots \qquad (53)$$

where τ, a constant for the given suspension, is known.

The apparatus actually used by Cavendish was rather large. The beam was 6 feet long, the torsion wire—which was of silvered copper—was over 3 feet long, the deflecting masses M were spheres of lead 1 foot in diameter. A special room was erected to house the apparatus, and all manipulations and readings were made from the outside. Despite this, it was found impossible to avoid all temperature gradients, and air currents produced erratic movements of the suspended system, so that the torsion-beam was never at rest. The equilibrium position was estimated by observing a number of swings, when the masses M were on either side of the beam. These readings were taken by means of a telescope, and the beam carried, at each end, a vernier moving over a fixed scale. Thus a value equal to 2θ was obtained.

Corrections were applied for the following errors :—

(i) Each large sphere attracted also the more distant small sphere, and thus an appreciable opposing gravitational couple was produced.

(ii) There was an attraction on the torsion-beam tending to increase Γ.

(iii) The rods supporting each large mass M tended to increase the deflecting couple.

The mean result calculated from 29 readings gave :—

$$G = [6 \cdot 754 \pm 0 \cdot 041] \times 10^{-8} \text{ C.G.S. units.}$$
$$D = 5 \cdot 448 \pm 0 \cdot 033 \text{ gm. per c.c.}$$

This experiment was repeated many times by other observers, and the results of these and other determinations are given in Table III.

(b) Boys' Modification of the Cavendish Experiment.—In the original Cavendish experiment the accuracy of determination was limited by the following factors :—

(i) The suspension was necessarily rather thick to support the heavy beam. This entailed a comparatively large value for τ and a correspondingly small deflection.

(ii) The method of measuring θ by verniers was not capable of great accuracy.

(iii) Temperature gradients in the large apparatus could not be avoided, and the elimination of the accompanying disturbances due to convection currents was impossible.

(iv) The counter gravitational couple still further reduced θ.

Professor C. V. Boys,[1] by using fine quartz fibres of great strength and regularity in elastic properties, constructed a smaller apparatus on the Cavendish principle with increased sensitiveness ; for quartz threads, though as strong as steel wires of the same size in breaking

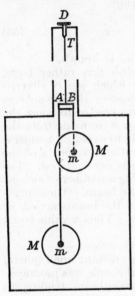

FIG. 19.—
BOYS' MODIFICATION OF
THE CAVENDISH EXPERI-
MENT.

stress, have a much smaller resistance to torsion. The deflection in his experiment was observed by means of a mirror and illuminated scale, and was therefore measurable to a much higher degree of accuracy. The small size of the apparatus made it easier to avoid air currents, and thus the most troublesome difficulty experienced in the earlier work was removed. Finally, owing to the short torsion-arm used, Boys found it necessary, in order to reduce the opposing gravitational couple, to place the pairs of masses M and m at different levels. The main features of the Boys apparatus are shown in Fig. 19. T is the torsion thread, 17 in. long, attached to a torsion head D and supporting the arm AB, which was about 1 in. long, and acted as the mirror for reflecting the light from the illuminated scale of an observing telescope. The small masses m were about $\frac{1}{4}$ in. in diameter and of gold, while the large masses M were lead spheres $4\frac{1}{2}$ in. in diameter.

The results obtained agreed well among themselves, and gave as final values :—

$$G = 6 \cdot 6576 \times 10^{-8} \text{ C.G.S. units.}$$
$$D = 5 \cdot 5270 \text{ gm. per c.c.}$$

P. R. Heyl [2] repeated a method of using the torsion balance first employed by Braun. Braun's apparatus was larger than that constructed by Boys, the distance between the centres of the small masses—each of 54 gm.—being about 25 cm. and that between the large masses—9 kg. each—about 42 cm. All the centres were at the same level, and the apparatus was maintained at a low pressure to minimise convection currents.

[1] Boys, *Phil. Trans.*, A, 186, 1 (1895).
[2] Heyl, *Bureau of Standards Journ. of Research*, 5, 1243 (1930).

Heyl's experiments were carried out in a constant-temperature room. The large attracting masses were steel cylinders, while the small masses were spheres of gold, glass, or platinum at the ends of an aluminium torsion rod, supported by a tungsten thread about 1 metre long. When set swinging with an angular amplitude of about 4°, the system continued to oscillate for about 20 hours. The attracting masses were arranged in two ways : (a) with all four centres in line horizontally, and (b) with the horizontal line joining the large masses bisecting the torsion bar at right angles. In the first, the " near " position, the gravitational attraction accelerates the swing, while in the second, the " distant " position, a retardation is produced. The calculation of the gravitational attractions is complicated by the cylindrical form of the large masses, but when performed for all the mass elements of the oscillating system, the restoring torques are respectively $(\tau + AG)$ and $(\tau - BG)$ per unit twist, A and B being instrumental constants—in practice A was 422,312 and B 176,229 C.G.S. units. Thus the periodic times increased from about 1750 sec. to about 2000 sec. and the elimination of τ from the periodic time equations rendered G in terms of known quantities. Heyl's weighted mean values are :—

$$G = [6 \cdot 670 \pm 0 \cdot 005] \times 10^{-8} \text{ C.G.S. units.}$$
$$D = [5 \cdot 515 \pm 0 \cdot 004] \text{ gm. per c.c.}$$

A redetermination made by Heyl and Chrzanowski,[1] using the same method, showed no significant variations from these results.

(c) *Poynting's Balance Experiment.*—It was suggested by von Jolly that, if the counterpoise of a balance is disturbed by placing, under the mass hanging from one arm of the balance, an additional large mass, then the extra attraction could be measured, and thus G might be found. The difficulty of the experiment lies in the fact that this extra pull is necessarily very small, so that the balance must be extremely sensitive—and therefore very susceptible to disturbing influences—and the corresponding deflection of the beam must be measured by some very delicate method. Von Jolly carried out such an experiment with fair success, and J. H. Poynting[2] performed a balance experiment on a much more elaborate scale. A sensitive bullion-balance was placed in an underground room, and was totally enclosed to diminish disturbances due to air currents. All manipulations were made by mechanisms controlled by rods from the outside. First the sensitivity of the balance was observed by noting the deflection, produced by a change in the position of a rider on the beam. Then the tilt, produced by introducing a large lead sphere underneath one of the suspended masses, was measured in the same way. The ratio of these deflections gave a measure of the additional pull in terms of the weight of the rider,

[1] Heyl and Chrzanowski, *Bureau of Standards, J. of Res.*, 29, 1 (1942).
[2] Poynting, *Phil. Trans.*, A, 182, 565 (1891).

and enabled G and D to be calculated. The general arrangement of Poynting's experiment may be seen in Fig. 20.

The masses m at A and B were lead spheres of about 50 lb. each, and the main deflecting mass M_1—which was also of lead and about 350 lb.—could be brought under A, or B, by rotating its supporting turntable about the pivot P. M_2, a compensating mass, to avoid tilting the floor as M_1 was moved, was about half the weight of M_1. The deflection produced by changing M_1 from position C to position D was due to the excess attraction in the two cases, and, to

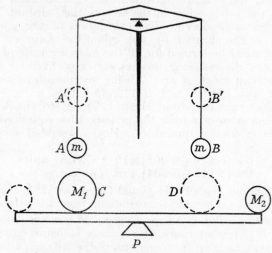

FIG. 20.—POYNTING'S BALANCE EXPERIMENT.

eliminate the effect of M_1 and M_2 on the beam of the balance, the experiment was repeated with the masses m at A' and B', about 1 foot higher. The change in deflection was then due only to this shift in position.

Neglecting the effect of M_2, G may be calculated as follows :—

Let the deflection due to the movement of a rider of weight ng, through a distance x, along the beam be ϕ. Then, $ngx = k\phi$, where k is a constant for small deflections of the balance.

Let d be the distance between the centres of M_1 and m in each position A and B. Then the change in torque is $G\dfrac{M_1 m}{d^2}2l$, where $2l$ is the length of the balance-beam. If the resulting deflection is θ, then

$$G\frac{M_1 m}{d^2} . 2l = k\theta,$$

or

$$G = \frac{ngxd^2}{2M_1 ml} . \frac{\theta}{\phi}$$

A correction has to be applied for the effect of M_2 and the cross effect of M_1 on the sphere m, suspended from the opposite end of the balance-arm.

Both the angles θ and ϕ are small, and to measure them the double-suspension mirror suggested by Lord Kelvin was used. Its action may be followed from Fig. 21. The balance-pointer P has an arm N fixed to it at right angles to its plane of swing, and a second fixed arm M is placed so that a small gap AB—which may

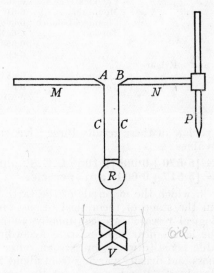

FIG. 21.—KELVIN'S DOUBLE-SUSPENSION MIRROR.

be varied by moving M—is formed. From A and B bifilar supports CC sustain a mirror R, which is used to detect the movement of P. If AB is small, the system becomes extremely sensitive—the effects of air currents on R are minimised by the damping vanes V, which are immersed in oil—and a very small movement of P produces a measurable deflection. If both ϕ and θ are measured with the same setting of the double suspension, there is no need to calibrate the system or to measure the distance AB. Poynting's final result was

$$G = 6 \cdot 6984 \times 10^{-8} \text{ C.G.S. units.}$$
$$D = 5 \cdot 4934 \text{ gm. per c.c.}$$

36. Summary of Results in Experiments on G and D.— Table III gives the values for G and D obtained in the most important of the experiments on the constant of gravitation.

TABLE III.—SUMMARY OF RESULTS FOR G AND D

Experimenter and Date.	Type of Experiment.	$G \times 10^8$ C.G.S. Units.	D gm. per c.c.
1775. Maskelyne and Hutton .	Mountain	7·4	5·0
1798. Cavendish . . .	Torsion balance	6·754	5·448
1843. Baily	,, ,,	6·49, 6·62	5·67, 5·56
1854. Airy	Mine	5·7	6·5
1878. Cornu and Baille . .	Torsion balance	6·618	5·56
1881. von Jolly . . .	Chemical ,,	6·465	5·692
1887. Preston	Mountain	6·61	5·57
1891. Poynting . . .	Chemical balance	6·698	5·493
1895. Boys	Torsion ,,	6·6576	5·5270
1896. Braun	,, ,,	6·658	5·527
1896. Eötvös	,, ,,	6·66	5·53
1898. Richarz and Krigar-Menzel . . .	Chemical ,,	6·684	5·505
1901. Burgess	Torsion ,,	6·64	5·55
1930. Heyl	,, ,,	6·670 '	5·517

In a recent review of these results Birge [1] has suggested as the most probable values :—

$$G = [6\cdot670 \pm 0\cdot005] \times 10^{-8} \text{ C.G.S. units.}$$
$$D = [5\cdot517 \pm 0\cdot004] \text{ gm. per c.c.}$$

The manner in which the materials of the earth are distributed is still largely in the stage of theoretical discussion, although the data of seismological research are continually adding precision to knowledge of the layers near the surface. According to Jeffreys [2] the most probable constitution comprises an outer shell of about 3000 km. thickness and density varying from about 2·7 gm. per c.c. at the surface to about 5·0 gm. per c.c. at the lowest level. This surface crust is solid in character and encloses a molten core which consists mostly of iron with a density, under the conditions of pressure existing, of about 12 gm. per c.c.

37. Qualities of Gravitation.—We shall now discuss some of the circumstances in which the law of gravitation might be expected to vary.

Permeability.—In both magnetism and electricity, where the fundamental laws of interaction between the relevant physical quantities have a close resemblance to the Newtonian Law of Gravitation, it is found that the attraction depends on the nature of the intervening medium. In the gravitational experiments described above, air was the medium between the attracting masses, but the accuracy of astronomical predictions, assuming the same law, indicates that G cannot be greatly different for free space than for air. This, however, is not conclusive, for a similar result is obtained in electrostatics

[1] Birge, *Phys. Soc. Prog. Reps.*, **8**, 90 (1941).
[2] Jeffreys, *Roy. Astron. Soc. M.N.*, **97**, 3 (1936).

and magnetism. The direct experiment performed by Austin and Thwing,[1] in which slabs of various materials were interposed between the attracting elements of a modified Boys' experiment, showed that no change in G could be detected within the limits of the experiment. The effect, if present, is certainly on a much smaller scale than in the cases of magnetic permeability, or specific inductive capacity. Finally, the agreement between pendulum experiments in which different materials are used for the base—and are thus interposed between the pendulum and the earth—indicates again that the effect sought, if present, is small.

Selectivity.—According to Newton's Law the nature of the attracting masses is unimportant, and it is the magnitude of the mass, and not the type of atom, which determines the gravitational field. If we could regard cohesion as merely a static aggregation, obeying the inverse square law of attraction, then the force of cohesion could be determined from molecular size and mass, and the varying tensile strengths of materials would appear to indicate a decided selectivity of gravitation. Such assumptions, however, are invalid, and no such conclusion may be drawn. The negative results of Bessel's hollow bob pendulum experiments, on the other hand, are not necessarily conclusive evidence of non-selectivity, since they merely show that the special case of the earth's gravitation —which is due to many types of material—is, on the whole, non-selective. This may be due to its various parts exerting an average equality of intensified and diminished attractions. The chief experimental foundation for the belief that the quality of the attracting matter is not important, is the agreement among the results of the Cavendish type of experiment which has been made with a variety of different substances as interacting masses.

Directivity.—When crystals grow from solution their characteristic molecular structure seems to indicate a directive action in the inter-molecular gravitation, and this supposition is supported by their well-known directive properties towards light, heat, and electricity. It is necessary, therefore, to test experimentally whether or not the gravitational attraction between crystalline masses depends on their mutual orientation. This was attempted, directly, by Dr. Mackenzie [2] in a type of Cavendish experiment but with negative results. Poynting and Gray,[3] with the same object in view, utilised the theory of forced oscillations by revolving a quartz sphere in close proximity to another suspended sphere. This continued revolution would, if directive action were present, cause a simple harmonic couple to act on the stationary sphere, and if the period of the forcing couple and the free period of the suspended system are nearly equal, a large oscillation of the latter should ultimately result. No positive

[1] Austin and Thwing, *Phys. Rev.*, 5 (1897).
[2] Mackenzie, *Phys. Rev.*, 2 (1895).
[3] Poynting and Gray, *Phil. Trans.*, A, **192**, 245 (1899).

evidence of such a forced vibration could be obtained. This experiment affords the best evidence that gravitation, even in the case of crystals, is not directive, at least for distances large compared with molecular dimensions.

Temperature.—Experiments by Poynting and Phillips,[1] by Landolt[2] and others,[3] show that gravitation is unaffected by temperature, although Shaw,[4] using a torsion-balance of the Boys-Cavendish type, found that G appeared to increase slightly as the attracting bodies were heated. Later results, however, showed that, within the limits of experimental error, if G varies according to the law, $G=G_0[1+\alpha t]$, then α is numerically less than $1 \cdot 6 \times 10^{-6}$, so that, for a temperature range $0°$ C. to $250°$ C., G remains appreciably constant. The earlier statement of a decided change was due to systematic errors introduced by slight displacements of the beam masses.

We are thus finally led to believe that gravitational attraction is a function only of the attracting masses and of their distance apart.

38. Evidence for the Newtonian Law of Gravitation. Kepler's Laws.—In the year 1618 Kepler published the third of his famous laws which were deduced from the astronomical data, especially those obtained by Tycho Brahe, on the motion of Mars. The first law dealt with the shape of a planet's orbit in its motion around the sun, the second with the relation between the orbital speed and the corresponding distance from the sun, and the third, whose discovery followed many fruitless attempts, with the connection between the size of the planetary orbit and the time for its description, *i.e.* the planet's year. The laws may be enunciated as follows :—

Law I.—Each planet moves in an ellipse with the sun at one focus.

Law II.—The line joining a planet to the sun traces out equal areas in equal times, *i.e.* the areal velocity of the radius vector [5] is constant.

Law III.—The square of the time for the completion of one circuit of the orbit (the planet's year) is proportional to the cube of the major axis of the orbit.

It should be realised that these laws are purely deductions from astronomical observations, and no special law of gravitation is assumed. Indeed, the formulation of the third law was long delayed through the accident that the numerical relation given above was not tested until many other possibilities had failed. It follows, therefore, that for any suggested law of gravitation to be provisionally accepted, it must immediately satisfy the test of these empirical laws. That the Newtonian Law does so without requiring sub-

---

[1] Poynting and Phillips, *Proc. Roy. Soc.*, A, **76**, 445 (1905).
[2] Landolt, *Preuss. Ak. Wiss. Berlin, Sitz. Ber.*, 8 (1906) ; 16 (1908).
[3] See above papers.   [4] Shaw, *Phil. Trans.*, A, **216**, 349 (1916).
[5] See Chapter XII, Article 193.

sidiary hypotheses is strong evidence in its favour. We shall see later [1] exactly how the inverse square law fulfils this condition. Briefly, the process is as follows. From any hypothetical law of gravitation—and, therefore, of gravitational accelerations—a system of particle dynamics may be built up by purely mathematical methods. The shapes of orbits under given initial conditions— *i.e.* their geometry—and the velocity-distance relations—*i.e.* their kinematics—follow from the assumed law of acceleration, and the results of immediate importance are :—

(i) If a particle moves so that its acceleration is always directed towards some fixed point, the areal velocity of the radius vector, drawn from that point, is constant.

(ii) If an inverse square law of acceleration towards that point is assumed, then the path is a conic with the point as one focus.

(iii) According to the same law, if the orbit is a closed curve— *i.e.* an ellipse or a circle—the periodic time t_0 is related to the semi-major axis of the ellipse, or radius of the circle, a, thus

$$t_0{}^2 \propto a^3.$$

If we compare these deductions with Kepler's Laws the following properties of celestial bodies become evident :—

From **Law II.**—Planets are under the action of central accelerations directed towards the sun.

From **Laws I** and **III.**—The central acceleration varies with distance according to the inverse square law.

This correspondence shows that, in so far as Kepler's Laws are strictly true, gravitation over planetary distances follows the Newtonian Law. The latter, however, is much more general than this, and its applicability to terrestrial distances is shown by the general agreement between determinations for G over distances, varying from many yards to a few inches, and also by the fact that the moon's motion is correctly accounted for by the assumption that the known attraction of the earth on a body, near its surface, is modified at the moon by the inverse square law. The minimum distance at which the law holds is not yet known with certainty, but it probably breaks down at distances of less than molecular magnitude.

39. Newton's Law as an Approximation. Einstein's Theory of Relativity.

—In the preceding paragraph it was shown that the Newtonian Law of Gravitation is upheld over a large range by a vast body of experimental evidence. It must follow, then, that, if any observations indicate divergences from its predictions, they are due to the law being only an approximation—though certainly an extremely close one—to the true law. Before the outstanding discrepancies are discussed, however, there are two difficulties inherent in Newton's enunciation which are the chief reasons for criticism. In the first place, the mass of a body varies with its

[1] See Chapter XII, Article 194.

velocity, and we are left in considerable doubt as to what value is the correct one for insertion in the formula. Secondly, distance is not as fundamentally simple as it appears to be, since the measurement assigned to a distance depends upon the circumstances of the observer making the measurement. It is not intended here to present a full description of Einstein's relativity theory, but reference to the Michelson-Morley experiment will indicate that the numerical value, assigned to the distance between two points, varies according to the system of space co-ordinates chosen, *i.e.* to the observer making the experiment. The negative result of this experiment is usually explained by the Fitzgerald contraction of bodies in their line of motion. There is therefore a similar ambiguity about the remaining term in the Newtonian Law. These two differences are, of course, small, but it was by taking them into account—an incidental consequence of the theory of relativity—that the outstanding deviations from the Newtonian Law were explained.

There are two main sections of the relativity theory, one, the restricted or special theory, which deduces the consequences of an invariable velocity of light to all co-ordinate systems having no relative accelerations. For our immediate purpose only three of these results need be mentioned. If a body A moves with reference to an observer O_1 with velocity u, while O_1 moves in the same direction with velocity v relative to a second observer O_2, then the velocity of A relative to O_2 is given by

$$V = \frac{u+v}{1+\dfrac{uv}{c^2}},$$

instead of $V = u+v$ of classical Newtonian mechanics. From this it follows that if u is the velocity of light in a medium stationary with reference to O_1, the velocity apparent to O_2 will be given by V above or, neglecting v^2, compared with c^2 we have

$$V = u+v\left(1-\frac{u^2}{c^2}\right), \quad \text{or,}$$

$$V = u+v\left(1-\frac{1}{\mu^2}\right),$$

where μ is the refractive index of the medium. This is the well-known Fizeau formula in optics. Secondly, by reason of relative motion the inertial effect of a body is increased, so that the mass is a function of the velocity. The connection between the rest mass m_0 and the moving mass m is :—

$$m = \frac{m_0}{\sqrt{1-\dfrac{v^2}{c^2}}},$$

and as a third immediate deduction the energy of a body is given by

$$E=mc^2,$$

so that a body at relative rest has an energy m_0c^2.

The other section of the relativity theory, the general theory, determines the necessary transformation equations for systems of co-ordinates with mutual accelerations, and again three conclusions are of particular importance. Firstly, the inertial mass which enters into normal dynamical formulæ and the gravitational mass are identical. Secondly, natural orbits undergo a continuous precessional motion, such as that of the perihelion in the orbit of Mercury, the exact amount of which was given by the theory. Thirdly, a ray of light has a mass which is appreciable by reason of its great velocity, and thus should be deflected when moving in a strong gravitational field. The deflections, and thus the apparent shift of the light source, may be calculated according to both laws. There is, at present, no possibility of making a test of this effect on a terrestrial scale, owing to the extremely minute lateral displacement in a moderately long ray path, but conditions are favourable during a total solar eclipse, when stars may be seen in a direction close to the edge of the sun. In these circumstances the apparent displacement is of the order of one second of arc which, with a long focal length telescope, is easily measured with accuracy. Einstein's theory predicts a movement double that given by Newton's Law, and experiment has shown again in this case that the former is verified, as accurately as experimental errors permit.

A further experiment in favour of the relativity law of gravitation, and to that extent against the older law, is concerned with the relative positions of lines due to similar sources on the sun, or other celestial body, and earth, respectively. The former should be displaced, relatively to the latter, towards the red end of the spectrum. The experiment is one of great difficulty by reason of the smallness of the effect and the relatively large movements produced by pressure, etc., but it has been successfully carried out by W. S. Adams [1] of the Mount Wilson Observatory. The observation was made on the companion of Sirius. The corrected value of the observed shift was 21 km. per sec., or 0·32 Angstrom units. This value, interpreted as a relativity displacement, gave a radius for the star of about 18,000 km. The result agrees with measurements of the size based on other methods, and affords direct evidence from stellar spectra for the validity of the third test of the theory of general relativity.

In conclusion, we may say that, for all except the smallest distances and one or two outstanding phenomena, the Newtonian Law of Gravitation is very approximately true, but to explain these differences and to achieve greater definiteness and philosophical satisfaction, the Einstein theory of relativity is necessary.

---

[1] Adams, *Proc. Amer. Acad. Sci., II* (1925).

EXAMPLES

1. Find the attraction due to a thin circular disc, of radius r and mass per unit area m, at a point, distant x from the disc, on the line through the centre and perpendicular to its plane. Find also the value of this attraction when the point is indefinitely close to the disc.
$$[2\pi Gm(1-x/\sqrt{(x^2+r^2)})\;;\;\; 2\pi Gm.]$$

2. If a spherical mass of radius a and density d has an eccentric spherical cavity of radius b, show that the attraction at any two points in the cavity is the same in magnitude and direction and find its value if the distance of the centre of the cavity from that of the sphere is c.
$$[4\pi Gdc/3.]$$

3. In a spherical mass the density varies inversely as the distance from the centre. Show that the attraction is the same at any two internal points.

4. If a uniform sphere has a mass M and radius r find the attraction which one hemisphere exerts upon the other. $[3GM^2/8r^2.]$

5. Find the attraction produced by a long, thin uniform rod of mass m per unit length at a distance r from the rod, if r is small compared with the length of the rod and the distance of each end of the rod is large compared with r. $[2mG/r.]$

6. Find the total gravitational potential energy of a uniform sphere of mass M and radius r. Discuss the significance of the negative sign.
$$[-3GM^2/5r.]$$

7. Prove that the value of gravity at a point on an elevated tableland of height h is given by Bouguer's rule :
$$g[1-2h/R+3hd/2RD],$$
where R is the earth's radius, d the surface density, D the mean density of the earth, and g the sea-level value of gravity. [Use the relation obtained in question 1 above.]

8. If the density of the earth at a distance x from the centre is $14\cdot5-12x/R$ gm. per c.c. where R is the radius of the earth, which is supposed to be spherical, show that the initial rate of increase of gravity per cm. below the surface of the earth is $14\cdot7\ G$ where G is the constant of gravitation in C.G.S. units.

9. If the moon's distance from the earth is 240,000 miles, the earth's radius is 4000 miles, g at the surface of the earth is $32\cdot2$ ft. per sec. per sec., find the time taken by the moon to complete one circuit of its orbit around the earth.   [27·37 days.]

10. Compare the minimum velocity with which a particle would circulate around the earth near its surface with the minimum vertical velocity with which the particle must be projected in order to move completely beyond the earth's influence. $[1:\sqrt{2}.]$

11. A smooth straight narrow tunnel is bored through an isolated uniform sphere of density d and a small particle is allowed to move in it from a position of rest. Show that the resulting motion is simple harmonic whose period is independent of the direction of the tunnel and of the size of the sphere. Find the periodic time of one vibration.
$$[T^2=3\pi/Gd.]$$

12. A sensitive bullion balance has a sensitivity such that when a milligram rider is moved 1 cm. along the balance arm the deflection of the balance is 500 scale divisions. Two small spheres each of mass 350 gm. and radius 2 cm. are counterpoised on the balance and hang at a distance of 20 cm. apart. Then a lead sphere of radius 10 cm. and density 11·4 gm. per c.c. is moved from under one hanging sphere to a position directly beneath the other in each case nearly touching the smaller sphere. Find the constant of gravitation if the consequent deflection of the balance is 68·6 scale divisions. $g = 981$.

$$[6·67 \times 10^{-8}.]$$

13. In a Cavendish type of experiment to measure the constant of gravitation the spheres at the end of the beam had masses of 2 gm. each. The length of the beam, whose mass could be neglected, was 10 cm., and the deflecting spheres were of mass 14 kg. each. The distance between centres of adjacent attracted and attracting spheres was 15·5 cm. in a horizontal direction perpendicular to the beam. If the restoring torque per radian twist between the ends of the suspension was 0·05 dyne-cm. find the deflection, on a screen placed 2 metres from the beam, of light rays incident upon a mirror fixed to the beam. Take G as $6·67 \times 10^{-8}$. [2·10 mm.]

14. Find the gravitational potential and the attraction at a point on the axis of a circular hoop of mass M and radius r if the distance of the point from the plane of the hoop is x. Hence find the value of x when (a) the potential and (b) the attraction is a maximum.

$$[-GM/\sqrt{(r^2 + x^2)} ; \quad GMx/(r^2 + x^2)^{3/2} ; \quad 0 ; \quad x = r/\sqrt{2}.]$$

15. A uniform sphere has a radius 2 cm. Find the percentage increase in its weight when a second sphere of radius 20 cm. and density 12 gm. per c.c. is brought underneath it and nearly touching it. $g = 981$; $G = 6·67 \times 10^{-8}$. $[5·65 \times 10^{-6}.]$

16. If the mean density of the earth is 5·5 gm. per c.c. and its radius 4000 miles, while the average surface density in the vicinity of a mine shaft 0·5 miles deep is 2·5 gm. per c.c., find the acceleration due to gravity at the bottom of the shaft given that the surface value of g is 981·200 cm. per sec. per sec. [981·278.]

CHAPTER IV

GYROSCOPIC MOTION

40. Precessional Torque.—It has been shown previously, in Article 10, that a rotating body under the action of a constant torque, whose axis is at right angles to the rotation axis of the body, reacts to the couple by changing its plane of rotation. This type of motion is called precession, and the couple causing it is called the *precessional torque*. Its magnitude may be obtained as follows.

If I is the moment of inertia of the rotating body about its revolution axis, and ω the angular velocity of rotation, then the angular momentum $I\omega$ may be represented vectorially at any instant by a line, drawn normal to the plane of rotation, of length proportional to $I\omega$. Thus, suppose the body is a disc revolving about its geometrical axis, and let MN (Fig. 22) be the edge of the disc whose plane is revolving about an axis, perpendicular to the figure at a

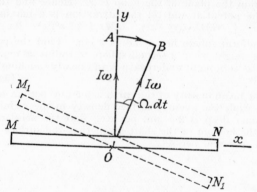

FIG. 22.—PRECESSION OF FLY-WHEEL.

precessional rate Ω. After a short interval of time, the disc moves to M_1N_1 through an angle $\Omega.dt$, and the angular momenta at the beginning and end of this interval are represented by OA and OB, where the angle AOB is $\Omega.dt$. The vectorial change in angular momentum is $AB=I\omega.\Omega.dt$, and thus the rate of change of angular momentum is $I\omega\Omega$. This rate of change is equal to the applied torque and, thus, the precessional torque Γ_1 is given by

$$\Gamma_1=I\omega\Omega,$$

or
$$\Omega=\frac{\Gamma_1}{I\omega} \qquad . \qquad . \qquad . \qquad . \qquad (54)$$

The change of angular momentum is along AB, *i.e.* it is parallel to the plane of rotation and perpendicular to the axis of rotation, so that AB must be the axis of the applied torque. Hence we see that, if the axis of rotation is along Oy and the axis of the applied torque is along Ox, then the body precesses about the third mutually perpendicular axis Oz. This fact is illustrated in Fig. 23, where the disc is shown in perspective. The two forces, P, form the couple about the axis Ox, and the precessional motion will tend to bring M towards R and N towards S. It will be noticed that, if the disc were not revolving, the couple would tend to move the disc about the line MN, and T would move towards R and U towards S. Thus the rule for the direction of precession may be ex-

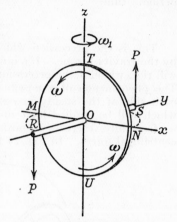

FIG. 23.—THE GYROSTAT.

pressed as follows : The direction of precession is such that a motion of 90° in that direction would bring the plane of the disc into the original plane of the precessional couple and, when this parallelism is complete, the direction of the rotation is that of the original torque.

41. Gravitational and Centrifugal Torques.—In most cases of precessional motion the body is supported at a point, not on the vertical through the centre of gravity of the body, and, as a result, there is a gravitational couple which tends to rotate the body into a position of smaller potential energy, *i.e.* to lower the centre of gravity. If the body is not revolving, this is the sole result of the gravitational couple, but if the body is also revolving about some axis, the gravitational couple supplies the torque necessary to produce precession, and if, further, no other couple acts on the body, these two torques are equal, and the precessional rate maintained by the gravitational torque, Γ_2, is given by

$$\Omega = \frac{\Gamma_2}{I\omega}.$$

This motion is termed *gyroscopic*, and the body is called a *gyroscope*.

Such a case is illustrated in Fig. 24, which represents a heavy disc revolving at high speed, ω, about its geometrical axis, AOB, which is supported at B by a vertical pivot BC. If $OB = l$ and mg is the weight of the disc, the gravitational couple acting on the disc is $\Gamma_2 = mgl$, and the precessional rate which can be maintained by this couple is

$$\Omega = \frac{mgl}{mk^2\omega} = \frac{gl}{k^2\omega}, \qquad . \qquad . \qquad . \qquad . \qquad (55)$$

where k is the radius of gyration of the disc about the axis AOB. Thus one complete cycle of the precessional motion is made in the periodic time

$$t_0 = 2\pi \frac{k^2 \omega}{gl}.$$

This is the precession which, once started, may be *maintained* by the gravity torque. If a quicker rate is given, then the axis AOB will rise, while, if the precession is retarded, the axis AOB will fall. The phenomenon of a possible oscillation of the rotation axis on each side of the steady precession position has important results, which will be studied later under the heading of *nutation*.

Generally, there is a third couple acting on the body, due to centrifugal forces. In Fig. 24 the centripetal reaction at B is along

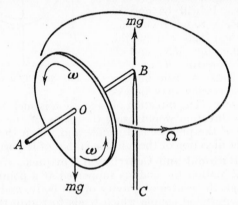

FIG. 24.—PRECESSION OF A GYROSTAT UNDER GRAVITY.

the line AOB, while the centrifugal effort is along BOA, and these two equal forces, acting in the same straight line, give an effect, in a practical case, which merely increases the frictional constraint, at the pivot, to precession. If the centrifugal effect and opposite reaction at the support are not in the same straight line, they constitute a third couple called the *centrifugal torque*.

42. Lanchester's Rule.—In order that the body shall not move outwards from the centre of precession, it is necessary for the centrifugal torque to be balanced by an equal and opposite centripetal torque. This balancing effect is derived from the gravitational torque, and the resultant is available to produce precession.

Let $\Gamma_1, \Gamma_2, \Gamma_3$ be the magnitudes, supposed in the same direction, of the gyrostatic, gravitational, and centripetal torques, respectively. Then, from the considerations above, we have

$$\Gamma_2 - \Gamma_3 = \Gamma_1, \qquad \cdot \qquad \cdot \qquad \cdot \qquad \cdot \qquad (56)$$

and if it happens that Γ_2 is clockwise when Γ_3 is anticlockwise, then in (56) above the sign of Γ_3 is negative. We have assumed here that the gravitational torque exceeds the centripetal torque, and that Γ_1 has the same sign as Γ_2. This is not obviously true, and it is necessary to enunciate some rule which shall give, for any given direction of precession, the necessary sense of the torque producing it. A general rule of this kind was enunciated by Lanchester in the form : View the gyrostat from a point in its plane with the line of sight perpendicular to the axis of the given precession. Now let the gyrostat move slightly in the direction of precession. A point on its circumference is seen to describe an ellipse, and the sense of its path gives the direction of the precessional torque, while the line of sight is its axis. An example of the application of this rule is given in the next section.

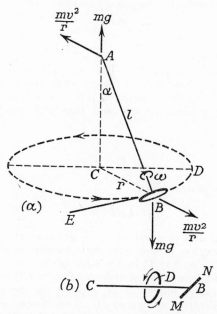

Fig. 25.—The Gyrostatic Pendulum.

43. Gyrostatic Pendulum.—As an example of the application of equation (56), consider the case of a small heavy gyrostat revolving about a light rigid rod AB (Fig. 25) as axis, with angular velocity ω, and precessing about the vertical AC at a rate Ω. Such an arrangement is called a *gyrostatic pendulum*. The three torques acting on the pendulum are :—

(i) *Gravitational Torque* Γ_2.—If the weight of the gyrostat, which may be supposed all concentrated at the point B, is mg, then the gravitational couple is composed of this force mg acting downwards through B, and an equal upward reaction of the support at A. These together form a couple given by

$$\Gamma_2 = mgl \sin \alpha,$$

where α is the angle BAC.

(ii) *Centripetal Torque* Γ_3.—The centripetal force on the gyrostat is $\dfrac{mv^2}{r}$ acting along CB, and an opposite reaction of the support, acting at A, produces a centrifugal couple equal to

$$\frac{mv^2}{r} l \cos \alpha,$$

where v is the speed of the gyrostat around the circle of radius $CB = r$. The opposing centripetal torque Γ_3 is thus

$$\Gamma_3 = \frac{mv^2}{r} l \cos \alpha,$$

and acts in the same direction as Γ_2.

(iii) *Gyrostatic Torque* Γ_1.—The rod AB is always perpendicular to the plane of rotation of the gyrostat, and so the rate of precession Ω is the angular velocity of AB. In a time dt the point B moves through a distance vdt, and thus AB moves through an angle $\dfrac{vdt}{l}$, or

$$\Omega = \frac{v}{l},$$

so that, from equation (54),

$$\Gamma_1 = I\omega\Omega = mk^2\omega\frac{v}{l},$$

where k is the radius of gyration of the gyrostat about the axis AB. To find the direction of this gyrostatic torque, apply Lanchester's rule. Let MN (Fig. 25) (b) be the edge of the gyrostat when at B the line of sight being EB at right angles to CB and AB. Then when the pendulum moves to D, a point on the disc appears to rotate in the direction shown at D. This is opposed to the sense of Γ_2 and Γ_3, and so

$$\Gamma_1 = -mk^2\omega\frac{v}{l},$$

if it is to be substituted in (56).

The periodic time t_0 is given by $vt_0 = 2\pi r$, and thus from (56),

$$-mk^2\omega\frac{2\pi r}{t_0 l} = mgl \sin \alpha - \frac{m}{r}\left(\frac{2\pi r}{t_0}\right)^2 l \cos \alpha,$$

or

$$-k^2\omega \sin \alpha\left(\frac{2\pi}{t_0}\right) = gl \sin \alpha - l^2 \sin \alpha \cos \alpha\left(\frac{2\pi}{t_0}\right)^2,$$

and, putting $\dfrac{2\pi}{t_0}=p$, we have

$$p^2l^2 \cos\alpha - pk^2\omega - gl = 0,$$

which gives

$$p = \frac{+k^2\omega \pm \sqrt{k^4\omega^2 + 4gl^3 \cos\alpha}}{2l^2 \cos\alpha} \qquad . \qquad . \quad (57)$$

To decide between the two possible values of p put $\omega=0$. The system then becomes a conical pendulum for which

$$\frac{2\pi}{t_0} = p = +\sqrt{\frac{g}{l\cos\alpha}},$$

so that the positive sign in (57) is required.

44. Rolling Disc.—Another familiar example of gyroscopic motion is that of a thin disc, projected to roll over a horizontal surface with its plane vertical. While its translational velocity is greater than a certain critical value, its path is a straight line, but below this velocity the plane of the disc inclines to the vertical, and, at the same time, the path becomes curved towards the " side

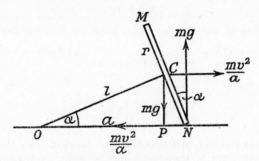

Fig. 26.—Rolling Disc.

of lean." This curvature of the resulting path increases as the velocity is decreased by friction. Thus the path followed on the horizontal surface is spiral in form until the disc falls flat.

Let MN (Fig. 26) be the edge of the disc when the linear velocity of its centre C is v, and its plane makes an angle α with the vertical. The three torques acting on the disc in a clockwise direction are

$$\Gamma_2 = -mg \cdot PN = -mgr \sin\alpha,$$

$$\Gamma_3 = -\frac{mv^2}{a} \cdot PC = -\frac{mv^2}{l\cos\alpha}r\cos\alpha = -mv^2 \tan\alpha,$$

$$\Gamma_1 = -mk^2\omega\Omega = -mk^2 \cdot \frac{v}{r} \cdot \frac{v}{l} = -mk^2 \cdot \frac{v^2}{r^2} \cdot \tan\alpha.$$

Hence, from (56),

$$mk^2 . \frac{v^2}{r^2} . tan\ \alpha = mgr\ sin\ \alpha - mv^2\ tan\ \alpha,$$

and thus

$$v^2 \left[1 + \frac{k^2}{r^2}\right] = gr\ cos\ \alpha,$$

or

$$cos\ \alpha = \frac{v^2}{gr}\left[1 + \frac{k^2}{r^2}\right].$$

This gives the angle of lean for a given velocity, and the critical velocity, or minimum forward speed for straight line motion, is

$$v^2 = \frac{gr}{1 + \dfrac{k^2}{r^2}}.$$

For a disc $k^2 = \frac{1}{2}r^2$, and

$$v = \sqrt{\tfrac{2}{3}gr}.$$

For a hoop $k = r$, and

$$v = \sqrt{\tfrac{1}{2}gr}.$$

The radius of curvature of the path on the horizontal surface is the distance $ON = \dfrac{r}{sin\ \alpha} = \dfrac{r}{\sqrt{1 - cos^2\ \alpha}}$, and thus is given by

$$\frac{r}{\sqrt{1 - \dfrac{v^4}{g^2 r^2}\left[1 + \dfrac{k^2}{r^2}\right]^2}}.$$

45. General Case of Precessional Motion.—In the preceding cases a simple form of treatment was possible by reason of a tacit assumption that, for the purposes of calculating the gravitational and centrifugal torques, the mass of the body could be assumed to be concentrated at its centre. A little reflection will show that this is not generally possible, because only points on the rotation axis move around the axis of precession in circular paths and, even for these points, the radius of the circular path is different for each. Other points have a much more complicated path, compounded of their motions about the axes of rotation and precession, respectively. It is necessary, therefore, to consider the results of these varied motions of different particles before the more general cases of precessional motion, such as that of the spinning top, can be treated fully.

46. General Expression for Angular Momenta.—Since in the following cases of gyroscopic motion it is more convenient to use axes fixed in the body and not in space, we shall deduce expressions for the angular momenta about such axes, the only limitation being that the origin is supposed fixed.

Let Ox, Oy, Oz (Fig. 27) be three mutually perpendicular axes, ω_1, ω_2, and ω_3 the angular velocities of the body about these axes, and h_1, h_2, and h_3 the corresponding angular momenta. Suppose that $P(x, y, z)$ is a point in the body at which is placed a particle of mass m, and let u, v, w be its velocity components along Ox, Oy, Oz, respectively. Then, from the figure,

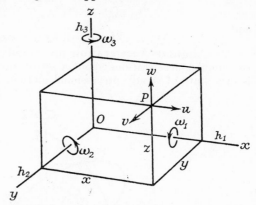

FIG. 27.—GENERAL EXPRESSION FOR ANGULAR MOMENTA.

$$u=\omega_3 y-\omega_2 z \atop v=w_1 z-\omega_3 x \atop w=\omega_2 x-\omega_1 y \Bigg\} \qquad . \qquad . \qquad . \qquad . \qquad (58)$$

$$h_1=\Sigma m(vz-wy)$$
$$=\Sigma m(w_1 z^2-\omega_3 zx-\omega_2 xy+\omega_1 y^2),$$
$$h_2=\Sigma m(wx-uz)$$
$$=\Sigma m(\omega_2 x^2-\omega_1 xy-\omega_3 yz+\omega_2 z^2),$$
$$h_3=\Sigma m(uy-vx)$$
$$=\Sigma m(\omega_3 y^2-\omega_2 yz-\omega_1 zx+\omega_3 x^2),$$

so that

$$h_1=I_1\omega_1-\omega_2\Sigma mxy-\omega_3\Sigma mzx, \atop h_2=I_2\omega_2-\omega_1\Sigma mxy-\omega_3\Sigma myz, \atop h_3=I_3\omega_3-\omega_2\Sigma myz-\omega_1\Sigma mzx, \Bigg\} \qquad . \qquad . \qquad . \qquad (59)$$

where I_1, I_2, and I_3 are the moments of inertia of the body about the three axes. The other factors such as Σmxy are called *products of inertia* and, in many cases of practical importance, disappear.

The kinetic energy of the mass m at P is given by

$$dE=\tfrac{1}{2}m(u^2+v^2+w^2),$$

so that the total kinetic energy of the body is

$$E=\tfrac{1}{2}\Sigma m(u^2+v^2+w^2)$$
$$=\tfrac{1}{2}\Sigma m[(\omega_3 y-\omega_2 z)^2+(\omega_1 z-\omega_3 x)^2+(\omega_2 x-\omega_1 y)^2]$$
$$=\tfrac{1}{2}\omega_1{}^2\Sigma m(y^2+z^2)+\tfrac{1}{2}\omega_2{}^2\Sigma m(z^2+x^2)+\tfrac{1}{2}\omega_3{}^2\Sigma m(x^2+y^2)$$
$$\qquad\qquad\qquad -\omega_2\omega_3\Sigma myz-\omega_3\omega_1\Sigma mzx-\omega_1\omega_2\Sigma mxy$$
$$=\tfrac{1}{2}I_1\omega_1{}^2+\tfrac{1}{2}I_2\omega_2{}^2+\tfrac{1}{2}I_3\omega_3{}^2-\omega_1\omega_2\Sigma mxy-\omega_2\omega_3\Sigma myz$$
$$\qquad\qquad\qquad\qquad\qquad -\omega_3\omega_1\Sigma mzx. \qquad (60)$$

Comparing this with equation (59) we have

$$h_1 = \frac{\partial E}{\partial \omega_1}, \qquad h_2 = \frac{\partial E}{\partial \omega_2}, \qquad h_3 = \frac{\partial E}{\partial \omega_3}, \qquad \text{. . (61)}$$

and

$$2E = h_1\omega_1 + h_2\omega_2 + h_3\omega_3 \qquad \text{. . . (62)}$$

47. Angular Acceleration for Steady Precession.—To find the angular accelerations about a set of moving axes, when a body is in a state of steady precessional motion, let Ox, Oy, Oz (Fig. 28)

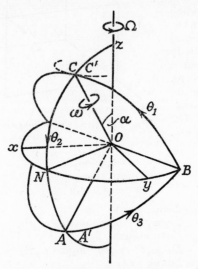

FIG. 28.—ANGULAR ACCELERATION FOR STEADY PRECESSION.

be three axes fixed in space, and suppose that Oz is the axis of precession. Let OC be the axis of rotation of the body whose angular velocity is ω, and suppose that the angular velocity of any point in OC, about Oz, is Ω. The line OA is fixed in the body at right angles to OC and in the plane zOC, while OB is perpendicular to both OA and OC. Let θ_1, θ_2, and θ_3 be the angular velocities of these axes OA, OB, and OC about their instantaneous positions, and suppose OA, OB, and OC are of unit length. In the time dt, C moves to C', so that $CC' = \Omega \sin \alpha \,.\, dt$, and the angular velocity of the body about OA is

$$\frac{1}{dt} \cdot \frac{CC'}{OC} = -\Omega \sin \alpha,$$

where the positive sign is used, in the conventional way, to indicate counter-clockwise rotations when viewed looking towards the origin. The angular velocity about OB is zero, and about OC is ω. If A moves to A' in time dt,

$$AA' = \Omega \cos \alpha \,.\, dt,$$

and thus we have

$$\theta_1 = -\Omega \sin \alpha, \qquad \theta_2 = 0, \qquad \theta_3 = \Omega \cos \alpha . \qquad . \quad (63)$$

Let the angular momenta of the body about the axes OA, OB, OC be h_1, h_2, h_3 (Fig. 29). The precession of the angular momentum h_1, with angular velocity θ_3 about OC, requires a torque about OB

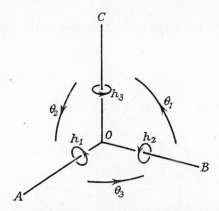

FIG. 29.—TORQUES FOR STEADY PRECESSION.

equal to $h_1\theta_3$. Similarly, h_3 precesses about OA at a rate θ_1, and requires a torque about OB equal to $-h_3\theta_1$. Finally, since h_2 may change with time, an additional torque $\dfrac{dh_2}{dt}$ is needed about OB. Thus, if τ_1, τ_2, and τ_3 be the torques about these three axes OA, OB, and OC,

$$\tau_2 = \frac{dh_2}{dt} - h_3\theta_1 + h_1\theta_3.$$

Similarly,

$$\tau_1 = \frac{dh_1}{dt} - h_2\theta_3 + h_3\theta_2, \qquad . \qquad . \qquad . \quad (64)$$

and

$$\tau_3 = \frac{dh_3}{dt} - h_1\theta_2 + h_2\theta_1.$$

In the case for steady precession these become from (63)

$$\tau_1 = \frac{dh_1}{dt} - h_2\Omega \cos \alpha,$$

$$\tau_2 = \frac{dh_2}{dt} + h_3\Omega \sin \alpha + h_1\Omega \cos \alpha, \qquad . \qquad . \quad (65)$$

$$\tau_3 = \frac{dh_3}{dt} - h_2\Omega \sin \alpha.$$

48. Steady Precession of a Top.—From these results we may now deduce the precessional motion of a spinning-top. Since the latter is a body of revolution about the rotation axis, the products of inertia vanish, and the angular momenta are, from (59),

$$h_1 = I_1 \omega_1, \qquad h_2 = I_2 \omega_2, \qquad h_3 = I_3 \omega_3, \qquad . \qquad . \qquad (66)$$

end

$$I_1 = I_2.$$

Thus, in Fig. 30, OC is the axis of rotation of the top, and it makes

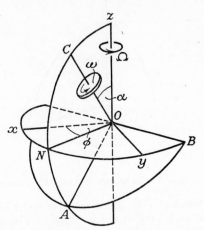

FIG. 30.—PRECESSION OF A SPINNING-TOP.

an angle α with the axis of precession Oz. The angular velocities about OA, OB, and OC are, from (63),

$$-\Omega \sin \alpha, \qquad 0 \qquad \text{and} \qquad \omega, \qquad . \qquad . \qquad (67)$$

and, on substituting these values in the expressions (66) for the angular momenta about these axes, we have

$$h_1 = -I_1 \Omega \sin \alpha,$$
$$h_2 = 0,$$
$$h_3 = I_3 \omega,$$

I_1 being the moment of inertia of the body about OA, and I_3 that about OC. Substituting these values in the expressions (65) for the torques about the axes,

$$\tau_1 = \frac{d}{dt}(-I_1 \Omega \sin \alpha) = 0,$$

$$\tau_2 = I_3 \omega \Omega \sin \alpha - I_1 \Omega^2 \sin \alpha \cos \alpha,$$
$$\tau_3 = 0.$$

If the torque τ_2 is produced solely by gravitational forces, then

$$\tau_2 = mgl \sin \alpha,$$

where mg is the weight of the top and l is the distance of its centre of gravity from O. Thus

$$mgl = I_3\omega\Omega - I_1\Omega^2 \cos\alpha \quad . \quad . \quad . \quad (68)$$

This gives the condition for the top to precess steadily at the given rate Ω. If $\alpha = 90°$, the conditions of Article 41, Equation (55), are obtained.

Since from (68) there are, in general, two values of Ω, two different rates of precession may be maintained by the gravitational couple, *i.e.* for the given inclination to the vertical. If k is the radius of gyration about OC, and k_1 that about an axis through the centre of gravity perpendicular to OC,

$$I_3 = mk^2, \quad \text{and} \quad I_1 = m(k_1^2 + l^2),$$

and thus

$$gl = k^2\omega\Omega - (k_1^2 + l^2)\Omega^2 \cos\alpha,$$

which gives

$$\Omega = \frac{2\pi}{t_0} = \frac{k^2\omega \pm \sqrt{k^4\omega^2 - 4(k_1^2 + l^2)gl\cos\alpha}}{2(k_1^2 + l^2)\cos\alpha}, \quad . \quad . \quad (69)$$

where t_0 is the periodic time of precession.

The minimum value of ω, which gives a real value for Ω, is obtained from

$$k^4\omega^2 = 4(k_1^2 + l^2)gl\cos\alpha,$$

or

$$\omega = \frac{2}{k^2}\sqrt{(k_1^2 + l^2)gl\cos\alpha} \quad . \quad . \quad . \quad (70)$$

Initial Conditions.—We have considered thus far only a maintained steady precession without imposing any initial conditions, but, in a more general case, both the rate of precession and the inclination to the vertical vary. Suppose that the initial conditions of the top are as indicated in Fig. 30, the original angle between the planes zOx and zOA being ϕ. The only external torque—neglecting friction—is that due to gravitation, and this acts about the axis OB. Thus the angular momentum h about Oz is constant, and the angular velocities of the axes OA, OB, OC are

$$-\frac{d\phi}{dt}\sin\alpha, \quad \frac{d\alpha}{dt}, \quad \omega,$$

and so

$$h_1 = -I_1\frac{d\phi}{dt}\sin\alpha = -m(k_1^2 + l^2)\sin\alpha\frac{d\phi}{dt},$$

$$h_2 = I_1\frac{d\alpha}{dt},$$

$$h_3 = I_3\omega.$$

The angular momentum about Oz is given by

$$h = h_1(-\sin\alpha) + h_3\cos\alpha = m(k_1{}^2 + l^2)\sin^2\alpha\frac{d\phi}{dt} + mk^2\omega\cos\alpha,$$

and since this must be constant,

$$m(k_1{}^2 + l^2)\sin^2\alpha\frac{d\phi}{dt} + mk^2\omega\cos\alpha = mk^2\omega\cos\alpha_0, \quad . \quad (71)$$

where α_0 is the initial value of the angle α.

Additionally, from the conservation of energy principle, the sum of the kinetic and potential energies must remain constant. The kinetic energy E_1 is given by (60), $i.e.$

$$E_1 = \tfrac{1}{2}m[k_1{}^2 + l^2]\left[\frac{d\phi}{dt}\sin\alpha\right]^2 + \tfrac{1}{2}m[k_1{}^2 + l^2]\left(\frac{d\alpha}{dt}\right)^2 + \tfrac{1}{2}mk^2\omega^2,$$

the products of inertia being zero. The potential energy E_2 is

$$E_2 = mgl\cos\alpha,$$

so that, by the conservation of energy,

$$m[k_1{}^2 + l^2]\left[\left(\frac{d\phi}{dt}\sin\alpha\right)^2 + \left(\frac{d\alpha}{dt}\right)^2\right] + 2mgl\cos\alpha = 2mgl\cos\alpha_0. \quad (72)$$

The subsequent motion is given by (71) and (72) and, from (71),

$$\frac{d\phi}{dt} = \frac{k^2\omega[\cos\alpha_0 - \cos\alpha]}{[k_1{}^2 + l^2]\sin^2\alpha}. \quad . \quad . \quad . \quad (73)$$

Nutation.—When $\alpha = \alpha_0$, $\dfrac{d\phi}{dt} = 0$, or the top placed in the given position does not immediately precess. Instead, it falls slightly under the action of gravity ; thus $\dfrac{d\phi}{dt}$ has a finite value, and precession begins. The fall of the axis, however, has a limit, α_1, after which it rises again to the value α_0, and this oscillation between the two inclinations α_1 and α_0, accompanied by a correspondingly varying precessional rate, is called *nutation*. To indicate this phenomenon we may combine equations (73) and (72) and, eliminating $\dfrac{d\phi}{dt}$, we have

$$\frac{k^4\omega^2[\cos\alpha_0 - \cos\alpha]^2}{[k_1{}^2 + l^2]\sin^2\alpha} + [k_1{}^2 + l^2]\left(\frac{d\alpha}{dt}\right)^2 = 2gl[\cos\alpha_0 - \cos\alpha]. \quad . \quad (74)$$

Maximum and minimum values of α are given by $\dfrac{d\alpha}{dt} = 0$, $i.e.$

$$k^4\omega^2[\cos\alpha_0 - \cos\alpha] = 2gl[k_1{}^2 + l^2]\sin^2\alpha \text{ or } \cos\alpha = \cos\alpha_0. \quad (75)$$

From (75)

$$sin^2\, \alpha + \frac{k^4\omega^2}{2gl[k_1{}^2+l^2]}(cos\, \alpha - cos\, \alpha_0) = 0,$$

or

$$cos^2\, \alpha - 2d\, cos\, \alpha + 2d\, cos\, \alpha_0 - 1 = 0, \qquad . \quad . \quad (76)$$

where $2d$ is written for $\dfrac{k^4\omega^2}{2gl[k_1{}^2+l^2]}$. The solution of (76) is

$$cos\, \alpha_1 = d \pm \sqrt{1+d^2-2d\, cos\, \alpha_0},$$

and since $cos\, \alpha$ must be less than unity, only the negative sign is possible, so that

$$cos\, \alpha_1 = d - \sqrt{1+d^2-2d\, cos\, \alpha_0}.$$

Hence the axis of the top, as it precesses, varies its inclination to the vertical between the values α_0 and α_1, and, since when $\alpha = \alpha_0$, $\dfrac{d\phi}{dt} = 0$, *i.e.* the precession momentarily ceases, at such times the end C of the axis reaches a cusp in its nutation movement. At the lower value α_1, however, the rate of precession is a maximum whose value may be obtained from (73) and (74). Thus

$$[k_1{}^2+l^2]\Big(\frac{d\phi}{dt}\Big)^2 sin^2\, \alpha = k^2\omega(cos\, \alpha_0 - cos\, \alpha)\frac{d\phi}{dt},$$

$$[k_1{}^2+l^2]\Big(\frac{d\phi}{dt}\Big)^2 sin^2\, \alpha + [k_1{}^2+l^2]\Big(\frac{d\alpha}{dt}\Big)^2 = 2gl(cos\, \alpha_0 - cos\, \alpha),$$

and so, when $\dfrac{d\alpha}{dt} = 0$,

$$k^2\omega(cos\, \alpha_0 - cos\, \alpha)\frac{d\phi}{dt} = 2gl(cos\, \alpha_0 - cos\, \alpha),$$

which gives $\alpha = \alpha_0$ when $\dfrac{d\phi}{dt} = 0$, or

$$\frac{d\phi}{dt} = \frac{2gl}{k^2\omega}.$$

Minimum Velocity for the Top to " Sleep."—A top is said to " sleep " when it spins with its axis vertical. The motion will be stable only if, when slightly displaced, the top returns again to the vertical position. The necessary condition may be obtained by putting $\alpha_0 = 0$ in the equation for $\dfrac{d\alpha}{dt}$, and finding in what circumstances, for a small displacement, $\dfrac{d^2\alpha}{dt^2}$ is negative. Thus, substituting

$\alpha_0 = 0$ in (74), we have

$$(k_1{}^2 + l^2)\left(\frac{d\alpha}{dt}\right)^2 = 2gl(1 - \cos\alpha) - \frac{k^4\omega^2(1 - \cos\alpha)}{(k_1{}^2 + l^2)(1 + \cos\alpha)},$$

or

$$2(k_1{}^2 + l^2)\left(\frac{d\alpha}{dt} \cdot \frac{d^2\alpha}{dt^2}\right) = 2gl\sin\alpha\frac{d\alpha}{dt} - \frac{k^4\omega^2}{k_1{}^2 + l^2} \cdot \frac{2\sin\alpha}{(1 + \cos\alpha)^2} \cdot \frac{d\alpha}{dt},$$

and since α is small,

$$(k_1{}^2 + l^2)\frac{d^2\alpha}{dt^2} = \sin\alpha\left[gl - \frac{k^4\omega^2}{4(k_1{}^2 + l^2)}\right],$$

so that, if $\dfrac{d^2\alpha}{dt^2}$ is negative,

$$\frac{k^4\omega^2}{4(k_1{}^2 + l^2)} > gl,$$

or

$$\omega^2 > \frac{4gl(k_1{}^2 + l^2)}{k^4}.$$

This result may also be deduced from equation (69).

49. Alternative Method for Spinning-Top.—The problem of the spinning-top may be investigated in a simpler way—though one which is open to objection—by considering the three torques of Article 41. If a particle of mass m_1 is situated at a distance l_1 from O (Fig. 30), it describes a circle, due to precession, about Oz of radius $l_1 \sin\alpha$, and the centrifugal force due to this motion is $\dfrac{m_1 v_1{}^2}{l_1 \sin\alpha}$, acting horizontally, where v_1 is its speed in the circle. This, together with the corresponding reaction at O, forms an elementary centrifugal couple of magnitude $\dfrac{m_1 v_1{}^2}{l_1 \sin\alpha} l_1 \cos\alpha$ and, if t_0 is the periodic time, $v_1 t_0 = 2\pi l_1 \sin\alpha$. The total centrifugal torque is given by

$$\Gamma_3 = \Sigma m_1\left(\frac{2\pi}{t_0}\right)^2 l_1{}^2 \sin\alpha \cos\alpha = I_1\left(\frac{2\pi}{t_0}\right)^2 \sin\alpha \cos\alpha,$$

where I_1 is the moment of inertia about OA.

If the top is viewed from the direction BO (Fig. 30), the three torques, acting in a clockwise direction, are

$$\Gamma_1 = -I_3\omega\Omega \sin\alpha,$$
$$\Gamma_2 = -mgl \sin\alpha,$$
$$\Gamma_3 = I_1\left(\frac{2\pi}{t_0}\right)^2 \sin\alpha \cos\alpha,$$

where I_3 is the moment of inertia about OC. Putting $\Omega t_0 = 2\pi$, and substituting these values in equation (56), we have

$$\left(\frac{2\pi}{t_0}\right)^2 (k_1{}^2+l^2)\cos\alpha-\left(\frac{2\pi}{t_0}\right)k^2\omega+gl=0,$$

or

$$\frac{2\pi}{t_0}=\frac{k^2\omega\pm\sqrt{k^4\omega^2-4gl(k_1{}^2+l^2)\cos\alpha}}{2(k_1{}^2+l^2)\cos\alpha},$$

which is the same as (69).

50. The Earth's Gyroscopic Effect.—The earth in its revolution about the polar axis may be regarded as an enormous gyrostat, which will be capable of precession and nutation, if a couple acts about an axis at right angles to the north-south line. If the earth were truly spherical and of uniform density, such a couple would be impossible, but the existence of equatorial protuberances gives rise to both solar and lunar precessions and nutations. The earth is represented in Fig. 31, with exaggerated ellipticity, by the ellipse *WE*. If the sun is situated along the direction *Ox*, then the eastern protuberance is nearer the sun, and its gravitational reaction to the sun is slightly greater than it would be if the sun were situated

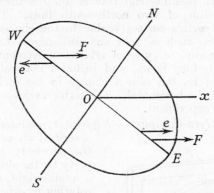

FIG. 31.—GYROSCOPIC MOTION OF THE EARTH.

along the line *NS*, at the same distance from the centre. In the latter case let the attraction on each half of the ellipsoid be *F*. Then, in the figure $F+e$ and $F-e$ are the forces of attraction on the two halves *NES* and *NWS*, respectively. Thus, in addition to the total attraction $2F$, there is a couple formed by the two forces e about an axis at right angles to *NS* and to the diagram. This couple constitutes a gyroscopic torque, which will cause the earth to precess, so that, under the conditions shown, *N* rises up from the plane of the diagram while *S* goes down. The polar axis thus intersects the celestial sphere in a point which describes a precessional circle, whose angular radius is 23° 27′ about the pole of the ecliptic. Owing to changes in the moon's position and in the sun's declination, the resultant torque fluctuates in value, and thus the simple circle becomes a " wavy " circular track, due to the corresponding nutation movement.

51. The Gyroscopic Compass.—If a gyrostat is suspended in frictionless gimbals, so that it has three degrees of freedom for any position of the outside frame, then no movement of the latter can cause a torque to act on the gyrostat. The latter therefore retains its direction in space. In particular, such a system, mounted on a ship, would be uninfluenced by the pitching, tossing, or direction of the vessel. This inherent stability of the gyrostat suggests its use as a compass, and the many practical difficulties have been overcome with sufficient success to render the gyro-compass preferable, particularly in submarines, to the magnetic compass.

The simple system just described lacks the essential property of returning, after a disturbance, to the original direction, as obviously any position of the gyrostat is inherently stable. It does, however, enable the rotation of the earth to be demonstrated, since the axle will, in the absence of disturbing torques, retain its original orientation, and, if this is truly north and south, it will apparently turn so that its north pointing end travels towards the east, owing to the non-parallelism of two north–south lines. This movement relative to the earth's surface is due to the changing orientation in space of lines—such as floor and wall edges—fixed relative to the earth. A complete cycle of relative movement will be completed in twenty-four hours, and includes not only the easterly rotation referred to, but also a change in the inclination of the rotation axis to the horizontal. The latter varies according to the latitude of the experiment.

Pendulum Gyro-Compass.—A gyrostat, mounted in the manner described above, may be given the necessary restorative property by the simple addition of a small weight, hung below the rotating fly-wheel. The essentials of such a pendulum gyro-compass are shown in Fig. 32. The gyrostat is mounted by its axle ends A, B, in a horizontal ring which carries a vertical stirrup, fixed rigidly to it, and weighted immediately below the centre of the fly-wheel by means of the weight W. This horizontal ring may turn freely around the axis CD within a vertical ring, which is similarly free to move about the vertical axis FG within the frame H.

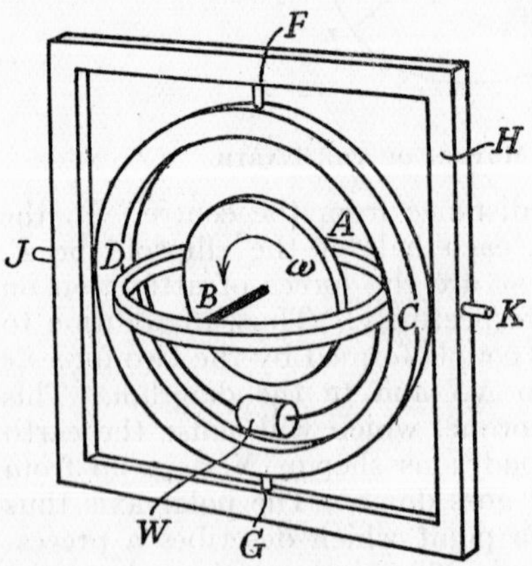

FIG. 32.—MODEL OF THE PENDULUM GYRO-COMPASS.

To ensure complete freedom of movement, this frame H is also carried
in horizontal gimbals, of which K, J form the first pair.   Such an
arrangement is stable only when the end B points truly north, as
will be understood by reference to Fig. 33.   Consider the gyro-
compass at the equator with its axis pointing North–South, the end
B towards the north.   The inner ring will be horizontal with the
weight directly beneath.   There is thus no torque due to gravity,
the system is stable, and, since the axis of the wheel is parallel to
the earth's polar axis, no tendency to move will accompany the
earth's rotation.   Suppose now the axis AB is forced into an east–
west direction with the end B pointing east (Fig. 33) (1).   The
earth's rotation from position (1) to (2) in Fig. 33 will tend to

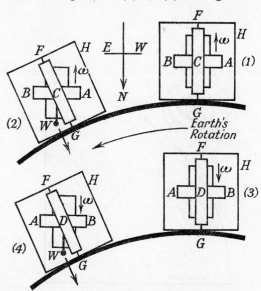

Fig. 33.—Pendulum Gyro-compass at the Equator.

produce the state of affairs shown at (2), with the axle AB parallel
to its previous direction.   This gives rise to a gravitational couple
owing to the weight W being no longer vertically below the centre
of AB, and precession occurs about FG, so that B swings around
towards the north.   When the north–south direction is achieved,
the position is, as seen already, stable.

If the end B had pointed west (Fig. 33) (3), the position (4) would
have resulted in a similar gravity torque, but, since the rotation of
the fly-wheel is reversed, relative to the diagram, the precessional
motion is reversed also, and B swings from the west towards the
north, instead of from the east to the north.   Thus B—viewed from
which the gyrostat rotation is anticlockwise—is the north-seeking

end of the revolution axis. (It is useful to remember the corresponding rule for the magnetic effects of currents.) It is therefore clear that an accidental disturbance of AB from the south–north line calls into existence a directive force of restoration.

When the gyro-compass is not at the equator, the effect is apparently different. In Fig. 34 the system is represented in latitude λ. The axle is horizontal and the end B is placed facing east. The gyroscopic action will, as already explained, tend to force AB into alignment with the polar axis, *i.e.* along LM. This can be done by a rotation about FG of 90°, succeeded by a rotation about CD equal to λ. The former movement takes place without any gravity

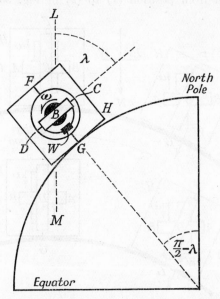

FIG. 34.—PENDULUM GYRO-COMPASS AT LATITUDE λ.

torque, and the axis AB is then in the meridian. The second movement, however, produces a gravitational couple which causes AB to precess, B moving towards the west. It seems then that the north–south direction of BA is immediately followed by a wandering of B towards the west, and that the readings of the compass are no longer to be relied on. This, however, is merely apparent because—except at the equator—this westerly movement is necessary to keep BA pointing north–south. The seeming contradiction in this statement will be understood by reference to the paragraph above, where it was shown that, if no such precessional movement of AB occurs, the end B apparently wandered off to the east. Thus the gravity torque produces just that change in the space direction of the gyrostat axis required to maintain it always parallel to the north–south direction of its immediate locality.

Magnitude of the Directive Effect.—The magnitude of the directive tendency depends on the three factors :—

(*a*) The moment of inertia of the fly-wheel,

(*b*) Its angular velocity,

(*c*) The rate of rotation of the earth.

Of these, the last is fixed, and thus, to make the gyro-compass sensitive, it is necessary to have the first two as large as possible. The limits of their magnitude are fixed by considerations of safety, and the necessity of avoiding temperature effects due to the irreducible minimum of friction. Since the three quantities (*a*), (*b*), and (*c*) above are constants for a given instrument, it would seem that the compass is equally sensitive at all latitudes. This is not so, because, although the restoring moment is the same everywhere, its horizontal effect diminishes from the equator to the pole. At the latter place the horizontal force is zero, and, except for the weight W, the axis AB would set itself vertically.

It should also be noticed that, although an increase in the directive forces may be obtained by a larger and stronger instrument, it does not follow that the sensitiveness is increased proportionally, since these forces then act upon a much more massive body. The sensitiveness depends to the greatest extent on the elimination of friction.

52. Errors of the Gyro-Compass.—Brown,[1] whose gyro-compass is used in the British navy, found that, in practice, many instrumental difficulties occur, and in most cases a compromise is necessary between the actual instrument and its simple ideal. This causes a number of errors in the reading which must be corrected for. The chief of these are :—

(*a*) *Latitude Error.*—The freedom of movement of the compass necessitates some form of damping to permit a reasonably quick reading to be taken. This damping agency prevents the gravity torque from acquiring its full value, and thus the compass has insufficient westerly precession. There is therefore an easterly deviation, called the latitude error, and this is usually corrected for by an alteration of the lubbar line—or zero mark—in the vessel.

(*b*) *North Steaming Error.*—If a vessel is travelling due north or south, the axis of rotation of the compass is now slightly inclined to the polar axis, due to the resultant velocity of the earth and vessel. This error applies equally to all forms of gyro-compass, and is corrected for by the use of tabulated values, giving the error for different northerly or southerly speeds.

(*c*) *Acceleration Error.*—When the vessel is changing speed in a north–south direction, the inertia effect of the control weight causes a virtual change in the direction of gravity, and the compass

[1] Brown, *Nature*, **105**, 44, 77 (1920).

will give an incorrect reading while the speed is changing. Readings are therefore taken under steady steaming conditions.

(d) *Error due to Pitching and Rolling.*—Rolling and pitching of the vessel, when on a due east–west or north–south course, is negligible in effect, but for intermediate directions the effect is extremely complicated, and the elimination of error from this cause necessitates a great increase in instrumental complexity. In one case—that of the Anschutz gyro-compass [1] designed in 1912—three extra gyroscopes were fitted. One of these has its axis in the north–south direction, while those of the other two are in the same horizontal plane and make angles of 30° on either side of the main rotor. The three are joined by a system of links in such a way that the virtual moment of inertia about the north–south line is increased. The whole assembly is attached to a spherical float, which swims in a vessel containing mercury in the interior of the instrument. There is also an attachment by means of which the master compass actuates a number of dials in different parts of the ship.

In recent years much development work on the design of gyro-compasses has resulted in their employment by both the United States Army Air Force and the Royal Air Force [2] in aircraft. Their special advantage, a direct result of the large rotational inertia, is their steadiness of reading during rapid changes of direction, when the magnetic compass is liable to errors which cannot be exactly computed, and can be allowed for only empirically. Additionally in large aircraft, repeater dials can be installed so as to give information of course changes to members of the crew at different stations. Such gyro-compasses still show precessional effects, and it is necessary to check their readings by reference to the magnetic compass at frequent intervals while on a straight and level course.

53. Other Gyroscopic Applications.—The inherent directional stability of a rapidly revolving body has other important applications of which a few may be mentioned. Rifle and artillery barrels are rifled to give their projectiles a rapid spin about an axis in the direction of motion. This ensures greatly increased uniformity of flight by improving their resistance to small deflective forces. The rolling of hoops, and the riding of bicycles—both cases of statical instability —are possible only because of the gyroscopic effect which, as in the rolling disc, produces a movement of the plane of rotation, tending to counterbalance the disturbing action of gravity. The single track train, or mono-rail, of Brennan is stabilised by gyrostats, while a similar use to stabilise vessels was suggested by Schlick.

More recently, aircraft instruments such as the automatic pilot, modern bomb sights, the artificial horizon, and turn and bank indicators have been developed on gyrostat-controlled principles.

[1] See Martienssen, *Zeits. Vereins. deutsch. Ing.*, 67, 182 (1923).
[2] Witherow and Hansen, *Trans. Amer. Inst. Elec. Eng.*, 63, 204 (1944) ; see also *Engineer*, London, 179, 177, 188 (1945).

In all such cases the operative process is the relation of a virtually fixed datum plane, provided by the gyrostat, to a movable plane in the aircraft, and the result of their relative change of orientation is an instrumental indication much more reliable than personal judgment.

EXAMPLES

1. A uniform disc of mass 500 gm. and radius 5 cm. revolves about an axis through its centre and perpendicular to its plane at a rate of 50 revolutions per sec. Find the periodic time of the horizontal precessional motion of the axis if the flywheel is supported at a point on the axis 3 cm. from the centre of the disc and projected with axis horizontal without subsequent nutational motion. $g = 981$.   [8·39 sec.]

2. If, as a result of friction at the support, the axis of the disc in the previous question dips below the horizontal at an angle of 30° while the rotational speed remains unaltered, find the new precessional period. Hence show that for large variations of axis inclination to the horizontal the precessional period is practically unchanged.   [8·39 sec.]

3. (a) An iron hoop of radius 2 ft. is bowled along a horizontal rough surface. Find the minimum forward speed of the hoop at which it will roll with plane vertical.

(b) If the coefficient of friction between the hoop and the ground is 0·4 find the forward speed at which the hoop finally slips and falls flat.
          [(a) 5·68 ft. per sec. ; (b) 5·47 ft. per sec.]

4. A top consists of a flat disc of radius 2 cm. with an axle, of negligible thickness, whose point is 2 cm. from the centre of the disc. Find the minimum rate of rotation at which the top will spin.
          [13·25 revs. per sec.]

5. If the top in the previous question is given a spin of 30 revs. per sec. and placed on a rough horizontal plane with its axis at 15° to the vertical, find the angle through which the axis sways in its initial nutation movement.   [2½°.]

6. Find the minimum rate of rotation of the top in question 4 if it is to spin stably with axis vertical.   [15·8 revs. per sec.]

7. An aeroplane has a rotary engine which revolves in a clockwise direction as seen by the pilot. Show that a pitching moment is experienced when the aeroplane is making a horizontal turn, and find the direction of this moment when the turn is being made to the right. If the aeroplane speed is 100 miles per hour, the engine revolutions 1500 per minute, the moment of inertia of the engine about its rotation axis 500 ft.-lb. units and the radius of the turn 200 yd., find the magnitude of the pitching moment.   [Nose down ; $1·92 \times 10^4$ ft.-lb. units.]

8. A bullet projected from a rifle has a right-handed spin imparted to it by the rifling and, in its flight, grazes a vertical wall. Show that the result is a deflection upwards, or downwards, according to whether the wall is on the left, or right, respectively of the bullet as judged by the firer.

CHAPTER V

ELASTICITY

54. Elastic Bodies.—The development of dynamics proceeds from the conception of a massive particle—*i.e.* a body so small that all its parts may be regarded as having the same displacement—to that of a rigid body, in which the distance between any two points is unaffected by forces acting on the body. In order to bring physical theory into line with the behaviour of actual bodies, it becomes necessary to take into account a possible relative movement in the parts of a body under the action of forces which, acting on a rigid body, would be in equilibrium, and thus have no effect. Actually, no body is perfectly rigid, although a substance, such as steel or glass, is practically so for small forces. Materials may be subdivided according to their behaviour when the forces which produce deformations are removed. If the body retains completely its altered shape and size, it is said to be *perfectly plastic*, as, for example, putty. If, on the other hand, the body recovers its original size and shape, it is said to be *perfectly elastic*. This method of differentiation is not absolute, since no body is perfectly elastic, when subjected to very large deformations, while it is probable that even putty recovers, at least partially, from very small alterations of shape or size.

55. Hooke's Law and Elastic Limits.—Over a considerable range it is found, by experiment, that the deformation, produced by forces, is proportional to the magnitude of those forces. This statement of proportionality is called *Hooke's Law* and is the basis of the theory of elasticity. The point at which Hooke's Law just ceases to hold is called the *elastic limit* of the substance, and is determined, experimentally, by plotting the magnitude of the special type of deformation against the value of the applied force system. The point of departure of the resulting curve from a straight line gives the elastic limit of the specimen, for that particular kind of alteration in its size or shape. Sometimes the elastic limit is defined as the magnitude of the applied forces which produce the maximum amount of recoverable deformation. In this case its experimental measurement is rather different, and consists in loading the specimen, and then measuring its dimensions on removal of the load. This is repeated with increasing loads until the recovery on unloading is not complete, *i.e.* until a definite permanent set—or change of shape—is formed. The amount of this permanent set is plotted against the load, and an estimate is made of the point at which the set begins.

With most materials these two definitions of the elastic limit give practically the same values.

The actual elastic limit can be obtained only by the use of very delicate instruments. The *yield point* occurs with greater forces, and is that point at which there is an increase in the deformation of the body, without a corresponding addition to its load. With some substances, such as iron and mild steel, the yield point is well marked, but it is non-existent in hard steel, bronze, and most alloys. For these substances the rate of extension with load increases beyond the elastic limit without discontinuity.

56. Stress and Strain.—The change in the dimensions of a body, produced by a system of forces in equilibrium, is called a *strain*, and its character will evidently depend on the nature of the force system producing it. The latter is called the *stress* and is always measured by the applied force per unit area of the body. The method of measuring the strain varies according to its character. Consider a long wire clamped at its upper end and loaded at the

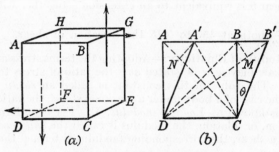

FIG. 35.—SHEAR STRAIN.

bottom. An increase in the load produces an elongation of the wire, and in this case the strain is measured by the increase in length, per unit length, of the wire. If, however, a body is uniformly compressed in all directions, it will be unaltered in shape if it is isotropic—*i.e.* if its elastic properties are uniform in all directions—but it undergoes a change of volume, and the strain is measured by the alteration in volume, per unit volume, of the original body. Finally, suppose (Fig. 35) a unit cube of a substance is under the action of tangential forces as shown in (*a*). The result will be a change in shape, the face $ABCD$ becoming the rhombus $A'B'CD$ (Fig. 35) (*b*), but its size remains constant, since the area $ABCD$ is equal to that of $A'B'CD$, and the body is unchanged in dimensions in a direction perpendicular to $ABCD$. This type of strain is called a *shear* and is measured by the angular deformation θ. The shear may be regarded as produced by progressive slidings of planes, such as $ABGH$, in a direction parallel to a chosen datum plane, say $DCEF$, the amount of the movement being proportional to the distance from the selected datum plane. The magnitude of the shear may also be defined as the relative displacement of two planes, whose distance apart is unity. This reduces to the same definition as before, since, if θ is small—a necessary assumption in the theory of elasticity and one which is realised in practice—we have

$$\theta = \tan \theta = \frac{BB'}{BC} = \frac{relative\ displacement}{distance\ of\ separation}.$$

A shear may, alternatively, be regarded as a combination of an extension, together with a contraction perpendicular to the extension, for (Fig. 35) (b) the diagonal DB becomes of length DB', and if BM is drawn perpendicular to DB', the extension along DB is

$$\frac{MB'}{DB} = \frac{MB'}{DM} = \frac{BB'}{\sqrt{2}} \cdot \frac{1}{\sqrt{2}.BC} = \frac{1}{2}\frac{BB'}{BC} = \frac{\theta}{2}.$$

Similarly, the fractional contraction of the diagonal AC is $\dfrac{AN}{NC} = \dfrac{\theta}{2}$.

Thus a shear θ is equivalent to an extension $\dfrac{\theta}{2}$ together with a compression $\dfrac{\theta}{2}$, both at $45°$ to AB, the direction of shear.

57. Moduli of Elasticity.—Adopting the terms stress and strain, Hooke's Law may now be stated as : the ratio of stress to strain is constant. The value of this constant is called an *elastic modulus*. Thus, in the case of a body under a tensional stress, the ratio of stress to strain is known as *Young's modulus, Y*. For a uniform volume compression, or dilation, the modulus is called the *bulk modulus, K* ; while, for a shear, the corresponding modulus is termed the *modulus of rigidity, n*.

Another elastic constant called the *axial modulus χ* is defined in terms of the principal stress needed to produce a simple elongation without lateral change. The complete stress is a Young's Modulus stress, together with two perpendicular stresses of such a magnitude as will prevent lateral contraction. The ratio of the extensional stress to increase in length per unit length is χ. We thus have

$$Y = \frac{Applied\ load\ per\ unit\ area\ of\ cross\text{-}section}{Increase\ in\ length\ per\ unit\ length},$$

$$K = \frac{Compressive,\ or\ tensile,\ force\ per\ unit\ area}{Decrease,\ or\ increase,\ in\ volume\ per\ unit\ volume},$$

$$n = \frac{Tangential\ force\ per\ unit\ area}{Angular\ deformation},$$

$$\chi = \frac{Longitudinal\ load\ per\ unit\ area\ of\ cross\text{-}section}{Increase\ in\ length\ per\ unit\ length}.$$

Although the definitions of Y and χ are similar, the total force system and complete strains differ in the two cases.

These moduli are not independent constants, since any possible change in the size and shape of a body may be obtained by first changing the size, but not the shape—*i.e.* by a volume strain—and then changing the shape, without altering the size—by means of shears. Thus a suitable combination of volume and shear strains may produce any kind of strain and, in particular, a linear tensile strain. This interrelation of the elastic moduli will be considered later.

Careful measurement shows that, when a body undergoes a linear tensile strain—*i.e.* is under the action of two equal and oppositely directed forces—it experiences a lateral contraction in addition to its longitudinal extension, and also that this contraction is directly proportional to the extension. The ratio of lateral strain—measured by the decrease in width per unit width—to the longitudinal strain is called *Poisson's ratio*, σ.

58. Direct Measurement of Young's Modulus.—The value of Y for a material in the form of a long thin wire may be obtained by an apparatus designed by G. F. C. Searle,[1] and shown in Fig. 36.

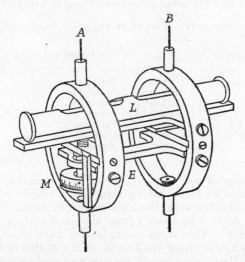

FIG. 36.—SEARLE'S SPIRIT-LEVEL APPARATUS FOR THE MEASUREMENT OF YOUNG'S MODULUS.

The wire A is clamped firmly at its upper end alongside another wire B. The lower ends of these wires are connected to the frame E, which carries a sensitive level L, and the latter may be tilted by means of the micrometer M. Each wire is initially loaded sufficiently to straighten it, and the bubble is adjusted. An additional load is then added to the specimen under test, and the corresponding move-

[1] G. F. C. Searle, *Camb. Phil. Soc. Proc.*, **10**, 318 (1900).

ment of the micrometer, necessary to restore the level, measures the extension produced. This loading is continued, and extensions are plotted against the corresponding loads. The result is a straight line whose slope gives the extension for unit load. From this result, knowing the length and radius of the wire, Young's modulus may be calculated.

For thicker and shorter specimens some form of extensometer is required, such as that devised by Ewing.[1]

59. Determination of Poisson's Ratio.—The most direct method of measuring Poisson's ratio consists in using an extensometer in combination with an instrument for the simultaneous measurement of lateral strain and this is the usual practice in engineering establishments where facilities exist for the application of the large stretching forces necessary for the production of measurable lateral strains in thick rods. For thinner rods and wires, indirect methods, such as are described in Articles 66 and 67, are available. It is clear from equation (110) of Article 65 that σ must lie between 0 and 0·5 and, for many materials, it is nearly 0·33.

The values of σ for some substances are given in Table IV below.

TABLE IV.—VALUES OF POISSON'S RATIO σ

Substance.	σ.	Substance.	σ.
Glass . .	0·25	Tin . . .	0·33
Steel . . .	0·27–0·30	Aluminium .	0·34
Copper . .	0·31–0·34	Cadmium . .	0·30
Brass . .	0·32–0·35	Silver . . .	0·38
Delta metal .	0·34	Platinum . .	0·39
Muntz metal .	0·34	Gold . . .	0·42
Lead . . .	0·43	Marble . .	0·27

60. Torsion of a Cylinder.—Consider a cylinder, fixed at one end and twisted at the other by means of a couple of moment Γ, whose axis coincides with the axis of the cylinder. The angular displacement ϕ, at a distance l from the fixed end, is proportional to both l and Γ. This is an example of a pure shear, since there can be no change in either the length, or the radius of the cylinder, for reversing the couple would reverse any such change, and the response of the cylinder to the couple is clearly independent of the latter's direction. Each circular cross-section is rotated about the cylinder's axis, by an amount which is determined by its distance from the fixed end. Thus, in Fig. 37 (a), a wedge of the cylinder is strained from the position $ABCD$ into the position $ABED$, so that $CE=r_1\phi$, where r_1 is the radius of the cylinder, and, in Fig. 37 (b), an element $FGHI$ of the lower end is moved to $JKLM$. Suppose $BF=r$ and $FG=dr$, while $FH=dx$, then the parallelepiped, with

[1] Ewing, *Proc. Roy. Soc.*, A, **58**, 123 (1895).

$FGHI$ as base, is sheared as shown in Fig. 37 (c), where $GK=r\phi$. The force, f, acting tangentially on the face $FGHI$ and producing the shear θ, constitutes a shearing stress of magnitude $\dfrac{f}{drdx}$. Thus the modulus of rigidity is given by

$$n=\frac{f}{\theta drdx},$$

or, since $l\theta=r\phi$,

$$f=ndrdx.\frac{r\phi}{l}.$$

This force f has a moment fr about the axis of the cylinder, and thus the total moment is

$$\Gamma=\frac{n\phi}{l}\iint r^2drdx.$$

The integral of dx must be taken round the circle of radius r, and so

$$\Gamma=\frac{2\pi n\phi}{l}\int r^3dr.$$

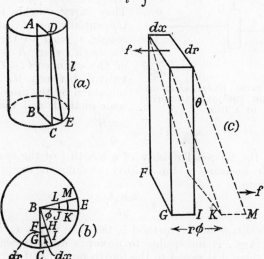

FIG. 37.—TORSION OF A CYLINDER;

If the cylinder is solid this becomes

$$\Gamma=\frac{n\pi r_1{}^4\phi}{2l}, \qquad . \qquad . \qquad . \qquad . \qquad (77)$$

and if hollow, of outer and inner radii r_1 and r_2, respectively,

$$\Gamma=\frac{n\pi\phi}{2l}[r_1{}^4-r_2{}^4] \qquad . \qquad . \qquad . \qquad . \qquad (78)$$

The quantity $\dfrac{\Gamma}{\phi}$ —the torque to produce unit twist between the ends of the specimen—is usually called the *torsional rigidity*, and is designated by τ.

Equations (77) and (78) may be applied directly to the measurement of τ for a cylindrical wire, using either a static method, or a torsional pendulum.[1] For the static experiment, which is suitable for comparatively thick specimens, an arrangement shown in Fig. 38 may be used. The specimen AB is clamped at A and fixed firmly into a wide cylinder C at B. Two mirrors M_1 and M_2 are fixed to AB at a distance l apart, and two flexible cords, attached to C, pass over freely running pulleys P_1 and P_2. They carry weights mg and act tangentially on C, so that the couple applied to the end B is $\Gamma = 2mgR$, where R is the radius of the cylinder C. The relative twist ϕ, between M_1 and M_2, is measured by the usual lamp-and-scale method, and thus we have

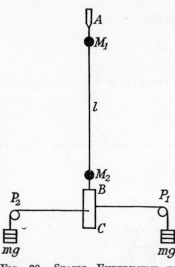

Fig. 38.—Static Experiment to Measure the Torsional Rigidity of a Rod.

$$\tau = \frac{\Gamma}{\phi} = \frac{2mgR}{\phi},$$

where τ is the torsional rigidity of a length l of the specimen. If an absolute measure of the rigidity modulus is required, this is obtained from

$$\tau = \frac{n\pi r_1^{\,4}}{2l}.$$

One advantage of the method is that the radius r_1, being comparatively large, is susceptible to accurate measurement. This is important since it is raised to the fourth power, and any error in r_1 becomes seriously magnified in n. Secondly, since this is a static experiment, the specimen is not subjected to periodic changes in the strain which may result in a slightly large value for n.[2]

In the torsional pendulum method, a body of known moment of inertia, I, is attached to the end B, and the system is made to execute torsional oscillations. Then, from (19), the period t_0 is given by

$$t_0 = 2\pi \sqrt{\frac{I}{\tau}},$$

[1] See Article 9.   [2] See Article 77.

and thus τ may be measured. For a sufficiently slow oscillation with a substance of high rigidity, a long and fairly thin wire is necessary.

61. Torsion of Bars of Non-circular Cross-section.—For bars of which the section is not circular, the problem of deducing the torsional rigidity becomes very much more difficult. The cases where the section is elliptic, equilaterally triangular, and square with rounded corners were treated successfully by St. Venant,[1] who showed that the torsion involved a longitudinal displacement in the cross-section. This displacement is not uniform, but is an axial elongation at some points in the section and an axial contraction at others. Thus the particles in any cross-section are no longer

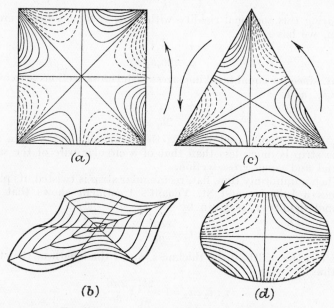

(a)   *(c)*

(b)   *(d)*

Fig. 39.—Torsion of a Bar—St. Venant.

coplanar when strained. The cross-section is divisible by radial lines into sectors, which are alternately places of axial extension and contraction, *i.e.* alternate depressions and protuberances, the magnitude of the axial movement increasing with distance from the axis, and from the radial lines demarking adjacent sectors. For example, St. Venant gives the following cases. For a square, Fig. 39 (a), the section is divisible into eight sectors by median and diagonal lines, and the axial displacement is alternately towards and away from the fixed end. If the twisting is in the direction of the arrow, then the dotted lines show displacements towards the fixed

[1] See Love, *Math. Theory of Elasticity*, 2nd ed., Chapter XIV.

end, while the full lines indicate opposite displacements. This effect is shown in perspective in Fig. 39 (b). For an equilateral triangle the effect is as shown in Fig. 39 (c), while, for an ellipse, it is as in Fig. 39 (d). For such an elliptic cross-section, St. Venant showed that the torsional rigidity τ_1 is given by

$$\tau_1 = \frac{n\pi}{l} \cdot \frac{a_1{}^3 b_1{}^3}{a_1{}^2 + b_1{}^2},$$

where a_1 and b_1 are the major and minor semi-axes, respectively. If a_1 is large compared with b_1, the specimen becomes a strip and

$$\tau_1 = \frac{n\pi a_1 b_1{}^3}{l}.$$

Comparing this torsional rigidity with that, τ, for a circular cross-section, we have

$$\frac{\tau}{\tau_1} = \frac{r_1{}^4}{2a_1 b_1{}^3},$$

so that, since for equal breaking stresses the cross-sections are equal, $r_1{}^2 = a_1 b_1$, and

$$\frac{\tau}{\tau_1} = \frac{a_1}{2b_1}.$$

As a_1 is large compared with b_1, the torsional rigidity of a flat elliptic strip is much less than that of a circular wire of the same material and equal cross-section.

When a uniformly thin, flat, rectangular strip is twisted, its plane becomes a helicoid, and St. Venant's treatment shows that the torsional rigidity τ_2 is given by

$$\tau_2 = \frac{ncd^3}{3l},$$

where c is the width, d the thickness, and l the length of the strip, and thus

$$\tau : \tau_1 : \tau_2 = 1 : \frac{2b_1}{a_1} : \frac{2\pi d}{3c}$$

for circular, elliptic, and rectangular strips of the same cross-sectional area and equal lengths. Rectangular strips are used as suspensions in galvanometers. These strips have very small torsional rigidity, and possess the additional advantage of offering a comparatively large surface area for the dissipation of heat produced by the current.

If such a rectangular strip acts as the suspension of a torsional pendulum, the period t_0 is given by

$$t_0 = 2\pi \sqrt{\frac{I}{\tau_2}} = 2\pi \sqrt{\frac{3Il}{ncd^3}},$$

where I is the moment of inertia of the suspended system. Thus n may be determined.

According to St. Venant's mathematical treatment of non-circular sections, if Ox, Oy, Oz are axes taken in a plane perpendicular to the axis of the bar, and if ϕ is the displacement at a point (x, y), due to the " warping " which occurs when the bar is twisted, ϕ must satisfy the equation

$$\frac{\partial^2 \phi}{\partial x^2} + \frac{\partial^2 \phi}{\partial y^2} = 0, \qquad \cdots \qquad (79)$$

and the boundary condition

$$\frac{\partial \phi}{\partial n} = y \cos \theta_x - x \cos \theta_y, \qquad \cdots \qquad (80)$$

where $\dfrac{\partial \phi}{\partial n}$ is the change of ϕ in a direction normal to the boundary of the section, and θ_x, θ_y are the angles between the normal at the point (x, y) and the axes of x and y, respectively. Functions which satisfy (79) always occur in pairs, and if ψ is the function conjugate to ϕ, it is related to ϕ by the equations

$$\frac{\partial \phi}{\partial x} = \frac{\partial \psi}{\partial y}, \qquad \frac{\partial \phi}{\partial y} = -\frac{\partial \psi}{\partial x} \qquad \cdots \qquad (81)$$

Thus, if we can find ψ, ϕ is given by (81). The function ψ must satisfy (79) and its boundary condition

$$\frac{\partial \psi}{\partial s} = y \cos \theta_x - x \cos \theta_y, \qquad \cdots \qquad (82)$$

where $\dfrac{\partial \psi}{\partial s}$ is the rate of change of ψ round the boundary. But $\cos \theta_x = \dfrac{\partial y}{\partial s}$ and $\cos \theta_y = -\dfrac{\partial x}{\partial s}$, so that (82) reduces to

$$\frac{\partial \psi}{\partial s} = \tfrac{1}{2} \frac{\partial}{\partial s} (x^2 + y^2),$$

and the boundary condition is

$$\psi = \tfrac{1}{2}(x^2 + y^2) + a \ constant \qquad \cdots \qquad (83)$$

If another function f is defined by

$$f = \psi - \tfrac{1}{2}(x^2 + y^2),$$

then it evidently satisfies

$$\frac{\partial^2 f}{\partial x^2} + \frac{\partial^2 f}{\partial y^2} + 2 = 0 \qquad \cdots \qquad (84)$$

at all points in the section, and

$$f = constant \qquad \cdots \qquad (85)$$

at the boundary.

For an elliptic cross-section, bounded by the curve

$$b^2 x^2 + a^2 y^2 = a^2 b^2,$$

the function f is given by

$$f = -(b^2 x^2 + a^2 y^2)/(a^2 + b^2),$$

since $f = -a^2b^2/(a^2+b^2)$ at all points of the boundary, and thus

$$\psi = \frac{x^2+y^2}{2} - \frac{b^2x^2+a^2y^2}{a^2+b^2},$$

which gives

$$\frac{\partial\phi}{\partial x} = \frac{\partial\psi}{\partial y} = -\frac{y(a^2-b^2)}{a^2+b^2},$$

and

$$\frac{\partial\phi}{\partial y} = -\frac{\partial\psi}{\partial x} = -\frac{x(a^2-b^2)}{a^2+b^2}.$$

This, on integration and putting $\phi=0$, at the centre gives,

$$\phi = -\frac{xy(a^2-b^2)}{a^2+b^2},$$

and the axial displacement is given by the family of hyperbolas, which have the axes of the ellipse as asymptotes, and agrees with the diagram of Fig. 39 (d).

The torque Γ on the bar in each case can be shown to satisfy the relation

$$l\Gamma = -2n\theta \iint f dx dy,$$

where θ is the twist between the ends of the bar. Thus

$$l(a^2+b^2)\Gamma = 2n\theta \iint (b^2x^2+a^2y^2)dx dy,$$

the integral being taken over the cross-section. This reduces to St. Venant's relation

$$l(a^2+b^2)\Gamma = n\pi\theta a^3b^3.$$

In only a few cases is it possible to obtain mathematical expressions for ϕ, ψ, and f, and thus there is no general method of expressing the strain in a bar in a mathematical form. In cases other than those of the ellipse, square, equilateral triangle, and a few more simple forms of cross-section, further investigation must be made by experiment, utilising equations (84) and (85). It has been pointed out by various experimenters that these equations represent other physical phenomena which are more susceptible of direct measurement. For example, Prandtl,[1] in what is known as *Prandtl's Analogy*, drew attention to the fact that there is a similarity between f and the deviation, from the plane, of a soap film which covers a hole of the same size as the cross-section, and which is under an excess pressure on one side. In such a case, if S is the surface tension, p the excess pressure, and z the displacement at any point (x, y) from the plane of the section, then

$$\frac{d^2z}{dx^2} + \frac{d^2z}{dy^2} + \frac{p}{2S} = 0, \qquad \cdot \quad \cdot \quad \cdot \quad (86)$$

[1] Prandtl, *Phys. Zeits.*, **4**, 758 (1903).

z being zero at the boundary. Thus, if z is measured on such a scale that $f = \dfrac{4Sz}{p}$, equations (84) and (86) are identical, and measurements of z at various points on the film will, together with a knowledge of p and S, give f everywhere over the cross-section. The soap film may be regarded as a graphical representation of the function f.

If n is the modulus of rigidity and Φ the twist in the bar, then the shear stress at any point may be found by multiplying the slope of the surface, representing f at that point, by $n\Phi$, so that if α is the inclination of the soap film to the cross-section, the stress P is given by

$$P = \frac{4S}{p} n\Phi\alpha,$$

while the torque Γ on the bar is

$$\Gamma = 2n\Phi \iint f . dxdy = \frac{8S}{p} n\Phi V,$$

where V is the volume between the film and the plane of the cross-section, Φ being equal to $l\theta$.

62. The Bending of Beams.—Cantilever.—When a rod is bent from its natural shape by the action of applied forces, it will recover

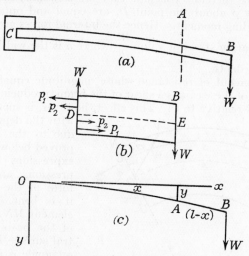

Fig. 40.—Bent Cantilever.

its original form on removal of those forces, provided that no part of it has been strained beyond the elastic limit. In the strained position, its shape will be governed by the opposing action of the rigidity of the rod against the type of stress applied, and by the magnitude of the stress system. In Fig. 40 (a) a beam CB is shown clamped at one end and supporting an applied load at the free extremity. Such a system is called a *cantilever*. If we imagine a section of the rod to be drawn at the point A, the internal forces, over the section A, applied by the remainder AC of the beam, must, together with the external load W, keep the part AB in equilibrium. The force W acting vertically downwards at B is balanced by an equal vertical force W, acting upwards at A. These two forces constitute a couple, of moment $W \times AB$, called the *bending moment* at A, and thus there must be, in addition, an internal couple of equal moment and opposite sense. Certain lines along the length of the beam are extended, others are compressed, while some are unaltered in length. The latter lie in a surface, called the *neutral surface*, which is parallel to the axis about which bending occurs. Thus DE, which is the intersection of the neutral surface by the plane of the diagram, retains its original length. Fibres within the beam above DE will be extended, and the extension will increase with greater distance from the neutral surface, while fibres below DE will undergo longitudinal contractions. The resultant elastic reaction will produce forces such as p_1, p_2 in both parts of the beam, and these will constitute a system of couples, whose resultant may be called the *moment of resistance*, and balances the bending moment $W \times AB$. We therefore conclude that the combined moments, due to the forces p about the point D, are equal and opposite to the external bending moment. Hence the internal forces give rise to :—

(i) A shearing stress of value $\dfrac{W}{ab}$, where a is the width of the rod and b is its depth.

(ii) A moment of resistance whose magnitude equals $W \times AB$.

The first of these causes a shear of the beam, producing a lowering of the end B relative to C. This effect, however, is small compared

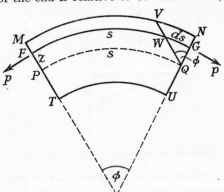

Fig. 41.—Expression for the Internal Bending Moment.

with the depression of B, due to the bending, as proved below. To obtain expressions for the depression, and for the form of the beam when it is bent, consider an element $MNUT$ (Fig. 41) of the beam. The neutral surface PQ subtends an angle ϕ at its centre of curvature, and, if the radius of curvature is R, then $PQ = R\phi$. Draw QV parallel to PM, and, since FG is the length of a stretched fibre, situated at a distance z above the neutral surface, $FW = PQ = s$, say, is the normal length, while $WG=ds$ is the extension it has under-gone. Thus its tensile strain is $\dfrac{ds}{s}$, and if p is the magnitude of the internal force which produced this extension,

$$\frac{p}{\alpha}=Y\frac{ds}{s}, \qquad . \qquad . \qquad . \qquad . \qquad (87)$$

where α is the cross-sectional area of the fibre and Y is Young's modulus for the material of the beam. But $PQ=s=R\phi$, and $ds=z\phi$.

Hence
$$\frac{ds}{s}=\frac{z}{R},$$

and
$$\frac{p}{\alpha}=Y\frac{z}{R}, \quad \text{or} \quad p=\frac{Y}{R}z\alpha.$$

The moment of p about Q is $pz=\dfrac{Y}{R}\alpha z^2$, and thus the internal bending moment—or moment of resistance—which is the sum of all such terms, is

$$\Sigma pz=\frac{Y}{R}.\Sigma\alpha z^2.$$

The quantity $\Sigma\alpha z^2$ is analogous to the moment of inertia about the neutral axis, and is called the *geometrical moment of inertia* of the cross-section about that axis. It is equal to Ak^2, where A is the cross-sectional area and k is the radius of gyration. We thus have

$$\textit{Internal Bending Moment}=\frac{YAk^2}{R}, \qquad . \qquad . \qquad (88)$$

and this must balance the moment of the external forces at the section. The quantity YAk^2, which measures the resistance of the beam to bending, and which is quantitatively defined as the external bending moment required to produce unit radius of curvature, is called the *flexural rigidity*.

To apply this fundamental equation, choose axes Ox, Oy (Fig. 40) (c) along, and perpendicular to, the unstrained position of the beam. Let the co-ordinates of A be x, y, and suppose that the curvature of the beam is small. The co-ordinates of B then are l, δ, where δ is the depression of B, due to bending, and l is the length of the beam. The external bending moment at A is $W(l-x)$ and, if we consider a short length ds of the beam, its curvature at a point is $\dfrac{d\psi}{ds}$, where ψ is the angle the tangent makes with the x axis. Hence the curvature

$$\frac{1}{R}=\frac{d\psi}{ds}=\frac{d}{ds}(tan\ \psi)=\frac{d^2y}{dx^2},$$

since ψ is small, and thus $\psi=tan\ \psi$. Hence

$$W(l-x)=\frac{Y}{R}Ak^2=YAk^2\frac{d^2y}{dx^2} \qquad . \qquad . \qquad . \qquad (89)$$

By integration, we have

$$YAk^2\frac{dy}{dx}=W\left(lx-\frac{x^2}{2}\right)+c_1.$$

When $x=0$, $\frac{dy}{dx}=0$, so that $c_1=0$, and

$$YAk^2\frac{dy}{dx}=W\left(lx-\frac{x^2}{2}\right) \quad . \quad . \quad . \quad . \quad (90)$$

At the loaded end $x=l$, and

$$\frac{dy}{dx}=\frac{Wl^2}{2YAk^2}, \quad . \quad . \quad . \quad . \quad (91)$$

which gives the slope of the beam at that point. If (90) is integrated, we have, since $x=0$ when $y=0$,

$$YAk^2y=W\left(\frac{lx^2}{2}-\frac{x^3}{6}\right), \quad . \quad . \quad . \quad (92)$$

which is the equation to the beam. At B the maximum displacement, δ, from the horizontal position occurs, $x=l$, and

$$\delta=\frac{Wl^3}{3YAk^2} \quad . \quad . \quad . \quad . \quad (93)$$

For a bar of rectangular section $k^2=\frac{b^2}{12}$, and thus

$$\delta=\frac{4Wl^3}{Yab^3}.$$

The depression δ_1, due to the shear stress $\frac{W}{ab}$, is

$$\delta_1=\frac{Wl}{abn},$$

where n is the modulus of rigidity. Therefore

$$\frac{\delta_1}{\delta}=\frac{Wl}{abn}\cdot\frac{Yab^3}{4Wl^3}=\frac{Y}{4n}\left(\frac{b}{l}\right)^2,$$

and for a moderately long and fairly thin beam $\left(\frac{b}{l}\right)^2$ is very small.

Thus δ_1 is small compared with δ, and the whole depression of B is sensibly equal to δ.

The foregoing treatment assumes that the weight of the beam produces no appreciable bending. If this is not so, we may take this weight into consideration by adding, to the external moment due to W, the moment about A, due to the portion AB of the beam. If the beam weight per unit length is w, this amounts to a force

$w(l-x)$, acting at the centre of gravity of AB, that is, at a distance $\frac{1}{2}(l-x)$ from A. Thus equation (89) becomes

$$YAk^2\frac{d^2y}{dx^2}=W(l-x)+\frac{w}{2}(l-x)^2,$$

or, on integrating twice,

$$YAk^2y=W\left(\frac{lx^2}{2}-\frac{x^3}{6}\right)+w\left(\frac{l^2x^2}{4}-\frac{lx^3}{6}+\frac{x^4}{24}\right),$$

which gives at B

$$YAk^2\delta=\frac{Wl^3}{3}+\frac{wl^4}{8}=\frac{l^3}{3}\left[W+\tfrac{3}{8}W_1\right], \quad . \quad . \quad (94)$$

where $W_1=wl$ is the weight of the beam.

Formula (93) may be used in determining the value of Young's modulus for the beam by measuring the depression produced by a given load. In a similar manner, by utilising equation (91), Y may be found in terms of the angular deflection of the loaded end of the beam. The latter method is more delicate, because the optical lever may be employed to magnify the movement.

Beam Supported at its Ends and Loaded at the Centre.— Suppose that the beam AB (Fig. 42) is supported at, or near, its ends, and carries a load W at the centre-point P. The external forces acting are $\frac{W}{2}$ at each end, due to the support thrusts, and W acting downwards at P. The tangent at P will be horizontal, and thus

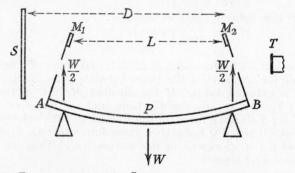

FIG. 42.—BEAM LOADED AT ITS CENTRE AND SUPPORTED NEAR ITS ENDS.

each half of the beam is equivalent to a cantilever, clamped at the point P and displaced by an end force $\frac{W}{2}$. The relative elevation δ of A, or B, above P is, from (93),

$$\delta=\frac{Wl^3}{48YAk^2} \quad . \quad . \quad . \quad . \quad (95)$$

A similar result may be obtained by the direct integration of

$$YAk^2\frac{d^2y}{dx^2}=W\left(\frac{l}{2}-x\right)-\frac{W}{2}(l-x),\qquad . \qquad . \qquad (96)$$

and correction for the weight of the beam is made in the same manner as previously. Equation (95) is used in the determination of Y by observing δ for a known value of W. Also, the first stage of integration of (96) gives

$$YAk^2\frac{dy}{dx}=\frac{Wl^2}{16}-\frac{Wx^2}{4}.$$

At the end of a rectangular bar $x=0$ and $Ak^2=\frac{ab^3}{12}$, so that

$$\frac{dy}{dx}=\tfrac{3}{4}\frac{Wl^2}{ab^3Y}.\qquad . \qquad . \qquad . \qquad . \qquad (97)$$

Thus Young's modulus may be found by means of the following experiment. A pair of pillars, with small mirrors M_1, M_2 (Fig. 42) attached to the upper ends, are fixed near the ends of the beam, the mirrors being practically normal to its length. A scale S is viewed by means of a telescope at T, the light from the scale having suffered two reflections from the mirrors. Suppose that the difference in the scale readings in the telescope, before and after putting on a load W at the centre of the beam, is s. If L is the horizontal distance between the two mirrors, and D the horizontal distance from the scale to the mirror M_2, then, from simple geometry,

$$\frac{dy}{dx}=\frac{s}{2(L+2D)},\text{ approximately.}$$

Equating this value to (97) we have

$$Y=\frac{3Wl^2(2D+L)}{2ab^3s}.$$

A more complete treatment of the internal forces of a bent beam is possible for any part of the beam between points of application of discrete external loads. If the element $MNUT$ of the beam, shown in Fig. 41, is only slightly bent, and the forces on the section MT are a shearing force f upwards and an anticlockwise couple G, while the length PQ is δx, then these forces become $f+\delta f$ downwards and $G+\delta G$ clockwise in the section NU. Thus for vertical equilibrium we have:—

$$f=f+\delta f+w\delta x,\quad\text{or}\quad\frac{df}{dx}=-w,\qquad . \qquad . \qquad (98)$$

w being the weight per unit length. Similarly by taking moments about T

$$G=G+\delta G+(f+\delta f)\delta x+w\frac{\delta x^2}{2},$$

or,

$$\frac{dG}{dx}=-f\qquad . \qquad . \qquad . \qquad . \qquad (99)$$

ignoring second and higher order terms.

The integration of these equations yields

$$f = f_0 - wx, \qquad \cdot \qquad \cdot \qquad \cdot \qquad \cdot \qquad (100)$$

and

$$G = G_0 - f_0 x + \frac{wx^2}{2}, \qquad \cdot \qquad \cdot \qquad \cdot \qquad (101)$$

where f_0 is the upward shearing force at the point $x=0$, and G_0 is the anticlockwise internal bending moment at the same point.

For example, in the beam shown in Fig. 42 taking the origin at the left-hand support and measuring x positively to the right, it is evident that

$$f_0 = \frac{W + W_1}{2}, \quad G_0 = 0,$$

where W_1 is the weight of the beam, and the supports are assumed at its ends. Thus

$$G = \frac{wx^2}{2} - \frac{W + W_1}{2}x,$$

and if this is equated to $YAk^2 \dfrac{d^2y}{dx^2}$, its integration will give the form of the beam when its own weight is not negligible. The result will be applicable between A and P.

63. Beam Bent with Considerable Curvature.—If a beam is so strongly bent that the tangent of its inclination to the unstrained position can no longer be regarded as small, and the curvature cannot be taken as equal to $\dfrac{d^2y}{dx^2}$, the original form of equation (88) must be retained. In many problems the resulting differential equation is not easily solved, but in some cases interesting results may be obtained by simple means. Consider a flexible cantilever—for example a piece of thin clock-spring—carrying a constant load and clamped successively at various points along its length. In this case the horizontal distance between the clamp and the loaded end approaches a maximum value. Thus OPQ (Fig. 43) is the spring in a strongly bent position, and P is a point with

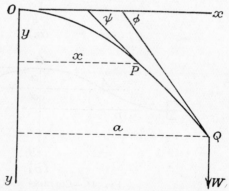

FIG. 43.—STRONGLY BENT CANTILEVER.

co-ordinates x, y. The tangent at P meets the Ox axis at an angle ψ, while that at the end Q—of which the co-ordinate is a—is ϕ. The bending moment at P is $W(a-x)$, so that

$$W(a-x)=YAk^2\frac{d\psi}{ds}=YAk^2 \cos \psi\frac{d\psi}{dx},$$

and

$$\int_0^a W(a-x)dx=YAk^2\int_0^\phi \cos \psi d\psi,$$

or,

$$\frac{Wa^2}{2}=YAk^2 \sin \phi \qquad . \qquad . \qquad . \qquad (102)$$

At $\phi=90°$ the x co-ordinate of the loaded end is given by

$$YAk^2=\frac{Wa_0^2}{2}, \quad \text{or} \quad a_0=\sqrt{\frac{2YAk^2}{W}} \quad . \qquad . \qquad (103)$$

The equation (102) may be employed to determine Y for a very flexible beam by observing the inclination to the horizontal of the loaded end, while (103) enables Y to be measured from the value of a_0, the maximum horizontal distance between clamp and loaded end. In these cases the limit of accuracy is imposed by the accuracy with which the thickness of the strip is measured, for, in a rectangular cross-section, the thickness is raised to the third power in Ak^2.

Columns and Supports.—When a beam is loaded in the direction of its length, as with vertical columns and supports, the method

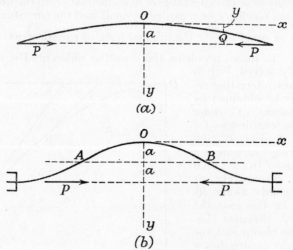

FIG. 44.—COLUMNS AND SUPPORTS.

of treatment is different. Suppose, for example, a long thin column, with rounded ends so that it can bend along its whole length, supports loads of P at each end, as shown in Fig. 44 (a). Then, for small bending, we have as the bending moment at Q,

$$YAk^2\frac{d^2y}{dx^2}=P(a-y),$$

where a is the lateral displacement at the central point O. The solution to this equation is

$$y=a(1-cos\ \lambda x),$$

where λ is equal to $\sqrt{\dfrac{P}{YAk^2}}$. When $x=\dfrac{l}{2}$, l being the length of the beam, $y=a$. Thus P is given by

$$P=\frac{\pi^2YAk^2}{l^2},$$

and is independent of a, *i.e.* the force P will maintain the beam in any slightly bent form. This value of P is the critical load since, for a smaller value, no bending will occur and the beam will be in stable equilibrium. For loads greater than this critical value the beam will bend more and more.

If the beam is clamped rigidly at each end, its slightly deformed shape is as shown in Fig. 44 (*b*). In this case the length AB is under similar conditions of bending as in the previous case, and, substituting the condition $y=a$ when $x=\dfrac{l}{4}$, we find that P, the critical load, is now

$$\frac{4\pi^2YAk^2}{l^2}.$$

64. Spiral Springs.—The principles and formulæ developed for bending and torsion are immediately applicable to the theory of spiral springs. A common spiral spring consists of a uniform wire, shaped permanently to have, when unstrained, the form of a regular helix. If the top end is held fixed and the lower end is attached to a bar, the spring may be acted on, through this bar, by forces such that, in its altered form, it is still a regular helix. This condition is obviously fulfilled if an infinitely small force, and an infinitely small couple, are applied to the bar along the axis of the spring and in a plane perpendicular to it. If the force and couple are increased to any degree, but always kept along and in the plane perpendicular to the axis of the altered spiral, this condition is still realised. We may imagine the spiral spring formed by winding the wire uniformly on a cylinder of radius R. Two cases arise. The plane of the wire may either be practically perpendicular to the axis of the cylinder, or it may make a small angle with it. The type of spiral spring formed in the first case is referred to as flat.

Flat Spiral Springs.—Suppose a weight W is attached to the free end. Then, considering the equilibrium of the part of the spring below a section at A (Fig. 45), there must be a shearing force equal to W acting vertically over the section, and a couple of moment WR. The effect of the latter is to produce a uniform twist, say ϕ, per unit length of the wire, and this is balanced by the torsional resistance $\frac{1}{2}n\pi r^4\phi$ where r, the radius of the wire, is supposed small compared with R. For equilibrium,

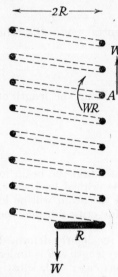

$$WR=\frac{n\pi r^4\phi}{2} \qquad . \quad . \quad (104)$$

If l is the total length of the wire, the twist at the free end is $l\phi$, and the work done in twisting the wire is

$$\frac{1}{l}\int_0^{l\phi}\tfrac{1}{2}n\pi r^4\phi d\phi=\tfrac{1}{4}n\pi r^4\phi^2 l,$$

which is stored up in the wire as potential energy. Suppose the weight W is depressed and then released. When its displacement is x, the twist in the wire is increased by an amount ϕ_1 per unit length, such that $x=lR\phi_1$, and the additional potential energy is

Fig. 45.—Spiral Spring.

$$\tfrac{1}{4}n\pi r^4\phi_1{}^2l=\frac{n\pi r^4 x^2}{4lR^2}.$$

In this position W has been lowered by x and the centre of gravity of the spring by $\dfrac{x}{2}$, so that the change of potential energy from these effects is

$$\frac{n\pi r^4 x^2}{4lR^2}-Wx-\frac{W_1 x}{2},$$

where W_1 is the weight of the spring. At the same position the weight W will have kinetic energy equal to $\frac{1}{2}\dfrac{W}{g}\left(\dfrac{dx}{dt}\right)^2$, and the spring itself possesses kinetic energy. The vertical depression at any point in the spring is proportional to its distance, s, from the fixed end, measured along the wire, and the velocity will be $\dfrac{s}{l}\left(\dfrac{dx}{dt}\right)$. If m is the mass per unit length, the kinetic energy of an element ds will be

$$\tfrac{1}{2}m\left(\frac{s}{l}\cdot\frac{dx}{dt}\right)^2 ds,$$

and of the whole spring,

$$\frac{m}{2l^2}\left(\frac{dx}{dt}\right)^2\int_0^l s^2 ds=\tfrac{1}{2}\frac{W_1}{3g}\left(\frac{dx}{dt}\right)^2.$$

Thus the total kinetic energy is

$$\frac{1}{2g}\left(W+\frac{W_1}{3}\right)\left(\frac{dx}{dt}\right)^2,$$

and, from the principle of energy conservation,

$$\frac{1}{2g}\left(W+\frac{W_1}{3}\right)\left(\frac{dx}{dt}\right)^2+\frac{n\pi r^4x^2}{4lR^2}-Wx-\frac{W_1x}{2}=const.$$

Differentiating this with respect to t and rearranging the terms, we have

$$\frac{d^2x}{dt^2}+\frac{n\pi r^4gx}{2lR^2\left(W+\frac{W_1}{3}\right)}-\frac{\left(W+\frac{W_1}{2}\right)g}{\left(W+\frac{W_1}{3}\right)}=0,$$

which represents periodic motion, taking place about a displaced zero with a period t_0, given by

$$t_0=2\pi\sqrt{\frac{2lR^2\left(W+\frac{W_1}{3}\right)}{n\pi r^4g}}.$$

The depression due to vertical shear has been neglected compared with that due to torsion, and that this is permissible may be shown as follows. The shearing strain at A (Fig. 45) is $\dfrac{W}{n\pi r^2}$, and so the total depression produced by this strain is $\dfrac{Wl}{n\pi r^2}$. The depression due to twist is $lR\phi$, and from (104) this is equal to $\dfrac{2WR^2l}{n\pi r^4}$. Hence

$$\frac{Depression\ due\ to\ vertical\ shear}{Depression\ due\ to\ torsion}=\frac{r^2}{2R^2},$$

and this ratio, in general, is very small.

Non-flat Spiral Springs.—If the spring is not flat, *i.e.* if an element of the spiral is inclined at an angle α with the horizontal, the section at a point of the wire, perpendicular to the length of the wire, will be inclined at the angle α to a plane passing through the point and the axis of the spiral. Thus the torsional moment, produced by the weight W, may be resolved into two components, one $WR\cos\alpha$ acting in the plane of the section at A and producing a twist ϕ per unit length given by

$$WR\cos\alpha=\frac{n\pi r^4\phi}{2}\qquad\cdot\qquad\cdot\qquad\cdot\qquad(105)$$

The other component, $WR\sin\alpha$, acting with its axis perpendicular to the section at A, constitutes a bending moment and produces a change in curvature at A given by (88), *i.e.*

$$\frac{WR \sin \alpha}{YAk^2} = \frac{4WR \sin \alpha}{\pi r^4 Y},$$

so that, if ds is an element of the length of the wire, this element is bent through an angle

$$\frac{4WR \sin \alpha ds}{\pi r^4 Y} \qquad . \qquad . \qquad . \qquad . \qquad (106)$$

Considering the vertical displacements of the free end resulting from the twisting and bending, we have, from (105), since the section is inclined at an angle α to the vertical, a vertical displacement equal to

$$Rl\phi \cos \alpha = \frac{2WR^2l \cos^2 \alpha}{n\pi r^4},$$

and, arising from (106), an additional vertical movement,

$$\frac{4WR \sin \alpha}{\pi r^4 Y}.R \sin \alpha \int_0^l ds = \frac{4WR^2l \sin^2 \alpha}{\pi r^4 Y}.$$

Hence the total vertical displacement is

$$\frac{2WR^2l}{\pi r^4}\left[\frac{\cos^2 \alpha}{n} + \frac{2 \sin^2 \alpha}{Y}\right].$$

In addition to this vertical movement of the free end, there will be an angular displacement in the horizontal plane. Thus, from (105), the torsion gives rise to a horizontal angular shift of

$$l\phi \sin \alpha = \frac{2WlR \sin \alpha \cos \alpha}{n\pi r^4},$$

and tends to coil up the spring. In a similar manner the bending will produce a horizontal angular rotation of the free end, which, from (106), is given by

$$\frac{4WR \sin \alpha \cos \alpha}{\pi r^4 Y} \int_0^l ds = \frac{4WRl \sin \alpha \cos \alpha}{\pi r^4 Y},$$

and this tends to uncoil the spring. The resultant movement tending to coil up the spring is

$$\frac{2WRl \sin \alpha \cos \alpha}{\pi r^4}\left[\frac{1}{n} - \frac{2}{Y}\right]$$

and is greatest when $\alpha = 45°$.

The spring tends to coil, or uncoil, according as

$$\frac{1}{n} > \quad \text{or} \quad < \frac{2}{Y}.$$

For most metals $Y > 2n$, and spiral springs formed of wires of circular cross-sections tend to coil up when an extending force is applied to their free ends.

65. Relations between the Elastic Constants.—Since a combination of a uniform volume strain and three perpendicular shears is capable of producing any homogeneous strain, it is evident that the elastic constants Y, K, n, and σ must be interrelated, and the connection between them may be obtained by a tabular method of designating stresses and their resultant strains. In Table V the first three columns indicate the applied stresses along any three perpendicular axes Ox, Oy, Oz, while in the remaining columns are the consequent strains. If the stress is extensional, it is given a plus sign; if compressional, it is regarded as negative and similarly with the strains. Thus a stress $+P$ in the Ox column and 0, 0, in the Oy and Oz stress columns mean that an extensional Young's Modulus stress is applied alone along Ox. The consequent strain is an extension $+\dfrac{P}{Y}$ along Ox and two contractions each equal to

$-\dfrac{\sigma P}{Y}$ along Oy and Oz.

In this way Table V (A) shows the result of applying three perpendicular stresses, each $+P$, in succession. The resultant stress is a pure volume stress $+P$ and the strain is three perpendicular extensions each equal to $\dfrac{P}{Y}(1-2\sigma)$, or a volume strain of $\dfrac{3P}{Y}(1-2\sigma)$. But by definition the volume strain is $\dfrac{P}{K}$ and thus

$$\frac{P}{K}=\frac{3P}{Y}(1-2\sigma), \quad \text{or} \quad Y=3K(1-2\sigma) \quad . \quad . \quad (107)$$

In Table V (B) two equal perpendicular stresses, one extensional the other compressional, are combined to produce an extension along Ox of $\dfrac{P}{Y}(1+\sigma)$ and an equal compression along Oy. But these strains have been shown in Article 56 to be equivalent to a shear strain of magnitude $\dfrac{2P}{Y}(1+\sigma)$ at $45°$ to Ox or Oy. Since the equivalent shearing stress is P, we have:—

$$\theta=\frac{P}{n}=\frac{2P}{Y}(1+\sigma), \quad \text{or} \quad Y=2n(1+\sigma) \quad . \quad . \quad (108)$$

Table V (C) shows the result of applying a set of stresses which will define the axial modulus if the lateral strains along Oy and Oz are zero, $i.e.$ if

$$P_1=\sigma(P+P_1), \quad \text{or} \quad P_1=\frac{\sigma P}{1-\sigma}.$$

In this case the extension along Ox is

$$\frac{P}{Y}\left(1-\frac{2\sigma^2}{1-\sigma}\right)=\frac{P}{Y}\frac{(1+\sigma)(1-2\sigma)}{(1-\sigma)}.$$

But as this by definition is also equal to $\dfrac{P}{\chi}$, we have

$$Y(1-\sigma)=\chi(1+\sigma)(1-2\sigma). \qquad . \qquad . \quad (109)$$

From these equations we may also obtain :—

$$Y=\frac{9nK}{3K+n}, \quad \sigma=\frac{3K-2n}{6K+2n}, \quad \chi=\frac{3K+4n}{3}. \qquad . \quad (110)$$

TABLE V.—STRESSES AND STRAINS

Stresses applied along			Strains produced along		
Ox	Oy	Oz	Ox	Oy	Oz	
$+P$	0	0	$+\dfrac{P}{Y}$	$-\dfrac{\sigma P}{Y}$	$-\dfrac{\sigma P}{Y}$	
0	$+P$	0	$-\dfrac{\sigma P}{Y}$	$+\dfrac{P}{Y}$	$-\dfrac{\sigma P}{Y}$	(A)
0	0	$+P$	$-\dfrac{\sigma P}{Y}$	$-\dfrac{\sigma P}{Y}$	$+\dfrac{P}{Y}$	
$+P$	$+P$	$+P$	$\dfrac{P}{Y}[1-2\sigma]$	$\dfrac{P}{Y}[1-2\sigma]$	$\dfrac{P}{Y}[1-2\sigma]$	(Sum)
$+P$	0	0	$+\dfrac{P}{Y}$	$-\dfrac{\sigma P}{Y}$	$-\dfrac{\sigma P}{Y}$	(B)
0	$-P$	0	$+\dfrac{\sigma P}{Y}$	$-\dfrac{P}{Y}$	$+\dfrac{\sigma P}{Y}$	
$+P$	$-P$	0	$\dfrac{P}{Y}[1+\sigma]$	$-\dfrac{P}{Y}[1+\sigma]$	0	(Sum)
$+P$	0	0	$+\dfrac{P}{Y}$	$-\dfrac{\sigma P}{Y}$	$-\dfrac{\sigma P}{Y}$	
0	$+P_1$	0	$-\dfrac{\sigma P_1}{Y}$	$+\dfrac{P_1}{Y}$	$-\dfrac{\sigma P_1}{Y}$	(C)
0	0	$+P_1$	$-\dfrac{\sigma P_1}{Y}$	$-\dfrac{\sigma P_1}{Y}$	$+\dfrac{P_1}{Y}$	
$+P$	$+P_1$	$+P_1$	$\dfrac{1}{Y}[P-2\sigma P_1]$	$\dfrac{1}{Y}[P_1-\sigma(P+P_1)]$	$\dfrac{1}{Y}[P_1-\sigma(P+P_1)]$	(Sum)

66. Searle's Method for the Elastic Constants.—G. F. C. Searle [1] has described a very convenient method for the measurement of the elastic constants of a material in the form of fairly short

[1] G. F. C. Searle, *Phil. Mag.*, **49**, 193 (1900).

and moderately thin wire. The specimen AB (Fig. 46) (a) passes into two small holes, drilled at the centres of two rods CD and EF of square or circular cross-section, and is fixed firmly by two set screws, which may conveniently be fitted with rings for the attachment of a bifilar form of support. The ends E, D are drawn together by means of a thread, thus forcing the wire into an arc, and when the system is released, the relaxation of the strain in the wire causes each rod to vibrate in a horizontal plane about its supporting thread with period t_1. This period is measured. If (Fig. 46) (b) l is the length of wire between the clamping screws, and α the angular

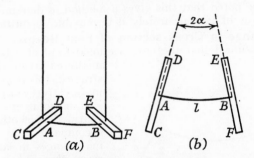

FIG. 46.—SEARLE'S APPARATUS FOR THE MEASUREMENT OF THE ELASTIC CONSTANTS OF A WIRE.

deflection of each bar from its equilibrium position, then, since the bending moment is constant at any point in AB, the latter will form a circular arc of radius R, such that $l=2R\alpha$. The bending moment is, from (88), equal to

$$\frac{YAk^2}{R}=\frac{2YAk^2\alpha}{l},$$

and this is the restoring couple acting on each bar when the system is released. Thus the torque τ per unit angular displacement is given by

$$\tau=\frac{2YAk^2}{l},$$

and the periodic time of oscillation is, from (19),

$$t_1=2\pi\sqrt{\frac{Il}{2YAk^2}},$$

where I is the moment of inertia of the bar about its supporting thread. For a circular wire AB the radius of gyration is $\frac{1}{2}r$, and thus

$$t_1=2\pi\sqrt{\frac{2Il}{\pi r^4 Y}} \qquad . \qquad . \qquad . \qquad (111)$$

If, now, the bar CD is clamped horizontally with the wire AB

vertical, and EF is made to execute torsional oscillations, from (19), the period t_2 of the oscillating bar is given by

$$t_2 = 2\pi \sqrt{\frac{2Il}{n\pi r^4}}, \qquad . \qquad . \qquad . \qquad (112)$$

the value of I being the same in both experiments. From (111) and (112) Y and n may be found, while, utilising relation (108), σ is given by

$$2(1+\sigma) = \frac{Y}{n} = \frac{t_2^2}{t_1^2}.$$

It should be noted that this gives a method of determining σ for a wire in terms of two accurately determinable quantities t_1 and t_2.

67. Change in Cross-section of Bent Beams.—Although it has been assumed that the cross-sectional form of a bent beam is

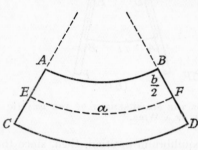

FIG. 47.—CROSS-SECTION OF A BENT BEAM.

unaltered when the beam is strained, this is only approximately true, since the extension of some fibres, and the contraction of others, will be accompanied by corresponding changes in lateral dimensions, those fibres which are stretched longitudinally decreasing in width and *vice versa*. Hence, in practice, the form assumed by a section, which in the unstrained condition is rectangular, will be similar to that shown in Fig. 47 when stress is applied, while a rod of circular cross-section changes into an oval form with maximum width on the compressed side of the rod. If the rectangular section had width a and depth b in the unstrained position, AB becomes $a\left(1 - \dfrac{\sigma b}{2R}\right)$, since the longitudinal extension at the distance $\frac{1}{2}b$ from

the neutral line is, from Article 62, equal to $\dfrac{b}{2R}$, where R is the radius of curvature of the beam. From Fig. 47, if r is the radius of curvature of the neutral surface EF in the plane of the diagram,

$$\frac{EF}{r} = \frac{AB}{r - \frac{1}{2}b}, \quad \text{and thus} \quad \frac{a}{r} = \frac{a\left(1 - \dfrac{\sigma b}{2R}\right)}{r - \dfrac{b}{2}}.$$

Hence

$$r - \frac{b}{2} = r\left(1 - \frac{\sigma b}{2R}\right), \quad \text{or} \quad \sigma = \frac{R}{r}.$$

This relation has been used in the measurement of σ, but, since r is of the order $3R$, and is measured by determining the mutual inclination of AC and BD, the method does not give accurate results. Whiddington's method [1] of measuring small distances might be employed. In this the alteration of pitch in a heterodyne beat note, consequent on the difference in capacity of an air condenser, produced by a change in the distance between its plates, is used to determine that small distance variation. The method has been successfully applied to measure the cantilever depression of a fairly rigid steel bar under very light loads, and seems likely to be of great value where exceedingly small changes in length are involved.

If the upper surface of the beam is optically flat, an optical interference method [2] is available for the measurement of σ, utilising the relation $r\sigma=R$. A test plate of glass is mounted on the beam at its mid point, and the beam is bent by being supported near its ends on knife edges as in Fig. 42, but with loads applied at A and B instead of at P. Interference fringes can then be seen by light which is reflected vertically, as in the well known Newton's Rings experiment. These fringes comprise two sets of hyperbolas having common asymptotes. If horizontal axes Ox, Oy are taken along and across the length of the beam, the depression z at any point (xy) is given by

$$8Rrz=4x^2r+R(a^2-4y^2),$$

where a is the width of the beam. Along each fringe z is constant and, for the fringes passing through the centre, $8rz=a^2$. Thus the equation to the asymptotes is

$$rx^2=Ry^2,$$

which is a pair of straight lines each making an angle θ with the x axis, given by $\cot^2\theta=R/r=\sigma$.

68. Expansion of a Hollow Isotropic Cylinder.—The expansion of a hollow cylinder under internal and external pressures is of importance in many experiments, designed to measure the bulk modulus of the material of the cylinder. Fig. 48 (a) shows the cylinder of internal and external radii R_1 and R_2, the internal and external pressures being p_1 and p_2. The cylinder is supposed to have a length large compared with its radius, and to be closed by thick and flat ends. In general, there will be both axial and radial displacements at each point in the material. Suppose the axial strain to be C, and the radial displacement at a point distant r from the axis to be ρ. Then, as is shown below, ρ is given by

$$\rho=Ar+\frac{B}{r},$$

where A and B are constants.

[1] Whiddington, *Phil. Mag.*, **40**, 634 (1920) ; *Engineering*, **110**, 384 (1920).
[2] G. F. C. Searle, *Experimental Physics*, p. 89 (1934).

Thus the radial strain is $\dfrac{d\rho}{dr}=A-\dfrac{B}{r^2}$, while the transverse, or circumferential, strain $\dfrac{\rho}{r}=A+\dfrac{B}{r^2}$. Suppose the corresponding axial, radial and transverse stresses are P, Q, R respectively. Then, by

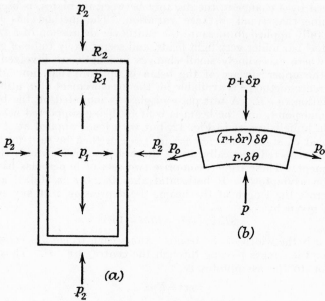

Fig. 48.—Expansion of a Cylinder.

the method given in Article 65, the strains are given by

$$C=\frac{P}{Y}-\frac{\sigma(Q+R)}{Y},$$

$$A-\frac{B}{r^2}=\frac{Q}{Y}-\frac{\sigma(R+P)}{Y},$$

$$A+\frac{B}{r^2}=\frac{R}{Y}-\frac{\sigma(P+Q)}{Y}.$$

If these equations are solved for P, Q, R we have

$$P=\frac{CY(1-\sigma)}{(1+\sigma)(1-2\sigma)}+\frac{2AY\sigma}{(1+\sigma)(1-2\sigma)}, \qquad . \qquad . \qquad (113)$$

$$Q=\frac{CY\sigma}{(1+\sigma)(1-2\sigma)}-\frac{BY}{r^2(1+\sigma)}+\frac{AY}{(1+\sigma)(1-2\sigma)}, \qquad . \qquad (114)$$

$$R=\frac{CY\sigma}{(1+\sigma)(1-2\sigma)}+\frac{BY}{r^2(1+\sigma)}+\frac{AY}{(1+\sigma)(1-2\sigma)}. \qquad . \qquad (115)$$

When $r=R_1$, $Q=-p_1$, and when $r=R_2$, $Q=-p_2$. Thus from (114).

$$p_2-p_1=\frac{BY}{(1+\sigma)}\left[\frac{1}{R_2{}^2}-\frac{1}{R_1{}^2}\right],$$

and, by eliminating BY,

$$\frac{Y(A+\sigma C)}{(1+\sigma)(1-2\sigma)}=-\left[\frac{p_2R_2{}^2-p_1R_1{}^2}{R_2{}^2-R_1{}^2}\right]. \qquad . \qquad . \quad (116)$$

The axial stress P is given by

$$P\pi(R_2{}^2-R_1{}^2)=p_1\pi R_1{}^2-p_2\pi R_2{}^2,$$

and so from (113)

$$\frac{Y[2\sigma A+C(1-\sigma)]}{(1+\sigma)(1-2\sigma)}=-\left[\frac{p_2R_2{}^2-p_1R_1{}^2}{R_2{}^2-R_1{}^2}\right]. \qquad . \quad (117)$$

Combining (116) and (117)

$$\frac{YA}{1-2\sigma}=\frac{YC}{1-2\sigma}=-\left[\frac{p_2R_2{}^2-p_1R_1{}^2}{R_2{}^2-R_1{}^2}\right].$$

From these values of A, B, C we have :
Axial Strain

$$C=\frac{\delta l}{l}=-\frac{(1-2\sigma)}{Y}\left[\frac{p_2R_2{}^2-p_1R_1{}^2}{R_2{}^2-R_1{}^2}\right].$$

Radial Strain

$$A-\frac{B}{r^2}=-\frac{(1-2\sigma)}{Y}\left[\frac{p_2R_2{}^2-p_1R_1{}^2}{R_2{}^2-R_1{}^2}\right]+\frac{(1+\sigma)}{Yr^2}\left[\frac{R_1{}^2R_2{}^2}{R_2{}^2-R_1{}^2}\right](p_2-p_1).$$

Transverse Strain

$$A+\frac{B}{r^2}=-\frac{(1-2\sigma)}{Y}\left[\frac{p_2R_2{}^2-p_1R_1{}^2}{R_2{}^2-R_1{}^2}\right]-\frac{(1+\sigma)}{Yr^2}\left[\frac{R_1{}^2R_2{}^2}{R_2{}^2-R_1{}^2}\right](p_2-p_1).$$

Thus the new dimensions of the cylinder can be obtained from :
Increase in length

$$\delta l=-\frac{l(1-2\sigma)}{Y}\left[\frac{p_2R_2{}^2-p_1R_1{}^2}{R_2{}^2-R_1{}^2}\right],$$

Increase in external radius

$$\delta R_2=AR_2+\frac{B}{R_2},$$

or $$\delta R_2=\frac{R_2}{Y}\frac{[p_1R_1{}^2(2-\sigma)-p_2R_1{}^2(1+\sigma)-p_2R_2{}^2(1-2\sigma)]}{R_2{}^2-R_1{}^2}.$$

Increase in internal radius

$$\delta R_1=AR_1+\frac{B}{R_1},$$

or $$\delta R_1=\frac{R_1}{Y}\frac{[p_1R_1{}^2(1-2\sigma)+p_1R_2{}^2(1+\sigma)-p_2R_2{}^2(2-\sigma)]}{R_2{}^2-R_1{}^2}.$$

The increase in internal volume δV_1 is given by

$$\frac{\delta V_1}{V_1} = \frac{\delta l}{l} + \frac{2\delta R_1}{R_1},$$

or
$$\frac{\delta V_1}{V_1} = \frac{3p_1R_1{}^2(1-2\sigma) + 2p_1R_2{}^2(1+\sigma) - p_2R_2{}^2(5-4\sigma)}{Y(R_2{}^2 - R_1{}^2)},$$

and the increase in external volume δV_2 is given by

$$\frac{\delta V_2}{V_2} = \frac{p_1R_1{}^2(5-4\sigma) - 2p_2R_1{}^2(1+\sigma) - 3p_2R_2{}^2(1-2\sigma)}{Y(R_2{}^2 - R_1{}^2)}.$$

The following special cases are of importance :—

(a) *Increase in length, for internal pressure only, the wall thickness being small, i.e. $p_1 = P$, $p_2 = $ zero.* Thus

$$\frac{\delta l}{l} = \frac{PR_1{}^2(1-2\sigma)}{Y(R_2{}^2 - R_1{}^2)} = \frac{PR}{6Kx},$$

where R is the mean radius and x the wall thickness. This is the theory of Mallock's experiment.

(b) *Increase in internal volume under the action of an external pressure alone, i.e. $p_1 = $ zero, $p_2 = P$.* Then

$$\frac{\delta V_1}{V_1} = \frac{PR_2{}^2(4\sigma - 5)}{Y(R_2{}^2 - R_1{}^2)} = \frac{PR(4\sigma - 5)}{2Yx}.$$

This is the basis of Amagat's experiments.

(c) *Increase in internal volume when external and internal pressures are the same, i.e. $p_1 = p_2 = P$.*

$$\frac{\delta V_1}{V_1} = -\frac{3P(1-2\sigma)}{Y} = -\frac{P}{K},$$

a result which would be obtained if the cylinder had been solid and under the action of an external pressure P alone. This result is of importance in Regnault's measurement of the bulk modulus of liquids.

To prove that the radial displacement p is of the form $Ar + \dfrac{B}{r}$ consider the following :—Fig. 48 (b) represents a small curved element of the cylinder wall of unit depth, p_0 being the circumferential stress. For radial equilibrium

$$pr\delta\theta - (p + \delta p)(r + \delta r)\delta\theta = p_0\delta r\delta\theta,$$

or
$$\delta(pr) = -p_0\delta r.$$

The resultant axial strain is $\dfrac{\sigma(p - p_0)}{Y}$ and, since this must be constant over the section,

$$p - p_0 = p + \frac{\delta(pr)}{\delta r} = \text{constant} = M.$$

Thus
$$r\frac{dp}{dr}=M-2p$$

which gives on integration,

$$M-2p=\frac{N}{r^2}, \; N \text{ being a constant.}$$

Therefore
$$2p_0=2p-2M=-M-\frac{N}{r^2}.$$

The total radial strain is

$$\frac{d\rho}{dr}=\frac{(p+\sigma p_0+\sigma P)}{Y}=-\frac{[Mr^2(1-\sigma)+2\sigma Pr^2-N(1+\sigma)],}{2Yr^2}$$

and thus

$$\rho=-\frac{1}{2Y}\int\left[M(1-\sigma)+2\sigma P-\frac{N}{r^2}(1+\sigma)\right]dr$$

or,

$$\rho=-\frac{M(1-\sigma)r}{2Y}-\frac{\sigma Pr}{Y}-\frac{N(1+\sigma)}{2Yr}$$

$$\rho=Ar+\frac{B}{r}.$$

69. The Bulk Modulus of Solids.—The bulk modulus of a solid may be calculated from the values of Y and n, using equation (110), and there are several methods by which a direct determination may be made. For example, Amagat measured K by observing the change in the internal volume of a cylinder under an applied traction. According to Article 65, this change is given by

$$\frac{\delta V}{V}=\frac{P}{Y}(1-2\sigma)=\frac{P}{3K}, \quad . \quad . \quad . \quad (118)$$

where P is the applied force per unit area, V the original volume, and δV the change in volume. In Amagat's work δV was measured by filling the cylinder with water, which extended into a narrow calibrated capillary tube, and noting the alteration in the position of the meniscus when the cylinder was loaded. In another experiment the change, δV_1, in internal volume, experienced by the cylinder under a uniform external pressure P, was measured by the same means. In such a case, as was proved in the previous article, δV_1 is given by

$$\frac{\delta V_1}{V}=\frac{PR_2^2}{R_2^2-R_1^2}\cdot\frac{1}{Y}(4\sigma-5), \quad . \quad . \quad . \quad (119)$$

where R_2 and R_1 are the external and internal radii of the cylinder. By dividing (118) by (119) we have

$$\frac{\delta V}{\delta V_1}=\frac{R_2^2-R_1^2}{R_2^2}\cdot\frac{1-2\sigma}{4\sigma-5},$$

and this gives an accurate means of determining Poisson's ratio.

In Mallock's method [1] of measuring K the material is in the form of a long and thin-walled tube which is subjected to internal pressure. The tube is supported in horizontal gimbals, one of which is held on a rocking support carrying a small reflecting prism. The latter has an index mark which is observed through a micrometer microscope, and thus the longitudinal extension is magnified and measured. If the thickness of the walls is small compared with the diameter of the tube, it is found that the change in length depends solely on the bulk modulus and, for isotropic substances,

$$K = \frac{PR}{6(R_2 - R_1)\delta l},$$

where δl is the longitudinal extension and R is the mean radius. Over the range of pressures employed—1 to 30 atmospheres—the extension was proportional to the applied pressure, and thus indicated a constant value of the bulk modulus. Mallock's experimental results, obtained with steel, brass, and copper, are included in Table VI, and it is noteworthy that hard-drawn copper tubing proved to be stiffer than steel. With steel and brass, annealing produced only a small change in the bulk modulus, but with copper the effect was very much greater.

Bridgman [2] made a number of measurements of K for solids in the form of rods or tubes, utilising pressures up to 6,500 kg. per square centimetre—about 6,300 atmospheres—by two different methods. In the first method the specimen, in the form of a rod, is enclosed in a heavy steel cylinder throughout the interior of which the hydrostatic pressure is applied. The rod shortens under this uniform external pressure while the cylinder lengthens, the latter effect being only about 5 per cent. of the former. The extension δl_1 of the cylinder is measured by placing it on the bed of a comparator, and noting the distance apart of two fine scratches before, and after, applying the pressure. In addition, the contraction δl_2 of the rod, relative to the cylinder, is measured. The rod passes through a ring which it fits with sufficient friction to retain it in position, and one end of the rod abuts against the cylinder end. The other end of the rod is free to contract through the ring, which is itself prevented from moving, relative to the cylinder, by pressing against an internal shoulder. Thus the relative movement, δl_2, is equal to the change of position of the ring on the rod, and this is observed by measuring the distance between two marks, one on each, before and after the pressure is applied. The absolute extension δl of the rod is then given by

$$\delta l = \delta l_2 - \delta l_1.$$

This gives the longitudinal strain, which is one-third of the volume compressive strain, and thus enables K to be calculated.

[1] Mallock, *Proc. Roy. Soc.*, A, **74**, 50 (1904).
[2] Bridgman, *Proc. Amer. Acad.*, **44**, 255 (1908). See also *The Physics of High Pressures*.

TABLE VI.—VALUES OF THE ELASTIC CONSTANTS OF SOLIDS

(K, Y, n in dynes per sq. cm. × 10¹¹)

Material.		K.	Y.	n.	σ.
Steel	(M)	18·3			
,, ...	(B)	19·4			
,, ...	(A)	14·9	20·7	..	0·267
,, ...		16·4	20·9	8·12	0·287
Copper . . .	(A)	11·8	12·3	..	0·327
,, (hard) .	(M)	23			
,, (annealed)	(M)	14·3			
Brass	(A)	10·6	11·00	..	0·328
,, . . .	(M)	10·9			
Copper . . .		13·1	12·3	4·55	0·337
Glass . . .	(A)	4·61	7·09	..	0·245
,, . . .	(B)	4·67			
Aluminium .	(B)	8·55			
Lead	(A)	3·78	1·58	..	0·428
Aluminium . .		7·46	7·05	2·67	0·339
Lead . . .		4·00	1·62	..	0·446
Silver . . .		10·9	7·90	2·87	0·379
Platinum . .		24·7	16·8	6·10	0·387
Gold		16·6	8·0	2·77	0·422
Quartz . . .		1·4	5·18	3·0	
Tin		5·29	5·43	2·04	0·33
Nickel . . .		17·6	20·2	7·70	0·309
Manganin . .		12·1	12·4	4·65	0·329
Constantan . .		15·5	16·3	6·11	0·325
Cadmium . .		4·12	4·99	1·92	0·30
Phosphor bronze .		..	12·0	4·36	0·38
Delta metal .	(A)	9·94	11·86	..	0·340
Zinc		6·0	8·28	3·80	
Bismuth . . .		3·26	3·13	1·22	0·33
Palladium . .		..	11·3	5·11	0·393
Bronze . . .		..	8·08	3·43	0·358
German silver .		..	11·6	4·5	0·37
Platinoid . .		..	13·6	3·6	0·37
India-rubber . .		..	0·05	0·00016	0·48
Oak		..	1·3		
Mahogany . .		..	0·88		
Boxwood . . .		..	3·0		
Catgut . . .		..	0·32		

(M) Mallock.   (B) Bridgman.   (A) Amagat.

In Bridgman's second method—which employs the same principles of measurement—the relative change in length of a rod with respect to a tube of another substance, when both are under a uniform pressure over the whole surface, is measured. If the bulk modulus of the material of the rod is known, that of the tube may be deduced. With glass tubes a seasoning effect is necessary, and this is produced by applying several cycles of pressure variation.

In a succession of further experiments Bridgman [1] has raised the

[1] Bridgman, *Proc. Amer. Acad. Arts. Sci.*, **74**, 13, 425 (1942).

maximum pressure used to about 100,000 kg. per sq. cm. or approximately 97,000 atmospheres. Indirect methods were necessary to measure such pressures. In one, resistance elements of various metals were used, and the resistances plotted against pressure over the directly measurable range. For some the resistance increased, for others it decreased, in a strictly linear manner, and it was found that when they were used at much higher pressures their extrapolated graphs, at the measured resistance values, gave practically the same value of the pressure which was therefore accepted. No containing vessel was reliably able to withstand such pressures applied internally alone, so Bridgman placed the operative vessel within another by means of which a suitable external pressure could be applied of sufficient intensity to guard against risk of bursting. In this important series of measurements data are provided for the P, V relations of 17 elements up to 100,000 kg. per sq. cm., and, to a lower maximum, of water and 20 organic liquids. In an investigation of the behaviour of substances under high shearing stress at high pressure, Bridgman found [1] that many normally stable substances become unstable and may detonate, while pairs of substances usually inert may combine explosively.

70. Single Metal Crystals.—Normal polycrystalline metals have practically the same properties in all directions, but this uniformity is the consequence of a chaotic crystal distribution giving a steady statistical average. The individual crystals are very small, and the discontinuities between them cause brittleness which increases with continuous, and particularly with continuously varying, strain. It is thus to be expected that the properties, especially those of elasticity, of large metal crystals are greatly influenced by the internal regularity of orientation of molecular fields.

Many different methods of producing rods of monocrystalline structure have been used. Bridgman [2] first melted the tip of the rod or wire and then placed it in a glass tube in an almost non-oxidising atmosphere so that the oxide coating, which serves to hold the wire in cylindrical form, is neither destroyed nor unduly developed. Then a furnace, maintained slightly above the melting point, is drawn slowly along the wire, the melted end entering first. For a wire 0·1 cm. diameter the rate of passage through the furnace should be about 1 mm. per minute, and then each element, as it melts and subsequently resolidifies, takes up the crystal orientation determined by the already treated portion. The defect of the method is that no control is exercised over the crystal orientation relative to the length of the wire. To overcome this drawback, Kapitza [3] describes a somewhat similar method in which a seed crystal, with the desired orientation, is fused to the leading end of the melted rod and thus directs the subsequent axial directions.

---

[1] Bridgman, *Phys. Rev.*, **48**, 825 (1935).
[2] Bridgman, *Proc. Amer. Acad. Sci.*, **60**, 307 (1925).
[3] Kapitza, *Proc. Roy. Soc.*, *A.*, **119**, 358 (1929).

In a third method Czochralski [1] melted the metal in a crucible maintained a few degrees above the melting point. A sheet of mica, with a hole giving the size of the desired rod, floats on the metal and a seed crystal, suitably oriented, is used to touch the melt through the hole, and is then drawn upwards by a clockwork or electric motor, at a rate which may be as great as 1 cm. per minute. By this means rods from 0·5 mm. to 5·0 mm. diameter may be produced.

As is to be expected, practically all the normal physical properties show directional variation in the monocrystalline state, and follow closely the law :—

$$P = P_1 \cos^2 \alpha + P_2 \sin^2 \alpha$$

in which P, P_1, and P_2 are the measures of that property at an angle α to the symmetry axis, parallel to that axis, and perpendicular to it, respectively. This is the case with electrical resistance, thermal conductivity, and thermo-electricity.

Strength, Elasticity, and Plasticity.—In general, single crystals have smaller elasticity and markedly greater plasticity than poly-crystalline samples, and these reactions to stresses vary notably with direction. Because of regular molecular patterning, there are directional variations in tensile strength, and marked tendencies for fracture to occur along fixed cleavage planes. Thus if various planes are drawn in the metal, the breaking stress normal to the planes will exhibit defined minima of different magnitudes. Therefore the actual direction of fracture depends upon the ratio of stress component, perpendicular to one of the cleavage planes, to its particular breaking stress, and the break occurs at that plane for which the ratio is greatest. The cleavage planes naturally tend to be where molecular spacing is a maximum, but since most molecular fields are polar, this is not always true ; for ionic crystals it is more usual for cleavage planes to be determined by the direction of iso-ionic planes, so that cleavage exposes opposite faces of similar ions.

It is in connection with plastic deformations that metal crystals show extraordinary and somewhat puzzling properties. For example, ordinary cadmium wire has a high value of n but single crystal wire shears into a permanent set under its own weight. Just as there are minimum breaking stress planes (cleavage planes), so there are minimum shearing stress planes, and plastic deformation occurs as a result of the mutual gliding of these planes over one another, but the exact mechanism is difficult to explain theoretically, as the glide elements are parallel slabs of metal about 10,000 cells apart. When the glide has gone on for some thousands of cell lengths the material stiffens considerably. This is the cause of the work-hardening process well known in engineering by which permanent sets produced by hammering, *etc.*, produce a tougher material. For example, a single crystal cadmium wire, after plastic extension to twice its old

[1] Czochralski, *Z.f. Phys. Chem.*, **92**, 219 (1917).

length, has its breaking stress increased tenfold. The process of glide deformation is shown diagrammatically in Fig. 49 (*a*) in which a longitudinal yield is indicated as the result of an inclined glide. The actual direction of glide depends, as with cleavage, on the plane in which the ratio of shearing stress to maximum bearable stress is greatest. For some simple crystalline forms, *e.g.* cadmium, there is only one glide direction.

The stress-strain diagram for such a plastic extension shows, Fig. 49 (*b*), that the glide occurs as a series of jerks during which extension occurs without increase of stress, followed immediately by a small range of pseudo-elasticity, and so on in sequence. Finally, there is a fairly extensive region of regular elastic expansion.

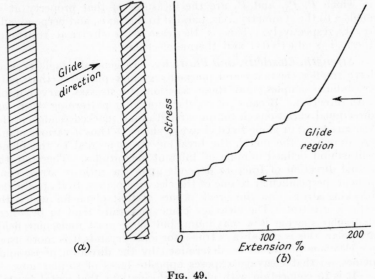

Fɪɢ. 49.

The onset of plasticity is most accurately delineated by the stress-strain graph, but it may also be studied by (*a*) the distortion produced in the Laue spots given by X-ray diffractions, or (*b*) the double refraction which is produced in transparent crystals.

71. Elasticity of Fluids.—A solid possesses both rigidity and bulk moduli, but a fluid has no rigidity and thus cannot permanently resist a tangential stress. In a solid the stress at any point on a given element of area may have any direction with reference to that area, but in a fluid *at rest* it must act along the normal to the plane, and it follows that, in liquids at rest, the pressure at a point is independent of direction, and is thus a function of the position of the point alone. In a *perfect* fluid, whether at rest or in relative motion, no tangential stress can exist, but, in practice, relative motion is accompanied by tangential forces tending to prevent that motion, and they persist as long as the motion lasts.   Thus the fluid may be regarded as yielding to these stresses, different liquids yielding at very different rates.   The condition at which yield takes place is determined by a property known as viscosity, and the latter may be regarded as a transient type of rigidity.   This point is discussed further in the chapter on viscosity.

A perfect liquid is usually described as a completely incompressible fluid.   No liquid, in practice, is quite incompressible, although in many cases the change in volume, for moderate increases in pressure, is sufficiently small to be neglected in many problems.   The quantitative study of the bulk modulus of liquids, and its relation to the other properties of the liquid, is a matter of great practical importance.   It must be remembered, however, that the value of the modulus depends on the rate of application and removal of the stress.   The two extreme cases, (i) slow stress changes under isothermal conditions, and (ii) rapidly alternating stresses under adiabatic conditions, are of special importance.   In either case the bulk modulus K is defined by the relation

$$K = -V\left(\frac{dP}{dV}\right),$$

where dP is an additional stress, causing an increase dV in an original volume V.   The *compressibility* β is defined as the reciprocal of K, or

$$\beta = -\frac{1}{V}\left(\frac{dV}{dP}\right).$$

A complete study of the isothermal compressibility of a substance involves a knowledge of the isothermal curves connecting P and V at various temperatures, so that the density of the substance must be known at all pressures and temperatures.   From such curves, or from corresponding data, the most important thermodynamical properties of the substance become known.

72.   Measurement of the Bulk Moduli of Liquids.—Experiments designed to measure K are beset with difficulties, which arise chiefly in the determination of the high pressures involved, the small change of volume to be measured, and, still more, the change in the size of the containing vessel.   To correct for the last factor, accurate knowledge of the bulk modulus of the material of the vessel is required.   In early experiments the vessels were of glass, but, since the elastic constants of glass are not very definite, it is essential to make preliminary measurements with the vessel to be used in the experiment.   If the vessel is subjected to the same internal and external pressure, its internal volume does not remain constant, but decreases by an amount equal to that which would be caused if the vessel were solid and were subjected to the given stress, applied externally. A cylinder with flat ends, under a pressure P, experiences a change in internal volume δV_1 given by

$$\frac{\delta V_1}{V} = \frac{P}{K_1},$$

where K_1 is the bulk modulus of the material of the vessel and V is its original volume. If measurements are made of the apparent change δV_2 in the volume of contained liquid under the pressure P, applied internally and externally, the true diminution δV is given by

$$\delta V = \delta V_2 + \delta V_1,$$

or

$$\frac{\delta V_2}{V} = P\left(\frac{1}{K} - \frac{1}{K_1}\right), \qquad \cdot \qquad \cdot \qquad \cdot \qquad (120)$$

where K is the bulk modulus of the liquid. This was the method used by Regnault, the liquid being placed in a glass piezometer enclosed in an outer vessel in such a way that, by means of three taps, pressure could be applied to the inside, to the outside, or on both sides of the piezometer. This flexibility of adjustment was necessary, since the previous theory assumes homogeneity of the elastic properties in the vessel, and this assumption, in the case of glass, is of doubtful validity.

Regnault's experiments were limited to moderate pressures up to 10 atmospheres. This range was extended by Tait to 500 atmospheres, by Parsons and Cook [1] to 2,000 atmospheres, and, more recently, in the important investigations by Bridgman [2] to about 12,000 atmospheres. The latter experiments are the most complete yet carried out, and the resulting isothermals, for pressure and volume of many liquids, are now accepted as standards. The substance under test was placed in a strong chrome-vanadium steel cylinder, and the pressure was produced by the advance of a piston of known cross-section, the amount of advance giving the apparent change in the volume of the liquid relative to the enclosing vessel. The pressure was determined by noting the change in the electrical resistance of a coil of manganin wire placed in the vessel, the resistance of this coil being about 100 ohms; and the relation between pressure and resistance was obtained by initial calibration with an absolute manometer of special type. This relation was found to be so accurately linear to pressures of the order of 12,000 atmospheres, that it could be extended by extrapolation to 20,000 atmospheres without serious error. To render the piston leak-proof at such high pressures, Bridgman used a special form of packing which, although somewhat inefficient at low pressures—thus necessitating an ordinary form of packing as an auxiliary—became automatically tighter with increase of pressure, so that the limit to the attainable pressure was

[1] Parsons and Cook, *Proc. Roy. Soc.*, *A.*, 85, 332 (1911).
[2] Bridgman, *Proc. Amer. Acad.*, 48, 309 (1912); 49, 3 (1913); 66, 185 (1931). See also *The Physics of High Pressures*.

determined by the strength of the cylinder. The principle of this packing is indicated in Fig. 50. Pressure is applied to the liquid L in the cylinder by the sliding mushroom head A which, in turn, is forced into the cylinder by the pressure of the rod P, acting on A through the hardened ring of steel D, the mild steel, or copper washers B, and the soft rubber packing C. Thus the compressional force on C must equal the total thrust on A and, since the cross-sectional area of C is less than that of A, the pressure in the packing exceeds the pressure of the liquid, and the liquid can never leak.

The whole apparatus was maintained at a constant temperature by thermostatic control, and, in the case of water, readings of the pressure and volume were taken to 80° C. The correction for the expansion of the cylinder was determined by a set of auxiliary experiments in which part of the liquid was replaced by steel, and the compressibility of the two together was found.

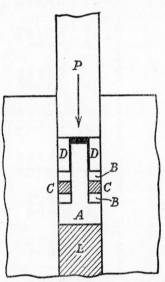

Some of the many additional important results obtained by Bridgman in these experiments are summarised below. As will be seen these results do not yet permit many simple generalisations and, as a rule, they show irregularities due in all probability to the overlapping of different effects. For example, the compression under pressure appears to be due partly to a reduction in the spacing of the molecules and partly to an actual change in the effective molecular size.

Fig. 50.—Bridgman's Experiments on the Bulk Moduli of Liquids.

The elastic constants do not show an invariable increase with pressure, with some substances decreases are observed. Thermal conductivity, electrical conductivity, and Peltier coefficients also yield no general rule, and the two former show little mutual relationship.

The value of K for water, obtained by different observers, is given in Table VII, where the units of K are 10^4 kg. per sq. cm.

73. Elasticity and Temperature.—As a general rule elastic moduli decrease with temperature, and for comparatively small ranges of temperature the relation is approximately linear. Schaefer indicated that, for temperatures from about 15° C. down to that of liquid air, the order of ascending temperature coefficients for Young's modulus is also the order of increasing thermal expansion and diminishing melting-point, but, since he assumed a linear relation,

Table VII.—Bulk Modulus of Water at Different Temperatures

Observer.	0° C.	10° C.	20° C.	30° C.	40° C.	50° C.	60° C.	70° C.	80° C.	Pressure Range.
Bridgman *	2·18	2·33	2·40	2·46	2·48	2·50	2·50	2·50	2·43	0–500 atmos.
	2·37	2·51	2·60	2·66	2·68	2·70	2·70	2·68	2·63	0–1000 ,,
	2·54	2·67	2·76	2·81	2·84	2·85	2·85	2·83	2·78	0–1500 ,,
	4·09	4·16	4·22	4·30	4·30	4·31	4·30	4·28	4·24	0–6500 ,,
	...	...	...	...	5·85	5·86	5·86	5·84	5·81	0–12500 ,,
Parsons and Cook at 4° C.	2·15	...	...	...	...	...	...	...	...	500 ,,
	2·43	...	...	...	...	...	...	...	...	1000 ,,
	2·79	...	...	...	...	...	...	...	...	2000 ,,
Tait	1·99	2·12	2·24	2·35	2·44	2·48	...	...	...	Low pressures.
	2·06	2·19	2·31	2·39	2·44	2·44	...	...	...	150 atmos.
	2·12	2·26	2·33	2·43	2·38	2·38	...	...	...	300 ,,
Landholt and Bornstein	2·00	2·13	2·24	2·34						
Grassi	2·06	2·13	2·24	2·26						

* More recently (*loc. cit.*) the upper pressure limit has been raised to 50,000 kg. per sq. cm.

his work does not indicate how the temperature coefficient changes. Wassmuth [1] determined the variation of Young's modulus with temperature by means of bent beams. Lee and Shave, [2] and Andrews, [3] working at temperatures to within 150° C. of the melting-points of the materials, found that the relation between Y and T was of an exponential form,

$$Y = Y_1 e^{-b_1 T},$$

where b_1 has one value for temperatures to about one-half the absolute temperature of the melting-point, and another value for higher temperatures. With quartz, Y was found to change only slightly over the range 0° C. to 800° C. In connection with this it is interesting to note that the thermal expansion of this substance is also very small over the same temperature range.

The first experiments on the temperature variation of the rigidity modulus were made by Kohlrausch and Loomis, who observed over a temperature range 15° C. to 100° C., and their results are expressible in the form :—

$$n_T = n_0(1 - aT - bT^2).$$

Schaefer [4] measured n at air temperature and at the temperature of liquid air, but again he assumed a linear law of change. Horton [5] carried out careful measurements with a number of metallic wires and also with quartz fibres. A torsional oscillation method was employed, and the temperature range was from 16° C. to 100° C., and in some cases to 126° C. A truly linear relation was found only for pure copper and steel, although it was very approximately linear with silver. In most other cases Horton found that the measured rigidity depended greatly on the previous heat treatment of the specimen.

In general, the compressibility of liquids increases with rise of temperature, although Amagat found a minimum value for water at about 50° C. Pagliani and Vicentini determined the temperature of minimum compressibility to be between 60° C. and 70° C., while Grassi obtained a maximum compressibility between 0° C. and 4° C. This result does not agree with those of other observers, and Bridgman [6] found a continually decreasing compressibility over the range 0° C. to 50° C. His results may be expressed in the form,

$$K = A + BT - CT^2,$$

which has a maximum value when $B = 2CT$, and for all pressures this temperature of minimum compressibility was approximately 50° C. Curves deduced from Bridgman's readings are shown (Fig. 51). For the other liquids studied by Bridgman no general rule can be

[1] Wassmuth, *Phys. Zeits.*, **6**, 755 (1905).
[2] Lee and Shave, *Proc. Phys. Soc.*, **36**, 5 (1924).
[3] Andrews, *ibid.*, **37**, 3 (1925).
[4] Schaefer, *Ann. d. Phys.*, **9**, 3 (1902).
[5] Horton, *Phil. Trans.*, A, **204**, 1 (1904).
[6] Bridgman, *loc. cit.*

stated, and in a few cases the compressibility increased with rise in temperature.

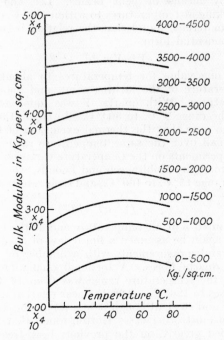

FIG. 51.—BULK MODULUS OF WATER AND PRESSURE (BRIDGMAN).

74. Elasticity and Pressure.—There is no essential distinction in compressibility between a substance, ordinarily liquid, and a gas, after the first few thousand atmospheres. Amagat showed that air, for example, at a pressure of 3,000 atmospheres is as dense as water, but the compressibility of solids is, in general, much less than that of fluids. In all cases the decrease in volume is the result of two effects, (a) a decrease in the space between the constituent molecules and (b) an actual decrease in the volume of the molecules themselves. The large initial compressibility of gases is due to the comparatively large distances between the molecules, and the initial decrease in volume is a result of effect (a), but after the first few thousands of atmospheres the major part of the loss of volume is due to (b).

In the case of all liquids the compressibility decreases with increase of pressure, at first rapidly and then much more slowly. The initial comparatively high compressibility arises by a decrease in the molecular spacing, while the final small value is probably due to a decrease in the volume of the molecules themselves. For water, at any given temperature, the bulk modulus K is a linear function of the pressure which, from Bridgman's results, is given by

At $0°$ C., $K=(2\cdot02+0\cdot000656P)\times10^4$.

At $50°$ C., $K=(2\cdot36+0\cdot000598P)\times10^4$,

where P is expressed in kg. per sq. cm.

In the case of solids the occurrence of an initial comparatively large compressibility is much less apparent, and the compressibility decreases only slightly at high pressures. It is therefore probable that by far the larger part of the volume decrease is due to a reduction in the size of the molecules.

The effect of pressure on rigidity was measured by Bridgman [1] by observing the change in extension of a helical spring, stretched by a constant weight and subjected to uniform pressure. The pressure range was about 12,000 atmospheres, measurements being made at intervals of 2,000 atmospheres, and the temperature was thermostatically controlled. As the spring stretched it drew a sliding manganin wire over a fixed contact, as in the potentiometer, and the consequent difference of potential between the contact and a fixed terminal on the wire was measured. The substances investigated were steel, glass, platinum, nickel, and several other metals. In general, the rigidity increases slightly under pressure, the order of the change being about 2 per cent. for an increase of pressure of 10,000 atmospheres, but the experiments were not of sufficient accuracy to show any non-linear connection between rigidity and pressure. For glass a decrease of rigidity with pressure was found.

Using these results Bridgman also deduced that both Young's modulus and Poisson's ratio show an increase of about 3 per cent. for 10,000 atmospheres increase in pressure.

75. Compressibility of Gases.—The relation between the pressure P, volume V, and absolute temperature T of a perfect gas is given by

$$PV=RT, \qquad \cdot \qquad \cdot \qquad \cdot \qquad \cdot \qquad (121)$$

and thus the bulk modulus, K, under isothermal conditions is

$$K_T=-V\left(\frac{dP}{dV}\right)_T=P.$$

For adiabatic compressions—in which the heat of compression remains in the gas—$PV^\gamma=const.$ and the adiabatic elasticity K_H is given by

$$K_H=-V\left(\frac{dP}{dV}\right)_H=\gamma P.$$

The adiabatic elasticity is greater than the isothermal value in the ratio γ, which depends on the nature of the gas, being $1\cdot66$ for monatomic gases, $1\cdot41$ for air, and approaching unity with increasing molecular complexity.

In real gases the relation (121) is very closely obeyed for moderate

[1] Bridgman, *Proc. Amer. Acad.*, **63**, 401 (1928) ; **64**, 39 (1929).

ranges of temperature, but at very low temperatures and at high pressures, considerable deviations from the perfect gas law occur. This is to be expected, since in these circumstances the assumptions made in deducing the perfect gas law from the kinetic theory of gases no longer apply.

At constant temperature the relation between pressure and volume for a perfect gas is

$$PV = constant,$$

and this equation is known as Boyle's Law. Despretz enclosed a number of gases in barometer tubes standing in the same cistern, so that they had equal volumes under the same initial pressure. This system was then placed in a vessel filled with water, and when pressure was applied it was found that the previous equality of volumes was destroyed. Thus some at least of the gases did not obey Boyle's Law. Of all the gases examined, hydrogen was found to be least compressible, although it was only at high pressures that a difference was observable between hydrogen and air. Regnault enclosed a gas in a closed tube which dipped into the mercury filling a vessel. By pouring more mercury into the vessel through a side tube, the volume of gas was approximately halved and the corresponding pressure recorded. Then gas was pumped into the closed tube to restore the old volume condition under the new pressure, and the latter was then increased again to compress the gas to half volume. In no case was PV found to be constant, and with all gases except hydrogen the product decreased with increasing pressure. A series of important experiments was begun by Amagat, who worked at the bottom of a mine-shaft and produced the pressures by means of mercury in a tube 300 metres long extending up through the shaft. He experimented with nitrogen, oxygen, air, carbon monoxide, marsh gas, and ethylene. At low pressure PV for nitrogen decreased to a minimum, and then increased as the pressure was continually raised. A similar variation, still more strongly marked, was found with ethylene, particularly at lower temperatures ; in fact, this type of variation occurs with all gases, including hydrogen, as the critical temperature is approached. For very high pressures the relation between PV and P is sensibly linear, and thus the curves are of the form,

$$P(V-b) = c,$$

where b and c are constants, the former depending on the nature of the gas and the latter on the temperature. When $V = b$ the pressure is infinite, and so b may be regarded as the least volume which can be occupied by the gas particles. Amagat found that the ratio $\dfrac{b}{V}$ at a pressure of 760 mm. of mercury was 0·00078 for hydrogen and 0·00231 for ethylene. The experiments of Amagat were extended to pressures as high as 3,000 atmospheres, using a method similar to that employed for studying the compressibility of liquids,[1] but the difficulties were much greater owing to the very small volumes into which the gas was compressed by such high pressures. The bulk moduli at 3,000 atmospheres of hydrogen, oxygen, nitrogen, and air were found to be

$$6 \cdot 39 \times 10^9, \quad 10 \cdot 15 \times 10^9, \quad 10 \cdot 15 \times 10^9, \quad \text{and} \quad 10 \cdot 90 \times 10^9$$

dynes per sq. cm., respectively.

76. Characteristic Equation of a Fluid.—Many attempts have been made to obtain a general expression connecting the pressure P, volume V, and absolute temperature T of a substance throughout the range from gas to liquid. Such equations are modifications of the perfect gas law $PV=RT$, to which they must approximate at high temperatures. The most celebrated of these is Van der Waals'[2] equation,

$$\left(P+\frac{a}{V^2}\right)(V-b)=RT,$$

in which the $\frac{a}{V^2}$ term is introduced to account for the intermolecular attractions of the gas particles which produce an internal, or intrinsic, pressure in addition to that, P, exerted on a confining boundary.[3] The quantity b is proportional to the effective volume occupied by the actual particles of the gas, and is shown [4] from considerations of probability to be four times the actual volume of the particles themselves. Van der Waals' equation is limited in its applicability, is not in accord with later experiments, and does not hold for any real liquid. The quantity a varies with the temperature, and Clausius [5] suggested the equation,

$$P=\frac{RT}{V-\alpha}-\frac{C}{T(V+\beta)^2},$$

where R, α, β, and C are constants. This formula gives, generally, good agreement with experiment, and it is a special form of the general relation suggested by Amagat,[6]

$$\left(P+\frac{a}{f(V,\ T)}\right)(V-b)=RT,$$

in which it is assumed that the internal pressure varies with volume and temperature. Finally, we may note the equation suggested by Dieterici,[7]

$$P=\frac{RT}{V-b}\cdot e^{-\frac{a}{RTV}},$$

which reduces to Van der Waals' form if quantities other than those of the first order of smallness are neglected.

[1] Amagat, *Comptes Rendus*, **115**, 638 (1892–3).
[2] See Threlfall and Adair, *Mems. Phys. Soc.*, Vol. I, part 3, p. 337.
[3] See Article 140.   [4] *loc. cit.*
[5] Clausius, *Wied. Ann.*, **9**, 337 (1880); *Phil. Mag.*, **9**, 393 (1880).
[6] Amagat, *Ann. d. Chim. et d. Phys.*, **28**, 480 (1893).
[7] Dieterici, *Wied. Ann.*, **69**, 685 (1899).

77. Isothermal and Adiabatic Elasticities.—When a body is suddenly strained, thermal effects are produced which tend to increase the resistance offered to further strain. This effect is quite general, and as a result it is necessary in measuring elastic moduli to note the conditions under which the straining occurs. The adiabatic modulus is always greater than the isothermal value, and in the case of a gas, the ratio of the two is given by

$$\frac{K_H}{K_T} = \gamma,$$

where γ is the ratio of the specific heats at constant pressure and constant volume. The same type of law applies to the bulk moduli of liquids, although the ratio is smaller than it is for gases.

The relation between the adiabatic and isothermal values of the different moduli may be obtained by an appropriate Carnot's cycle. For example, suppose that a stretched wire undergoes the cycle represented in Fig. 52. The independent variables are F, the stretching force, and x, the increase in length. Let AB be the T isothermal whose slope gives the value of the isothermal modulus. From A to B the wire is stretched isothermally by an increase $\delta F = BM$ in the stretching force, and the corresponding extension is $x = AM$. The heat absorbed is, say, h ergs. From B to C a further expansion occurs adiabatically, the temperature changing from T to $T - \delta T$. An isothermal contraction CD at $T - \delta T$, followed by the adiabatic contraction DA, restores the wire to its original state, and by the laws of thermodynamics

$$\frac{h}{T} = \frac{Area\ ABCD}{\delta T} = \frac{ABGN}{\delta T} = \frac{AN.BM}{\delta T}.$$

But AN is the decrease in length at constant tension for a fall of temperature δT. Thus $AN = l\alpha\delta T$, where l is the length of the

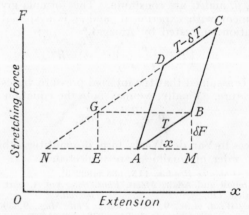

FIG. 52.—ISOTHERMAL AND ADIABATIC VALUES OF YOUNG'S MODULUS.

wire and α is its coefficient of linear expansion, while $BM=\delta F$. Hence

$$\frac{h}{T}=\frac{l\alpha\delta T.\delta F}{\delta T}=l\alpha.\delta F,$$

or, h, the heat supplied to maintain constant temperature conditions, when an increase δF is made in the stretching force, is given by

$$h=lT\alpha.\delta F,$$

and if α is positive, h and δF are either both positive, or negative, so that a stretching under adiabatic conditions for such a wire or rod results in a cooling effect.

If this cooling effect is conserved, a fall of temperature dT will occur and

$$h=J\varsigma\rho la_1 dT,$$

where ς, ρ, and a_1 are the specific heat, density, and cross-sectional area of the wire, respectively. Thus

$$dT=\frac{T\alpha}{J\varsigma\rho}.\frac{\delta F}{a_1}=\frac{T\alpha\delta P}{J\varsigma\rho}, \quad . \quad . \quad . \quad (122)$$

where δP is the increase in tensile stress. This result has been verified within the limits of experimental accuracy by Joule.[1]

During an adiabatic expansion, the actual increase in length is due to the combined results of the increased tension and the consequent cooling. Thus, if a change δP is made suddenly in the stress on a wire, and the total resultant fractional extension is δe, then

$$\frac{\delta P}{\delta e}=Y_H,$$

where Y_H is the adiabatic value of Young's modulus. The extension δe may also be produced by a combination of the isothermal expansion and the contraction due to cooling. Hence

$$\delta e=\frac{\delta P}{Y_T}-\alpha.dT=\frac{\delta P}{Y_T}-\frac{T\alpha^2\delta P}{J\varsigma\rho},$$

where Y_T is the isothermal value of Young's modulus. By equating these values of δe, we have

$$\frac{\delta P}{Y_H}=\frac{\delta P}{Y_T}-\frac{T\alpha^2\delta P}{J\varsigma\rho},$$

or

$$\frac{1}{Y_T}-\frac{1}{Y_H}=\frac{\alpha^2 T}{J\varsigma\rho} \quad . \quad . \quad . \quad . \quad (123)$$

From a knowledge of Y_T, Y_H may be calculated and thus their ratio obtained. For metals, equation (123) gives a value of the order 1·005.

Acoustic experiments give Y_H, and Wertheim and Breguet found that the ratio of Y_H to Y_T was greater than that given by (123)

[1] Joule, *Phil. Trans.*, 149, 91 (1859).

above. No satisfactory explanation of this discrepancy has been suggested.

The cooling of a wire, when it is suddenly stretched, is a particular example of a general principle which states that, in the case of bodies which expand on being heated, an increase of pressure is accompanied by the development of heat and *vice versa*. This general principle may be proved thus : From the first law of thermodynamics,

$$dQ=dE+P.dV,$$

where $P.dV$ is the work done on the body, dE and dQ being the resulting change of internal energy and heat within the body. Since dQ is $T.d\Phi$, where $d\Phi$ is the change of entropy,

$$dE=T.d\Phi-P.dV$$
$$=T\left(\frac{d\Phi}{dT}\right)_P dT+T\left(\frac{d\Phi}{dP}\right)_T dP-P\left(\frac{dV}{dT}\right)_P dT-P\left(\frac{dV}{dP}\right)_T dP,$$

or

$$\left(\frac{dE}{dT}\right)_P=T\left(\frac{d\Phi}{dT}\right)_P-P\left(\frac{dV}{dT}\right)_P, \qquad . \qquad . \quad (124)$$

and

$$\left(\frac{dE}{dP}\right)_T=T\left(\frac{d\Phi}{dP}\right)_T-P\left(\frac{dV}{dP}\right)_T \qquad . \qquad . \quad (125)$$

But dE and $d\Phi$ are perfect differentials, and we may differentiate (124) and (125) with respect to P and T, respectively, and equate the results so that

$$\left(\frac{d\Phi}{dP}\right)_T=-\left(\frac{dV}{dT}\right)_P,$$

or

$$\left(\frac{dQ}{dP}\right)_T=-TVk,$$

where $\frac{1}{V}\left(\frac{dV}{dT}\right)_P$ is the volume coefficient, k, at constant pressure.

Hence, if k is positive, $\left(\frac{dQ}{dP}\right)_T$ is negative, and a quantity of heat must be taken away from a body in order to maintain its temperature constant when the pressure is increased, so that a sudden increase of pressure is accompanied by a development of heat, in the case of bodies which expand on being heated, and similarly a lowering of temperature results with those bodies, such as india-rubber, which contract when heated. This principle was verified experimentally by Joule,[1] who found that, for water above 4° C. when suddenly compressed, there was a rise in temperature, while, at temperatures below 4° C., the opposite effect occurred. He enclosed the liquid in a strong vessel, furnished with a cylinder in which a piston worked.

[1] Joule, *Phil. Trans.*, **149**, 133 (1859).

The pressure could be changed by a sudden addition of weights to the piston. The change of temperature was measured by means of a thermo-electric couple of copper and iron wires, one junction of which was placed in the centre of the liquid and the other in a bath of water.

78. The Theory of Elasticity.—The mathematical theory of elasticity is developed from the dynamics of a particle, of rigid bodies, and thence to the action of forces on deformable bodies. Its application is limited to the extent to which actual bodies fulfil certain fundamental hypotheses. One of these is that their behaviour is independent of their previous history, and it is also usual to assume that the elastic displacements are small quantities whose products and powers may be neglected. The former assumption is approximately true, unless overstraining—which may materially affect subsequent values of the moduli—has occurred, and the second is included in the applications made of Hooke's Law, except for abnormally elastic substances such as india-rubber.

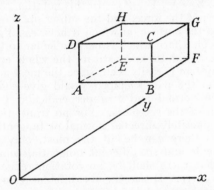

FIG. 53.—THEORY OF ELASTICITY—STRESS AND STRAIN.

Consider a body, in equilibrium when subjected to any external system of forces, and choose axes Ox, Oy, Oz (Fig. 53). A small rectangular parallelepiped of the material will be in equilibrium under the action of a number of internal forces. Acting on the face $ABCD$ will be a force P, and $\dfrac{P}{ABCD}$ is the *average* stress over that face. As the area of the face is continually decreased by the approach of D and B towards A, the value of this average stress tends towards some definite limit which is called the stress at A. It may act at any angle to an element of area at A, and thus may be fully represented by its components P_x, P_y, and P_z acting along Ox, Oy, and Oz, respectively.

Under the action of the stresses on its faces, the parallelepiped may be strained so as to produce a change in length of any, or all, of its edges and an alteration in the size of its angles. If $A'B'$ the new position of AB, its fractional elongation is $\dfrac{A'B'-AB}{AB}$, and the limit of this ratio as B approaches A is termed the extension at A along Ox. In a similar way the change in the angle DAE is measured by the quantity $\theta_x = DAE - D'A'E'$. Hence there are two fundamental types of strain, longitudinal and shear.

From Hooke's Law we have $\dfrac{stress}{strain} = constant$, and to give definite significance to this constant it is necessary to consider various types of strain. The stress on any plane may be resolved into three components, one normal and two tangential, to the plane, of which the former produces compression or dilation, while the latter are shearing stresses. If the co-ordinate axes are parallel to these stresses, and we consider the deformation of a rectangular parallelepiped, there will be, in general, three different normal stresses which may conveniently be called X_x, Y_y, Z_z, and three different pairs of shearing stresses $X_y = Y_x$, $Z_x = X_z$, $Y_z = Z_y$. In this notation the capitals indicate the direction of the force, and the subscripts show the direction of the normal to the surface on which it acts, e.g. Y_z means a force acting along Oy on a face which is perpendicular to the Oz axis, i.e. in the xy plane. That these constitute the whole components of a uniform stress system is easily seen, since the most general distribution of forces on the parallelepiped would give eighteen different values, viz., one normal and two perpendicular tangential components on each of the six faces. For no translational motion in any direction, oppositely directed normal or tangential forces must be equal. Thus there can be, at the most, only three different normal components and six different tangential components, while the condition that there shall be no rotation reduces the number of the latter to three. Hence the six different values given above represent the most general homogeneous stress system.

In a similar way a uniform strain may be resolved into six components which will represent the effect of the stress system. The extensions along the co-ordinate axes, due to normal displacements, may be designated e_{xx}, e_{yy}, e_{zz}, the double subscript being used to indicate that it is the relative displacement of two planes, originally unit distance apart, which is being considered, and both of these planes are normal to the Ox, Oy, Oz axes, respectively. The shears can be converted into extensions by the alternative definition of the shear strain as the relative tangential displacement of planes unit distance apart. They will thus take their places in the notation adopted as

$$e_{yz} = e_{zy}, \quad e_{zx} = e_{xz}, \quad e_{yx} = e_{xy},$$

where e_{yz} is the relative displacement of planes perpendicular respectively to Oy and Oz. Thus, again, only six different values are required to specify the strain completely.

Principal Strains.—Through any point of the body there will be three directions which are mutually perpendicular before and after straining. These are called the *axes of the strain*, and the corresponding magnitudes are called the *principal strains*. For isotropic substances these axes will be the directions of the normal stresses, and thus the complete stress-strain relations may be given by the ratios of the principal stresses and their corresponding strains. Consider a simple linear tensile stress P_1. It might be expected that there would be a corresponding strain in the same direction, and none at right angles. Such is not the case, for it is found that the resulting tensile strain is accompanied by compressions which are perpendicular and proportional to the tensile strain. If P_1 acts along Ox, then

$$X_x = P_1, \qquad Y_y = 0, \qquad Z_z = 0,$$

and

$$e_{xx} = \frac{P_1}{Y}, \qquad e_{yy} = e_{zz} = -\sigma\frac{P_1}{Y},$$

where Y is Young's modulus and σ Poisson's ratio.

Principle of Superposition.—At a point the most general stress is P_1 along Ox, P_2 along Oy, and P_3 along Oz. Thus $X_x = P_1$, $Y_y = P_2$, $Z_z = P_3$, and $X_y = Y_z = Z_x = 0$. It is assumed that each component stress produces the same effect if acting alone, as it contributes to the final result when acting in conjunction with the others. This assumption is known as the *Principle of Superposition*.

The strains corresponding to these stresses will be

$$e_{xx} = \frac{1}{Y}[P_1 - \sigma(P_2 + P_3)],$$

$$e_{yy} = \frac{1}{Y}[P_2 - \sigma(P_3 + P_1)],$$

$$e_{zz} = \frac{1}{Y}[P_3 - \sigma(P_1 + P_2)],$$

and

$$e_{xy} = e_{yz} = e_{zx} = 0.$$

Solving these equations, for P_1, P_2, and P_3 we have

$$P_1 = \frac{(1-\sigma)Y}{(1+\sigma)(1-2\sigma)}\left[e_{xx} + \frac{\sigma}{1-\sigma}(e_{yy} + e_{zz})\right],$$

$$P_2 = \frac{(1-\sigma)Y}{(1+\sigma)(1-2\sigma)}\left[e_{yy} + \frac{\sigma}{1-\sigma}(e_{zz} + e_{xx})\right],$$

$$P_3 = \frac{(1-\sigma)Y}{(1+\sigma)(1-2\sigma)}\left[e_{zz} + \frac{\sigma}{1-\sigma}(e_{xx} + e_{yy})\right],$$

or, as they are more generally written,

$$\left.\begin{aligned}P_1 &= \lambda\delta + 2n \cdot e_{xx}\\ P_2 &= \lambda\delta + 2n \cdot e_{yy}\\ P_3 &= \lambda\delta + 2n \cdot e_{zz}\end{aligned}\right\}, \qquad . \qquad . \qquad . \quad (126)$$

where $\delta=e_{xx}+e_{yy}+e_{zz}$, $\lambda=\dfrac{\sigma Y}{(1+\sigma)(1-2\sigma)}$, and $2n=\dfrac{Y}{1+\sigma}$. The *dilation*, δ, is the sum of the principal elongations, and measures the fractional change of volume. By adding equations (126),

$$P_1+P_2+P_3=\delta(3\lambda+2n).$$

If $$P_1=P_2=P_3=P,$$

$$\delta=\frac{3P}{3\lambda+2n}, \quad \cdot \quad \cdot \quad \cdot \quad \cdot \quad (127)$$

and we obtain the fractional change of volume under a uniform tension in all directions. By definition the bulk modulus K is given, from (107), as

$$K=\frac{P}{\delta}=\tfrac{1}{3}[3\lambda+2n]=\frac{Y}{3(1-2\sigma)}.$$

Considering a cube which is subject to a simple stress of magnitude F on four of its sides (Fig. 54), the stress across the diagonal

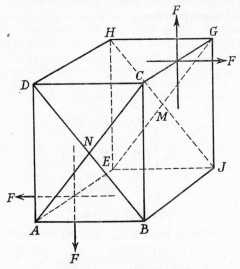

FIG. 54.—STRESS IN DIAGONAL PLANE.

plane $DBJH$ will be purely normal, tensile, and of magnitude F. Across a diagonal plane $ACGE$ it will be normal but compressive. Thus, if axes Ox, Oy, Oz are chosen parallel to NC, ND, NM, the stress system is

$$X_x=F, \qquad Y_y=-F, \qquad Z_z=0, \qquad X_y=Y_z=Z_x=0,$$

and the corresponding strains are

$$e_{xx}=-e_{yy}=\frac{1+\sigma}{Y}F, \;\; e_{zz}=0.$$

After the strain has taken place,

$$tan\ D'A'N' = \frac{D'N'}{A'N'} = \frac{1+e_{yy}}{1+e_{xx}} \cdot \frac{DN}{AN} = \frac{1+e_{yy}}{1+e_{xx}}.$$

The change produced in the right angle DAB is

$$DAB - D'A'B' = \frac{\pi}{2} - 2D'A'N',$$

and is the shear strain θ. Thus

$$\frac{\theta}{2} = \frac{\pi}{4} - D'A'N',$$

so that

$$tan\ \frac{\theta}{2} = \frac{1 - tan\ D'A'N'}{1 + tan\ D'A'N'} = \frac{e_{xx} - e_{yy}}{2 + e_{xx} + e_{yy}} = \tfrac{1}{2}[e_{xx} - e_{yy}].$$

Hence

$$\theta = e_{xx} - e_{yy} = 2(1+\sigma)\frac{F}{Y}.$$

The coefficient, or modulus, of rigidity is defined by

$$n = \frac{F}{\theta} = \frac{Y}{2(1+\sigma)},$$

and is thus identified with the n of equation (108).

The principle of superposition, from which these results are deduced, is not self-evident. Indeed, its use limits subsequent applications of the theory. However, experiment shows that in the case of isotropic bodies under small strains, the deductions from the principle may be verified. It follows from the principle, that the order of applying the stresses is immaterial, and this deduction affords a means of testing its applicability. Thus, by experiment, one might measure Young's modulus for a wire in a twisted and untwisted state, respectively. If the above principle is true, the values should agree.

79. Strain Ellipsoid.—With a uniform homogeneous strain a parallelepiped becomes strained, in general, into another parallelepiped, a circle into an ellipse, and a sphere into an ellipsoid. Projective properties are retained, and thus conjugate diameters of the sphere become conjugate diameters of the ellipsoid. In particular, the three principal diameters of the ellipsoid are derived from three perpendicular diameters of the sphere and thus are, by the previous definition, the axes of the strain. The ellipsoid, resulting from the deformation of a sphere, is called the *strain ellipsoid*, and its equation assumes a simple form, when referred to the axes of strain. Calling the principal strains along Ox, Oy, Oz, a, b, c, respectively, unit length becomes $1+a$, $1+b$, $1+c$ in these directions, and a sphere of unit radius becomes the ellipsoid,

$$\frac{x^2}{(1+a)^2} + \frac{y^2}{(1+b)^2} + \frac{z^2}{(1+c)^2} = 1 \qquad . \qquad . \quad (128)$$

In some cases this ellipsoid reduces to a spheroid. For example, in a Young's modulus extension along Ox, the elongations are

$$a=a, \qquad b=-\sigma a, \qquad c=-\sigma a,$$

and the strain ellipsoid becomes the prolate spheroid,

$$\frac{x^2}{\left(\dfrac{1+a}{1-\sigma a}\right)^2}+y^2+z^2=(1-\sigma a)^2.$$

For a uniform dilation $a=b=c$, and the unstrained sphere is still spherical when strained, while for a uniform shear in the zx plane we have $b=0$, $c=-a$, and the ellipsoid becomes

$$\frac{x^2}{(1+a)^2}+y^2+\frac{z^2}{(1-a)^2}=1.$$

To find the directions in which the elongation has a given value —which must, of course, be intermediate between the largest and smallest of a, b, and c—it is necessary to determine the intersection of the strain ellipsoid and a sphere, of radius equal to the given extended length. Thus, if the extension is d, the required directions are found by solving the equations,

$$\frac{x^2}{(1+a)^2}+\frac{y^2}{(1+b)^2}+\frac{z^2}{(1+c)^2}=1,$$

and

$$\frac{x^2}{(1+d)^2}+\frac{y^2}{(1+d)^2}+\frac{z^2}{(1+d)^2}=1.$$

Subtracting, we have

$$x^2\left[\frac{1}{\alpha^2}-\frac{1}{\delta^2}\right]+y^2\left[\frac{1}{\beta^2}-\frac{1}{\delta^2}\right]+z^2\left[\frac{1}{\gamma^2}-\frac{1}{\delta^2}\right]=0,$$

where α is written for $(1+a)$, δ for $(1+d)$, *etc.* This is the equation to a general conical surface, called the *cone of constant elongation*, with its vertex as origin. In some cases this equation may be simplified. For example, a Young's modulus extension along Ox gives

$$Ax^2-B(y^2+z^2)=0,$$

which is a right circular cone with axis along Ox. For a simple shear we have, if $\delta=1$,

$$\frac{x^2}{\alpha^2}-\frac{z^2}{\alpha^2}=0, \quad \text{or} \quad x=\pm z,$$

which gives two planes intersecting along the y axis and inclined at 45° to the axes of shear. These planes evidently give the two circular sections of the ellipsoid, and indicate the directions of no change in size or shape.

EXAMPLES

1. Two cylindrical shafts have the same length and mass and are made of the same material. One is solid, while the other, which is hollow, has an external radius twice the internal radius. Compare their torsional rigidities and the maximum strains produced by equal twisting torques. [3 : 5 ; 1 : 1·44.]

2. A suspension thread of length $2l$ consists of a wire of length l and radius r rigidly joined to a second wire of equal length, of radius $2r$ and similar material. The top end is clamped, while the lower end is twisted about the axis. Find (a) the torsional rigidity of the complete suspension thread if the rigidity modulus is η and (b) the ratio of the relative angles of twist between the ends of the two parts.
[(a) $8\pi\eta r^4/17l$; (b) 16 : 1.]

3. A horizontal bar of weight W is suspended by two parallel vertical wires each of length l and radius r. The rigidity of the wires is η and they are at a distance d apart. If the upper end of each wire is twisted about its own axis through an angle θ, find the angle through which the bar is deflected. [$4\pi\eta r^4\theta/(Wd^2+4\pi\eta r^4)$.]

4. Prove that if a number of rods are joined end to end the torsional rigidity of the combination is given by the same formula as that for a number of resistances in parallel. Hence, or otherwise, find the torsional rigidity of a tapering wire of length l, rigidity modulus η and end radii a and b. [$3\pi\eta a^3b^3/2l(b^2+ab+a^2)$.]

5. A long thin rod has a length 100 cm. and an elliptic cross-section 2 cm. wide and 0·5 cm. deep. When clamped at its upper end and supporting at the lower end a body of inertia moment $5\cdot21\times10^5$ C.G.S. units, the periodic time of torsional oscillations is 0·313 sec. When supported horizontally on knife edges at its ends and carrying a load of 450 gm. at its mid-point, the sag produced is 6·12 mm. Find the value of each of the usual elastic constants.
[$\eta=4\cdot55\times10^{11}$; $Y=12\cdot25\times10^{11}$; $K=13\cdot3\times10^{11}$; $\sigma=0\cdot35$.]

6. A cantilever beam mounted horizontally has a negligible weight. Show that the depression at any point P due to a vertical load applied at a second point Q is the same as the depression at Q produced by a similar load at P.

7. A flexible steel strip is bent into a strongly curved form by a string tied to its ends. Find the value of Young's modulus for the strip if the tension in the string is 3 kg., the distance between the centre points of string and strip being 15 cm. The strip has a width of 2 cm., a thickness of 1 mm., and string and strip meet at right angles. $g=981$.
[$1\cdot99\times10^{12}$ dynes per sq. cm.]

8. A light cantilever beam is clamped horizontally and carries a load of 3 kg. at its free end, this being such as to produce only a slight amount of bending. When depressed and released the beam vibrates with a periodic time of 0·30 sec. The projecting length of the beam is 50 cm., its width is 2·5 cm. and depth 0·5 cm. Find the value of Young's modulus for the beam. If the mass of the projecting beam is 500 gm., what percentage error in the value of Young's modulus is made by neglecting to take this mass into account ?
[$2\cdot105\times10^{12}$ dynes per sq. cm. ; 4 per cent.]

9. A spiral spring whose diameter is 3 cm. consists of 200 turns of wire of radius 1·0 mm., the length of the spring when hanging vertically being 50 cm. The rigidity modulus of the wire is 8×10^{11} dyne per sq. cm., while its Young's modulus is 20×10^{11} dyne per sq. cm. Calculate the depression of the free end when a weight of 50 gm. is hung on the lower end, the upper end being fixed. How much of this depression is due to (a) bending, (b) torsion ?

[1·655 cm. ; (a) negligible ; (b) practically all.]

10. A thin-walled brass tube closed at each end is mounted horizontally, so that one end is prevented from moving and the pressure inside is gradually increased from 1 to 5 atmospheres. The other end, free to move, carries one mirror of a Michelson interferometer and 44·5 complete fringe displacements are observed using light of 6000 A.U. The tube has a length of 100 cm., an external radius of 2 cm. and a wall thickness of 1 mm. Find the value of the bulk modulus of brass.

[$10·12 \times 10^{11}$ dynes per sq. cm.]

11. A glass vessel of volume 1 litre is filled with water and placed under the receiver of a compression pump ; the pressure is increased from 1 to 3 atmospheres. The meniscus, formed in a capillary tube of internal radius 0·160 cm., is found to descend through a distance of 1·18 cm. If the bulk modulus of the glass is $4·61 \times 10^{11}$ dynes per sq. cm., find the bulk modulus of water at the temperature of the experiment. [$2·04 \times 10^{10}$ dynes per sq. cm.]

12. A body is under stress along three perpendicular axes Ox, Oy, Oz such that there is no linear strain along Oy or Oz. It is then stressed along the same axes so that the linear strains along Oy and Oz are equal and there is no strain along Ox. Compare the ratio of stress to strain along Ox in the first case with that along Oy or Oz in the second.

[$(1 - \sigma) : 1.$]

13. Taking the same stresses and strains as in the last question express each of these stress-strain ratios in terms of the bulk modulus k and the rigidity modulus η. [$k + 4\eta/3$; $2k + 2\eta/3.$]

14. A 400-day clock is controlled by the torsional oscillations of a horizontal brass disc supported by a fine brass wire. If the coefficient of linear expansion of brass is 18×10^{-6} and the thermal coefficient of rigidity of brass is $4·6 \times 10^{-4}$, find the error of the clock in 24 hours at 10° C. if it keeps correct time at 0° C. [Loses 3 min. 11 sec.]

15. A circular bar, supported horizontally on horizontal knife edges 40 cm. apart, has a length of 60 cm. and carries a load of 10 kg. suspended from each end. The radius of the bar is 4 mm., and when the loads are applied the centre point rises by 4·88 mm. Find the value of Young's modulus for the bar. [$20·0 \times 10^{11}$ dynes per sq. cm.]

16. The bar in the previous question is now rigidly clamped in a vertical position and at a distance of 50 cm. below the clamp a couple of magnitude 5×10^{7} dyne-cm. is applied. As a result a mirror fixed to the lower end of the bar deflects a spot of light by 155 mm. on a scale 1 metre away. Find the value of the modulus of rigidity for the bar.

[$8·02 \times 10^{11}$ dynes per sq. cm.]

17. Calculate the bulk modulus and Poisson's ratio for the material of the rod in the previous two questions.

[$13·2 \times 10^{11}$ dynes per sq. cm. ; 0·24.]

EXAMPLES 149

18. A uniform thin rod of weight W is supported at its ends and is initially horizontal. If it bends slightly under its own weight and the final sag of the middle point below the horizontal through the supports is δ, show that the loss of gravitational potential energy is $16W\delta/25$, and that half of this is represented by the energy of strain, in the final equilibrium position.

19. A rod of uniform cross-section is supported horizontally at three points, one at each end and one in the middle at the same level. Show that the greatest sags occur very nearly at one-fifth of the length from each end.

CHAPTER VI

SURFACE TENSION

80. Molecular Forces.—Any two particles of matter exercise a mutually attractive influence, whose magnitude depends upon the masses of the particles and upon their distance apart. Let us fix our attention on any one molecule, m, inside a body. It is surrounded by a group of molecules, and if we take all those molecules which lie within a sphere of extremely small radius and whose centre is m, there is a special action exerted on m by each of these molecules, those nearest to m exerting a more powerful influence than those near the surface of the sphere. This is true, whatever be the sizes and shapes of, or distances between, the molecules. Beyond a certain distance these special actions are assumed to be negligible, and this distance is the radius of the sphere, called *the sphere of molecular activity*.

If dm_1 and dm_2 are two elements of mass, the linear dimensions of each being very small, the mutual action is a force of magnitude

$$f(r)dm_1dm_2,$$

where r is the separation distance.

In the study of the forms, assumed by liquid surfaces in contact with each other and with solid bodies, it is these molecular forces with which we have to deal. The component of the force along the x axis is

$$\frac{x_1-x_2}{r}f(r)dm_1dm_2,$$

where x_1 and x_2 are the co-ordinates of dm_1 and dm_2, and the total force acting on dm_1 is

$$dm_1\int_0^{r_0}\frac{x_1-x_2}{r}f(r)dm_2,$$

the integration being performed between the limits 0 and r_0, where r_0 is the radius of the sphere of molecular activity.

If these molecular forces exist, it follows that, within a layer of fluid at the surface and of extremely small thickness, r_0, there is a special intensity of pressure, which increases in magnitude as we travel from any particle in the surface, along the normal to the surface, and towards the interior of the fluid. Now, if we describe round this surface particle as centre, the sphere of molecular activity, only a hemisphere exists in the fluid, and the molecular forces acting on the particle arise from the molecules of this hemisphere. It is obvious that the symmetrical grouping of these molecules results in the production of a resultant force, directed towards the interior of the fluid.

It is well known that if a glass tube of small bore be dipped in water, the water rises inside the tube to a higher level than that of the water outside ; and if a liquid is spilt on a table, it has a definite boundary, the curved edges clinging to the table. These phenomena, and many others, are explained by the fact that, at the surface of a homogeneous body, the sphere of molecular activity of a particular molecule is incomplete, and that the molecule also falls within the field of action of the particles of whatever matter is on the other side of the boundary surface.

Also, if we assume that the dimensions of the field of action are very small, compared with the radius of curvature of the surfaces, then at all points on the surface of separation between the two substances, there are similar conditions as far as molecular forces are concerned. Thus the surface potential energy, due to these molecular forces, must be in a constant ratio to the surface area, the constant depending on the nature of the substances in contact.

If a liquid is contained within a vessel, the containing walls of the latter will have their own sphere of attraction and corresponding resultant forces opposed to those of the liquid itself. The tendency of a particle to move will be determined by the direction of the resultant of these forces. For the liquid surface in contact with a gas, the tendency to move will be towards the interior of the liquid, and over such a surface there will be a universal trend to inward movement, or an attempt to reduce the number of surface molecules to a minimum. For a given volume the geometrical form with a minimum surface area is a sphere, and thus we conclude that the natural shape of a uniformly gravitating liquid will be, in the absence of other forces, a sphere. If, however, the earth's attraction on the parts of the liquid is not negligible, the natural form will depart from the spherical into one more closely approximating to a horizontal plane as the earth's effect increases. The various forms assumed by mercury drops illustrate this, for with very small drops the shape is practically spherical. Slightly larger drops are approximate spheres, with a slight flattening at the top and bottom, while a large pool of mercury is flat.

The fact that a liquid surface contracts spontaneously shows that there is free energy associated with it, that work must be done to extend the surface. This *free surface energy* is of fundamental importance, but to simplify calculations it is usual to substitute for it a hypothetical tension, acting in all directions parallel to the surface and equal to the free surface energy. This tension is known as *surface tension* and it has the same dimensions as a surface energy, as well as the same numerical magnitude. The work done in extending a surface which is pulling with a tension S dynes per cm., by 1 sq. cm., will be S ergs per sq. cm., hence the free surface energy of such a surface will be S ergs per sq. cm.

The conception of surface tension can always be used in considering the properties of surfaces which depend solely on the existence of free surface energy. It should be realised, however, that the term " surface tension " is misleading by reason of its suggestion that there is a real stretching force tangential to the surface of a liquid. There is no special " contractile skin," or physical tension, parallel to the surface of liquids. It is more useful to regard the surface tension as that force which, as a tension in the surface, would produce the real effects actually due to the asymmetrical spacing of intermolecular attractions at, and near, a boundary between two media.

81. Total Surface Energy.—It is important to notice that the above quantity of work does not represent the whole of the energy expended when a fresh surface is formed. If the enlargement is made suddenly, the liquid is cooled, or the surface energy is increased at the expense of the internal energy. At the same time the force to be overcome increases, by reason of the increase in surface tension with falling temperature. During a slow isothermal change an equivalent amount of heat flows in from neighbouring bodies to maintain the temperature constant. Thus, when the surface area is increased by 1 sq. cm. the additional total surface energy, E, is related to the mechanical work, S, done in stretching the surface isothermally, and to the heat, h, absorbed, according to the equation,

$$E=S+h.$$

To find the corresponding value of h, we may suppose that the film is subjected to a Carnot cycle. Thus (Fig. 55) let the surface tension

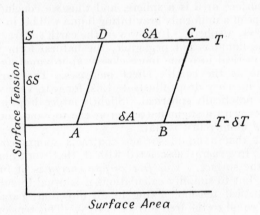

Fig. 55.—Total Surface Energy.

at absolute temperatures T, $T-\delta T$ be S and $S-\delta S$, respectively. Then, since surface tension is independent of area, the work done when the film is stretched isothermally from a condition represented by D, to that represented by C, is $S.\delta A$, and the heat taken in is $h.\delta A$. From C to B there is an adiabatic contraction, the temperature changing from T to $T-\delta T$. From B to A, let the surface contract isothermally, so that when it expands adiabatically, it finally arrives back at its original state, as represented by D. This cycle is clearly reversible, and so, from the laws of thermodynamics,

$$\frac{Net\ work\ done\ during\ cycle}{Heat\ absorbed\ at\ higher\ temperature} = \frac{\delta T}{T},$$

or

$$\frac{\left(S-\dfrac{dS}{dT}\delta T\right)\delta A-S.\delta A}{h.\delta A} = \frac{\delta T}{T},$$

and

$$h=-T\frac{dS}{dT}.$$

Hence

$$E=S-T\frac{dS}{dT}. \quad . \quad . \quad . \quad . \quad (129)$$

We thus see that the total surface energy is numerically equal to the surface tension only if $T=0$, *i.e.* at the absolute zero, or if $\frac{dS}{dT}=0$. With all liquids the surface tension decreases with rise in temperature, and thus $\frac{dS}{dT}$ is negative, E being greater than S. If, however, we are concerned with the *net* gain in energy of the surface and its surroundings, this is evidently equal to S, since the heat given to the surface is taken from its surroundings.

82. Liquid in Contact with a Solid.—The surface of a liquid near its place of contact with a solid body must, in general, be curved, even when gravity is the only external force acting throughout the mass of the liquid. Thus let PAB (Fig. 56) represent the

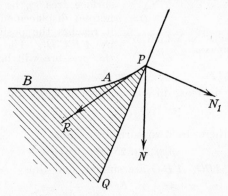

FIG. 56.—INCLINATION OF FREE LIQUID SURFACE TO THE HORIZONTAL.

surface of a liquid in contact at P with the surface PQ of a solid body. If we consider the forces acting on a molecule at P, we have the force of gravity acting vertically along PN, the molecular forces of the solid producing a resultant along PN_1—normal to the solid at P—and the molecular forces of the liquid molecules, adjacent to P, giving a resultant PR, which acts somewhere between the tangent plane to the liquid surface at P and the surface of the solid. In all cases the resultant of these forces, acting on a molecule of a perfect fluid at its free surface, must be normal to that surface. Hence the resultant of PN, PN_1, and PR will determine the direction of the normal to the fluid surface at P. In general this resultant will not act along PN, so that the surface of the fluid at P is not usually horizontal.

At points remote from the solid body there are only two forces acting, *viz.*, gravity and the molecular attraction, the latter of which is normal to the free surface. Thus the former must act in the same direction and the free surface is horizontal.

83. Pressure on a Curved Membrane of Uniform Tension.

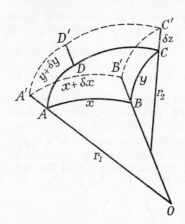

FIG. 57.—PRESSURE ON A CURVED MEMBRANE.

—If we consider a curved membrane, it is evident that an element of the membrane is in equilibrium, only if an excess pressure acts on the concave side to counterbalance the surface tension effect. The magnitude of this excess pressure may be obtained as follows :—

Let $ABCD$ (Fig. 57) be an element of the curved surface having principal radii of curvature r_1 and r_2. Suppose the excess pressure on the concave side is p dynes per sq. cm., and let the surface area xy be given a small normal displacement, δz, so that it reaches the position indicated by $A'B'C'D'$. The work done by the pressure will be

$$pxy \cdot \delta z,$$

and, since the increase in surface area is $\delta(xy)$, the work done is also given by

$$2S \cdot \delta(xy),$$

remembering there are two surfaces. Thus

$$pxy \cdot \delta z = 2S(x\delta y + y\delta x). \qquad . \qquad . \qquad . \qquad (130)$$

The triangles ABO, $A'B'O$ are similar, and thus

$$\frac{x+\delta x}{r_1+\delta z} = \frac{x}{r_1} = \frac{\delta x}{\delta z}, \quad \text{or} \quad \delta x = \frac{x}{r_1}\delta z.$$

Similarly, $\delta y = \dfrac{y}{r_2}\delta z$, so that, from (130),

$$p x y \delta z = 2S\left[\frac{xy\delta z}{r_2} + \frac{xy\delta z}{r_1}\right],$$

or
$$p = 2S\left[\frac{1}{r_1} + \frac{1}{r_2}\right] \qquad . \qquad . \qquad . \qquad (131)$$

This expression is true also for the excess pressure inside a liquid bubble. If there is only one surface—as, for example, in the case of a liquid drop, or an air bubble in a liquid—

$$p = S\left[\frac{1}{r_1} + \frac{1}{r_2}\right] \qquad . \qquad . \qquad . \qquad (132)$$

84. The Shape of Films.—If the pressure is the same on both sides of the surface, the latter must fulfil the condition $r_1 = -r_2$, or the principal curvatures at any point are equal in magnitude and oppositely directed. A series of films which satisfy this condition may be obtained experimentally by the use of two funnels. A coating of soap solution is obtained by dipping the broad end of one funnel into a soap solution and sharing it with the second funnel

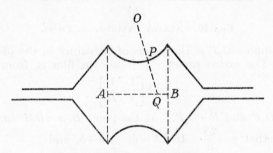

FIG. 58.—CATENOIDAL FILMS.

by placing the two, rim to rim. On drawing the funnels apart, the required film surface is produced between them, and in this case is a surface of revolution. A section of such a film is shown in Fig. 58. If P is any point on the curve, and O is the centre of curvature in the plane of the diagram, then, when OP is produced to meet the axis of symmetry AB in Q, PQ is the other radius of curvature, and $PO = -PQ$. Such a relation is a property of the catenary curve, and the surface is a catenoid of revolution about AB as axis.

If the film collected between the two funnels is given an additional pressure inside, it may be rendered nearly cylindrical. Such films, however, are not perfectly cylindrical; for consider a section which has the general form shown in Fig. 59. The points A and B are points of inflexion, and if P is any other point on the surface, the normal at P cuts the axis of symmetry UM in O_1. Then O_1P is the radius of curvature in a plane perpendicular to the plane of the

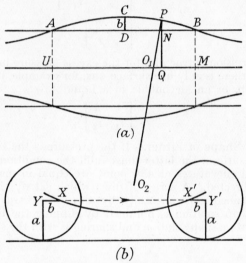

Fig. 59.—Nearly Cylindrical Films.

figure. Suppose O_2P is the radius of curvature in the plane of the diagram. The excess pressure p inside the film is, from (131),

$$p = 2S\left[\frac{1}{r} + \frac{1}{R}\right],$$

where $r = O_1P$ and $R = O_2P$. At the point B, $r = BM = a$, say, and $R = \infty$, so that $p = \dfrac{2S}{a}$. If $PN = \delta$, $r = a + \delta$, and

$$\frac{1}{R} = \frac{1}{a} - \frac{1}{r} = \frac{1}{a} - \frac{1}{a+\delta} = \frac{\delta}{a^2}, \qquad . \qquad . \qquad . \quad (133)$$

approximately. This equation represents the locus of a point X (Fig. 59) (b) situated at a distance $b = CD$ from the centre Y of a circle of radius a, as the circle rolls along the line UM. Points such as A and B (Fig. 59) (a) are obtained with successive horizontal positions of XY, the distance between two such adjacent positions being given by $UM = AB = \pi a$.

The following typical cases occur :—

(i) The film has a length *less* than half the circumference of the generating circle and is *convex*. In this case, as shown in Fig. 60 (a),

$$p_1 = \frac{2S}{a_1} = \frac{2S}{BM},$$

whereas if the film were truly cylindrical between the same ends, the excess pressure p inside would be $p = \dfrac{2S}{FG}$, where FG represents the radius of the funnel. Hence in this case $p < p_1$.

(ii) The film has a length *less* than half the circumference of the generating circle and is *concave*. Fig. 60 (b) represents this case and, if p_2 is the excess pressure,

$$p_2 = \frac{2S}{a_2}, \quad \text{and} \quad p = \frac{2S}{FG}.$$

Also, since

$$a_2 > FG > a_1, \qquad p_1 > p > p_2.$$

(iii) Similarly, if the film length is *greater* than half the circum-

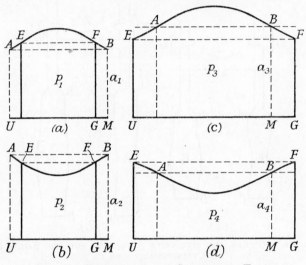

FIG. 60.—PRESSURE INSIDE CYLINDRICAL FILMS.

ference of the generating circle and is *convex* at the centre, while p_3 is its excess pressure,

$$p_3 = \frac{2S}{a_3}, \quad \text{and} \quad p = \frac{2S}{FG}.$$

(iv) Finally, the film length may be *greater* than half the circumference of the generating circle, while there is a *concavity* at the centre. In this case, if p_4 is the excess pressure inside,

$$p_4 = \frac{2S}{a_4}, \quad \text{and} \quad p = \frac{2S}{FG}.$$

Since

$$a_3 > FG > a_4, \qquad p_3 < p < p_4.$$

Such films are shown in Fig. 60 (c) and (d).

These results have been confirmed experimentally with the apparatus shown in Fig. 61 by Rucker and Reinold. A tube shaped like the letter H was fitted with three taps T_1, T_2, T_3, and the vertical ends terminated in cups A and B, which were placed over end-pieces. If a film is collected between A and C, and a little air is drawn out through T_1, the film is *constricted* at the centre and is stable, while T_2 and T_1 remain closed. A short film *widened* at the centre may be collected between B and D. If now the tap T_2 is opened, then, since the excess pressure p_1 in the film BD is greater than that p_2 in AC, air flows from B to A and the films tend to the same form. On the other hand, if the films have lengths greater than half the circumference of the generating circle (Fig. 61) (b), the excess pressure p_3

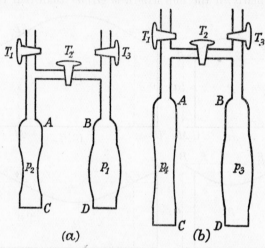

FIG. 61.—RUCKER AND REINOLD'S APPARATUS FOR THE STUDY OF
CYLINDRICAL FILMS.

is less than p_4, and air flows from A to B, so that B becomes still more convex, while A collapses to disruption. Both these predicted results were confirmed by the experiment.

Cylindrical films of the type described above are stable only if their lengths are less than their circumferences, because, if we imagine a movement of air from one half to the other within a film of length greater than $2\pi a$, then the half which loses air will be constricted at the centre, and since its length is greater than half its circumference, the pressure rises to p_4. In the other half, which becomes convex, the pressure is reduced to p_3, so that the resulting pressure change produces a continued movement of air in the same direction as the original disturbance, and the film is unstable. This is evident also from Fig. 61 (b), since such a long film may be represented by placing the two films shown in the figure end to end. Thus any small change from the purely cylindrical form, produced by an infinitesimal movement of air, will introduce the instability shown by the experiment, one half expanding at the expense of the other. On the other hand, if the film length is less than $2\pi a$, it will be stable, as may be seen by imagining the two films of Fig. 61 (*a*), placed end to end. These considerations, and the foregoing theory, need modification if the film communicates with a large volume of air in addition to that enclosed within the film. For example, G. F. C. Searle [1] shows that if $V^2/\pi^2 a^3$ is *very* large, V being the volume of air enclosed by the film, connecting tubes and any communicating vessel, then instability begins for a film length greater than πa.

Similar conclusions apply to liquid cylinders, and explain the tendency of a jet of liquid to break up into drops when its length exceeds its circumference. If the liquid has a large coefficient of viscosity, the relative movements of the parts of the jet which accompany disruption will be opposed, and greater length of cylindrical drop is possible without instability. For this reason very viscous liquids, such as molten glass and quartz, may be drawn into fine threads of great length.

85. The Forms of Liquid Films in General.—Equation (133) above was obtained on the assumption that δ was very small. If this restriction is removed, the general shape of a liquid film may be obtained as follows.

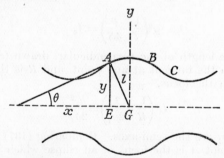

FIG. 62.—GENERAL FORM OF FILM SURFACES OF REVOLUTION.

Consider a film in equilibrium under its own molecular forces, the existence of practically flat films indicating that the action of gravity may be neglected compared with the tension of the film. In this case we have, from (131),

$$\frac{1}{r_1} + \frac{1}{r_2} = \frac{p}{2S},$$

where p, the excess pressure inside the film, may be maintained by closing its ends and assuming that the volume of air enclosed remains constant. We shall consider only surfaces of revolution. In Fig. 62

[1] G. F. C. Searle, *Experimental Physics*, p. 150 (1934).

the curve ABC generates the surface by revolution around the x axis, and, if r is the radius of curvature in the plane of the diagram and the length of the normal AG is l, the principal radii of curvature are r and l, and

$$\frac{1}{r}+\frac{1}{l}=\frac{p}{2S} \qquad . \qquad . \qquad . \qquad . \qquad (134)$$

Let the tangent at A make an angle θ with the x axis so that $r=-\dfrac{ds}{d\theta}$, where ds is an element of the arc measured along the curve from A towards B, and $AE=y=l \cos \theta$. Hence, from (134),

$$-\frac{d\theta}{ds}+\frac{\cos \theta}{y}=\frac{p}{2S} \qquad . \qquad . \qquad . \qquad (135)$$

But

$$\frac{d\theta}{ds}=\sin \theta \frac{d\theta}{dy},$$

and, from (135),

$$y \cos \theta=\frac{y^2 p}{4S}+A_1, \qquad . \qquad . \qquad . \qquad (136)$$

where A_1 is a constant. All curves satisfying (136) are traced out by the foci of conic sections rolling, without sliding, along the axis of x. Thus, substituting in (136) $\cos \theta=\dfrac{y}{l}$,

$$y^2\left(\frac{1}{l}-\frac{p}{4S}\right)=A_1 \qquad . \qquad . \qquad . \qquad (137)$$

But, if L is the length of the perpendicular, drawn from the focus of an ellipse on the tangent at any point, and R is the distance of this point from the focus,

$$L^2\left(\frac{1}{R}-\frac{1}{2a_1}\right)=\frac{b_1{}^2}{2a_1}, \qquad . \qquad . \qquad . \qquad (138)$$

where a_1 and b_1 are the semi-axes. Comparing (137) and (138) we see that the point A is the focus of an ellipse which touches the x axis at G, the semi-axes being given by

$$a_1=\frac{2S}{p}, \qquad b_1=\sqrt{\frac{4A_1S}{p}}.$$

This is true for any position of A, and thus the locus of A is traced out by the focus of the ellipse as it rolls along EG. This curve is known as the unduloid and is sinuous in form.

If the pressure is the same on both sides of the film, (137) becomes

$$\frac{y^2}{l}=A_1 \qquad . \qquad . \qquad . \qquad (139)$$

In a parabola the ratio of the square of the perpendicular, from the focus on a tangent at a point, to the distance of the point from the focus is constant. Hence we see that the locus of A in this case is the curve traced out by the focus of a parabola as it rolls along EG. This curve is a catenary, and the surface of revolution is a catenoid. Under certain conditions two catenaries can be drawn between two points, the surface generated by the revolution of the upper one being a minimum. On the other hand, it is not always possible to draw a catenary, which shall pass through two given points and have a given line as directrix, so that it is not always possible to obtain a film joining two circular lines, or the ends of two funnels. In other cases two catenoid films are possible, but only one of these is stable.

Plateau realised the case of liquid drops, unacted upon by external forces, by immersing a drop of olive oil in an alcohol-water mixture of the same specific gravity. By holding the drop between two wires in the shape of closed curves, or by allowing it to form around a solid of any shape held in the water-alcohol mixture, a large number of liquid surfaces may be obtained. They may also be produced by a suitable manipulation of soap bubbles.

86. Experimental Methods for the Measurement of Surface Tension. (*i*) *Jaeger's Method.*—If a spherical air bubble is produced in a liquid, the excess pressure inside the bubble is $p=\dfrac{2S}{r}$, where r is the radius of the bubble. Jaeger utilised this relation in measuring surface tensions by observing the pressure necessary to produce such bubbles. The apparatus is shown diagrammatically in Fig. 63. A pressure pump is connected to a large vessel A, which acts as a reservoir and is joined, through a tap T, to the manometer M and the vertical tube BC, the latter having a fairly narrow orifice of radius r at C. As the tap is opened, the pressure at C increases until a bubble breaks off with a corresponding change in the manometer reading. Another bubble begins to form, and the manometer registers a pressure difference h, which is a maximum when the bubble is completely formed. The experiment consists in noting the value of h when the bubbles form at the rate of about one every second or even slower. The maximum pressure p_1 inside the bubble is then given by

$$p_1=g\rho h+B,$$

where B is the atmospheric pressure and ρ is the density of the manometer liquid. The pressure p_2 just outside the bubble is

$$p_2=B+xdg,$$

where d is the density of the liquid and x is the depth of C below its surface. Thus the excess pressure p inside the bubble is

$$p=p_1-p_2=g[\rho h-xd]=\frac{2S}{r},$$

so that

$$S=\frac{gr}{2}[\rho h-xd] \quad . \quad . \quad . \quad . \quad (140)$$

The experiment in this form does not give accurate values for S, chiefly because instability of the bubble is not reached when its radius is equal to that of the orifice. For a given tube and a steady rate

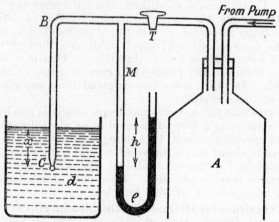

FIG. 63.—JAEGER'S METHOD OF MEASURING SURFACE TENSIONS.

of bubbling, the equilibrium position will be some definite function of the radius r, say $f(r)$, and the equation should be

$$S = f(r) \cdot \frac{g}{2}[\rho h - xd].$$

This result may be utilised to measure the relative values of the surface tension at different temperatures, since then $f(r)$ will be the same for all the experiments. These relative values may be converted into absolute determinations if the surface tension at any one temperature is known.

Jaeger [1] has also described a method by which the bubble is produced in the liquid contained in a long narrow bulb. A tube of glass, or platinum, is sealed into the top of this bulb and dips into the liquid, while its upper end is connected to a reservoir of pure nitrogen. A second tube, sealed into the bulb near its top and placed horizontally, is joined to one side of a manometer whose other limb connects to the first tube. The manometer measures the maximum excess pressure p of the bubble as in the earlier method, and the surface tension is given by [2]

$$S = \tfrac{1}{2}rp\left[1 - \tfrac{2}{3}\frac{r}{h_1} - \tfrac{1}{6}\left(\frac{r}{h_1}\right)^2\right],$$

where

$$h_1 = \frac{p}{(\rho - \rho_1)g},$$

[1] Jaeger, K. Akad. Amsterdam Proc., 17, 521 (1914).
[2] Schrodinger, Ann. d. Phys., 46, 413 (1915); Verschaffelt, K. Akad. Amsterdam Proc., 21, 366 (1919).

r is the internal radius of the tube, and ρ, ρ_1 are the densities of the liquid and of the fluid issuing from the orifice, respectively. This formula renders Jaeger's method probably the most accurate one for determining surface tensions, and the above modification enables the apparatus to be maintained at any temperature, while no large quantity of liquid is required.

The same principle was applied by Bircumshaw[1] to measure the surface tension of liquid metals from their melting points to about 1000° C. in some cases. The liquids used were tin, lead, bismuth, cadmium, zinc and antimony, and in all cases the maximum pressure was measured when bubbles were blown at a depth t below the liquid surface from each of two coaxial tubes of radii r_1 and r_2. The values of r_1 and r_2 were too large to use in the formula given above, and so use was made of Sugden's[2] correction in the form :—

$$B^2 = \frac{S}{g\rho} = \tfrac{1}{2}rk(h-t),$$

in which ρ is the liquid density, $(h-t)$ the excess pressure inside the drop expressed in cm. of the same liquid and k the numerical correction obtained by Sugden from the basic capillary curve data provided by Bashford and Adams.[3] The value of k has been given by Sugden for all values of $\frac{r}{B}$ from 0 to about 2, and thus by successive approximation, the exact value may be obtained from an approximately deduced value of S. Hence if k_1 and k_2 are the values of rk for the two tubes, we have :—

$$h_1 - t = \frac{2B^2}{k_1}; \quad h_2 - t = \frac{2B^2}{k_2},$$

from which $2B^2 = \dfrac{(h_1-h_2)k_1k_2}{k_2-k_1}$. When this method is used for the surface tension of mercury difficulties are caused by the insufficient adhesion between the liquid and the jet. The difficulty can be overcome by using an amalgamated copper jet of which the internal and external radii are practically the same.

(*ii*) *Rayleigh's Jet Method.*—The breaking up of a liquid jet into drops was used by Rayleigh[4] in determining the surface tension of a liquid. When the drops first form, their various parts are in relative motion, and the shape oscillates about the mean spherical form. This effect is noticeable also just before the drops have separate existence, by reason of the cyclic alteration in the lateral dimension of the jet, measured in a particular direction. Thus, in Fig. 64, two points A and B include one complete cyclic change in the cross-section of the jet. The time, t_0, of vibration of a liquid

[1] Bircumshaw, *Phil. Mag.*, 2, 341 (1926) ; 3, 1286 (1927).
[2] Sugden, *Journ. Chem. Soc.*, 121, 858 (1922).
[3] Bashford and Adams, *Capillary Action*, Cambridge (1883).
[4] Rayleigh, *Proc. Roy. Soc.*, 29, 71 (1879).

drop, about its spherical form, is given by dimensional formulæ (Article 236) as

$$t_0 = K\sqrt{\frac{r^3\rho}{S}},$$

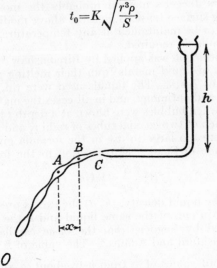

FIG. 64.—BREAKING UP OF A JET OF LIQUID INTO DROPS.

where r is the radius of the drop, ρ, the liquid density, and S, its surface tension. Experiment and analysis agree in assigning the value $\dfrac{\pi}{\sqrt{2}}$ to the constant K, and so

$$t_0 = \pi\sqrt{\frac{r^3\rho}{2S}}.$$

The jet follows a mean parabolic path after issuing from the orifice of the funnel C (Fig. 64), and the horizontal velocity v—if the delivery end of the funnel is horizontal—is, by equation (396),

$$v = \sqrt{2gh},$$

where h is the vertical height of the free liquid surface above the orifice. Thus the horizontal distance x between A and B is $x = v . t_0$ and

$$S = \frac{\pi^2 ghr^3\rho}{x^2}.$$

The distance x may be measured by means of a travelling microscope, and r is taken to be the radius of the orifice.

(*iii*) *Ferguson's Method.*—A capillary tube method, which requires only a few cubic mm. of liquid and no determination of the liquid density, was described by Ferguson [1] as a modification of a

[1] Ferguson, *Proc. Phys. Soc.*, 44, 511 (1932).

previous experiment. If the liquid is within a horizontal capillary tube with no pressure difference between its ends, its two meniscus surfaces will be similar, but if an excess pressure is applied to one of them, the liquid will be blown to the far end where its meniscus changes from concave, through plane, to convex form. If this meniscus is used as a reflecting surface, an image of a source of light will be formed near the pole of the meniscus while its radius of curvature is relatively small, but the appearance of the illuminated surface changes very rapidly to become a practically uniform field in the observing microscope at the instant of planeness. Assuming that the bore is sufficiently small, that the distorting effects of gravity are negligible—Ferguson suggests 1 mm. bore to be the limiting size—and that the angle of contact is small, then the simple formula connecting the necessary excess pressure p and the radius of the tube is,

$$p = \frac{2S}{r},$$

r being the radius of the tube. The method is also applicable to an interfacial tension if the surface tension of either liquid—air interface is known, and it can be assumed that the interface contact angle is small.

87. Application of the Principle of Virtual Work.—When, under the action of any forces, a system of particles is in equilibrium, and this system receives, or is imagined to receive, any small disturbance, the total amount of work done by all the forces acting on the various particles is zero. In other words, the potential energy of the system is a minimum. We shall now apply this principle to the equilibrium of a homogeneous liquid at rest in a vessel under the action of gravity.

Let z be the height of an elementary volume, $dxdydz$, of the liquid. The potential energy of the whole system is composed of four parts.

(a) Gravitational energy equal to

$$g\rho \iiint z \, . \, dxdydz.$$

(b) Energy of the liquid-air surface.
(c) Energy of the liquid-solid surface.
(d) Energy of the air-solid surface.

Hence

$$g\rho \iiint z \, . \, dxdydz + AS_1 + BS_2 + CS_3$$

must be a minimum, where A, B, C represent the areas of the surfaces (b), (c), (d), and S_1, S_2, S_3 are the surface tensions.

Consider a slight displacement of the surface A, so that if δl

denotes the movement of A along its normal, the gravitational

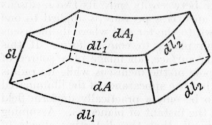

energy varies by $g\rho\iint z.\delta l dA$, and if we suppose that the line of contact of the liquid with the v e s s e l remains stationary, B and C are constant and A changes to A_1. Let the elementary area dA (Fig. 65) change to dA_1, so that if r_1 and r_2 represent the principal radii of curvature of the arcs dl_1, dl_2,

FIG. 65.—VIRTUAL DISPLACEMENT OF LIQUID SURFACE.

$$dl_1' = \left(1-\frac{\delta l}{r_1}\right)dl_1, \quad \text{and} \quad dl_2' = \left(1-\frac{\delta l}{r_2}\right)dl_2 ;$$

also

$$dA_1 - dA = dl_1'dl_2' - dl_1 dl_2$$

$$= -\left(\frac{1}{r_1}+\frac{1}{r_2}\right)\delta l.dl_1 dl_2,$$

or,

$$\delta(dA) = -\left(\frac{1}{r_1}+\frac{1}{r_2}\right)\delta l dA.$$

From the principle of virtual work,

$$g\rho\iint z\delta l dA + S_1\iint \delta(dA) = 0,$$

or,

$$\iint\left[g\rho z - S_1\left(\frac{1}{r_1}+\frac{1}{r_2}\right)\right]\delta l dA = 0, \quad . \quad . \quad (141)$$

subject to the condition that the volume remains constant, *i.e.*

$$\iint \delta l dA = 0 \quad . \quad . \quad . \quad . \quad (142)$$

The condition of unchanged volume, combined with the principle of virtual work, is expressed by multiplying (142) by an arbitrary constant and adding it to (141). Hence the complete equation is

$$\iint\left[g\rho(z-k) - S_1\left(\frac{1}{r_1}+\frac{1}{r_2}\right)\right]\delta l dA = 0,$$

where k is a constant. Integrating this, we have

$$S_1\left(\frac{1}{r_1}+\frac{1}{r_2}\right) = g\rho(z-k),$$

or,

$$S_1\left(\frac{1}{r_1}+\frac{1}{r_2}\right) = p + constant,$$

where p is the pressure just within the surface of the liquid. If the left-hand size is zero—which is the case when the surface is flat—then $p=p_0$, where p_0 is the atmospheric pressure. Hence, finally,

$$S_1\left(\frac{1}{r_1}+\frac{1}{r_2}\right)=p-p_0,$$

so that the effect is the same as if the surface were in a state of tension.

Again, suppose that the line of contact of the liquid with the vessel is displaced from WX to YZ (Fig. 66). Draw normals to

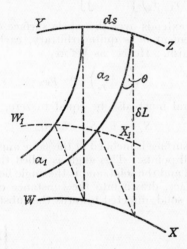

FIG. 66.—VIRTUAL DISPLACEMENT OF MENISCUS.

the surface A from all points on WX, and let these normals meet the surface A_1 along the line W_1X_1, so that the surface A_1 may be supposed to consist of two parts, that enclosed by the line W_1X_1 and denoted by a_1, and that enclosed between W_1X_1 and YZ and denoted by a_2. Then

$$a_1-A=-\iint\left(\frac{1}{r_1}+\frac{1}{r_2}\right)\delta l\, dA, \text{ as before.}$$

If δL denotes the distance between the lines WX and YZ, a_2 may be considered as the projection of the elements $\delta L ds$ of the surface of the vessel on the new liquid surface A_1, where ds is an element of the line of contact. Thus, if θ is the angle between the normals to the surfaces A and B,

$$a_2=\int\cos\theta.\delta L ds.$$

But $\delta B = -\delta C = \int \delta L ds$, and since the potential energy is stationary,

$$\delta\left[g\rho \iint z \, . \, dxdydz + AS_1 + BS_2 + CS_3 \right] = 0,$$

or

$$g\rho \iint z \, . \, \delta l dA + S_1(a_1 + a_2 - A) + S_2\delta B + S_3\delta C = 0,$$

i.e.

$$\iint\left[g\rho z - S_1\left(\frac{1}{r_1} + \frac{1}{r_2}\right) \right]\delta l dA + \iint (S_1 \cos \theta + S_2 - S_3)\delta L ds = 0.$$

The first integral extends over the whole surface of the liquid, and since the displacement δl is quite arbitrary, each element of this integral must vanish. Hence, as before,

$$S_1\left(\frac{1}{r_1} + \frac{1}{r_2}\right) = p - p_0.$$

The second integral must also be equal to zero, and thus

$$S_1 \cos \theta + S_2 - S_3 = 0,$$

so that the liquid surface is inclined at the same angle θ to the surface of the vessel at all points. This angle is called the *angle of contact* between the liquid and the solid, and is the angle between the normal to the liquid surface, drawn into the substance of the liquid, and the normal to the solid, directed towards the substance of the solid.

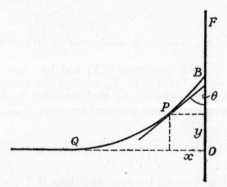

FIG. 67.—CAPILLARY CURVE.

88. The Capillary Curve.—If a perfectly clean glass plate dips vertically in a liquid then, close to the plate, the surface of the liquid assumes a definite shape. A section of the surface made by a vertical plane, perpendicular to the glass plate, gives the form assumed by the liquid at the place of contact, and is termed the *capillary curve.* Let the glass plate, or wall, be supposed normal to the plane of the diagram (Fig. 67), which represents the section of the plane and the liquid surface, this section being far removed from the edges of the plate OF. Of the two principal radii of curvature of the liquid surface at any point P, one will be infinite and the other will be r, the radius of curvature of BPQ at P.

Taking the x axis horizontally and the axis of y vertically, we obtain

$$\frac{S}{r}=p=g\rho y,$$

where p is the difference of pressure on the two sides of the surface at P, and y is measured from the level of the horizontal portion, while ρ is the liquid density. Denoting $\frac{S}{g\rho}$ by B^2, we have

$$\frac{\frac{d^2y}{dx^2}}{\left[1+\left(\frac{dy}{dx}\right)^2\right]^{\frac{3}{2}}}=\frac{y}{B^2}, \qquad . \qquad . \qquad . \qquad (143)$$

and putting $\frac{dy}{dx}=q$, from (143),

$$\frac{\frac{dq}{dx}}{(1+q^2)^{\frac{3}{2}}}=\frac{q\frac{dq}{dy}}{(1+q^2)^{\frac{3}{2}}}=\frac{y}{B^2}.$$

Integrating,

$$-\frac{2}{\sqrt{1+q^2}}=\frac{y^2}{B^2}+C_1 \qquad . \qquad . \qquad . \qquad (144)$$

When $y=0$, $q=\frac{dy}{dx}=0$, so that $C_1=-2$, and thus

$$q=\frac{dy}{dx}=\pm\frac{y\sqrt{4B^2-y^2}}{2B^2-y^2} \qquad . \qquad . \qquad . \qquad (145)$$

Putting $y=2B \sin \phi$,

$$\left(\frac{1}{\sin \phi}-2 \sin \phi\right)d\phi=\pm\frac{dx}{B} . \qquad . \qquad . \qquad (146)$$

If the angle of contact is acute, $\frac{dy}{dx}$ cannot be ∞, or $\frac{dx}{dy}$ cannot be zero, so that $\frac{dy}{dx}$ is always negative. Hence y is always less than $B\sqrt{2}$, the negative sign of (145) must be used, and the integration of (146) gives

$$2 \cos \phi+\log \tan \frac{\phi}{2}=-\frac{x}{B}.$$

When $\phi=0$, or $y=0$, $x=\infty$, and the capillary curve is asymptotic to the plane surface of the liquid.

If θ is the angle of contact $\left(\dfrac{dy}{dx}\right)_B = -\cot\theta$ and, from (144)

$$-\frac{2}{\sqrt{1+\cot^2\theta}} = \frac{OB^2}{B^2} - 2,$$

or,

$$OB = B\sqrt{2(1-\sin\theta)} = \sqrt{\frac{2S}{g\rho}(1-\sin\theta)},$$

which determines the height to which the liquid rises against the plate. If θ is known, the surface tension may be found by measuring this height. If the angle of contact is zero, $\dfrac{dy}{dx}=\infty$ at B, and $y=B\sqrt{2}$, or

$$OB = \sqrt{\frac{2S}{g\rho}}.$$

89. The Problem of a Floating Needle.—A needle carefully placed on the surface of water floats. This well-known experiment can be explained by means of surface-tension effects. Let Fig. 68 represent a section of the needle lying on the surface of the water, the section being perpendicular to the axis of the needle. The forces acting are :—

(a) The tensions at A and B.

(b) The weight of the needle ; and

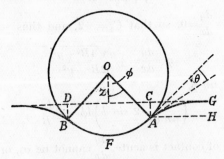

FIG. 68.—FLOATING NEEDLE.

(c) The water-pressure acting on AFB, equal to the weight of a volume of water whose cross-section is $DCAFBD$.

These forces are in equilibrium, and, resolving horizontally, the horizontal component of the surface tension at A, together with the horizontal pressure on GH due to the water, is equal to the surface tension at G, where GH and AH are, respectively, vertical and horizontal. Hence

$$2S \ sin \ (\phi-\theta)+g\rho[r^2\phi+r^2 \ sin \ \phi \ cos \ \phi-2zr \ sin \ \phi]=mg \quad (147)$$

and

$$g\rho(r \ cos \ \phi-z)^2=4S \ sin^2 \ \tfrac{1}{2}(\phi-\theta), \qquad . \qquad . \quad (148)$$

where θ is the angle of contact between the liquid and the tangent to the needle at A, m, the mass per centimetre of the needle of radius r, z, the height of its axis above the free level of the water, 2ϕ, the angle BOA, and ρ, the density of the liquid.

Equations (147) and (148) determine the equilibrium of the needle, and if $\theta=0$, they become

$$2S \ sin \ \phi+g\rho[r^2\phi+r^2 \ sin \ \phi \ cos \ \phi-2zr \ sin \ \phi]=mg,$$

and

$$g\rho(r \ cos \ \phi-z)^2=4S \ sin^2 \ \frac{\phi}{2}.$$

When z is eliminated from these, the equilibrium position is defined by the resulting relation between r and ϕ.

90. Shape of a Large Drop.—It was shown in Article 80 that, under the combined action of the earth's attraction on its parts and its own intermolecular forces, a moderately large drop has a form intermediate between a sphere and a horizontal plane. Some of the characteristics of such a drop may be deduced in the case where the liquid does not wet the surface, *i.e.* if the potential energy is not reduced by a spreading of the liquid over the supporting surface, as, for example, mercury on glass, or water on paraffin wax. Suppose the drop is sufficiently large, so that its upper surface is horizontal and its diameter is large compared with its thickness. A section

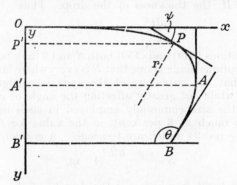

FIG. 69.—SHAPE OF A LARGE DROP.

of such a drop is shown in Fig. 69. At any point $P(x, y)$ on the surface, draw a tangent making an angle ψ with the x axis. Since P is distant, $OP'=y$ below the horizontal surface, the pressure at

P is $p=p_0+g\rho y$, where p_0 is the external pressure. But if the principal radii of curvature at P are r and R, in and perpendicular to the plane of the diagram, respectively, then

$$p=S\left[\frac{1}{r}+\frac{1}{R}\right]+p_0,$$

and since R is large compared with r,

$$\frac{S}{r}=g\rho y.$$

The curvature is $\frac{1}{r}=\frac{d\psi}{ds}$, where ds is an element of the periphery of the drop at P in the plane of the diagram, and since

$$\frac{d\psi}{ds}=\frac{d\psi}{dy}\cdot\frac{dy}{ds}=\frac{d\psi}{dy}\ sin\ \psi,$$

$$S\ sin\ \psi\frac{d\psi}{dy}=g\rho y,$$

or,

$$g\rho\int_0^y ydy=S\int_0^\psi sin\ \psi d\psi,$$

which gives

$$\frac{g\rho y^2}{2}=S[1-cos\ \psi].$$

At the point A, where the tangent is vertical, $y=OA'=h$, and $cos\ \psi=0$. Hence

$$\frac{g\rho h^2}{2}=S. \qquad . \quad . \quad . \quad . \quad (149)$$

At the point of contact B, the angle ψ becomes θ, the angle of contact, and $y=OB'=H$, the thickness of the drop. Thus

$$\frac{g\rho H^2}{2}=S[1-cos\ \theta], \qquad . \quad . \quad . \quad (150)$$

and from equations (149) and (150) both S and θ may be determined.

The assumptions made above that R is everywhere large compared with r and that the curvature at the apex is negligible, produce errors which, while not greatly affecting the angle of contact, may, for drops of the size commonly employed in such measurements, amount to as much as 8 per cent. in the value for S, the simple formula giving results which are too high. A corrected formula,[1]

$$S=\frac{g(\rho-\sigma)h^2}{2}(1-\eta),$$

is more nearly exact in which σ is the density of the air while η is the positive root of the cubic

$$\eta=\frac{0\cdot6095h}{c}(1-\eta)^{\frac{3}{2}},$$

[1] See G. F. C. Searle, *Experimental Physics*, p. 197 (1934).

c being the maximum horizontal radius of the drop. For a drop with $c=2$ cm. and $h=0.3$ cm., $\eta=0.080$.

The same treatment is possible in the case of a large gas bubble entrapped under a horizontal plate and within the liquid. In either case, a formula of sufficient accuracy has been derived by elementary means by Ferguson.[1] In the expression for the excess pressure we have, from Fig. 69,

$$\frac{1}{R}=\frac{\sin \psi}{x} \quad \text{and} \quad \frac{1}{r}=\sin \psi \frac{d\psi}{dy},$$

and, putting B^2 for $\dfrac{S}{g\rho}$,

$$y=\frac{B^2}{x} \sin \psi + B^2 \sin \psi \frac{d\psi}{dy}.$$

Neglecting the small term

$$y=2B^2(1-\cos \psi), \text{ approximately,}$$

from which

$$\cos \psi=\frac{2B^2-y^2}{2B^2} \quad \text{and} \quad \sin \psi=\frac{y\sqrt{4B^2-y^2}}{2B^2}.$$

If the origin is transferred to a point above A and $AA'=c$ we have, dividing throughout by c,

$$\frac{xy}{c}+y=\frac{B^2}{c} \sin \psi + B^2 \sin \psi \frac{d\psi}{dy}+\frac{B^2x}{c} \sin \psi \frac{d\psi}{dy}.$$

The first and last terms are small and very nearly equal and therefore

$$y^2=B^2 \sin \psi \cdot \frac{d\psi}{dy}+\frac{y}{2c}\sqrt{4B^2-y^2}$$

and this when integrated gives, after substituting $y=0$ when $\psi=0$,

$$y^2=2B^2(1-\cos \psi)-\frac{1}{3c}(4B^2-y^2)^{\frac{3}{2}}+\frac{8B^3}{3c}.$$

Therefore

$$h^2=2B^2-\frac{1}{3c}(4B^2-h^2)^{\frac{3}{2}}+\frac{8B^3}{3c}$$

and, after simplification,

$$H^2=4B^2 \cos^2 \frac{\theta}{2}+\frac{8B^3}{3c}\left(1-\sin^3 \frac{\theta}{2}\right)$$

the angle θ being assumed acute.

A simple method of producing and measuring such gas bubbles has been described by Bate.[2]

91. Force between Two Plates separated by a Thin Layer of a Liquid.—If two glass plates are well wetted and placed

[1] Ferguson, *Proc. Phys. Soc.*, 53, 554 (1941).
[2] Bate, *Proc. Phys. Soc.*, 53, 403 (1941).

together, it will be found that, although they slide over each other comparatively easily, it requires considerable force to draw them apart normally. Indeed, in doing so there is great risk of breakage. The force required for this normal separation—which measures the attractive force produced by surface tension—may be evaluated as follows :—

If the wetted area of each plate is A, its circumference B, and the angle of contact θ, while the distance between the plates, which are assumed to be parallel, is d, then the normal component of the surface tensional force around the periphery is $BS \sin \theta$. The pressure inside the film is less than that outside by an amount $S\left[\dfrac{1}{r}-\dfrac{1}{R}\right]$, where r and R are the principal radii of curvature of the meniscus. The former is given by $d=2r \cos \theta$ and thus the resultant excess pressure force acting downwards on the upper plate is $\dfrac{2AS}{d} \cos \theta$, and the resultant attraction is

$$F=2AS\left(\frac{\cos \theta}{d}-\frac{1}{2R}\right)+BS \sin \theta. \qquad . \qquad (151)$$

For most liquids which wet the plates this becomes, with sufficient accuracy,

$$F=\frac{2AS}{d},$$

and with very nearly plane surfaces d will become so small that F will be large, showing that the liquid can withstand a state of great tension.

92. Force to Pull a Plate from a Liquid Surface.—If a flat plate is placed in the surface of a liquid and then raised, a layer of the liquid will adhere to the plate and will thus be elevated. Considerable force is necessary to produce separation by a purely normal pull, and the magnitude of this force may be determined by considering Fig. 70 (*a*), which represents the state of affairs when the liquid, having been raised the maximum amount, h, is about to break away. If the area of the plate is A, and p_0 is the external pressure, the force acting downwards on the top surface of the plate is $p_0 A$. At a point Q just below the plate, the pressure p is given by

$$p=p_0-g\rho h,$$

where ρ is the density of the liquid. Thus the force acting upwards is $pA=A[p_0-g\rho h]$, and the tension F, necessary to pull the plate away from the liquid, is

$$F=p_0 A -A[p_0-g\rho h]=Ag\rho h \qquad . \qquad (152)$$

To find h, consider the horizontal equilibrium of a slice of the elevated liquid, 1 cm. wide (Fig. 70) (*b*). Two forces, each equal to S, will act tangentially to the meniscus, while the hydrostatic pressure P on the vertical rectangular end of the slice acts in the same direction. The magnitude of this force is

$$Ph=h[p_0-\tfrac{1}{2}g\rho h].$$

The external pressure p_0 will be directed in the opposite direction and

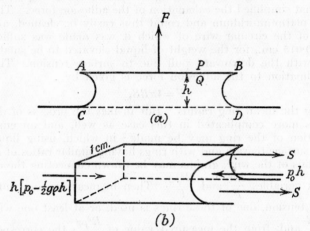

FIG. 70.—FORCE TO SEPARATE A PLATE FROM A LIQUID SURFACE.

will produce a force equal to p_0h. Thus, for horizontal equilibrium,

$$p_0h=h[p_0-\tfrac{1}{2}g\rho h]+2S,$$

or,

$$\tfrac{1}{2}g\rho h^2=2S; \qquad h=2\sqrt{\frac{S}{g\rho}}.$$

Substituting this value in (152) we have

$$F=2Ag\rho\sqrt{\frac{S}{g\rho}}=2A\sqrt{g\rho S} \ . \qquad . \qquad . \qquad (153)$$

If this force is measured by means of a chemical or torsion balance, it enables an approximate value to be obtained for S. The formula (153), however, is only approximately true, and the correct expression was given by Ferguson [1] in a form which may be expressed as

$$F=2Ag\rho\left[B-\frac{B^2}{3r}-\frac{B^3\sqrt{2}}{3r^2}\right], \qquad . \qquad . \qquad (154)$$

where B is written for $\sqrt{\dfrac{S}{g\rho}}$ and r is the radius of the plate. Thus (153) is only the first of these three terms. The last term is small,

[1] Ferguson, *Phil. Mag.*, 26, 925 (1913).

but needs inclusion for accurate work, unless r is over 6 cm. It must be remembered also that we have assumed the plate to be perfectly wetted by the liquid, and thus the expression will be modified if the liquid has a finite angle of contact. When equation (154) is used this method is capable of measuring S with considerable accuracy.

Adhesion Ring.—By replacing the plate with a ring du Nouy [1] somewhat simplified the calculation of the adhesion force. The ring was of platinum-iridium and could thus easily be cleaned, and the radius of the circular wire of which it was made was sufficiently small, 0·015 cm., for the weight of liquid elevated to be small compared with the downward pull due to surface tension. Thus an approximation to the adhesion force is given by

$$F=4\pi RS,$$

R being the mean ring radius. But in fact the process of detachment is more complicated in this case as well, and an empirical calibration of the ring may be made [2] in which, using liquids of known surface tension and with rings having similar ratios of R to r, the radius of the wire, graphs may be drawn connecting the dimensionless variables $\dfrac{RS}{F}$ and $\dfrac{R^3\rho g}{F}$. Then in measuring an unknown surface tension, one of these rings is used, or at least one with the same $\dfrac{R}{r}$ and, from the measured value of $\dfrac{R^3\rho g}{F}$, the corresponding $\dfrac{RS}{F}$ value is found.

93. Capillary Ascent.—If a clean narrow-bore tube is placed vertically with one end below the surface of a liquid, the latter will rise inside the tube—except in the case of mercury with which a depression occurs—to a level above that in the vessel outside. The height h of this *capillary ascent* may be calculated by considering the forces maintaining the elevated liquid column. If h is measured vertically from the bottom of the meniscus to the horizontal part of the free surface, the weight of a cylinder of liquid of height h, density ρ, and radius r—which is the internal radius of the capillary tube—is balanced by the surface tension acting around the contact circle, whose radius is also equal to r. If the angle of contact is θ, the equation for equilibrium is

$$2\pi rS \cos\theta=\pi r^2 h\rho g,$$

or,

$$S=\frac{rh\rho g}{2\cos\theta} \qquad . \qquad . \qquad . \qquad . \qquad (155)$$

This ignores the weight of liquid in the meniscus above the horizontal part. As a first approximation the meniscus is a hemisphere of radius

---

[1] du Nouy, *Journ. Gen. Physiol.*, **1**, 521 (1919).
[2] Harkins, Young and Cheng, *Science*, **64**, 333 (1926).

r, and the weight of liquid above the horizontal tangent plane to the meniscus is $\frac{1}{3}\pi r^3 \rho g$. The corrected formula is

$$S = \frac{r\rho g}{2 \cos \theta}\left[h + \frac{r}{3}\right] \qquad . \qquad . \qquad . \qquad (156)$$

Thus the correction becomes appreciable only if, within the limits of an experiment, $\frac{1}{3}r$ is comparable with h. The approximate formula may be used with a very narrow capillary tube.

A further simplification occurs for liquids such as water, alcohol, chloroform, *etc.*, whose contact angle is usually assumed to be zero. In these cases

$$S = \frac{r\rho g}{2}\left[h + \frac{r}{3}\right].$$

If the radius of the capillary tube is so large that $\frac{r}{h}$ approximates to unity, this correction for the meniscus will not be sufficiently accurate. For slightly wider tubes the meniscus may be treated as having a semi-elliptical section, and the corrected formula [1] is

$$S = \frac{r\rho g h}{2}\left[1 + \frac{r}{3h} - 0\cdot 111\frac{r^2}{h^2} + 0\cdot 0741\frac{r^3}{h^3}\right],$$

which is substantially the same as that obtained by Rayleigh [2] by more complicated analysis, *viz.*

$$S = \frac{r\rho g h}{2}\left[1 + \frac{r}{3h} - 0\cdot 1288\frac{r^2}{h^2} + 0\cdot 1312\frac{r^3}{h^3}\right].$$

This degree of approximation gives results accurate to 1 in 2000 for values of r up to $0\cdot 2\ h$. Beyond this, Sugden [3] calculated the values of $\frac{g r\rho h}{2S}$ against $r\sqrt{\frac{g\rho}{2S}}$ by the methods suggested by Bashford and Adams.[4] In use, an approximate value of S is used to give $r\sqrt{\frac{g\rho}{2S}}$ from which a corrected value of h is determined from the $\frac{g r\rho h}{2S}$ table. Thus a corrected figure of S is determined, and the process may be repeated until a constant value is found for S. Usually no more than two such references are needed to the tables.

If two vertical plates are placed close together, each with one edge beneath a liquid surface, then a corresponding ascent is obtained between the plates. Considering the forces maintaining

[1] Ferguson, *Mechanical Properties of Fluids*, p. 24 (1925).
[2] Rayleigh, *Proc. Roy. Soc.*, A, **92**, 184 (1916).
[3] Sugden, *Journ. Chem. Soc.*, **119**, 1483 (1921).
[4] *loc. cit.*

equilibrium of the elevated liquid, it may be shown that

$$S = \frac{d\rho g}{2\ cos\ \theta}\left[h + \frac{d}{4}\left(2 - \frac{\pi}{2}\right)\right]$$

$$= \frac{d\rho g}{2\ cos\ \theta}[h + 0.107d],$$

where d is the distance between the plates. If $\theta = 0$, this becomes

$$S = \frac{d\rho g}{2}[h + 0.107d],$$

and if d is very small compared with h, the equation reduces to

$$S = \frac{hd\rho g}{2},$$

or

$$hd = constant.$$

This is the equation to a hyperbola with the axes as asymptotes, and it gives the shape of the surface line between the plates when they are inclined at an angle to one another in a horizontal plane. It should be remembered, however, that this is true only when the separation distance is small.

94. Measurement of Contact Angles.—The direct measurement of contact angles is difficult and uncertain. More accurate and consistent values are obtained by measuring the surface tension separately by two methods, one of which is independent of, and the other involving in a known manner, the angle of contact. Thus Jaeger's method may be combined with an experiment such as that due to Wilhelmy,[1] in which the additional force, due to surface tension, on a plate suspended vertically from a balance-arm is measured. If the lower edge of the plate is in the level of the undisplaced liquid surface, the equation of equilibrium is

$$mg = Sl\ cos\ \theta,$$

where mg is the additional weight required to balance the vertical effect of surface tension, and l is the length of the line of contact. This method is superior to the capillary tube experiment, since the plate is easily cleaned and its contour line can be accurately measured.

An alternative method due to Anderson and Bowen[2] utilises the variation of the meniscus radius of curvature R at its apex with radius r of the capillary tube in which the meniscus is formed. The former, R, is measured by using the meniscus as a refracting surface for parallel light and when it is plotted against r, the curve approaches the origin at an angle ϕ for which $tan\ \phi = cos\ \theta$.

After reviewing this and other methods Ferguson[3] suggested

[1] Wilhelmy, *Pogg. Ann.*, **119**, 176 (1863).
[2] Anderson and Bowen, *Phil. Mag.*, **31**, 143 (1916).
[3] *loc. cit.*

that direct methods, *e.g.* the tilting of a plate until the liquid met the plate without meniscus formation, are probably preferable.

95. Measurement of Surface Tension by Means of Ripples.
—The rate at which short waves or ripples travel over the surface of a liquid depends on the surface tension, their velocity being given in Article 220,

$$v^2 = \frac{2\pi S}{\rho\lambda} + \frac{g\lambda}{2\pi},$$

where λ is the wave-length. Rayleigh [1] and Dorsey [2] used these ripples when determining the surface tension, by causing a style attached to an electrically maintained tuning-fork to touch the liquid surface. A coperiodic ripple system was formed and viewed stroboscopically by means of another fork having the same frequency. The ripples then appeared stationary and the wave-length could be measured. If n is the frequency of the fork, $v = n\lambda$, and

$$S = \frac{n^2\lambda^3\rho}{2\pi} - \frac{g\rho\lambda^2}{4\pi^2}.$$

In the case of mercury, the procedure may be simplified by using the mercury in the fork circuit. Each time the platinum wire, which is attached to the prong, leaves the surface of the mercury, a small spark occurs at the same phase of the ripple formation, and the system, viewed by means of this spark illumination, appears at rest. The wave-length is measured by means of a travelling microscope, and for $n = 100$, λ is about 3 mm. Since the wave-length is raised to the third power, it is this measurement which limits the accuracy of the experiment.

A review of possible stroboscopic methods of illumination which render possible the projection of ripple images upon a screen has been given by Tyler.[3] This improves the accuracy of measurement of the wave-length, and Tyler shows that the most satisfactory method of utilising the results consists in graphing λn^2 against $\frac{1}{\lambda^2}$ and measuring the slope of the resultant straight line. Another recent measurement of considerable precision was made by Brown,[4] in which current from a valve oscillator was used to produce both the ripple system and its intermittent illumination.

96. Surface Tension and Temperature.
—The surface tension of all liquids decreases linearly with rising temperature, over small temperature ranges, so that the surface tension S_t at $t°$ C. is given by

$$S_t = S_0(1 - \alpha t), \quad \text{and} \quad \frac{dS}{dt} = -k,$$

[1] Rayleigh, *Phil. Mag.*, **30**, 386 (1890).
[2] Dorsey, *ibid.*, **44**, 369 (1897).
[3] Tyler, *ibid.*, **31**, 209 (1941).
[4] Brown, *Proc. Phys. Soc.*, **48**, 312 (1936).

where S_0 is the value at $0°$ C., α is the temperature coefficient, and $k = S_0\alpha$.

At the critical temperature the value of S is zero, and the interface between liquid and vapour disappears, so that the absolute value of the surface tension depends on how far the temperature is from the critical value. Van der Waals suggested the relation,

$$S_T = A\left(1 - \frac{T}{T_c}\right)^{\frac{3}{2}},$$

where S_T is the surface tension at absolute temperature T, and T_c is the critical temperature, A being a constant for a given liquid. From this

$$\frac{1}{A}\frac{dS}{dT} = -\frac{3}{2T_c}\sqrt{1 - \frac{T}{T_c}},$$

and both S and $\dfrac{dS}{dT}$ are zero at the critical temperature.

A modified formula

$$S_T = A\left(1 - \frac{T}{T_c}\right)^{n},$$

where n varies for different liquids, but is in the neighbourhood of 1·21, is more accurate.[1]

In practice, however, the surface tension curve approaches the critical point tangentically, and becomes negligibly small at some degrees below the critical point.

If M is the molecular weight and ρ the density of the liquid, the surface area occupied by a gramme molecule, assuming the molecules are symmetrical in shape, is proportional to $\left(\dfrac{M}{\rho}\right)^{\frac{2}{3}}$, and is known as the *molar surface*. The surface energy in the molar surface is proportional to $S\left(\dfrac{M}{\rho}\right)^{\frac{2}{3}}$, and is termed the *molar energy*, so that

$$S\left(\frac{M}{\rho}\right)^{\frac{2}{3}} = K(T_c - T),$$

K being a universal constant of approximate value 2·2. This relation is known as *Eötvös' Law*,[2] which states that the molar free surface energy of any liquid should be proportional to the difference between its temperature and the critical temperature, and to a universal constant. This law is analogous to the gas law $pv = RT$, where pv corresponds to the free molar energy of the gas. Ramsay and Shields [3] modified the relation giving

$$S\left(\frac{M}{\rho}\right)^{\frac{2}{3}} = K(T_c - T - \delta),$$

[1] Ferguson, *Trans. Far. Soc.*, **19**, 408 (1923).
[2] Eötvös, *Wied. Ann.*, **27**, 448 (1886).
[3] Ramsay and Shields, *Zeits. Phys. Chem.*, **12**, 433 (1893).

where $(T_c - \delta)$ is the temperature at which the surface tension vanishes. This may be written

$$\frac{d}{dT}\left[S\left(\frac{M}{\rho}\right)^{\frac{2}{3}}\right] = constant = -K,$$

and, as already stated, K is 2·2 for many liquids. With some organic liquids, however, much higher values of K are obtained, and this is explained by the now generally accepted theory of molecular orientation in the liquid-gas surface. A high value of K corresponds to an arrangement of the molecules with their greatest dimension placed normally to the surface, and, from the value of K for a substance, interesting conclusions may be drawn as to the orientation of its surface molecules.

A more satisfactory relationship between the molar free energy and temperature is obtained by taking into account the effect of the vapour atmosphere above the liquid, and Katayama [1] suggested the definition of the molar free energy E_1 as $S\left[\dfrac{M}{\rho - \rho_1}\right]^{\frac{2}{3}}$, ρ_1 being the vapour density. Then it is found that

$$E_1 = a(T_c - T),$$

where a is a constant.

From equation (129) we see that the total surface energy E is greater than S, and since $\dfrac{dS}{dT}$ is approximately constant, so that

$$\frac{dE}{dT} = -T\frac{d^2S}{dT^2} = 0, \text{ approximately,}$$

the total surface energy remains constant over a considerable range of temperatures. From a critical examination of the total surface energies of various liquids, Langmuir [2] and Harkins [3] have concluded that pure liquid surfaces consist of a layer of oriented molecules, with their active parts drawn inwards. In the case of water, for example, there is supposed to be such a layer of directed molecules, while with benzene the molecules probably lie on the surface in a flat ring.

It must be remembered, however, that these surface molecules are continually evaporating and recondensing on the surface, the rate of evaporation and recondensation being given by $\dfrac{C_1 p}{\sqrt{MT}}$, where p is the vapour pressure and C_1 is a constant. In the case of water at 20° C. the rate of evaporation is about 10^{22} molecules per sq. cm. per sec., so that the life of a molecule on the surface is only about 10^{-7} seconds, and during this time the molecule must become oriented

[1] Katayama, *Tohoku Univ. Sci. Rep.*, **4**, 373 (1916).
[2] Langmuir, *Amer. Chem. Soc. Journ.*, **38**, 2221 (1916).
[3] Harkins, *ibid.*, **39**, 354 (1917); **39**, 541 (1917); **42**, 700 (1920); **43**, 35 (1921).

in a vertical position about which it oscillates. Since the moment of inertia of a molecule is extremely small, the short time available for taking up a definite position does not necessarily invalidate the theory.

97. Liquid—Liquid Interfaces.—It is to be expected that, at the interface between two immiscible liquids, a new phase will come into existence possessing a definite surface energy dependent on the composition of the two liquids. Antonow [1] stated that the interfacial tension between two liquids in equilibrium is equal to the difference between the surface tensions of each separately. This rule applies only to mutually saturated solutions. Since the surface tension of one is often reduced by the addition of the second, the measurements must be made with the liquids in equilibrium. For example, the difference between the surface tension of an aqueous layer on benzene and that of a benzene layer on water is equal to the tension of the water-benzene interface. The following results obtained by Reynolds [2] may be quoted in support of this rule :—

TABLE VIII.—INTERFACIAL SURFACE TENSIONS

Liquid.	Surface Tension in dynes per cm.		S for Pure Liquid.	Tension of Interface in dynes per cm.	
	Water Layer.	Liquid Layer.		Cal-culated.	Ob-served.
Benzene	63·2	28·8	28·4	34·4	34·4
Ether	28·1	17·5	17·7	10·6	10·6
Aniline	46·4	42·2	41·9	4·2	4·8
Chloroform . . .	59·8	26·4	27·2	33·4	33·3
Carbon tetrachloride . .	70·2	26·7	26·7	43·5	43·5
Amyl alcohol . . .	26·3	21·5	24·4	4·8	4·8
Cresol	37·8	34·3	37·1	3·5	3·9

Since the interfacial tension between two liquids can be expressed as the difference of two surface tensions, the value is, as a rule, small, and increases as the solubility in the second liquid diminishes. It also decreases with rise of temperature.

A consideration of the magnitude of various interfacial tensions leads to interesting conclusions concerning chemical constitution. Thus if S_1, S_2, and S_{12} are the surface tensions of two pure liquids and of their interface, then, by Antonow's rule,

$$S_1 + S_2 > S_{12},$$

and during the process of mutual saturation there will be a decrease in the free energy of the system. The work of cohesion, which is the work done when a liquid of unit cross-section is pulled apart

[1] Antonow, *Journ. d. Chim. Phys.*, 5, 372 (1907).
[2] Reynolds, *Journ. Chem. Soc.*, 119, 460 (1921).

against the cohesive forces, is given by

$$W_c = 2S_1, \quad \text{or} \quad 2S_2,$$

for the two liquids, respectively. The work of adhesion W_a is the work required to separate a composite layer, consisting of two liquids, at the junction, and is evidently equal to the decrease in free energy when the two liquids are brought into contact, *i.e.*

$$W_a = S_1 + S_2 - S_{12}.$$

A break should occur with the least expenditure of energy, and so the molecules are oriented at the surfaces such that this work of separation is a minimum. On this theory, W_c for some liquids should be the same. For instance, the molecules of octyl alcohol should orient themselves so that the break occurs between parts of the molecule which are similar to those parts of the octane molecule at which a break occurs, *i.e.* between the ends of the hydrocarbon chains. We should, therefore, expect W_a to be the same for octane as for octyl alcohol. Harkins [1] finds the values slightly different, and he accounts for this by assuming imperfect orientation due to thermal agitation.

Similarly, with an octyl alcohol-water interface, the polar groups of the alcohol molecules are immersed in the water and, to separate the surfaces, polar groups must be separated from their strong mutual attraction. In this case W_a must be large. Differences between W_c for an organic liquid, and W_a for the liquid and water, is a measure of the asymmetry of the organic liquid molecules.

The interfacial tension between two liquids may be measured by the drop-weight method.[2] In this experiment the weight mg is found for a drop of one liquid, density ρ_1, falling from a tube, of external radius r, which dips below the surface of the second liquid of density ρ_2. If the detachment is regarded as a case of approximately static equilibrium, at the moment when the pendulous drop has a cylindrical form where it is attached to the tube, the equation of equilibrium of that portion of the drop which is hanging is

$$mg\frac{(\rho_1 - \rho_2)}{\rho_1} + p\pi r^2 = 2\pi r S_{12},$$

where p is the excess pressure inside and is equal to $\dfrac{S_{12}}{r}$. Thus

$$m = \frac{\pi S_{12} r \rho_1}{g(\rho_1 - \rho_2)}.$$

But the detachment of the drop is essentially a dynamical problem for which dimensional analysis gives [3]

$$m = \frac{S_{12} r \rho_1}{g(\rho_1 - \rho_2)} \phi\left[\frac{S_{12}}{gr^2(\rho_1 - \rho_2)}\right], \qquad . \qquad . \quad (157)$$

[1] Harkins, *Amer. Chem. Soc. Journ.*, 38, 228 (1916); 42, 700 (1920).
[2] See Guye and Perrot, *Arch. Sci. Phys. et Nat.*, 11, 225 (1901).
[3] Article 234.

where ϕ is some arbitrary function of the non-dimensional variable

$$\frac{S_{12}}{gr^2(\rho_1-\rho_2)}.$$

The same problem was attacked by Harkins and Brown [1] who observed that the non-dimensional quantity $\frac{mg}{Sr}$ must be given by equal values of the other non-dimensional ratios $\frac{r}{V^{\frac{1}{3}}}$ and $\frac{r}{B}$, where V is the volume of the drop and B is written for $\sqrt{\frac{S}{g\rho}}$ as before, Thus

$$\frac{mg}{Sr}=\phi\left[\frac{r}{V^{\frac{1}{3}}}\right]=f\left[\frac{r}{B}\right].$$

Using liquids of known S, thus giving B, the values of $\frac{mg}{Sr}$ and $\frac{r}{B}$ were obtained together with $\frac{r}{V^{\frac{1}{3}}}$. Curves were then drawn connecting

(a) $\frac{r}{V^{\frac{1}{3}}}$ with $\frac{mg}{Sr}$, or $\phi\left[\frac{r}{V^{\frac{1}{3}}}\right]$,

(b) $\frac{r}{B}$ with $\frac{mg}{Sr}$, or $f\left[\frac{r}{B}\right]$.

This was done with water, benzene, carbon tetrachloride, and ethylene dibromide and the points for different liquids and different tips fell smoothly on the same curves. Therefore these curves could be used subsequently to find an unknown surface tension by determining m and r. Then $\frac{r}{V^{\frac{1}{3}}}$ can be calculated, and the graph determines the value of $\phi\left[\frac{r}{V^{\frac{1}{3}}}\right]$ or $\frac{mg}{Sr}$ from which S is directly derivable.

Instead of using the graph with its unavoidable limit of accuracy, reference may be made to the tabulated values from which the graphs were constructed and, since the tabulated values of $\frac{r}{B}$ with $f\left[\frac{r}{B}\right]$ are obtained with greater smoothness, it is preferable to determine $\phi\left[\frac{r}{V^{\frac{1}{3}}}\right]$ from the one set of results, transfer this value to the other set, and thus obtain $\frac{r}{B}$ from which S is calculable. If the value of an interface tension is being measured, and strictly all are

[1] Harkins and Brown, *Journ. Amer. Chem. Soc.*, **1**, 499 (1919).

interface tensions, it is obtained by substitution in

$$S = \frac{(m - m_1)g}{r\phi\left(\dfrac{r}{V^{\frac{1}{3}}}\right)}$$

m_1 being the mass of an equal volume of the lighter fluid.

Lord Rayleigh, using water drops in air, showed that the value of the non-dimensional variable in equation (157) was nearly constant at 3·8 for a large variation in r. Therefore

$$m = \frac{3 \cdot 8 S_{12} r \rho_1}{g(\rho_1 - \rho_2)}.$$

If the drop forms in air so that ρ_2 may be neglected, the tension S of the liquid-air surface is given by

$$mg = 3 \cdot 8 S r.$$

The weight of one drop is obtained by collecting and weighing a known number of drops, and the value of r should be about 3 or 4 mm. The method gives accurate values, and is probably the best means of measuring the tension of liquid interfaces.

The Wilhelmy method, in conjunction with a torsion balance, may also be used for measuring interfacial tensions. The two liquids are contained in a beaker, and the vertical plate, suspended from the arm of the torsion balance, is fully immersed in the upper liquid. When the beaker is raised, equilibrium is maintained until the interface is reached. Then the additional pull on the plate forces it downwards from the balanced position. The plate is restored to its original position by twisting the torsion head, and the angle of twist measures the force $l S_{12}$ where l is the horizontal perimeter of the plate and S_{12} is the interface tension. This assumes that the angle of contact is zero or, more accurately, that $cos\ \theta$ does not vary appreciably from unity.

98. Surface Tension and Other Constants of the Liquid.— Several attempts have been made to connect the surface tension of a liquid with its other constants. For instance, Macleod [1] showed that, for any given liquid at different temperatures,

$$S = C_1(\rho - \rho_1)^4,$$

where C_1 is a constant and ρ, ρ_1 are the densities of the liquid and saturated vapour, respectively. Ferguson [2] indicated that the constant C_1 could be expressed in the form

$$C_1 = \frac{A_1 T_c}{M^{\frac{2}{3}} \rho_c^{\frac{10}{3}}},$$

where A_1 is a constant independent of the liquid, M, the molecular weight, T_c, the critical temperature, and ρ_c, the critical density.

Attempts to test the Macleod law in its generalised form,

[1] Macleod, *Trans. Far. Soc.*, **19**, 38 (1923).

[2] Ferguson, *ibid.*, **19**, 407 (1923).

$S = C_1(\rho - \rho_1)^n$, by a logarithmic graph of S and $(\rho - \rho_1)$, show that, for many liquids for which the power law is closely followed at lower temperatures, there are considerable deviations from the Macleod law in the neighbourhood of the critical temperature. Moreover, in the range for which the logarithmic curve is linear, there are deviations from the value $n = 4$. These are sufficient to produce appreciable errors into the numerical value of *the parachor*, if the common practice is followed of taking the fourth root instead of the nth root in the calculation for the parachor.

Richards and Matthews [1] found that, for a large number of non-associated liquids,

$$S\beta^{\frac{3}{4}} = constant,$$

where β is the compressibility. Finally, Bennett and Mitchell [2] showed that, as already mentioned, the total surface energy E is constant over a large range of temperatures, and suggested this relation as a test of association into molecular aggregates.

99. The Parachor.—Macleod's equation, given above, can be written in the form :—

$$MC = \frac{MS^{\frac{1}{4}}}{\rho - \rho_1},$$

and since both M and C are constants for a given liquid, $MS^{\frac{1}{4}}/\rho$ is constant. It has been termed by Sugden [3] the parachor of the substance, and is independent of temperature over a wide range, Neglecting ρ_1 in comparison with ρ, we may express the parachor. P, in the form

$$P = VS^{\frac{1}{4}},$$

where V is the molecular volume of the substance. Thus we may regard the parachor as the molecular volume of a substance when the surface tension of the latter is unity, and parachors of different substances should be proportional to the molecular volumes, at temperatures at which the liquids have the same surface tension. For example, the ratio of the parachor to the molecular critical volume V_c of a given compound should be constant for all substances, as illustrated in the following table :—

Substance.	P	V_c	P/V_c
Hydrogen . . .	35·1	46·9	0·75
Benzene	206·3	256·1	0·81
Chlorobenzene . . .	244·5	307·8	0·80
Methyl ether . . .	211·7	281·9	0·75
Carbon tetrachloride . .	219·9	276·1	0·80
Methyl formate . .	138·6	172·0	0·81
Ethyl acetate . . .	217·1	286·0	0·76

[1] Richards and Matthews, *Zeits. Phys. Chem.*, **61**, 49 (1908).
[2] Bennett and Mitchell, *ibid.*, **84**, 475 (1913).
[3] Sugden, *Journ. Chem. Soc.*, **125**, 32, 1177 (1924). See also *The Parachor and Valency*, by Sugden (1930).

The additivity law applies to parachors ; isomeric substances of similar constitution have the same parachor, and the difference in parachor between successive members of a homologous series is constant and independent of the type of compound.   Thus the parachor of the group CH_2 is the difference between the parachors of C_2H_6 and C_3H_8.

The additivity law applies also to atomic parachors, so that by subtracting from the parachor for a paraffin, C_nH_{2n+2}, that for n CH_2 groups, as determined above, the parachor equivalent to two atoms of hydrogen can be found.   Thus the atomic parachor of hydrogen can be determined, and in a similar manner other atomic parachors. The most interesting applications of the parachor have been made in connection with problems of chemical structure.

100. Surface Tension of Solutions.—We have hitherto regarded the boundary separating two phases, such as liquid and vapour, simply as a geometrical surface, upon one side of which there is a phase of uniform properties, and on the other a second phase, everywhere distinct from the first and homogeneous in itself. Actually this is not the case, nor do the contiguous layers shade, as it were, rapidly but continuously one into the other.   We must regard the boundary as a film or lamina of finite, though minute, thickness, consisting of an entirely different phase with definite and measurable properties.

With solutions, the composition of the interface phase, or surface layer, is mostly different from that of the solution itself in bulk. In the case of a pure liquid, the interface energy is a minimum—as indeed it must be for all interfaces—but with pure liquids S is constant, and the energy can decrease only by a contraction in area. With solutions this is not so, for the surface tension varies with the concentration, and the possibility exists that S tends to a minimum value with changing concentration.   To effect this, the surface layer must be more dilute than the remainder of the solution, if S increases with concentration.   If, on the contrary, S decreases as the concentration is raised, then the dissolved substance will collect in the surface layer.   This enrichment, or impoverishment, of the surface phase does not continue indefinitely, for a point is reached at which the action is balanced by the counter-movement due to diffusion. The excess, or deficiency, of solute in the superficial phase may be calculated by Gibbs' equation, which may be developed from his *adsorption theorem.*

101. Gibbs' Adsorption Theorem.[1]—Consider a solution of which the surface, area A, and the volume, v, are subjected to independent reversible alterations, and let the osmotic pressure of the solute be p.   Then the work done on the system by increasing the area by dA—the volume remaining constant—is SdA, and that on increasing the volume by dv—the surface remaining constant—is

---

[1] See Milner, *Phil. Mag.*, 13, 96 (1907).

pdv. These operations may be performed successively, and the final result is independent of the order in which they occur. Hence

$$SdA - \left(p + \frac{dp}{dA}dA\right)dv = -pdv + \left(S + \frac{dS}{dv}dv\right)dA,$$

so that

$$\frac{dS}{dv} = -\frac{dp}{dA} \qquad \cdot \qquad \cdot \qquad \cdot \qquad (158)$$

Thus the surface tension will vary with the volume of the solution, *i.e.* with the concentration, only when the osmotic pressure depends upon the surface area. In other words the concentration of the solute in the thin surface film, which is the seat of the capillary forces, must be different from what it is in the bulk of the solution. If there is an excess concentration within the surface, any surface area increase will result in the removal of a certain amount of solute from the interior of the solution, and the osmotic pressure within the latter will decrease. Let C_1 be the number of gram-molecules of the solute in the bulk of the solution originally, and C_2 the number of gram-molecules of solute, per sq. cm. of the surface, which are withdrawn from the interior of the solution. Then the final concentration C in the interior, upon which both the osmotic pressure and the surface tension depend, will be given by

$$C = \frac{C_1 - AC_2}{v}.$$

Thus

$$\frac{dS}{dv} = \frac{dS}{dC} \cdot \frac{dC}{dv} = -\frac{C}{v} \cdot \frac{dS}{dC},$$

and

$$\frac{dp}{dA} = \frac{dp}{dC} \cdot \frac{dC}{dA} = -\frac{C_2}{v} \cdot \frac{dp}{dC}.$$

Utilising equation (158)

$$-C\frac{dS}{dC} = C_2\frac{dp}{dC}.$$

If the osmotic pressure obeys the ordinary gas laws, then $p = CRT$ and so

$$C_2 = -\frac{C}{RT} \cdot \frac{dS}{dC}.$$

In all inorganic solutions the surface tension increases linearly with concentration, so that C_2 is negative, C_2/C is constant, and there is a defect of salt in the surface film of an amount proportional to the concentration.

Gibbs' theorem has been verified experimentally and the field which it covers is very wide. Thus the addition of a solute to a solvent will cause marked changes in the composition of the surface phase, if the solvent and solute possess different surface tensions.

For example, on the addition of a material of low surface tension to water, the surface phase becomes rich in the solute and the surface tension of the solution will fall rapidly.

The surface-tension-concentration curve for mixtures of two substances will, as a rule, run a simple course between the surface tension lines of the two substances, but there is a large number of substances which raise the surface tension of water. For these

$$\frac{S_L - S_M}{S_M} = kC,$$

where S_L, S_M are the tensions of the solution and solvent, respectively, k is a constant, and C is the concentration. Jaeger [1] found a similar behaviour in the case of solutions of benzoic acid, camphor, aniline, naphthalene in methyl and ethyl alcohols. Aqueous solutions of sodium chloride and other inorganic salts, sugars, glycerine, *etc.*, produce similar results. On the other hand, substances which lower the surface tension of water are alcohols, aldehydes, fatty acids, camphor, *etc.* Considerable lowering of the surface tension is caused at low concentrations, but at intermediate and high concentrations, S_L changes comparatively little and mostly tends towards the value possessed by the organic liquid. An experimental formula proposed by Szyszkowski [2] to represent the change is

$$\frac{S_M - S_L}{S_M} = b \log \left(\frac{C}{k} + 1\right),$$

where k and b are constants.

The marked lowering of the surface tension of water by small amounts of some substances is evident in many phenomena. Thus ether vapour produces a lively motion in a water surface, as the lowering of S_L does not proceed equally strongly at all parts of the surface, and the water is drawn from a place with lower surface tension to one where the surface tension has a higher value. The same local differences in S_L cause the motion which pieces of camphor exhibit upon a pure water surface. It is actually the camphor vapour which is responsible for this effect.

102. Theories of Capillarity.—Many attempts have been made to associate the results of surface tension with the conception of intermolecular forces, and their variations are due mainly to the possible hypotheses regarding surface structure and the law of force. The Newtonian law of gravitation, *i.e.* the inverse square law of attractions, is not adequate to explain capillary phenomena, and various alternatives have been suggested. In one of the early attempts, Young [3] solved many of the problems of capillarity, including most of those afterwards treated by Laplace,[4] by assuming

[1] Jaeger, *Wien. Akad. d. Wiss.*, **101**, 158 (1892).
[2] Szyszkowski, *Zeits. f. Phys. Chem.*, **64**, 385 (1908).
[3] Young, " Cohesion of Fluids," *Phil. Trans.*, A, **95**, 65 (1805).
[4] Laplace, *Mécanique Celeste*, Suppl. to Book 10.

that intermolecular action was the resultant of two opposed types of force ; one, an attraction which remains constant throughout its effective range, and the other a repulsion which, though preponderating at very close distances of approach, decreases rapidly with distance. Young's explanations were rendered obscure by his avoidance of mathematical symbols.

Laplace [1] offered a treatment of the subject which was entirely mathematical, while his results agreed in many respects with those of Young. He investigated, without assuming any special distance law of attraction, the force acting on the fluid contained in an infinitely thin canal normal to the fluid surface and arising from the attraction of the fluid outside the canal. The pressure at a point in the interior of a fluid was of the form

$$p = K + k\left(\frac{1}{r_1} + \frac{1}{r_2}\right),$$

where K is a constant pressure which is probably large but which is not a surface effect, and k is another constant upon which all capillary phenomena depend.

Gauss [2] in 1830 developed the principle of virtual displacements into practically what is now called the conservation of energy, and by its means he formed an expression for the total potentials arising from the action between each pair of particles. This aggregate—which with reversed sign is now called the potential energy—is the result of three different actions :

(i) The external effect of gravity ;
(ii) The mutual actions of the fluid particles ;
(iii) The interactions between the fluid and its boundary media.

The condition of minimum potential energy gave the equation to the free surface in Laplace's form, and also indicated the conditions governing angles of contact. Thus Gauss supplemented the results of Laplace's theory.

In 1831 Poisson published his *New Theory of Capillary Action* in which the chief advance was the suggestion, for which he gave strong reasons, that there is a rapid variation in density near the liquid surface. Laplace's assumption of uniform density is not necessarily true—indeed, as we have seen, recent developments indicate that it is certainly not the case—and thus Poisson rendered valuable service in directing attention to this fundamental point.

Gauss' method has been modified in the light of Poisson's suggestion and its language brought more into line with modern descriptions.

Because of the influence which it has exerted on surface tension theory, a brief indication of Laplace's method will now be given.

In Fig. 71 AB is the boundary surface of the liquid, P, any point in AB, and CD, the tangent plane at P. A narrow cylinder PR is

[1] Laplace, *loc. cit.*
[2] Gauss, *Principia generalia theoriæ figuræ fluidorium in statu equilibrii.*

described, having its length normal to the surface at P and with cross-sectional area α.   At a distance PQ—equal to the extreme range of molecular action—a surface FQG is drawn parallel to APB. Thus the liquid between APB and FQG represents the surface layer in which the surface effects are built up, and the molecular pressure produced at Q will relate also to all points in QR, or QR continued. It is thus necessary to deal only with the transition distance PQ.

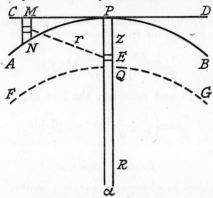

FIG. 71.—LAPLACE'S THEORY OF CAPILLARITY.   PRESSURE INSIDE A CURVED SURFACE.

Laplace assumed that the attraction between two elementary masses m_1 and m_2, whose separation distance is r, is given by

$$F = m_1 m_2 . f(r), \qquad . \qquad . \qquad . \qquad . \qquad (159)$$

where $f(r)$ is a function of the distance, such that when r is indefinitely small, F is large but finite, while, when r equals r_0, the range of molecular action, F is zero.   The cylinder PR is maintained in equilibrium under the action of the pressure at R and the attraction along PR of the rest of the liquid.   If we suppose the liquid to extend up to CPD, the attraction thus calculated will differ from the true value by the amount contributed by the liquid between APB and CPD, both reckoned in the direction PR.   But since the latter evidently acts along RP, it must be added to the former.   Let the attraction of the completed liquid be $K\alpha$, where K is a constant.

At a point M erect a small cylinder of length MN, width in the plane of the diagram dx, and breadth at right angles to the figure $x . d\theta$, where θ represents the angle between the tangent PC and that at P in the principal plane, $PM = x$, the principal radius of curvature being R_1.   If the radius of curvature in the plane of the figure is R, then $MN = \dfrac{x^2}{2R}$, and if $PE = z$ and $EM = r$, then by (159) the attraction on an elementary mass dm at E is

$$F = dm \frac{x^2}{2R} x dx . \rho d\theta . f(r),$$

where ρ is the liquid density, and the component of this force along QP is

$$Z = \rho dm \frac{x^3}{2R} dx \,.\, d\theta \,.\, f(r) \frac{z}{r}.$$

But since

$$\frac{1}{R} = \frac{\cos^2\theta}{R_1} + \frac{\sin^2\theta}{R_2},$$

where R_2 is the second principal radius of curvature, we have, on integrating this expression from $\theta = 0$ to $\theta = 2\pi$,

$$\frac{\pi}{2}\rho dm\left(\frac{1}{R_1} + \frac{1}{R_2}\right)\frac{z}{r}x^3 dx \,.\, f(r),$$

and since $r^2 = x^2 + z^2$ and $xdx = rdr$, the last expression becomes

$$\frac{\pi}{2}\rho dm\left(\frac{1}{R_1} + \frac{1}{R_2}\right)z(r^2 - z^2)f(r)dr \qquad . \qquad . \qquad (160)$$

Let

$$f(r)dr = -d[\phi(r)].$$

Since $f(r)$ diminishes as r increases, $\phi(r)$ is positive. On integrating (160) from $r = z$ to $r = r_0$ or ∞, we obtain

$$\frac{\pi\rho}{2}\left(\frac{1}{R_1} + \frac{1}{R_2}\right)zdm\int_z^\infty (z^2 - r^2)d[\phi(r)] \qquad . \qquad . \qquad (161)$$

But

$$\phi(\infty) = 0 \quad \text{and} \quad \int -r^2 d[\phi(r)] = -r^2\phi(r) + 2\int r\phi(r)dr.$$

Hence

$$\int_z^\infty -r^2 d[\phi(r)] = z^2\phi(z) + 2\int_z^\infty r\phi(r)dr,$$

and thus (161) becomes

$$\pi\rho\left(\frac{1}{R_1} + \frac{1}{R_2}\right)zdm\int_z^\infty r\phi(r)dr \qquad . \qquad . \qquad . \qquad (162)$$

Again, define a function $\psi(r)$ such that $r\phi(r)dr = -d\psi(r)$, $\psi(r)$ being positive and $\psi(\infty) = 0$. Then (162) becomes

$$\pi\rho\left(\frac{1}{R_1} + \frac{1}{R_2}\right)z\psi(z)dm \qquad . \qquad . \qquad . \qquad (163)$$

But $dm = \rho\alpha dz$, where dz is the thickness of the element at E, measured along PQ. Thus we have for the meniscus attraction,

$$\pi\rho^2\alpha\left(\frac{1}{R_1} + \frac{1}{R_2}\right)z\psi(z)dz,$$

and this, integrated from $z=0$ to $z=r_0$ or ∞, gives the action of the meniscus liquid on the cylinder PR. Putting

$$\int_0^\infty z\psi(z)dz=H,$$

(163) becomes

$$\pi\rho^2\alpha H\left[\frac{1}{R_1}+\frac{1}{R_2}\right].$$

If p is the molecular pressure at any point in PR below Q, we have

$$p\alpha=K\alpha+\pi\rho^2\alpha H\left[\frac{1}{R_1}+\frac{1}{R_2}\right],$$

or,

$$p=K+\pi\rho^2 H\left[\frac{1}{R_1}+\frac{1}{R_2}\right] \quad . \quad . \quad . \quad (164)$$

Thus the distance function $\psi(z)$ is connected with the surface tension S by the relation

$$S=\pi\rho^2 H=\pi\rho^2\int_0^\infty z\psi(z)dz, \quad . \quad . \quad . \quad (165)$$

and from (164) we have the following results :

(i) Inside a liquid with a flat surface the molecular pressure is K, which was called by Rayleigh the *intrinsic pressure* and is the $\frac{a}{V^2}$ term of Van der Waals' equation (see Article 140).

(ii) The pressure within a liquid, bounded by a convex surface, is greater than K by an amount $\pi\rho^2 H\left[\frac{1}{R_1}+\frac{1}{R_2}\right]$.

(iii) Both of these molecular pressures are built up in a surface layer of thickness equal to the range of molecular action.

To find the relation between K, r_0, and ψ, consider Fig. 72 (a) in which PR is a similar thin cylinder of the liquid whose bounding surface is MP, and its cross-sectional area is again α. Then $K\alpha$ has been defined as the attraction of the remainder of the liquid on the cylinder. Construct a coaxial thin cylindrical shell of radius $PM=x$, and thickness dx, extending indefinitely into the liquid. Let $MA=y$, and consider an element at A of length dy and depth, perpendicular to the figure, db. Its mass will be $\rho\,.dxdydb$, and its attraction on a mass dm at B is

$$\rho\,.dm\,.dxdydb\,.f(r),$$

where $r=AB$. The vertical component will be

$$\rho\,.dm\,.dxdydb\,.f(r)\frac{z-y}{r}, \quad . \quad . \quad . \quad (166)$$

where $z=PB$. But since $r^2=x^2+(z-y)^2$, then, keeping both x and z

constant, $rdr=(y-z)dy$, and (166) becomes, on integrating from $r=BM=a$ to $r=\infty$,

$$\rho . dm . dx db . \phi(a) . \qquad . \qquad . \qquad . \qquad (167)$$

Maintaining x constant, the integral of db around the cylindrical shell is $2\pi x$, and so we obtain from (167)

$$\rho . dm . 2\pi x dx . \phi(a),$$

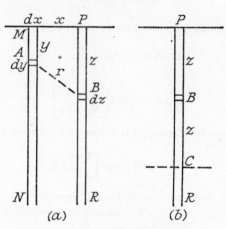

FIG. 72.—LAPLACE'S THEORY OF CAPILLARITY. INTRINSIC PRESSURE AND LATENT HEAT OF EVAPORATION.

and this must be integrated from $x=0$ to $x=\infty$. Since $xdx=ada$, the limits for a are $a=z$ and $a=\infty$, and thus

$$2\pi\rho dm \int_z^\infty a\phi(a)da = 2\pi\rho dm . \psi(z) \qquad . \qquad . \qquad (168)$$

If the element of mass dm is due to a thickness dz of the cylinder PR, we have $dm=\rho\alpha dz$, and integrating (168) from $z=0$ to $z=\infty$,

$$K\alpha = 2\pi\rho^2\alpha \int_0^\infty \psi(z)dz,$$

or,

$$K = 2\pi\rho^2 \int_0^\infty \psi(z)dz \qquad . \qquad . \qquad (169)$$

From (169) and (165) we have

$$\frac{K}{S} = \frac{2\int_0^\infty \psi(z)dz}{\int_0^\infty z\psi(z)dz}.$$

Since the denominator must be less than $r_0 \int_0^\infty \psi(z)dz$,

$$\frac{K}{S} > \frac{2}{r_0}, \quad \text{or} \quad r_0 > \frac{2S}{K}.$$

For water, S may be taken as 73 dynes per cm., and Van der Waals gives $K = 10,500$ atmospheres or $10 \cdot 5 \times 10^9$ C.G.S. units. Thus, for water,

$$r_0 > \frac{146 \times 10^{-9}}{10 \cdot 5} > 1 \cdot 4 \times 10^{-8} \text{ cm.}$$

Equation (168) shows that the attraction on a particle of mass dm, at a distance z below a flat surface, is

$$2\pi\rho dm\psi(z).$$

In moving this particle an extra distance, $-dz$, towards the surface, the work done is $-2\pi\rho dm\psi(z)dz$, and thus to bring the particle to the surface, from well inside the liquid, requires a total expenditure of work W equal to

$$2\pi\rho dm \int_0^\infty \psi(z)dz = \frac{K}{\rho}dm.$$

When at a distance z above the surface the attraction of the liquid will be $2\pi\rho dm\psi(z)$, for (Fig. 72) (b), if through C, such that $BC = BP$, a surface is constructed parallel to the true surface, the attraction due to the liquid between B and P is equal and opposed to that of the liquid between B and C. Therefore, in taking an element dm from the surface to a distance outside the range of attraction, an equal expenditure of work is required. Thus the total work in *evaporating* the element dm is, ignoring work done against external pressure,

$$2W = 2Kdm/\rho,$$

but since $dm/\rho = dv$, the volume of the element, the internal work done in evaporating unit volume of the liquid is $2K$. Thus $2K = \rho L_i$ where L_i is the internal latent heat. For water at atmospheric temperature (15° C.) the internal latent heat is about 556 calories, or $556 \times 4 \cdot 2 \times 10^7$ ergs, and this gives

$$K = 278 \times 4 \cdot 2 \times 10^7$$
$$= 11 \cdot 7 \times 10^9 \text{ C.G.S. units,}$$

which is of the same order of magnitude as Van der Waals' results.

Laplace's theory is usually criticised because he assumed uniform density, and, also, the integration methods are not above suspicion. It must be remembered that the upper limit of integration r_0 is comparable with molecular dimensions, and, on this scale, a liquid has not the homogeneity, tacitly assumed in an application of the integral calculus. It is particularly difficult to realise what the lower limit $z = 0$ means. Even if molecules may be regarded as rigid spheres, and that true collisions occur, the closest distance of approach of their centres would be the molecular diameter. It is this distance which forms the lower integration limit. Additionally, the separation distance between the molecules of a liquid is comparable with the size of the molecules, and thus it is only over very much larger distances than r_0 that the liquid may be regarded as homogeneous in structure. To some extent this objection is countered by the undefined character of the distance function $\psi(z)$, but we should expect the two effects to produce real divergences between the predictions of the theory and the results of experiment. For example, the theory does not give correctly the dependence of surface tension on temperature in the neighbourhood of the critical point.

Modern theory suggests that the interface is a special phase, and its thickness may be assumed equal to the radius of molecular action. All layers of molecules lying at the boundary, which have properties different from those of the molecules in bulk, may be regarded as belonging to the surface layer, and all layers which still have above them, in the direction of the vapour, sufficient molecules to exert the regular internal pressure attraction are under similar conditions of internal pressure. This necessary thickness is also equal to the range of molecular action, and thus the total transition layer will be of thickness equal to twice the radius of molecular activity. Many considerations lead to the conclusion that the latter is not sensibly greater than the diameter of the molecule, so that the transition layer at the boundary of two phases would consist of two unimolecular layers, one in each phase. Einstein [1] has shown that the radius of molecular action is equal to the diameter of the molecule, *i.e.* that only adjacent molecules are under the influence of mutual forces, and he considers the surface layer to be a particular phase of unimolecular thickness.

It has been shown by Langmuir [2] that films do occur which are only one molecule in thickness, such, for example, as the very thin films of oil and other substances on water. If C_1 is the surface concentration in gramme molecules per square centimetre of a unimolecular layer, then the surface area occupied by each molecule is

$$a = \frac{1}{C_1 N_m},$$ where N_m is the number of molecules in a gramme molecule. He measured a by dropping a known quantity of oil on water, and stretching this oil film until its measured surface tension changed. This occurred when the film occupied its maximum area, *i.e.* when it was only one molecule thick. His values, calculated for different substances, are in agreement with those found experimentally for insoluble films by X-ray methods.

Langmuir's theory [3] of capillary phenomena supposes that solids and liquids consist of atoms held together entirely by chemical forces. The ordinary conception of the molecule is thus almost completely eliminated, except in the case of gases, and a solid, or liquid, is looked

[1] Einstein, *Ann. d. Phys.*, **34**, 165 (1911).
[2] Langmuir, *Amer. Chem. Soc. Journ.*, **38**, 2221 (1916).
[3] Langmuir, *ibid.*, **39**, 1857 (1917).

upon as consisting of a single large molecule. Solid polar compounds are, in general, built up of atoms bound together by secondary or residual valencies. Solid non-polar compounds consist, in general, of group molecules in which the atoms are usually held together by primary valencies. Since energy must be expended in separating the atoms of a solid, the surfaces of solids must contain more potential energy than that corresponding to atoms in the interior, and thus the interatomic forces are more intense in the surface than in the interior.

In view of the work of Laue and Bragg [1] on crystalline structure, it is believed that solid bodies are not built up of molecules but of atoms arranged in definite ways, and that the atoms are arranged in groups which are called *group molecules*. These group molecules are held together by chemical forces to form single large molecules, and Langmuir proposes a similar theory for the structure of liquids. Each atom of a liquid is regarded as being combined with all the adjacent atoms, this union being effected by primary and secondary valencies. The atoms held together by primary valency usually constitute group molecules, while the secondary valency serves to hold the group molecules together. The structure of the surface layer of atoms is regarded as the principal factor in determining the surface tension, or rather the surface energy of liquids. This theory is supported by numerous data on the surface tension of organic liquids. The group molecules of these liquids arrange themselves in the surface layer, so that the active portions are drawn inwards ; by active portion is meant a part which is characterised by a strong stray field or residual valency. Since chemical action may be assumed to be due to the presence of electromagnetic fields surrounding the atoms, surface tension, or surface energy, is a measure of the potential energy of the electromagnetic stray field which extends out from the surface layer of atoms. The molecules in the surface layer arrange themselves so that the stray field is a minimum. The surface energy of a liquid depends, therefore, upon the least active portion of the molecule. The fact that the surface energies of the hydrocarbons of the paraffin series and the corresponding alcohols are practically identical, is explained by the fact that the surface layer in these cases is always CH_3. Further experimental verification of this orientation of the molecules at the surface will be encountered when we consider the spreading of films.

There is now almost conclusive evidence that the surface phase of films is only one molecule thick, and that the molecules of an insoluble material adsorbed on the liquid are oriented in a vertical direction, being attracted to the liquid surface in the case of a complex molecule by some particular group or groups. Even more conclusive evidence, in favour of the hypothesis of at least partial orientation, is that derived from a consideration of the latent heats of evaporation and the divergences noted in the Eötvös constant for unsymmetrical and undissociated molecules.

[1] Bragg, *X-Rays and Crystal Structure.*

103. Surface Tension and Evaporation.—When a drop is evaporating under constant temperature conditions, energy must be supplied to provide the latent heat of the vapour, and part of this is obtained from the surface energy which is lost through decreasing the surface area. Thus a drop will continue to evaporate into a space which would be in vapour equilibrium with a flat surface, and there can be no equilibrium between a drop and a surrounding atmosphere of saturated vapour, for, as the drop becomes smaller, a stage is reached when the surface energy loss, due to contraction, is sufficient to supply all the latent heat of vaporisation. The converse is also true, and a drop requires a nucleus for its initial stage of formation, and, for condensation, a degree of supersaturation is required to an extent dependent on the size of available nuclei. Wilson [1] showed experimentally that these nuclei may be dust particles—for which only a small degree of supersaturation is necessary—or electrically charged molecules. Electrification of a drop virtually opposes the surface tension effect owing to the mutual repulsion of similar charges.

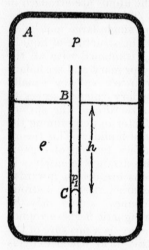

FIG. 73.—VAPOUR PRESSURE OVER A CURVED SURFACE.

To determine how the equilibrium between a vapour and a liquid surface depends on the curvature, suppose a closed vessel A (Fig. 73) contains the liquid and its vapour only, and that a narrow capillary tube, of material which is not wetted by the liquid, is placed in the liquid. The meniscus, which may be regarded as a hemisphere, is depressed to a depth h below the outside horizontal surface. Let p be the saturation pressure above the flat surface, and p_1, the equilibrium pressure above a curved surface of radius r. The pressure difference p_1-p equals the weight of a column of vapour of height h, and thus

$$p_1-p=\int g\sigma dh, \qquad . \qquad . \qquad . \qquad (170)$$

where σ is the vapour density. The pressure at B is p, while that at C, at the same horizontal level as the meniscus, is $p+g\rho h$, and, since there is an excess pressure inside the curved surface of $\dfrac{2S}{r}$, we have

$$p+g\rho h-\frac{2S}{r}=p_1,$$

or,
$$p_1-p=g\rho h-\frac{2S}{r}, \qquad . \qquad . \qquad . \qquad (171)$$

[1] Wilson, *Phil. Trans.*, A, **189**, 265 (1897); **192**, 403 (1899); **193**, 289 (1899).

where ρ is the density of the liquid and r is the radius of the capillary tube. Equating (170) and (171), we have

$$\int g\sigma dh = g\rho h - \frac{2S}{r},$$

or,

$$\frac{2S}{r} = \int g(\rho - \sigma)dh.$$

But σ is connected with the pressure by the relation $\sigma = \dfrac{p}{RT}$ and $dp = g\sigma dh$. Hence

$$\frac{2S}{r} = \int_p^{p_1} \frac{\rho - \sigma}{\sigma} dp = \int_p^{p_1} \frac{\rho}{\sigma} dp,$$

since σ is small compared to ρ. Thus

$$\frac{2S}{r} = \rho RT \int_p^{p_1} \frac{dp}{p} = \rho RT \log \frac{p_1}{p},$$

or,

$$\log \frac{p_1}{p} = \frac{2S}{\rho RT r}.$$

This equation gives the ratio of the vapour pressures, p_1 and p, for equilibrium with the curved surface of radius r and a flat surface, respectively. For a given degree of supersaturation—*i.e.* a given value of p_1—drops of radius less than r will continue to evaporate, while those of greater size will continue to grow. To obtain an idea of the magnitude of this effect, it may be noticed that for water at $0°$ C., the ratio of p_1 to p is as follows :—

Diameter of Water Drop in mm. $\times 10^{-6}$.	Ratio $\dfrac{p_1}{p}$.
100	1·02
10	1·26
5	1·59
2	3·2
1	10·2

These considerations apply also to the phenomenon of boiling. A pure liquid may be raised to a temperature, much in excess of its normal boiling-point, if no dissolved gas affords possible nuclei for the bubbles of vapour to form. When this formation occurs, however, the growth of the bubble is very rapid, since the surface tension is increasingly insufficient to counteract the excess pressure inside. Then boiling with bumping occurs. In the normal process of boiling, the bubble contains some gas, as well as vapour, and is in equilibrium when the pressure p_2, due to the gas, equals the necessary excess pressure inside over that outside the bubble. If p is the external pressure and p_1 the vapour pressure inside the bubble,

$$p_1 + p_2 = p + \frac{2S}{r}.$$

For constant temperature $p_2 r^3$ is constant $= k$, and

$$(p_1 - p) = \frac{2S}{r} - \frac{k}{r^3}.$$

At the equilibrium position

$$\frac{d}{dr}(p_1 - p) = 0 \quad \text{or} \quad k = \tfrac{2}{3}Sr^2,$$

so that

$$p_1 - p = \frac{4S}{3r}.$$

Hence ebullition begins with a bubble of radius r, when the vapour pressure in it exceeds the outside pressure by $\dfrac{4S}{3r}$.

104. Latent Heat and Surface Energy.—The internal latent heat of a liquid is, presumably, a measure of the work done against the internal pressure ; and that done by the molecules in reaching the surface—*i.e.* half-way from the interior to the outside—is measured by the potential energy acquired as surface energy. From this it is argued, according to the Laplace theory, that one-half of the latent heat must be equal to the molar surface energy, which is proportional to $\dfrac{S}{\rho^{\frac{2}{3}}}$, or $SV^{\frac{2}{3}}$, where V is the volume of a gramme molecule.

Bakker has suggested that

$$\int_{V_1}^{V_2} K\,dV = L_1, \qquad . \qquad . \qquad . \qquad . \qquad (172)$$

where K is the intrinsic pressure which is identical with the $\dfrac{a}{V^2}$ term of Van der Waals' equation, V_1 is the volume of 1 gm. of the liquid, V_2 that of the vapour, and L_1 is the internal latent heat. Bakker used the values of a at the critical temperature and deduced the value of L_1 at the boiling-point for many liquids.

Harkins and Roberts [1] found that the relationship between surface energy and latent heat, as expressed by

$$\frac{Molar\ total\ surface\ energy}{Molar\ internal\ latent\ heat} = constant,$$

is not true. Instead, the value of this expression increases with temperature, and is less for strongly unsymmetrical molecules, such as $C_2H_5.OH$, than for symmetrical molecules, such as those of nitrogen.

[1] Harkins and Roberts, *Amer. Chem. Soc. Journ.*, **44**, 653 (1922).

The process of evaporation, as already indicated, takes place in two stages. During the first stage, molecules are brought from the interior up to the surface, overcoming the surface tension effect, and during the second, they vaporise from the surface film. An equality of work in these two actions—such as is indicated by the Laplace theory—can be obtained only for perfectly symmetrical molecules. With more complicated asymmetrical molecules the second stage becomes more important, and the energy associated with the rupture from the surface is a large fraction of the total energy of vaporisation. An examination of the surface energy and latent heat of vaporisation, for a large series of compounds, confirms this theory. These results, obtained by Harkins and Roberts, are given in Table IX.

TABLE IX.—MOLECULAR ENERGY VALUES FOR THE VAPORISATION OF LIQUIDS AT A CORRESPONDING TEMPERATURE EQUAL TO 0·7 OF THE CRITICAL TEMPERATURE.

Liquid.	Total Surface Energy per molecule $\times 10^{14}$ ergs. e.	Internal Latent Heat of Vaporisation per molecule $\times 10^{14}$ ergs. λ.	Energy changed from Potential to Kinetic when Molecule moves from Surface to Vapour per molecule $\times 10^{14}$ ergs. $j = \lambda - e$.	$\dfrac{e}{\lambda}$.
Nitrogen . . .	3·84	8·7	4·8	0·441
Oxygen . . .	4·50	10·8	6·1	0·417
Ethyl ether . .	15·6	36·5	20·9	0·427
Carbon tetrachloride .	18·2	40·2	22·0	0·453
Benzene . . .	18·4	41·7	23·3	0·441
Chloralbenzene .	20·3	48·8	28·5	0·416
Methyl alcohol .	8·5	51·6	43·1	0·165
Ethyl alcohol . .	11·2	59·3	48·1	0·189

The effect of lack of symmetry in the molecule is to lower the molecular free surface energy, latent heat of surface formation, and total surface energy, and to increase the energy of thermal emission. An increasing value of $\dfrac{e}{\lambda}$ indicates an increasing symmetry of the molecule.

105. Drop of Liquid resting on Another Liquid.—When liquids do not spread on other liquids, there is a definite contact angle as with solids, but usually no two of the three surfaces concerned are continuous. Let Fig. 74 represent a drop of one liquid resting on the surface of another, the area of contact being B, the free surface of the drop in contact with air having an area A, and that of the supporting liquid in contact with air, C. When the sides of the containing vessel are very distant from the drop, we may neglect the change in the area separating the liquid and the vessel in considering a small deformation of the system.

Let S_1, S_{12}, S_2 be the surface tensions in the surfaces A, B, C, and θ_1, θ_{12}, θ_2 the angles these surfaces make, respectively, with the x axis at P, where $\theta_2 = \theta_1 + \theta_3$, and suppose that P is displaced to P_1, a point in the xz plane. This displacement may be resolved into components δx and δz along the x and z axes, respectively, and

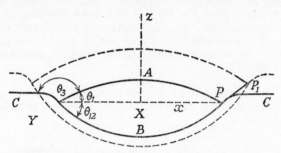

FIG. 74.—LIQUID DROP ON A LIQUID SURFACE.

the sum of the potential energy changes for these two component displacements is equivalent to that taking place during the displacement from P to P_1.

From Article 87 the change of potential energy in the surface A, due to the displacement δx, is

$$\iint \left[g\rho_1 z - S_1 \left(\frac{1}{r_1} + \frac{1}{r_2} \right) \right] \delta l_1 dA + \int S_1 \cos \theta_1 \delta x ds,$$

where ds is an element of the line of contact of the drop on the liquid. Thus the equation of virtual work for the whole system is

$$\iint \left\{ \left[g\rho_1 z - S_1 \left(\frac{1}{r_1} + \frac{1}{r_2} \right) \right] \delta l_1 dA + \left[g\rho_2 z - S_{12} \left(\frac{1}{r_3} + \frac{1}{r_4} \right) \right] \delta l_2 dB \right.$$

$$\left. + \left[g\rho_2 z - S_2 \left(\frac{1}{r_5} + \frac{1}{r_6} \right) \right] \delta l_3 dC \right\}$$

$$+ \int (S_1 \cos \theta_1 + S_{12} \cos \theta_{12} - S_2 \cos \theta_2) \delta x ds = 0,$$

where δl_1, δl_2, δl_3 are the normal displacements of the surfaces A, B, C, and ρ_1, ρ_2 are the densities of the drop and the supporting liquid, respectively. The r terms are the corresponding principal radii of curvature. To the left-hand side of this equation must be added the terms,

$$k_1 \int \delta l_1 dA + k_2 \int \delta l_2 dB + k_3 \int \delta l_3 dC,$$

which are rendered necessary by the constancy of volume in the liquids during the supposed displacement of the system. As before, the coefficients of δl_1, δl_2, δl_3, and also the coefficient of δx, vanish. Hence, for example, we have

$$S_1 \cos \theta_1 + S_{12} \cos \theta_{12} - S_2 \cos \theta_2 = 0 \quad . \quad . \quad (173)$$

Similarly, by considering the displacement, δz, of P along the z axis, the equation of virtual work for the whole system is

$$\iint \left\{ \left[g\rho_1 z - S_1\left(\frac{1}{r_1} + \frac{1}{r_2}\right) \right] \delta l_1' dA + \left[g\rho_2 z - S_{12}\left(\frac{1}{r_3} + \frac{1}{r_4}\right) \right] \delta l_2' dB \right.$$
$$\left. + \left[g\rho_2 z - S_2\left(\frac{1}{r_5} + \frac{1}{r_6}\right) \right] \delta l_3' dC \right\}$$
$$+ \int (S_{12} \sin \theta_{12} - S_1 \sin \theta_1 - S_2 \sin \theta_2) \delta z ds = 0,$$

and so, as before,

$$S_{12} \sin \theta_{12} - S_1 \sin \theta_1 - S_2 \sin \theta_2 = 0 \quad . \quad . \quad (174)$$

Thus, from equations (173) and (174), we see that the three forces S_1, S_{12}, S_2 are in equilibrium, and must therefore be represented by the three sides of a triangle, if the drop is to remain on the surface without spreading. This condition of equilibrium is sometimes referred to as *Neumann's triangle*,[1] and we have

$$S_2 < S_1 + S_{12}.$$

Thus if one liquid rests as a drop on another, without spreading, then none of the three surface tensions is greater than the sum of the other two. The experimental verification of Neumann's triangle is not accurate because the angles, and probably the surface tension of the various liquids resting on another, change with time.

A drop of liquid placed upon the surface of another liquid does not, in general, remain stationary but spreads out into a thin layer. If the liquids in equilibrium are completely miscible, S_{12} tends to become zero and the drop will spread if $S_2 > S_1$. Experiment confirms this rule, that of two completely miscible liquids, the one having the lower surface tension spreads over the other. From Gibbs' Theorem we have seen that a small quantity of a dissolved substance can lower the surface tension greatly, but cannot raise it to any great extent. If a substance raises the tension, its concentration in the surface layer is less than in the bulk of the solution, but on the other hand, if the dissolved substance lowers the surface tension, practically all of it may be contained in the surface. Spreading occurs if $S_2 > S_1 + S_{12}$, and any condition which lowers S_{12} favours spreading. This happens with a dissolved substance which markedly depresses S_{12}. If the substance is soluble in the drop, both S_1 and S_{12} are lowered, and the conditions for spreading are doubly favoured. In the case of substances, which are soluble also in the liquid, the formation of drops is favoured. Adsorption occurs

[1] Neumann, *Vorlesungen uber d. Theorie der Kapillaritat* (1894).

with great ease on mercury surfaces, and such contamination lowers considerably the surface tension. A drop of liquid placed upon such contaminated mercury may not spread if S_2, for the mercury surface, is less than S_1+S_{12}. On the other hand, if the mercury surface is perfectly clean, S_2 may be greater than S_1+S_{12} and spreading occurs.

Harkins has called the difference $S_2-S_1-S_{12}$, or W_a-2S_1, the spreading coefficient of liquid A on liquid C. Since W_a is the work of adhesion of A to C and $2S_1$ the cohesion of A, the condition of spreading is simply that the upper liquid must adhere to the lower one more strongly than it adheres to itself.

Water has a high cohesion and therefore does not spread on organic liquids. The latter have usually a moderate cohesion and spread on water unless the adhesion to water is unusually low. Any diminution of the surface tension of the lower liquid by a film decreases the tendency of the upper liquid to spread. This may be regarded as due to the surface pressure of the film opposing the outward spreading pressure of the liquid A.

The condition for spreading is clearly the same as that for zero contact angle in the liquid A, and is therefore the same as that for complete wetting of a solid surface by a liquid. If A spreads on B, then it is clearly impossible for B to spread on A. It is, however, possible for neither liquid to spread on the other. A non-spreading liquid, such as a heavy paraffin, may be caused to spread on water by dissolving in it a fatty acid, or some substance which increases W_a, the adhesion between the oil and the water. If neither liquid will spread on the other, a denser liquid can be made to float on a lighter one in just the same manner as solid substances, which have a finite contact angle, can float on water.

If the spreading is imagined to take place very slowly, with time allowed for the complete mutual saturation of the upper and lower liquids, the spreading coefficient will gradually diminish, as the surface of the lower liquid C becomes covered by a surface film of liquid A, and its surface tension diminishes. The contact angle remains zero as long as the spreading coefficient is positive, the sum of the two surface tensions S_1+S_{12} being less than S_2. Spreading ceases when S_2 is equal to S_1+S_{12}; at this point the contact angle is still zero, but any further diminution in surface tension of the lower liquid S_2 would result in the angle becoming finite.

Hence in the case of two liquids whose surface and interfacial tensions are such that one would spread on the other before they are mutually saturated, it is to be expected that when they are mutually saturated, one will rest on the other with zero contact angle and

$$S_1+S_{12}=S_2.$$

From this follows Antonow's claim that for two liquids, mutually saturated with each other, interfacial tension is equal to the difference between the surface tensions of the two liquids separately. Summarising we have :—

(a) If $S_1+S_{12}=S_2$, it is evident that the system will be in equilibrium, as no decrease in free energy can take place by the spreading, of the contraction of the drop.

(b) The drop will spread over the surface of the supporting liquid if $S_2>S_1+S_{12}$, as, for example, a drop of ether on water.

(c) The drop assumes the shape of a lens, forming a re-entrant angle with the liquid, if $S_2<S_1+S_{12}$. An example of this is a drop of petroleum placed on water. The actual shape of the drop depends on a complicated balance between spreading coefficients, densities of liquids, and the linear tension round the perimeter of the drop.

(d) Although $S_2>S_1+S_{12}$, the effect of dissolved substances may result in $S_2'<S_1+S_{12}$—where S_2' is the surface tension of the contaminated liquid. This occurs with benzene, or oils containing fatty acids, dropped on water.

It appears then that, in spreading, the drop does not extend as a homogeneous thin lamina but undergoes a superficial solution. If the spreading substance is volatile, it may vaporise from the surface of the liquid and condense on the clean surface. This decreases the free energy of the latter, and we obtain another type of spreading through the vapour phase, even if $S_2<S_1+S_{12}$. For example, carbon sulphide will spread on water by this means.

106. Spreading of Films on Liquids.—When a drop of some fluids is placed upon a clean water surface, a film of small thickness— about 1 micron—rapidly spreads from it in all directions. Hardy,[1] who has investigated the phenomenon, calls this *primary spreading*. In addition, sometimes the drop itself extends into a film, of thickness from 50 to 500 microns, which is in tensile equilibrium with the invisible film. The whole may then settle down into an irregular pattern, the apparent spaces of which are occupied by the invisible film. There are thus two distinct processes, the spreading into the very thin film, and the extension of the drop into a layer. The latter effect is called *secondary spreading*. Drops of certain fluids of low chemical activity and negligible vapour pressure, such as paraffin, can be placed on a clean water surface without the formation of the film.

Hardy placed drops of acetic acid on a glass plate, water vapour being rigorously excluded. Although, apparently, all the drop remained in position, there had, in fact, spread from it an invisible film, and existence of the latter was proved by a measurement of the static friction of the glass surface before and after the drop had been placed upon it.

Secondary spreading occurs when a drop of acetic acid containing water is placed on a glass plate, and if several drops of acetic acid are present on the plate, the existence of the invisible film is

---

[1] Hardy, *Proc. Roy. Soc.*, A, **88**, 316 (1913).

manifested in a curious way. Drops which are not more than one or two centimetres apart attract one another. They become oval in outline, the long axes being directed towards one another, and move slowly across the plate until they meet and coalesce. The invisible film is nowhere greater than 1 micron in thickness, and yet it is capable of pulling larger drops of fluid along.

If a layer of sensible thickness of a pure liquid, such as benzene, is formed on water and allowed to thin or evaporate, a sudden rupture occurs when a critical layer thickness is reached, and the benzene collects into a number of flat discs, or lenses. If evaporation is stopped, these lenses will coalesce into a single large lens surrounded by an area of water, covered with a very thin layer of benzene. The liquid underneath is saturated with benzene, so that the vapour pressure above the lens must be identical with that above the thin layer. The formation of such primary layers on water takes place from the drop itself, only when the sum of the tensions of the upper and lower surfaces of the lenticular drop is considerably less than that of water, or

$$S_2 > S_1 + S_{12}.$$

For example, with oleic acid,

$$74 > 15 + 31.$$

When $S_1 + S_{12}$ is only slightly less than S_2, the drop does not flash over the water surface, but remains apparently unaltered. It is, however, the vapour phase which condenses to form the primary composite surface. Thus, with octane,

$$74 > 20 \cdot 6 + 53.$$

Whether primary, or secondary, spreading does, or does not, occur on a fluid face depends mainly upon the relative values of the surface tensions, but on a clean solid face it must depend wholly upon the vapour tension. If vapour is given off, it will condense to form a primary composite surface, and this, being contractile, may pull the drop itself into a secondary surface. The fact that paraffin and castor oil do not spread at all on clean glass is due to their low vapour tensions, and is no evidence as to the tension of the glass-oil interface.

It has been noted previously that, in the case of the spreading of insoluble oils on water, the thin layer in equilibrium with a lens of an oil, such as oleic acid, is unimolecular in character. Langmuir pointed out that, if the molecules in the film are regularly oriented on the surface of the water owing to the attraction between the latter and the active groups of the organic liquid, such groups as $COOH$ and CH_3OH are dissolved in the water. Long hydrocarbon chains are attached to these groups, and these molecules have no tendency to dissolve, but stand vertically in the surface. There is no particular reason, therefore, for another layer of oil molecules to spread out over the first to form a second layer. Langmuir measured the cross-section and length of the molecules in the surface layer, and showed that in many cases, such as oleic acid, palmitic acid, *etc.*, the length is greater than the cross-section, *i.e.* the molecules are asymmetric. As the chain length increases, the lateral adhesion increases, and the area occupied by two adjacent molecules is reduced. This has been noted experimentally.

As regards the mechanism of the spreading of liquids, Langmuir [1] suggested that the molecules of water cause an expanding movement of the oil drop. The water molecules are in constant motion parallel to the surface, diffusing long distances. The oil molecules adhere to them and are carried outwards along the surface by reason of these surface-diffusing motions. If the liquid is one which spreads stably, then the spread film has a lower potential energy than the drop, so that the molecules which have left the drop to form a film, adhere to the surface—the surface-diffusing motions go on continually being pushed out farther by the surface pressure of those just leaving the drop. If the liquid is a non-spreading one, a few molecules may diffuse out along the surface a little way, but being less stable on the surface than in the drop, they will soon return to the drop, and will not adhere to the surface.

Since the films of fatty acids and other substances appear to be only one molecule in thickness, and to have all the molecules arranged in similar orientation—often simply perpendicular to the surface—measurement of the mechanical properties of films, consisting of a known number of molecules of a pure substance, affords unusually direct information concerning the force fields round individual molecules.

It is very useful to look upon the lowering of the surface tension of water, produced by the presence of an oil film, as being the result of a spreading force F, produced by the action of the adsorbed molecules on one another. This force may be defined as

$$F = S_0 - S,$$

where S_0 is the surface tension of pure water, and S is the surface tension of the water after the introduction of the film.

The spreading force F, which characterises any given adsorbed film, is entirely analogous to the pressure p which a gas or liquid exerts on the walls of a container. The pressure of a gas, or liquid, depends upon the concentration and on the temperature, the relation between these quantities being referred to as an equation of state. F may be measured by a surface tension balance. In this apparatus the surface of water in a long rectangular tray is divided by a floating barrier, which is attached to the pointer of a balance, so arranged that a horizontal force exerted on the barrier can be measured. When there is pure water on both sides of the barrier the balance reads zero. A definite amount of an oil is placed on the water on one side of the barrier, and this is confined in area by a

[1] Langmuir, *Trans. Faraday Soc.*, **17**, 673 (1922).

second barrier parallel to the first. By moving the second barrier the film can be compressed, or extended, so that it exerts a force on the balance and at the same time the area, a, covered by the film can be measured. By progressively changing the area, by moving the second barrier, the force F may be measured in terms of a and the absolute temperature T.

A typical surface tension balance—due to Adam [1]—is illustrated in Fig. 75. The trough A is completely filled with water and the barrier C is a glass strip. The lower torsion wire GG carries a mirror F in a light holder which has a lug projecting downwards to within about 2 mm. from the water surface. The float B is of thin metal foil having a small upward projecting lug J. The upper torsion wire MM has a light rigid framework PRS soldered to its mid-point—the lower end, a stirrup H, coming to about 2 mm. from

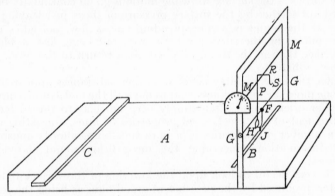

FIG. 75.—SURFACE TENSION TROUGH.

the surface of the water. This stirrup and the two lugs are joined by fine wire so that all three move together when twist is applied to the wire—the tension being secured by means of the torsion head on the lower wire. The upper wire has a large divided torsion head.

The instrument is calibrated by suspending weights on the hook S which forms the end of the framework PRS. Knowing the distance from the end of R to the junction with the wire, and the distance from this place to the bottom of the stirrup, the force in dynes on the centre of the float is determined for a known weight on the hook. From this the force in dynes per cm. on the float can be calculated.

In practice, the surface is first cleared by sweeping the barrier across the water surface. The main torsion head is set to zero, and the spot of light brought to the zero position on the scale. The film-forming substance—preferably dissolved in a solvent immiscible with water—is then put on the water surface, and the spot

[1] Adam, *Proc. Roy. Soc.*, A, **110**, 423 (1926).

of light brought back to the zero position by turning the torsion head. The area of the film may be varied by altering the position of the barrier—the area being bounded by the latter and the float. Forces from 0·01 dyne upwards may be measured with the apparatus.

Any equation which expresses F as a function of a and T is thus an equation of state for the two-dimensional adsorbed film. If the adsorbed molecules do not exert any force on one another, but exert forces only on the barriers which prevent the thermal agitation of the molecules from causing indefinite spreading, then they should behave as an ideal two-dimensional gas. The equation of state should be

$$Fa = kT,$$

or, if a is the area per molecule,

$$F = \sigma kT,$$

where k is Boltzmann's constant, and σ is the number of molecules per unit area in the adsorbed film. Thus these two-dimensional gases should be analogous to a typical three-dimensional one, and experiments by Adam have shown that there are some substances which form films on water that behave in this manner.

The typical films, produced on water by fatty acids and other substances have, however, properties which indicate that they are two-dimensional liquids, or solids, rather than gases, for they do not spread indefinitely, but the value of F becomes zero when the surface concentration σ falls to a definite value. The mechanical properties of these films indicate clearly that they can exist in either the liquid or the solid state. For example, films of fatty acids on water which is slightly alkaline are definitely solid, as is seen from the fact that without external pressure they can withstand considerable shearing stresses. On the other hand, a monomolecular film of cetyl alcohol on water behaves like a two-dimensional liquid, for even under high surface compression it can be made to circulate freely by gently blowing upon it.

When films are below a critical temperature, the value of which depends upon the constitution of the molecules, there is a region of constant surface pressure, apparently analogous to vapour pressure. In this region of constant pressure, the isothermals indicate that there must be two surface phases in equilibrium, liquid and gaseous. The liquid film, to which the gas film condenses, may be either what is termed a *condensed film*, or a *liquid-expanded film*. In the former the molecules are closely packed and oriented nearly perpendicular to the surface. The liquid-expanded films are more compressible, and have a greater area than the condensed films.

The latter are the most closely packed form of films, but a considerable variety of different packings is possible. When the polar group adjacent to the water is small enough, the molecules pack to 20·4 square Angstrom units per molecule under the forces of cohesion alone, without external compression. In the closely-packed-heads type of film the area generally depends upon the nature of the head, and is a measure of the maximum cross-section of the end group, as packed in the films.

Many substances, the amides, acids, bromo-acids and nitriles, condense from the gaseous state of the films into the liquid-expanded film. The area is about 48 square Angstrom units per molecule at no compression; the films are compressible to two-thirds, or less, of this area by forces of the order of 20 dynes per cm. The area of the liquid-expanded film of 48 square Angstrom units does not appear to depend, either upon the length of the chain, or upon the nature of the head; it must therefore be determined by the chain, oriented in such a way that the length does not affect the area. The area of the chain, packed as nearly vertical as possible, is 20·4 square Angstrom units.

In conclusion it may be stated that the experimental facts of surface tension may be interpreted in a qualitative way, by assuming a similar orientation of the surface film of a homogeneous liquid. We may say that the surface phase of pure liquids consists of a layer of oriented molecules with the active portions drawn inwards, and that the total surface energy is determined by the nature of the external groups of the molecules.

107. Contact Angle and Wetting.—The properties of a solid surface may be modified, when it is exposed to the vapour of a liquid, on account of the formation upon it of an adsorbed layer of the liquid. Moreover, the properties of the adsorbed layer differ from those of the liquid in bulk, especially if the liquid is strongly polar, so that there is a high degree of orientation of its molecules. For example, the contact angle between an organic liquid and a hydrophilic solid, *i.e.* a water-attracting one, such as quartz or Pyrex glass, is increased by previous exposure of the solid to water vapour, and the higher the vapour pressure, the greater is the contact angle. In addition, the contact angle in the organic liquid becomes practically independent of the nature of the solid, if the latter is covered with an adsorbed film formed from saturated water vapour, even though, in the absence of the water layer, the angles for the various solids may be very different. If organophilic solid surfaces—organic vapour—attracting ones—are exposed to organic vapours, and measurements made of the contact angle in a water drop on the surface, it sometimes happens that when the liquid is being removed from the drop, that the contact angle becomes zero. This indicates that the advancing water drop has swept the organic film off the solid surface. Taking the case of an organic liquid—of surface tension S_L—on a surface completely covered with a water film—of surface tension S'_W—and assuming that interfacial tension S_{LW} between the water and the drop is the same as that between the two liquids in bulk, we have

$$S'_W = S_{LW} + S_L \cos \theta,$$

where θ is the static contact angle. Calculations carried out for adsorbed organic films indicate that the surface tension of such films is greater than the bulk value in the case of polar liquids, but that there is little difference with non-polar liquids.

A thick film of liquid on a solid surface is not stable. Water poured on a freshly-formed glass surface breaks up into drops, which are separated by a monomolecular layer of water adhering strongly to the glass surface. On the other hand, if water is poured on to a wax surface, the area not occupied by drops is not covered with a monomolecular layer, although the drops themselves are held fixed to the surface by adhesion. This suggests that good and bad " wetting " are characterised, respectively, by the formation, or absence, of the monomolecular film—conditions which in turn are indicated by the time taken for the formation of drops after wetting. Thus rapidly formed drops represent poor " wetting." The hydrophobic, or hydrophilic nature, of the surface of a particular substance depends very much upon the mode of preparation of the surface. Its nature is not likely to be uniform over large areas ; in some places the water-attracting ends of the molecules may be exposed, and in others they may be hidden. This explains the adhesion of water drops to a window pane—the drops attaching themselves to regions where the surface is hydrophilic. Some substances when dissolved in water increase its tendency to wet a given solid surface. One such agent, aerosol O.T. Dry, will overcome the proverbial non-wetability of the duck.

EXAMPLES

1. If the surface tension of mercury is 520 dynes per cm., its angle of contact with glass 140°, its density 13·6 gm. per c.c., find the maximum length of a mercury thread which can be supported by surface tension in a vertical capillary tube of radius 0·010 cm. [1·81 cm.]

2. If the rate of change of the surface energy E of a liquid with temperature is proportional to the absolute temperature T, show that $dE/dT + dS/dT$ is constant, and that the surface tension S is a quadratic function of the temperature.

3. A cylindrical film with closed ends is formed between two wire rings of radius 2 cm., and distance apart 5 cm. Find the volume of air enclosed by the film. [69·7 c.c.]

4. A small hollow vessel which has a small hole in it is immersed in water to a depth of 40 cm. before any water penetrates into the vessel. If the surface tension of water is 73 dynes per cm., find the radius of the hole. [0·0037 cm.]

5. The surface tension of water is calculated by measuring the thickness of the meniscus of a water surface in contact with a vertical plane glass surface. The measurement is made with a travelling microscope reading to 0·005 mm., and is found to be 3·85 mm. Determine the limits within which the surface tension must lie. $g = 981$; density of water 1 gm. per c.c. [71·8 and 73·7 dynes per cm.]

6. A large air bubble is collected between the lower side of a concave glass surface of radius 50 cm. and the upper surface of some ether. The following observations are made : radius of circle of contact of air bubble and glass plate 5 cm., depth of ether surface below centre of glass surface 0·565 cm., height of widest horizontal section of bubble above bottom point 0·225 cm. If the density of ether is 0·714 gm. per c.c. and $g = 981$, find the surface tension of an air-ether surface and the angle of contact between ether and glass. [17·7 dynes per cm. ; $10\frac{1}{2}°$.]

7. A convex lens of which the lower face has a radius of curvature of 40 cm. stands on a flat glass plate, and a little water, surface tension 73 dynes per cm., is run between them. If the angle of contact between water and glass is very small and the wetted surface has a radius of 2 cm., calculate the force due to surface tension with which lens and plate are drawn together. [36·9 gm. wt. ; $3·62 \times 10^4$ dynes.]

8. Calculate the vertical force necessary to detach a horizontal flat circular plate of radius 4 cm. from the surface of a liquid of surface tension 30 dynes per cm., density 1 gm. per c.c., and zero angle of contact. [17·1 gm. wt.]

9. The molecular weight of ether is 74 and its density at 0° C. is 0·737 gm. per c.c. If the surface tension at 0° C. is 19·2 dynes per cm. and the Eötvös constant k is $-2·16$, calculate approximately the critical temperature of ether. If, also, the coefficient of thermal expansion of ether at 0° C. is 0·00163, find the rate of change of surface tension with temperature. [192° C. ; 0·121 dyne per cm. per deg. C.]

10. In a drop-weight determination of the surface tension between water and chloroform a glass tube of 4 mm. external diameter was used and 50 drops of chloroform, density 1·50 gm. per c.c., were allowed to fall in the water. The weight of these drops was 3·43 gm. Find the interfacial surface tension. [29·5 dynes per cm.]

11. If the latent heat of water is 600 calories per gm., its density 1 gm. per c.c., and its surface tension 73 dynes per cm., calculate the minimum radius a drop can have if it is free to evaporate but prevented from receiving heat. [6×10^{-9} cm.]

12. At 100° C. the saturation vapour pressure of water increases by 27 mm. of mercury per 1° C. If water under an external pressure of 76 cm. of mercury has to be superheated to 100·6° C. before boiling occurs, calculate the radius of the largest air bubble available as a vaporisation locus. The surface tension of water at 100° C. is 58·4 dynes per cm. [$3·6 \times 10^{-3}$ cm.]

13. A narrow-bore tube of internal radius r is in the form of an inverted ∪, and at its top point air can be forced in through a tube connected by a T joint. If the vertical limbs stand at depths h_1 and h_2 in two liquids of densities d_1, d_2, and surface tensions S_1, S_2, find the condition that bubbles shall be formed in the liquid of density d_1, and show that as the depth h_1 is increased the bubbling will suddenly change over to the other liquid. [$(h_2 d_2 - h_1 d_1)gr > 2(S_2 - S_1)$.]

14. A capillary tube of internal radius 0·025 cm. stands vertically in water of surface tension 73 dynes per cm. It is then slowly depressed vertically until a length of only 3 cm. is above the outside level. Describe what happens. Would any difference occur (a) if the lowering of

the tube were rapid and (b) if the tube were inclined continuously side-ways, instead of being lowered vertically, until the top is 3 cm. above the outside level ?

[Angle of contact 60° ;   (a) small oscillations ;
(b) radius of meniscus still 0·0496 cm.]

15. A large drop of aniline of radius 3 cm. and sp. gr. 0·975 is sus-pended in water at 75° C., and floats in equilibrium. When slightly deformed the drop oscillates about its mean spherical form with a periodic time of 5·25 sec. Calculate the interfacial surface tension.
[4·71 dynes per cm.]

16. A soap bubble of surface tension 30 dynes per cm. is slowly en-larged from a radius of 2 cm. to a radius of 20 cm. Calculate the amount of work necessary for this enlargement and explain why this is less than if the increase were made at a faster rate.   [2·99 × 10⁵ erg.]

17. Two soap bubbles of radii a and b coalesce to form a single bubble of radius c. If the external pressure is B, show that the surface tension S is given by $B(c^3 - a^3 - b^3)/4(a^2 + b^2 - c^2)$.

18. A soap film of surface tension S has energy e per unit area. If at any subsequent time the mass per unit area of the film is m, show that

$$S = e - m \cdot de/dm.$$

19. One gram of mercury is placed between two plane sheets of glass which are pressed together until the mercury forms a circular disc of uniform thickness and 5 cm. radius. Calculate the force exerted upon the upper plate by the mercury if its surface tension is 440 dynes per cm., its angle of contact 140°, its density 13·6 gm. per c.c.
[5·51 × 10⁷ dynes.]

CHAPTER VII

VISCOSITY

108. Introduction.—It is customary to define a fluid as a substance which is incapable of sustaining shearing stress. In the case of actual fluids, however, this property applies only when the fluid is at rest. If relative motion occurs, a measurable resistance is experienced, and the fluid is said to exhibit *viscosity*, or internal friction. It was assumed by Newton that, for a fluid moving in parallel layers, the shearing stress at any point—where the velocity gradient perpendicular to the direction of motion is $\dfrac{du}{dz}$—is directly proportional to the value of the gradient, so that the frictional force, f, per unit area is given by

$$f = \eta \frac{du}{dz}, \qquad \cdot \quad \cdot \quad \cdot \quad \cdot \quad (175)$$

where η, a characteristic constant for the fluid, is called the *coefficient of viscosity*.

This assumption is found, by experiment, to be true when the fluid is in stream-line motion, but does not hold for turbulence, or disorderly flow.

109. Critical Velocity.—In practically all experiments designed to measure coefficients of viscosity, stream-line flow is assumed to be present, and it is of importance to consider the conditions favourable to its production. With steady flow the work done by the agent causing motion is dissipated, chiefly in overcoming the viscous drag exerted between different layers of the liquid, and thus the viscosity coefficient will affect the critical velocity which marks the transition from stream-line motion into turbulence. The dimensions of the channel through which the liquid flows will also have effect, and, in general, steady motion will continue at higher velocities for viscous than for mobile liquids, and will be aided by restricting the width of the channel. On the other hand, when turbulence occurs, the energy required to produce the motion is used mainly in causing eddy currents, and thus the density of the liquid is involved. Osborne Reynolds showed, by experiment, that the critical velocity v is related to the density ρ of the liquid, its viscosity η, and the lateral dimension r of the channel by the equation

$$v = \frac{k\eta}{\rho r} \qquad \cdot \quad \cdot \quad \cdot \quad \cdot \quad (176)$$

and also that, for narrow tubes, k which is called *Reynold's number*, is approximately 1000.   This formula may be deduced by the method of dimensions as shown in Chapter XV.

For velocities well below the critical value, the rate of flow is independent of the density of the liquid, while for high velocities, *i.e.* under large pressures, the rate of flow depends to a far greater extent on the density than on the viscosity.   This explains the comparatively rapid flow of the very viscous lava during volcanic eruptions.

110. Fugitive Elasticity.—Maxwell [1] regarded viscosity as a limiting case of an elastic solid when the material breaks down under shear.   This conception is a useful one when applied to those substances, such as pitch and sealing-wax, whose behaviour is sometimes that of a solid, but which have also properties characteristic of fluids.   In an elastic solid the shearing stress on any plane is proportional to the displacement gradient, perpendicular to the direction of shear, while the viscous drag in a fluid is proportional to the velocity gradient, perpendicular to the direction of motion. It is thus possible to regard a liquid as capable of exerting and sustaining a certain amount of shearing stress for a short time, after which it breaks down, and the shear recommences.   Suppose the rate at which the shear breaks down is proportional to the magnitude of the shear θ and is given by $\lambda\theta$.   Then, if x is the displacement, the shear is given by $\theta = \dfrac{dx}{dz}$, and the rate of formation of shear is

$$\frac{d\theta}{dt} = \frac{d}{dz}\left(\frac{dx}{dt}\right) = \frac{du}{dz},$$

where u is the velocity in the same plane.   Thus $\lambda\theta = \dfrac{du}{dz}$ and, since the shearing stress f is given by $f = n\theta$, where n is the fugitive rigidity, we have

$$f = \frac{n}{\lambda}\cdot\frac{du}{dz}, \quad \text{or} \quad \eta = \frac{n}{\lambda}.$$

The quantity $\dfrac{1}{\lambda}$ is called the time of relaxation, and measures the time for the shear to disappear if its formation is discontinued.

111. Flow of a Liquid through a Narrow Tube.—When a liquid flows through a narrow tube under a pressure difference P between its ends, and in stream-line motion, a relation may be established between P, the radius a of the tube, its length l, the viscosity coefficient η, and the volume V of liquid flowing through the tube per second.   The stream lines will be parallel to the axis of the tube, and, from Bernoulli's theorem, [2] since there is no radial flow, the pressure will be constant over any given cross-section.   It

---

[1] Maxwell, *Phil. Trans.*, **156** (1866) ; *Scientific Papers*, **2**, 1.
[2] See Article 202.

was further assumed by Poiseuille,[1] who applied this method to a series of accurate viscosity determinations, that the liquid in contact with the walls of the tube was at rest. This assumption has been proved by experiment to be correct.

Suppose that, when steady conditions are reached, the velocity at a distance r from the axis of the tube is u. Then the velocity gradient is $\dfrac{du}{dr}$, and the viscous drag per sq. cm. is $\eta\dfrac{du}{dr}$. This acts over the surface of the inner cylinder of liquid in a direction opposed to the pressure gradient. The force, due to the pressure difference, tending to accelerate this liquid cylinder is $P\pi r^2$ and, for steady conditions,

$$P\pi r^2 = -\eta\frac{du}{dr}2\pi rl,$$

or,

$$-rdr = \frac{2\eta l}{P}du \qquad . \qquad . \qquad . \qquad (177)$$

At the wall of the tube $r=a$ and $u=0$, so, integrating from $r=a$ to $r=r$, we have

$$a^2 - r^2 = \frac{4\eta l}{P}u,$$

or,

$$u = \frac{P}{4\eta l}(a^2 - r^2) \qquad . \qquad . \qquad . \qquad (178)$$

This gives the velocity at any distance from the axis of the tube
The volume dV of liquid which flows through the tube per second between the radii r and $r+dr$ is given by

$$dV = 2\pi r dr \cdot u = \frac{P\pi}{2\eta l}(a^2 - r^2)rdr,$$

and the total volume V flowing through the tube per second is

$$V = \int_0^a \frac{P\pi}{2\eta l}(a^2 - r^2)rdr = \frac{P\pi a^4}{8\eta l} . \qquad . \qquad . \qquad (179)$$

112. Corrections to Poiseuille's Formula.—Although equation (179) represents approximately the flow through a long narrow tube, under a pressure difference sufficiently small for the liquid to drop from the outlet end, in accurate work it is necessary to insert corrections for two factors which have been neglected in the treatment above. In the first place, the pressure difference P is utilised partly in communicating kinetic energy to the liquid, and, secondly, it has been assumed that there are no accelerations along the axis of the tube. This second condition is not fulfilled near the inlet end of the tube, as the accelerations do not decrease to zero value until

---

[1] Poiseuille, *Comptes Rendus*, 15, 1167 (1842).

an appreciable length of the flow tube has been traversed, after which the velocity distribution becomes uniform. To correct for this error, the value of l is increased by a factor $k_1 a$, where k_1 is a constant which may be taken to be 1·64 in all cases.

To evaluate the other correction factor, suppose that P_1 is the effective pressure difference which overcomes viscosity. In one second the work done against viscosity is $P_1 V$, while the kinetic energy given to the liquid is

$$\left.\begin{aligned}
\int_0^a \tfrac{1}{2}\rho . 2\pi r dr . u . u^2 &= \pi\rho\left(\frac{P_1}{4\eta l}\right)^3 \int_0^a r(a^2-r^2)^3 dr \\
&= \pi\rho\left(\frac{P_1}{4\eta l}\right)^3 \frac{a^8}{8} = \left(\frac{P_1\pi a^4}{8\eta l}\right)^3 \frac{\rho}{\pi^2 a^4} .
\end{aligned}\right\} \text{from (178)}$$

The total loss of energy is

$$P_1 V + \frac{V^3\rho}{\pi^2 a^4},$$

and thus must equal PV. Hence

$$P_1 = P - \frac{V^2\rho}{\pi^2 a^4}.$$

This correction has been investigated experimentally, notably by Hagenbach, Couette, and Wilberforce, and has been found to render results more consistent and accurate. It is, however, only approximately true, and the correction should be

$$P_1 = P - \frac{k_2 V^2\rho}{\pi^2 a^4},$$

where k_2 is a constant whose value depends upon the form of apparatus, and, although always nearly unity, its value must, for the most accurate work, be obtained by calibration.

When these two corrections are applied to Poiseuille's formula, (179), it becomes

$$\left[P - \frac{V^2\rho k_2}{\pi^2 a^4}\right]\pi a^4 = 8\eta[l + k_1 a]V,$$

or,

$$\eta = \frac{P\pi a^4}{8V[l + 1\cdot 64a]} - \frac{V\rho k_2}{8\pi[l + 1\cdot 64a]} \qquad . \qquad . \qquad (180)$$

The coefficient η is sometimes called the *dynamic viscosity* and its C.G.S. unit is named the *poise*, but the ratio $\dfrac{\eta}{\rho}$ is called the *kinematic viscosity* and the name *stokes* has been suggested for its C.G.S. unit.

113. Measurement of the Viscosity of Water.—The direct application of this equation to the measurement of the viscosity coefficient for water may be made with fair accuracy by means of the apparatus shown in Fig. 76. A is a moderately large vessel in which water is maintained at a constant level by the inflow and outlet tubes B and C. The capillary tube DE, of length l and radius a, is fixed horizontally at a depth h below the free surface in A. The volume, V, of water flowing per second is obtained by collection, during a measured time, in a weighed vessel. The total pressure difference P is given by $P = g\rho h$, and thus all the quantities in equation (180), except η, are known.

A modification of the experiment may be used to determine the variation of η with temperature. In Fig. 77, A is a wide vessel con-

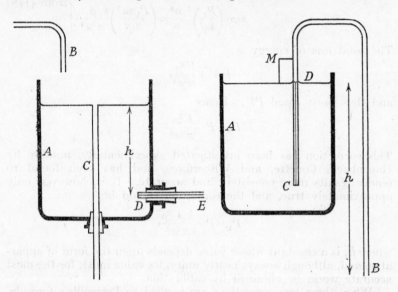

FIG. 76.—MEASUREMENT OF VISCOSITY   FIG. 77.—VISCOSITY OF LIQUIDS
COEFFICIENTS FOR LIQUIDS.   AND TEMPERATURE.

taining water, or other liquid, at a measured temperature, while the outflow tube BDC has a fairly wide bore from B to D, and DC is the capillary tube. An index point M is fastened to the tube on the same level as D, and as the level of liquid in A falls slowly, the tube BDC is lowered to keep M just touching the surface. The excess pressure P is given by $P = g\rho h$, where h is the vertical distance between B and D.

114. Effect of Temperature on the Viscosity of Liquids.—
The viscosity of liquids is dependent on temperature to a very marked extent, but although the relationship has been the subject of many investigations, no satisfactory simple formula has been suggested to express the connection with any great degree of accuracy. The

empirical formula of Slotte,

$$\eta_t = \frac{\eta_0}{1 + at + bt^2},$$

is not very accordant with experiment, while a modification,

$$\eta_t = \frac{A}{(1 + Bt)^c},$$

where A, B, and c are constants, though applicable to pure liquids, is inconveniently cumbersome, and does not apply to the important practical case of oils, which are mixtures of chemical compounds not easily separable.

In Andrade's theory [1] of liquid viscosities it is suggested, on certain assumptions of the mechanism of liquid viscosity, that a temperature relation of the form $\eta = Ae^{\frac{c}{T}}$ applies as a first approximation, A and c being constants. This formula gives very fair agreement with experimental results, and satisfies the empirical criterion pointed out by Porter [2] that if T and T_0 are two temperatures at which two liquids have the same viscosity, then the graph of $\frac{T}{T_0}$ against T is a straight line. A more detailed application of Andrade's theory gives the more complex viscosity-temperature relation :—

$$\eta v^{\frac{1}{3}} = Ae^{\frac{c}{vT}},$$

in which v is the specific volume. This formula agrees closely with the results for many liquids.

In Table X the viscosity coefficient for water is given at various temperatures.

TABLE X.—VARIATION OF THE VISCOSITY OF WATER WITH TEMPERATURE

Temp. °C.	Viscosity, C.G.S. units.	Temp. °C.	Viscosity, C.G.S. units.
0	0·01793	40	0·00657
5	0·01522	50	0·00550
10	0·01311	60	0·00469
15	0·01142	70	0·00406
20	0·01006	80	0·00356
25	0·00893	90	0·00316
30	0·00800	100	0·00284

115. Torque on a Cylinder placed in a Rotating Fluid.— If a cylinder is suspended inside a coaxial cylinder, which is made to rotate about the common axis with constant angular velocity, and the space between the two cylinders is filled with a viscous

[1] Article 122.
[2] Porter, *Phil. Mag.*, **23**, 458 (1912).

fluid, a measurement of the viscosity may be obtained from the couple which acts on the stationary cylinder. Suppose the inner and outer cylinders have radii a and b, respectively, and the fluid covers a length l of the inner one. The inmost layer of fluid will be at rest, while the outer layer has a speed $b\omega_1$, where ω_1 is the angular velocity of the external cylinder. Consider the forces acting over the side of the fluid cylinder whose radius is r, where r is intermediate in value between a and b. The velocity gradient at the distance r from the centre will be

$$\frac{d}{dr}(r\omega)=\omega+r\frac{d\omega}{dr},$$

but of these terms only the second one is operative in producing viscosity effects, since the velocity gradient ω is necessary to *prevent* any relative slipping in a uniformly rotating fluid. Thus the viscous torque τ_1, acting over the side of the cylinder of radius r, will be

$$\tau_1=2\pi rl.r.\eta.r\frac{d\omega}{dr}=2\pi\eta lr^3\frac{d\omega}{dr},$$

and, since the fluid between this boundary and the inner cylinder is in a steady state, τ_1 must also be the torque on the inner cylinder. Thus

$$\tau_1\frac{dr}{r^3}=2\pi\eta ld\omega,$$

and, if this is integrated between the limits a and b, we have, assuming no slipping,

$$\tau_1\left[\frac{1}{a^2}-\frac{1}{b^2}\right]=4\pi\eta l\omega_1, \qquad . \qquad . \qquad . \quad (181)$$

τ_1, however, gives merely the torque over the side of the cylinder. There is also a couple τ_2, due to viscosity, acting over the bottom surface. The magnitude of this will depend on the values of a and b and the distance between the bases of the two cylinders. If this distance remains fixed while the length of the inner cylinder acted upon by the fluid varies, τ_2 retains the same value and may be expressed by $\tau_2=f(a, b)$. Thus, for two different lengths of the inner cylinder,

$$\tau=\tau_1+\tau_2=\frac{4\pi\eta.\omega_1.a^2b^2}{b^2-a^2}l_1+f(a, b),$$

$$\tau'=\tau_1'+\tau_2=\frac{4\pi\eta.\omega_1.a^2b^2}{b^2-a^2}l_2+f(a, b),$$

whence

$$\tau-\tau'=\frac{4\pi\eta.\omega_1.a^2b^2}{b^2-a^2}[l_1-l_2].$$

This expression, derived from first principles, applies equally to liquids and gases, and may be used over a considerable range. In the case of liquids, the change from l_1 to l_2 is made by increasing the liquid used in the first determination, while, for gases, two cylinders are used of the same cross-section but of different lengths. The torques τ and τ' are generally measured by the twist produced in a suspension of known tor-sional rigidity.

G. F. C. Searle [1] has described a simple viscometer for the measurement of the viscosity coefficient for very viscous liquids, which is a modification of the rotating cylinder method. In Fig. 78 a solid cylinder C, of radius a, is fixed to an axle AB which is pivoted freely at its ends. Attached to the same spindle are a disc F and a drum K. The former is used, in conjunction with an index G, to measure the rotation period of C under the combined action of the two weights mg and the viscous friction of the liquid L. The weights are supported by flexible strings which pass over

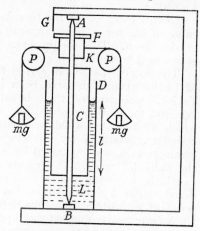

FIG. 78.—SEARLE'S EXPERIMENT TO DETERMINE THE VISCOSITY OF VISCOUS LIQUIDS.

ball-bearing pulleys PP. An outer cylinder D, of radius b, contains the liquid, and a length l of the cylinder C is acted upon by the viscosity drag. In the experiment the period t_0 of rotation of C is measured.

If the steady angular velocity of C is ω_1, then—neglecting the end effect—we have, from equation (181),

$$\omega_1 = \frac{\tau}{4\pi\eta l}\left[\frac{1}{a^2} - \frac{1}{b^2}\right],$$

where τ is the couple due to gravity and η is the viscosity coefficient of the liquid. If d is the diameter of K, since $\omega_1 t_0 = 2\pi$,

$$\eta = \frac{gd(b^2 - a^2)}{8\pi^2 a^2 b^2} \cdot \frac{mt_0}{l} \qquad . \qquad . \qquad . \qquad (182)$$

Thus, if the end correction is negligibly small, the graph of mt_0 and l should be a straight line passing through the origin. Actually, this curve, which is linear, intersects the l axis on the negative side of the origin, showing that the term l should be corrected to $(l+k)$, where k is obtained from the curve. Equation (182) then becomes

$$\eta = \frac{gd(b^2 - a^2)}{8\pi^2 a^2 b^2} \cdot \frac{mt_0}{(l+k)},$$

and all the quantities, except η, are known. Searle used liquids

[1] Searle, *Proc. Camb. Phil. Soc.*, **16**, 600 (1912).

of large viscosity—syrup and treacle—and thus comparatively large values—about 30 sec.—were obtained for t_0 when the other constants were $a=1\cdot9$ cm., $b=2\cdot5$ cm., $m=100$ gm., $l=6\cdot4$ cm., and $d=1\cdot91$ cm.

In this case, as for the flow in a tube, there will be a limiting value of ω_1, for a given apparatus, beyond which the simple law breaks down. This occurs when the assumed stream-line motion ceases and turbulence begins.

The conditions which govern the transition point from orderly to turbulent motion have been investigated, mathematically, by Taylor,[1] who showed that, beyond a certain fixed value of the velocity, the motion changed into a form containing helical vortices, which were located within compartments, in the space between the cylinders, produced by consecutive planes perpendicular to the common axis, and separated by a distance approximately equal to the radii difference. This result was confirmed by an experiment in which, following the method of Reynolds, the motion was rendered visible by the introduction of a little coloured liquid. The onset of turbulence was thus determined.

An alternative method was described by Andrade and Lewis [2] and appears to have many advantages, since it may be applied to other cases of liquid flow. Using a coaxial cylinder apparatus, Andrade and Lewis introduced suspended colloidal particles into the liquid. This enabled them to illuminate any portion, and to study its behaviour either visually or photographically. The advantages of this method are : (1) the motion may be studied for any length of time, since the transitory effect of interdiffusion, which limits the other method, is avoided ; and (2) the velocity distribution may be found by giving a known exposure, in which case each particle shows a distance of travel proportional to its velocity.

116. Viscosity of Very Viscous Liquids.—A simple method of determining the viscosity of very viscous liquids is one which depends on Stokes' Law.[3] According to this law, the resistance P, due to viscosity, acting on a small sphere falling through the liquid, is given by $P=6\pi\eta rv$, where v is the velocity, η, the viscosity, and r, the radius of the sphere. In such a case of resisted fall, the body attains a terminal velocity which then remains constant, the retarding viscous drag being equal to the gravitational force, i.e.

$$6\pi\eta rv = \tfrac{4}{3}\pi r^3 g(\rho-\sigma), \qquad \cdot \qquad \cdot \qquad \cdot \qquad (183)$$

where ρ and σ are the densities of the sphere and liquid, respectively. Thus, by measuring the terminal velocity v, a value is obtained for η. Stokes' formula is true only if vr is small compared with η, and this rule affords a test of its application in any special case. The viscous drag, $6\pi\eta rv$, is deduced for a sphere falling in an infinite ocean of

[1] Taylor, *Phil. Trans.*, A, **223**, 289 (1923).
[2] Andrade and Lewis, *Journ. Sci. Inst.*, **1**, 373 (1924).
[3] Stokes, *Collected Papers*, **3**, 1.

the liquid, and in a practical case there will be two corrective factors, due to boundary conditions at the walls and bottom of the cylinder containing the liquid. If the length of liquid is divided into three equal parts, and the centre one of these is used for the velocity measurement, then, as was shown by Ladenburg,[1] to correct for the wall effect, the true velocity v_∞ is given by

$$v_\infty = v\left(1 + 2\cdot 4\frac{r}{R}\right),$$

where v is the observed velocity, R is the radius of the vessel, and v_∞ is the velocity in a medium of infinite width.

To correct for the end effect,

$$v_\infty = v\left(1 + 3\cdot 3\frac{r}{h}\right),$$

where h is the total height of the liquid. Thus the corrected formula is

$$\eta = \frac{2}{9}\frac{(\rho - \sigma)gr^2}{v\left(1 + 2\cdot 4\dfrac{r}{R}\right)\left(1 + 3\cdot 3\dfrac{r}{h}\right)} \qquad . \qquad . \qquad . \qquad (184)$$

A more accurate form of the wall correction, due to Faxen, has been verified by Bacon[2] in the form :—

$$v = v_\infty\left[1 - 2\cdot 104\left(\frac{r}{R}\right) + 2\cdot 1\left(\frac{r}{R}\right)^3 - 0\cdot 95\left(\frac{r}{R}\right)^5\right].$$

A good method of producing very small spheres is to blow melted Wood's metal through the fine aperture of a glass tube into cold water. The radii of these spheres may be measured by means of a microscope.

117. Effect of Pressure on the Viscosity of Liquids.—With fairly mobile liquids the effect of pressure on viscosity is small. For example, at 20° C. the viscosity of ether is raised by about 60 per cent. for an increase of 500 atmospheres, while with water at atmospheric temperature, the viscosity decreases for the first few hundred atmospheres. With some liquids, however, the effect is much greater— *e.g.* for liquids of large viscosity, such as mineral oils, the ratio of the coefficients under 1 and 1,000 atmospheres is of the order 1 to 10, and with all liquids, except water, the effect of pressure increases at higher pressures. For pressures up to about 2,000 atmospheres, Andrade's theory gives reasonably good agreement with the experimental results obtained by Bridgman,[3] the formula connecting η with pressure being :—

$$\frac{\eta_p}{\eta_1} = \left(\frac{v_1}{v_p}\right)^{\frac{1}{6}}\sqrt{\frac{K_p}{K_1}} \cdot e^{\frac{c}{T}\left(\frac{1}{v_p} - \frac{1}{v_1}\right)}$$

[1] Ladenburg, *Ann. der Physik.*, **23**, 9, 447 (1907).
[2] Bacon, *Jour. Franklin. Inst.*, **221**, 251 (1936).
[3] Bridgman, *Proc. Amer. Acad.*, **11**, 603 (1925).

where v is the specific volume and K is the adiabatic bulk modulus. At high pressures it would be unreasonable to anticipate any good agreement since, in these circumstances, the molecules undergo deformation.

118. Torque on a Disc in the Surface of a Rotating Liquid. —A method of measuring viscosity coefficients, which is very similar to that of the rotating cylinder, is based on the couple which acts on a suspended disc when it is in contact with a rotating fluid. Two discs are mounted coaxially, and the lower one is made to rotate with angular velocity ω. A layer of fluid between them will suffer no slipping at either disc, and thus the vertical velocity gradient at a distance r from the common axis will be, on an average, $\dfrac{r\omega}{x}$, where x is the separation distance between the discs. Thus the elementary torque $d\tau$, acting on an annulus, radius r and width dr, of the upper disc, is

$$d\tau = 2\pi r\, dr \frac{r\omega}{x} \eta r,$$

and, for the total torque τ,

$$\tau = \int_0^a \frac{2\pi\eta\omega}{x} r^3\, dr = \frac{\pi\eta\omega a^4}{2x}, \qquad . \qquad . \qquad . \qquad (185)$$

where a is the radius of the upper disc.

This relation is only approximate, because the average velocity gradient $\dfrac{r\omega}{x}$ is not necessarily that at the surface of the disc, and also because, at the edge of the disc, the distribution of stream lines is complex. To reduce error arising from this second effect, it is usual to mount a guard ring around the suspended disc, of sufficient width to reduce the edge effect to a minimum.

This method, also, is applicable to both liquids and gases, and, of course, has similar restrictions on the maximum value of ω as in the case of the rotating cylinder experiment.

119. Damping due to Viscosity.—If a body is oscillating in a viscous fluid, its motion will be damped by the internal friction of the medium, and the corresponding logarithmic decrement affords a measure of the viscosity. The calculation of the effect is not a simple one, and readers may be referred to Maxwell's treatment of the problem.[1] The method, which is again applicable to both liquids and gases, has been used by Maxwell,[1] Coulomb, and Meyer,[2] the formula given by the latter for use with liquids being

$$\eta = \frac{16M^2}{\pi\rho t_0 (R^4 + 2R^3\delta)^2}\left[\frac{\lambda_1 - \lambda_0}{\pi} + \left(\frac{\lambda_1 - \lambda_0}{\pi}\right)^2\right]^2,$$

[1] Maxwell, *Collected Papers*, **2**, 1.
[2] Meyer, *Pogg. Ann.*, **113**, 55 (1861).

where

$$M=\text{moment of inertia of the suspended system,}$$
R and $\delta=$radius and thickness of the disc,
$\quad t_0=$periodic time in air,
λ_0 and $\lambda_1=$logarithmic decrements in air and in the liquid
$\qquad$ respectively,
$\quad \rho=$density of the liquid.

Meyer's theoretical deduction of this formula is not above criticism, but it may be regarded as an empirical formula which accords well with measurements made by other methods.

TABLE XI.—VISCOSITY COEFFICIENTS (LIQUIDS)

Liquid.	Viscosity. C.G.S. units.	Temp. °C.	Liquid.	Viscosity. C.G.S. units.	Temp. °C.
Mercury	0·0170	0	Benzene	0·00759	10
	0·0157	20		0·00649	20
	0·0122	100		0·00562	30
Glycerine	42·2	3	Ether	0·00258	10
	8·30	20		0·00234	20
	4·94	26·5		0·00212	30
Olive oil	0·989	15	Turpentine (dens. 0·87)	0·0178	10
Rape oil	3·85	10		0·0149	20
	1·63	20		0·0127	30
	0·96	30	Carbon di-oxide (liq.)	0·00089	0
Aniline	0·0440	20		0·00085	10
	0·0319	30		0·00071	20
	0·0241	40	Black treacle	400	12·3
Chloroform	0·00626	10	Glacier ice	12×10^{13}	—
	0·00564	20	Pitch	$1\cdot3\times10^{10}$	15
	0·00511	30	Soda glass	11×10^{12}	575
Sulphuric acid (dens. 1·03)	0·00973	25		4×10^{10}	710

Other applications of the damping, produced by viscosity as a means for measuring η, are Stokes'[1] decrement measurements for a pendulum vibrating in a fluid, and Helmholtz's and Piotrowski's determinations of the damped vibrations of a hollow sphere filled with the liquid and oscillating about a diameter. This last method has been examined anew by Andrade and Chiong[2] and a more satisfactory formula obtained for the torque on a revolving sphere, due to the viscosity of an internal liquid. This was utilised as a means of measuring the viscosity by observing, either the resultant logarithmic decrement, or the necessary electrical energy which will maintain the torsional oscillations at constant angular amplitude.

120. Commercial Viscometers.—The absolute determination of viscosity, necessitating an exact measurement of the dimensions

[1] Stokes, *Trans. Camb. Phil. Soc.*, **9**, 8 (1850).
[2] Andrade and Chiong, *Proc. Phys. Soc.*, **48**, 247, 261 (1936).

of the viscometer, is laborious, and in industrial practice some simpler instrument is used and calibrated by means of liquids of known viscosity. Such instruments, known as commercial viscometers, make use of either the capillary flow or rotational torque principle. Of the former the best known, and most widely used, is that due to Ostwald. It comprises a U-tube, of which one side is occupied by the capillary tube, and its use involves the time of fall of the meniscus from one fixed mark to another, the instrument containing a standard volume of the liquid. In these circumstances the operative formula is

$$k = \frac{\eta}{\rho} = At - \frac{B}{t},$$

k being the kinematic viscosity, t the time of flow, A, B instrumental constants. For liquids of high viscosity the second term, which is the kinetic energy correction, is very small and, if it is neglected, the ratio of kinematic viscosities is simply $\frac{k_1}{k_2} = \frac{t_1}{t_2}$ which was the formula used by Ostwald. It is, however, much more satisfactory to calibrate with more than one liquid and to obtain the graph of k against t.

In England the Redwood [1] viscometer is widely used. It comprises a cylindrical vessel in the bottom of which is a small capillary outlet, drilled through an agate plug, 1 cm. long and 1·5 mm. diameter. All the dimensions are standardised, and the time is taken for the level of liquid to fall between two fixed marks. In testing the instrument at the National Physical Laboratory it was found that, as suggested by theory, a graph of $\frac{k}{t}$ against $\frac{1}{t^2}$ was a straight line, the intercept giving A and the slope B. The values obtained were $A = 0 \cdot 00260$ and $B = 1 \cdot 715$ in C.G.S. units. During the test the apparatus is surrounded by a constant-temperature bath. The Engler [2] viscometer, widely used on the Continent, operates in a similar manner, as also does the Saybolt instrument designed by the Standard Oil Company and used in the United States.[3] If only a small quantity of the liquid is available, the Michell, cup and ball, instrument is available. A few drops of liquid are placed in a hemispherical cup, which is then inverted over a steel ball, internal contact being prevented by three small projections. The whole is then lifted, and the time is measured for which the sphere is held in position. A graph connects the viscosity with this time.

121. Viscosity of Colloidal Solutions.—The theoretical treatment of the viscosity of colloidal solutions is one of considerable difficulty. If the usual definition of η, equation (175), is employed,

[1] Redwood, *Chem. Ind. Soc. J.*, **5**, 121 (1886).
[2] Engler, *Zeits. Chem.*, **9**, 189 (1885).
[3] Bureau of Standards, *Tech. Paper* No. 100 (1917), No. 112 (1918).

i.e. if it is assumed that the frictional force between contiguous layers is proportional to the velocity gradient, then the experiments show that η is not a constant independent, for example, of the pressure difference between the ends of a flow tube. This may be expressed by saying that the apparent viscosity decreases with increasing pressure in the capillary tube experiment, or increasing angular velocity in the concentric cylinder experiment. In other words the viscosity coefficient must be assumed to vary according to some function of the velocity gradient. Many attempts have been made to formulate such a relationship,[1] but it is likely that little progress will be made until some method, analogous to that of Andrade and Lewis, is available for a point to point study of the moving liquid.

In this connection it is relevant to mention the study of thixotropy, or the property possessed by gels of changing from a jelly or semi-solid state into the fluid form as a result of agitation, by means of viscometers.[2] The quantity generally measured in such experiments is the apparent viscosity, but it is not easy to assess the significance of a quantity, defined on the assumption of equation (175) when, in all probability, that assumption does not apply.

122. Andrade's Theory of Liquid Viscosity.—It was suggested by Andrade[3] that, since the viscosity of liquids decreases with rising temperature, the mechanism of its occurrence must differ from that in gases, and a simple momentum interchange process is inadequate. The molecular spacing, and therefore the density and molecular force intensity, cannot be greatly different in liquids and solids, particularly at low temperatures, and thus many of the characteristics of solid molecular qualities must survive in the liquid. Among these Andrade assumes to be the normal frequency of vibration about the equilibrium position which however is liable, as a result of fluidity, to movement. There is, in no real sense, a liquid mean free path, but the amplitude of vibrational movement is taken to be larger than in the solid, and sufficient for molecules in adjacent laminæ with relative velocity to come into contact and by this method of interaction to share momenta. Thus the manner by which interlayer force is produced has similarities with the kinetic theory explanation of gaseous viscosity, but the frequency of such interchange, and the factors determining its efficiency, are derived from the theory of solids. When the temperature changes it will affect several of the relevant factors, but chiefly the probability that the contacts of adjacent molecules will be effective in the momentum sharing. The time of mutual association will depend on mutual molecular orientation on encounter, and this will be less regular at higher temperatures. If this is alone considered as the temperature effect on viscosity, the simpler exponential expression of Article 114

[1] See Hatschek, *The Viscosity of Liquids*, p. 211 (1928).
[2] Pryce Jones, *Journ. Oil and Colour Chem. Assocn.*, **17**, 305 (1934).
[3] Andrade, *Phil. Mag.*, **17**, 497, 698 (1934).

results. In addition, however, two smaller effects are taken into account; the change in molecular spacing which affects the specific volume and the change in vibrational frequency. The first is allowed for in the second formula of the same article, but an incorporation of a frequency change produces results less in accord with experimental data. It is interesting that this is the case also for solids.

To account for the effect of pressure, Andrade uses the previously obtained relationship of the viscosity with vibrational frequency which, in the theory of solids, is connected with the adiabatic bulk modulus. The constant A of the previous formulæ includes the vibrational frequency, and taking account of its variation with density, Andrade defines another constant A' by

$$A'v^{\frac{1}{3}} = A\sqrt{K},$$

K being the adiabatic bulk modulus. The substitution of this modification into the previous formula gives the final expression stated in Article 117.

123. Flow of a Compressible Fluid through a Narrow Tube.—In deducing Poiseuille's formula it was assumed that the volume crossing any section of the tube was constant. This is the same as supposing that the density is independent of the pressure, and although true for liquids, it is not the case for compressible fluids, *i.e.* gases. For these, it is the mass which crosses any section in a given time which is constant, *i.e.*

$$\rho \alpha v = constant,$$

where ρ is the density at a point in the section, area α, of a tube of flow and v is the velocity. The product αv is the volume flowing through the area per second. Considering an element of the tube of length dx, if the difference in pressure between its ends is dP, then from (179) the volume V leaving the element per second is given by

$$V = -\frac{\pi a^4}{8\eta} \cdot \frac{dP}{dx}, \qquad . \qquad . \qquad . \qquad (186)$$

the negative sign being used, since P decreases as x increases. If P_1 is the pressure at the inlet end, and V_1 is the volume entering the tube per second, then, since the cross-sectional area is constant, $P_1V_1 = PV$, and

$$P_1V_1 = -\frac{\pi a^4}{8\eta} \cdot P\frac{dP}{dx},$$

so that

$$\int_0^l P_1V_1 dx = -\frac{\pi a^4}{8\eta}\int_{P_1}^{P_2} P dP,$$

where P_2 is the pressure at the outlet end of the tube. Hence

$$P_1V_1 = \frac{(P_1{}^2 - P_2{}^2)\pi a^4}{16\eta l} \qquad . \qquad . \qquad (187)$$

124. Viscosity of Gases.—Grindley and Gibson [1] determined the viscosity of a gas by noting the pressure difference between the ends of a flow tube, through which the gas streamed from one container to another. The flow was produced by forcing water into one container, and thus the volume passing through per second was known. The coefficient of viscosity was then calculated from (187). The flow tube and containers could be raised to any desired temperature between $0°$ C. and $100°$ C., and it was found that the variation in η agreed closely with Sutherland's theoretical formula,[2]

$$\eta = \eta_0 \frac{k\sqrt{T}}{1 + \dfrac{C}{T}},$$

and was independent of the pressure. Both of these results are in accordance with the predictions of the kinetic theory of gases.

The value of η for air may be determined by means of the following simple experiment. One side of a U-tube consists of tubing—radius about $1{\cdot}5$ mm.—while the other side is a capillary tube of length l and radius a. The excess pressure at the lower end of the latter is produced by means of a pellet of mercury, weight mg. The time t, taken by the pellet to fall between two marks on the wider tube, is noted. If Q is the volume between these marks, then the volume of air, V_1, passing through the capillary tube per second is $\dfrac{Q}{t}$. The pressure P_1 at the entrance end is $P_1 = B + b - \delta$, where B is the atmospheric pressure, b the pressure due to the pellet, *i.e.* $\dfrac{mg}{\pi r^2}$, and δ the sticking coefficient, or virtual reduction of the excess pressure due to friction between the pellet and the walls of the fall tube. If these values of P_1 and V_1 are inserted in (187), we have

$$(B + b - \delta)\frac{Q}{t} = \frac{(B + b - \delta)^2 - B^2}{16\eta l}\pi a^4,$$

or,

$$Q = \frac{\pi a^4 t}{16\eta l}\left[(B + b - \delta) - B\left(1 + \frac{b - \delta}{B}\right)^{-1}\right]$$

$$= \frac{\pi a^4 t}{16\eta l}\left[B + b - \delta - B + b - \delta - \frac{b^2}{B}\right],$$

ignoring terms in $\dfrac{\delta}{B}$. Thus

$$Q = \frac{\pi a^4 t}{8\eta l}\left[b - \frac{b^2}{2B} - \delta\right],$$

or,

$$\left[b - \frac{b^2}{2B} - \delta\right]t = const = \frac{8\eta l Q}{\pi a^4}. \qquad . \qquad . \qquad (188)$$

[1] Grindley and Gibson, *Proc. Roy. Soc.*, A, 80, 114 (1908).
[2] See Articles 126, 133.

If experiments are carried out with two pellets of different sizes and the times of fall are t and t_1, we have

$$\left[b-\frac{b^2}{2B}-\delta\right]t=\left[b_1-\frac{b_1{}^2}{2B}-\delta\right]t_1,$$

and thus δ is determined and may be inserted in (188) to give η.

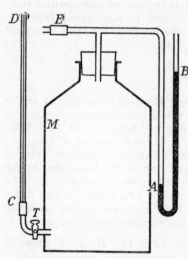

FIG. 79.—SEARLE'S METHOD OF DETERMINING THE VISCOSITY OF AIR.

Another method, suggested by Searle,[1] may be carried out with the apparatus shown in Fig. 79. A large vessel M, of volume V, is filled with air through a cycle valve E, until the initial difference in level, h_1, between A and B of the mercury manometer, is somewhat less than that for which turbulent flow occurs. When the gauge readings have become steady the tap is opened, for a measured time, and is then closed. The new difference in level, h_2, is then recorded. Suppose P_1 and P_2 are the pressures in M at the beginning and end of the experiment, and let P be the pressure at an interval t after the gas has commenced to flow. Then

$$P_1=(H+h_1)dg,$$
$$P_2=(H+h_2)dg,$$
$$P=(H+h)dg,$$

H being the height of the barometer, and h the difference in the mercury levels after a time t sec. Let V_1 be the volume of air entering the capillary tube CD per second at time t. In the interval dt the pressure changes to $P+dP$, and for a slow rate of flow

$$(P+dP)(V+V_1dt)=PV,$$

or,

$$V\frac{dP}{dt}=-PV_1.$$

But, from (187),

$$PV_1=\frac{P^2-B^2}{16\eta l}\pi a^4,$$

where $B=Hdg$. Hence

$$\frac{dP}{P^2-B^2}=-\frac{\pi a^4}{16\eta lV}dt=Adt,$$

[1] G. F. C. Searle, *Camb. Phil. Soc. Proc.*, **17**, 183 (1912).

A being written for the constant $-\dfrac{\pi a^4}{16\eta l V}$. Thus

$$2BAt = \int_{P_1}^{P_2} \frac{dP}{P-B} - \int_{P_1}^{P_2} \frac{dP}{P+B}$$

$$= -\log \frac{(P_1-B)(P_2+B)}{(P_2-B)(P_1+B)},$$

or,

$$\frac{H dg \pi a^4 t}{8\eta l V} = \log \left(\frac{h_1}{h_2} \cdot \frac{2H+h_2}{2H+h_1} \right).$$

Finally, we may notice an experiment due to Rankine [1] which is applicable to various gases and enables the effect of pressure to be studied. In this experiment a closed-tube system (Fig. 80) is used. The tube $ABCDEF$, of about 3 mm. diameter, is joined to FA the capillary tube. Two fixed marks M and N are made, such that the volume V_4 of ABM equals that of FEN. A mercury pellet P again produces the excess pressure, and in this case the time t is the interval between the top surface of the pellet passing M and the bottom surface reaching N. Let V_3 be the total volume $ABMNEF$. If the apparatus be placed horizontally, the pressure throughout has a uniform value, p say, and let the density of the gas at this pressure be $p\rho$, where ρ is the density at unit pressure. The mass of gas enclosed is $p\rho V_3$ and remains constant. At the beginning of the interval t, the pressure in ABM is p_1, while that in MDF is P_1, given by $P_1 = p_1 + \dfrac{w}{\alpha}$, where w is the weight of the pellet and α is the cross-sectional area of the fall-tube. Then, as the mass of gas is constant,

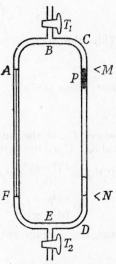

Fig. 80.—Rankine's Apparatus for the Measurement of Viscosity Coefficients for Gases.

$$p\rho V_3 = p_1 \rho V_4 + \rho(V_3-V_4)\left(p_1 + \frac{w}{\alpha} \right),$$

or,

$$p_1 = p - \frac{w}{\alpha} + \frac{w}{\alpha} \cdot \frac{V_4}{V_3}, \qquad . \qquad . \qquad . \qquad (189)$$

and

$$P_1 = p + \frac{w}{\alpha} \cdot \frac{V_4}{V_3} \qquad . \qquad . \qquad . \qquad . \qquad (190)$$

[1] Rankine, *Proc. Roy. Soc.*, A, **83**, 265 (1910).

At the end of the time t these become

$$p_2 = p - \frac{w}{\alpha} + \frac{w}{\alpha} \cdot \frac{V_3 - V_4}{V_3}$$

$$= p - \frac{w}{\alpha} \cdot \frac{V_4}{V_3}, \qquad \cdot \qquad \cdot \qquad \cdot \qquad \cdot \qquad (191)$$

and

$$P_2 = p + \frac{w}{\alpha} \cdot \frac{V_3 - V_4}{V_3} \qquad \cdot \qquad \cdot \qquad \cdot \qquad (192)$$

Hence the mass of gas which has passed through the capillary is

$$P_1 \rho (V_3 - V_4) - P_2 \rho V_4$$

$$= \rho(V_3 - V_4)\left(p + \frac{w}{\alpha} \cdot \frac{V_4}{V_3}\right) - \rho V_4\left(p + \frac{w}{\alpha} \cdot \frac{V_3 - V_4}{V_3}\right) = p\rho(V_3 - 2V_4).$$

Thus the average rate of flow in grams per second is

$$\frac{p\rho}{t}(V_3 - 2V_4) \qquad \cdot \qquad \cdot \qquad \cdot \qquad \cdot \qquad (193)$$

But, from (187),

$$P_1 V_1 = \frac{(P_1{}^2 - p_1{}^2)\pi a^4}{16\eta l},$$

where V_1 is the initial volume per second entering the capillary tube. Thus the initial mass per second entering is

$$P_1 V_1 \rho = \frac{P_1{}^2 - p_1{}^2}{16\eta l}\pi a^4 \rho$$

$$= \frac{\pi a^4 \rho}{16\eta l} \cdot \frac{w}{\alpha}\left(2p - \frac{w}{\alpha} + \frac{2w}{\alpha} \cdot \frac{V_4}{V_3}\right) \quad \text{from equations (190) and (189),}$$

and the average rate of flow in grams per second is

$$\frac{\pi a^4 \rho}{16\eta l} \cdot \frac{w}{\alpha} \cdot 2p.$$

Equating this value to that obtained in expression (193), we have

$$\frac{V_3 - 2V_4}{t} = \frac{w}{\alpha} \cdot \frac{\pi a^4}{8\eta l}, \qquad \cdot \qquad \cdot \qquad \cdot \qquad (194)$$

where $(V_3 - 2V_4)$ is the volume between the two marks M and N, less the volume of the pellet.

In this experiment correction must be made for the sticking of the pellet in the fall tube in the manner already described.

Rankine, by means of this apparatus, measured the viscosities of many gases and showed that they were, as predicted by the kinetic theory, independent of the pressure.

If it is required to measure a gas viscosity with the highest degree of accuracy as, for example, in the determination of the electronic charge by Millikan's oil-drop method, the uncertainties of the capillary tube experiment render it unsuitable, and a rotating cylinder apparatus is employed. In Bearden's form [1] the inner cylinder, which was hollow, closed at both ends and revolved between accurately machined centres, was magnetically driven. The outer cylinder was much shorter and end effects were rendered negligible by the provision of coaxial guard cylinders, the effective length of the driven cylinder being its actual length plus half the sum of the small clearance distances. The space between the cylinders could be evacuated and subsequently filled with any gas at controllable pressure. The formula, of course, is exactly the same as that applicable to liquids. Bearden's value for air at 23° C. was

$$(1 \cdot 82462 \pm 0 \cdot 00006) \times 10^{-4} \text{ poises.}$$

In Table XII are given the values of η for a number of the more important gases.

TABLE XII.—VISCOSITY COEFFICIENTS (GASES)

Gas.	Temp. °C.	Viscosity $\times 10^4$ C.G.S. units.	Sutherland's Const. C.
Air	−21·4 0 15 99·6	1·64 1·71 1·81 2·21	120
Hydrogen . .	0 99	0·86 1·06	72
Oxygen . . .	0 54	1·87 2·16	127
Nitrogen . . .	0 54	1·66 1·90	110
Helium . . .	0 67	1·89 2·35	80
Argon . . .	0 100	2·10 2·74	170
Chlorine . . .	0 20	1·29 1·47	
Carbon dioxide .	0 99	1·39 1·86	240
Water (vapour) .	0 100	0·90 1·32	72
Nitrous oxide . .	0 100	1·35 1·83	313
Carbon monoxide .	0 20	1·63 1·84	102

125. Effect of Pressure on the Viscosity of Gases.—Maxwell showed from the kinetic theory of gases that viscosity is independent of pressure, and this result has been found to be true over a wide range of pressures. At low pressures—such that the mean free

[1] Bearden, *Phys. Rev.*, **56**, 1032 (1939).

path of the molecules becomes of the same order of magnitude as the dimensions of the containing vessel—the viscosity continually decreases as the pressure falls ; the value of the pressure, at which this effect begins, depends upon the size of the containing vessel and upon the nature of the gas. The diminution in gas friction at low pressures is shown by the long-continued vibrations of a broken filament in a vacuum tube, and this effect is utilised in a number of decrement type pressure gauges.

When the pressure is low, there is relative motion between the wall of the vessel and an adjacent layer of gas. In fact, appreciable " slipping " occurs, and this fact reduces the value of the coefficient of viscosity. For liquids no such effect has been detected, but with gases it has been observed—notably in the experiments of Kundt and Warburg [1]—for pressures up to several millimetres of mercury. Maxwell suggested that this slipping effect could be corrected for, by assuming an imaginary displacement of the walls away from one another by an amount which depends on the mean free path, and which, from the experiments of Kundt and Warburg, would amount to four times the mean free path. If this were done, the gas may be taken as at rest on the new boundaries. Thus, when the dimensions of the vessel approach in magnitude the mean free path, this slipping effect becomes very noticeable.

126. Effect of Temperature on the Viscosity of Gases.—The viscosity of a gas increases with temperature, and Sutherland [2] deduced the relation

$$\frac{\eta_t}{\eta_0} = \frac{273+C}{T+C}\left(\frac{T}{273}\right)^{\frac{3}{2}},$$

where η_t and η_0 are the viscosities at $T°$ absolute and $0°$ C., respectively, and C is usually termed Sutherland's constant. The value of C for various gases is given in Table XII.

Sutherland's formula agrees well with experimental data.

127. Solid Friction and Lubrication.—When one solid surface slides over another, the force necessary to maintain motion measures the amount of kinetic friction between the surfaces. The ratio of this force to the normal reaction between the surfaces is nearly constant, and is called the coefficient of kinetic friction. It is independent of the velocity and of the apparent area of contact,[3] but the work of Bowden and Tabor [4] shows that the latter is not a useful measurement, since actual contact occurs over a limited area, and this is a self-adjusting quantity in that greater mutual force between two surfaces produces a plastic deformation at the small areas of contact, thus increasing the area. This increase adjusts the area of contact so as to reduce the pressure to that at which the solid

[1] Kundt and Warburg, *Pogg. Ann.*, **155**, 357 (1875).
[2] See Article 133.
[3] Beare and Bowden, *Phil. Trans.*, A, **234**, 329 (1935).
[4] Bowden and Tabor, *Proc. Roy. Soc.*, A, **169**, 391 (1939).

material no longer flows plastically. The real area of contact is thus necessarily proportional to the load. Therefore the area of contact of a body with a supporting surface is independent of the way it is oriented. The friction which is normally measured is that between surfaces covered with adsorbed gases, or even thin films of oxide, and the coefficient for these is usually less than unity ; if two metal surfaces are thoroughly degassed by heating in a vacuum, the coefficient rises very considerably, *e.g.* to values of 10 or more.[1] Although it is usually stated that kinetic friction is less than static friction, the difference at low speeds is very small, and in all cases is probably due more to the effect of heating than to any difference in mechanism. When sliding is occurring, however, oscillographic study shows that the relative motion is very complex and includes momentary pauses between positions of rapid slip ; this discontinuous motion is accompanied by equivalent temperature changes. Since the electrical conductance across the contact falls momentarily at the slip times, this is evidence of temporary welding over the real contact area, the frictional force being that necessary to break these bonds. It is not yet certain that this theory of sheared welds is, by itself, adequate to explain all the effects of friction. In particular it makes no allowance for the roughness of the surface by reason of which there is some degree of mutual fitting together between the surfaces, so that in their relative movement, surface irregularities must be surmounted or shorn off. It was to this expenditure of energy that Coulomb attributed the whole of the frictional resistance and, according to his theory, there would be no friction between mathematically smooth surfaces whereas, as we have seen, degassed smooth metal surfaces exhibit large forces of friction.

Lubricants separate the solid surfaces, either so completely that projections do not touch, or sufficiently to reduce greatly the consequent degree of seizure. From this point of view, therefore, the normal adsorbed films on the surfaces may be regarded as lubricants, but the name is more usually applied to substances added to the surfaces, in order to reduce the residual friction between the normally adulterated solids. When the amount of lubricant present is sufficient to form a film at least several molecules thick, then the ultimate force to be overcome is due to the viscosity of the lubricant. The theory of this film lubrication was first given by Osborne Reynolds.[2] In all the cases to which it applies, the common feature is that the surfaces in relative motion are slightly inclined to one another, and into the wedge-shaped clearance between them the lubricant is forced, until the pressure so developed equals the pressure between the moving surfaces, which are thus maintained a sufficient distance apart for the liquid between to have the normal bulk properties, and thus to resist shear merely by its viscosity.

[1] Bowden and Hughes, *Proc. Roy. Soc.*, A, **172**, 263 (1939).
[2] Reynolds, *Phil. Trans.*, A, **177**, 157 (1886).

Hence this type of lubrication substitutes inter-liquid shear for the shearing of bridging welds. In order that the wedging action shall be effective, two conditions are necessary ; the liquid must have enough viscosity for one layer to drag another with it, and it must adhere adequately to the solid surface. From the first condition it is seen that there will be, in any given circumstances, a minimum viscosity which will enable the film to be maintained. When allowance has been made for the normal rise of working temperature and the adulteration, which is progressive with use, it is economic to use the minimum viscosity, but even more important as a practical consideration is the chemical stability of the lubricant. In this matter the mineral oils have a superiority over the vegetable oils, which tend more easily to oxidation and a consequent formation of tarry residues. The second condition was formerly disguised by the term oiliness, but is now recognised as the power of forming strongly adherent coatings on the solid surface. That this is of importance is shown by the fact that the most efficient lubricants have a high heat of wetting with metals, but this may not be the only essential property as there is evidence that, to produce good lubrication by such an adsorbed layer, some other property—possibly flexibility in the molecules—is needed.

Such an adsorbed layer, even if only monomolecular on each surface, diminishes the friction very greatly and this form of lubrication, called boundary lubrication, has been very fully studied by Hardy [1] and his colleagues who measured the tangential force necessary to move a spherical slider which stands in a pool of the lubricant. In a short time the sphere penetrates the lubricant until only a boundary layer remains. It is not quite certain, though probable, that this layer is one molecule thick on each surface. According to Hardy's results, ring compounds are less effective than long chain compounds, and in a homologous series it was possible to evaluate the contribution of each portion of the molecular chain to the resultant frictional reduction. For example, in the compound $CH_3(CH_2)_nX$ the coefficient of friction μ is given by

$$\mu = \mu_0 - d - c(n-1),$$

in which μ_0 is the clean surface coefficient, d the effect due to the end groups CH_3 and X, and c is that caused by each CH_2 group. The quantity d is very nearly independent of the kind of solid surface, and c also is independent of the solid, but varies with the series. The coefficient for two different solids A and B was the mean of those for A with A and B with B. Thus each solid, plus its adherent film, makes an individual contribution to the residual friction. The ability of substances to form these monomolecular films is governed by the same considerations as those which cause oriented unimolecular surface layers on liquids, and the better boundary lubrication of long chain molecules may be due to the

[1] Hardy, *Collected Papers*, Cambridge, (1936).

consequent reduction in attractive force to that of the weak methyl groups at the outer ends of the hydrocarbon chains. This is supported by the fact that vegetable oils, which contain free fatty acids, are able to produce more strongly adherent boundary films than mineral oils. In order to obtain the value of both methods of lubrication, engineers now frequently use mineral oils with an admixture of vegetable oil, such as castor oil. The latter produces and maintains the boundary layer, while the former fulfils the rôle of film lubricant. As an additional precaution colloidal graphite also is sometimes added, with the resultant deposition of a thin film of graphite to the metal surfaces, so that even if solid contact should occur, the seizure would be between graphite layers in which the resistance to tangential slip is small.

EXAMPLES

1. A soap bubble of radius 4 cm. and surface tension 30 dynes per cm. is blown at the end of a tube of length 10 cm. and internal diameter 0·200 cm. If the viscosity of air is $1·85 \times 10^{-4}$ C.G.S. units, find the time taken by the bubble to be reduced to a radius of 2 cm.

[4 min. 56 sec.]

2. Water flows through a horizontal tube of length 20 cm. and internal radius 0·081 cm. under a constant head of the liquid 20 cm. high. In 12 minutes 864 c.c. of liquid issues from the tube. Calculate the viscosity coefficient for water and verify that the conditions for stream-line flow exist. The density of water is 1 gm. per c.c. and $g = 981$.

[0·0114 C.G.S. units ; crit. vel. 140 cm. per sec. ;
max. vel. 116 cm. per sec.]

3. Two vessels of equal cross-section, α, are joined near their bases by a horizontal narrow tube of length l and internal radius r. Initially the liquid surfaces are at heights $3h$ and h, respectively, above the capillary tube. Calculate the time taken for the difference in level to become h if the coefficient of viscosity is η and the density d. The flow is assumed to be slow. $[4\eta l\alpha \log 2/\pi r^4 dg.]$

4. If the vessel with the lower level of liquid in the previous question is removed, find the new time for the liquid in the first vessel to fall in level from $3h$ to $2·5h$. $[8\eta l\alpha \log 1·2/\pi r^4 dg.]$

5. A cylinder of radius 5 cm. and mass 1 kg. is suspended with axis vertical by a long fine thread of torsional rigidity τ and is immersed to a depth of 10 cm. in a liquid of viscosity 1·50 C.G.S. units contained in a coaxial cylinder, of radius 5·10 cm. Neglecting forces on the base of the suspended cylinder, find the condition that, on being twisted through a small angle, the cylinder returns to its equilibrium position without oscillation. $[\tau < 2·95 \times 10^5$ C.G.S. units.]

6. If the viscosity of water at 0° C., 20° C., 40° C., 60° C., and 80° C. is 0·01795, 0·01000, 0·00650, 0·00462, and 0·00339 C.G.S., find the rate of variation of viscosity η with temperature t at these temperatures if $\eta(1 + kt)^{\frac{3}{2}} = A$; A and k being constants.

[0·000242 ; 0·000120 ; 0·000069 and 0·000043.]

7. An air bubble, radius 1 cm., is allowed to rise through a long cylindrical column of syrup of radius 5 cm., and travels at a steady rate of 0·21 cm. per sec. If the density of the syrup is 1·47 gm. per c.c. find its viscosity at the temperature of the experiment.

$$[1·03 \times 10^3 \text{ C.G.S. units.}]$$

8. A U-tube consists of a length of 40 cm., of capillary radius 0·0135 cm., and 80 cm. of wider tubing, radius 0·150 cm., and is placed vertically. Two marks are made on the wider tube 30 cm. apart, and a mercury pellet of weight 1·890 gm. is found to take 53·2 sec. to fall from one mark to the other. A second pellet of mass 1·360 gm. takes 78·6 sec. If the atmospheric pressure is $1·00 \times 10^6$ dynes per sq. cm. calculate the viscosity of air at the temperature of the experiment.

$$[1·82 \times 10^{-4} \text{ C.G.S. units.}]$$

9. A glass bulb of volume 500 c.c. has a capillary tube of length 40 cm. and radius 0·020 cm. leading from it. The bulb is filled with hydrogen at an initial pressure of 86 cm. of mercury, density 13·6 gm. per c.c., and it is found that if the volume of the gas remaining in the vessel is kept constant the pressure falls to 80 cm. of mercury in 25·4 sec. If the height of the barometer is 76 cm. and $g=981$, find the viscosity of hydrogen. $\qquad [9·21 \times 10^{-5} \text{ C.G.S. units.}]$

10. Two bulbs, each of 500 c.c. internal volume, are connected by a tube of length 20 cm. and internal radius 0·0150 cm. The whole system is filled with oxygen, the initial pressures being 10 and 15 cm. of mercury respectively. Calculate the time taken for the pressures to become 12 and 13 cm. of mercury respectively. The viscosity of oxygen may be taken as 0·000199 C.G.S. $\qquad$ [483 sec.]

11. A cylindrical vessel is maintained full of a liquid to a depth of 20 cm., and has protruding from it three similar horizontal capillary tubes, each 45 cm. long, fixed at heights 0, 5, and 10 cm., respectively, from the base. Show that the rate of supply to the cylinder is the same as would be necessary for a single outflow tube of length 20 cm. and similar radius protruding horizontally at the bottom of the cylinder.

12. Two circular horizontal discs of radius 5 cm. and distance apart 1 mm. are separated by a layer of oil of viscosity 1·01 C.G.S. The upper disc is fixed while the lower one is revolved in vertical frictionless bearings by the tangential pull of a flexible string, the tension in which is 6000 dynes, which unwraps from a cylinder, radius 2 cm., coaxial with the disc and fastened rigidly to it. Find approximately the time taken by the rotating system to make one complete revolution. [5·2 sec.]

13. A thin wire of radius b is placed coaxially in a narrow tube of length l and radius a. Find the volume of liquid which flows per second through the annular space between the wire and tube when a pressure difference P is maintained between the ends of the tube if η is the viscosity of the liquid and steady-flow conditions exist.

$$[V = \{P\pi/8\eta l\} \{a^4 - b^4 - (a^2 - b^2)^2/(\log a - \log b)\}.]$$

14. Emery powder particles are stirred up in a beaker of water 10 cm. deep. Assuming the particles to be spherical find the radius of the largest particle remaining in suspension after 24 hours. Take the density of emery as 4 gm. per c.c. and the viscosity of water as 0·010 poise. $\qquad [3·8 \times 10^{-5} \text{ cm.}]$

CHAPTER VIII

THE KINETIC THEORY OF MATTER

128. The Kinetic Theory of Matter.—The kinetic theory of matter, and more especially that of gases, rests essentially upon two fundamental assumptions. The first of these postulates is that matter is composed of extremely small particles, atoms, and molecules, and that the molecules of the same chemical substance are exactly alike as regards size, shape, mass, *etc*. The second postulate is that the molecules of a gas are in constant motion, and this motion is intimately related to the temperature. In fact, the temperature of a gas is a manifestation of the amount of molecular motion. The energy associated with atoms may exist as *rotational* and *translational* kinetic energy together with *potential* energy, but polyatomic molecules possess, in addition to these forms, intramolecular energy, the constituent atoms of a molecule being in relative motion and contributing energy according to these motions.

Solids, which are not subjected to external forces, maintain their shape indefinitely, and from this fact it is assumed that, on the whole, their constituent molecules and atoms move about some mean position. Their movements are, to a large extent, limited. Bragg has shown that the atoms, which constitute the molecules, are arranged in definite space lattices, and in this case the effect of temperature increase consists in augmenting the kinetic energy of vibration of the atoms about their mean equilibrium positions.

The molecules of liquids not only move about mean positions but, by means of diffusion, they are slowly translated. The molecules and atoms in solids and liquids are sufficiently close together to react considerably on one another, and there is, accordingly, an internal or *intrinsic pressure*. This fact is confirmed by the great cohesion and resistance to compression which they exhibit. In gases the average distance between molecules, although it varies with temperature, is many times greater than that existing in solids and liquids ; and the rapidity with which gas molecules diffuse indicates that they are in a state of rapid motion. A relatively simple calculation, based on these assumptions, enables us to calculate the velocities of the molecules at any temperature. Their movements are assumed to be rectilinear and, on an average, uniform, provided that they do not approach too closely to other molecules. They continually collide with one another, and as there are many molecules present, even in the smallest volume, the time occupied in an actual collision must be extremely small, compared with the time-interval between successive collisions. At each impact the direc-

tion and magnitude of the velocity is suddenly changed, but th
total translational energy before and after collision must be the sam
This statement is true, only if the gas temperature remains constan
so that, although the kinetic energy of a particular group of mol
cules may change, the mean value of the kinetic energy of the who
remains constant. Each molecule as it rebounds from the wall
a containing vessel suffers a change in velocity, similar to that origi
ating from intermolecular collisions, and so it imparts momentu
to the wall, equal and opposite to that which it receives.   Th
change of momentum gives rise to a pressure on the boundary su
face.   When we consider that at normal pressure and temperatu
there are approximately 10^{19} molecules per c.c., we see that,
any appreciable area of the boundary surface, there must be
enormous number of impacts per second, the average number
which over the whole area remains constant.   Hence the averag
pressure exerted by the gas molecules will be the same everywher

129. Laws of a Perfect Gas.—A perfect, or ideal, gas is o
in which the molecules are assumed infinitely small, and exert on
negligible forces on one another, except in the case of their collision
Suppose there are N molecules per unit volume of gas, and let the
be divided into classes, so that all the molecules in any one cla
have approximately the same velocity, both as regards magnitud
and direction. Let N_1, N_2, . . . be the numbers of molecules
these classes, so that $N_1 + N_2 + \ldots = N$.

Let u_1, v_1, w_1 denote the components, along the x, y, z axes,
the velocity of the molecules of the first class, so that these mol
cules may be regarded as forming a group of molecules of densit
N_1 per unit volume, in which every molecule moves with the sam
velocity.   The value of $\Sigma N_1 u_1{}^2$ is the sum of the values of suc
terms for all the molecules in unit volume, and this is equal to $N\bar{u}$
If m is the mass of each molecule, the mean kinetic energy
translation of a single molecule is given by

$$\tfrac{1}{2}m[\bar{u}^2 + \bar{v}^2 + \bar{w}^2] = \tfrac{1}{2}mC^2,$$

where $C^2 = \bar{u}^2 + \bar{v}^2 + \bar{w}^2$ and C is called the *root mean square velocit*
the square of which is equal to the average of the squares of a
the velocities.

If we consider n molecules of a gas moving in all possible dire
tions, the probability that the velocity of a molecule shall lie alo
any one direction is the same for all directions.   Let us take son
fixed point O (Fig. 81) as origin, and draw from this point a syste
of lines of length C to represent, in magnitude and direction, th
velocities of the different molecules of the gas.   These lines will er
on a sphere of radius C.   With O as centre and any direction O
as axis, construct cones of which the generatrices make with O
angles equal to θ and $\theta + d\theta$.   The difference between the solid angl
of these two cones is the solid angle $\dfrac{2\pi C \, \sin\theta \, . \, C d\theta}{C^2}$, and the numb

of lines, *i.e.* the number of molecules moving between the directions θ and $\theta + d\theta$ is n_θ where.

$$\frac{n_\theta}{n} = \frac{2\pi \, \sin \, \theta d\theta}{4\pi},$$

or,

$$n_\theta = \frac{n \, \sin \, \theta d\theta}{2} \qquad . \qquad . \qquad . \qquad (195)$$

On XY, of area a_1, construct a cylinder of which the generatrix makes with ST an angle θ, and of which the length is C, ST being parallel to AB. The number of molecules within it is $Na_1C \cos \theta$,

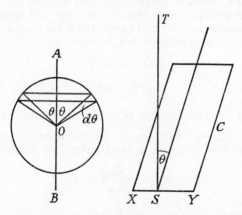

FIG. 81.—SPACE DISTRIBUTION OF MOLECULAR PATHS.

and all pass through the area XY per second. The number, $N\theta$, of these molecules whose directions make angles with ST comprised between the limits θ and $\theta + d\theta$ is, from equation (195),

$$N\theta = Na_1C \, \cos \, \theta \frac{\sin \, \theta d\theta}{2}, \qquad . \qquad . \qquad . \qquad (196)$$

and all these molecules impinge against the area a_1 per second. The change of momentum, normal to the area, at each impact is $2mC \cos \theta$, so that the total force, *i.e.* the rate of change of momentum, acting on the area a_1 is

$$\int_{\theta=0}^{\theta=\frac{\pi}{2}} N_\theta 2mC \, \cos \, \theta = \int_0^{\frac{\pi}{2}} mNa_1C^2 \, \cos^2 \, \theta \, \sin \, \theta d\theta = \frac{mNa_1C^2}{3},$$

and the force per unit area, or the pressure, exerted by the gas is given by

$$p = \frac{mNC^2}{3} = \frac{\rho C^2}{3}, \qquad . \qquad . \qquad . \qquad (197)$$

where ρ is the density. If V_0 represents the molecular volume of the gas and M its molecular weight, $\rho = \dfrac{M}{V_0}$ and

$$pV_0 = \frac{MC^2}{3} \qquad . \qquad . \qquad . \qquad . \qquad (198)$$

From this equation are derived the laws of *perfect gases*, the well-known formula for perfect gases being written

$$pV_0 = R_m T, \qquad . \qquad . \qquad . \qquad . \qquad (199)$$

where T is the absolute temperature and R_m the gas constant referred to one *gram-molecule* ($8\cdot318 \times 10^7$ ergs per degree absolute). Comparing equations (198) and (199), the total kinetic energy of all the molecules in a gram-molecule is equal to

and so
$$\left.\begin{array}{c} \tfrac{1}{2}MC^2 = \tfrac{3}{2}R_m T, \\[4pt] \tfrac{1}{2}mC^2 = \tfrac{3}{2}RT. \end{array}\right\} \qquad . \qquad . \qquad . \qquad (200)$$

Denoting $\dfrac{M}{m}$, *i.e.* the number of molecules contained in 1 gram-molecule, by N_m, we have, for the kinetic energy of translation of a molecule or free atom, at a temperature $T°$ absolute,

$$\tfrac{1}{2}mC^2 = \tfrac{3}{2}\frac{R_m}{N_m}T = \alpha T, \qquad . \qquad . \qquad . \qquad (201)$$

where

$$\alpha = \tfrac{3}{2}\frac{R_m}{N_m}.$$

The formulæ obtained for the pressure contain within them all the well-known gas laws. Thus, from equation (197), the value of N is equal to $\dfrac{3p}{mC^2}$, a quantity which depends only on the physical state of the gas and not on the structure of its molecules, so that two different gases, at the same temperature and pressure, contain equal numbers of molecules in equal volumes. This result is known as *Avogadro's Law*. The actual number of molecules in a cubic centimetre of gas at standard pressure and temperature is $2\cdot687 \times 10^{19}$. This number is frequently referred to as *Loschmidt's number*, the term *Avogadro's number* being reserved for the number of atoms in a gram-atom, or the number of molecules in a gram-molecule. Avogadro's important hypothesis on the identity of the numbers of molecules in equal volumes of different gases at the same pressure and temperature was formulated in 1811, but Avogadro made no quantitative estimate of either of the above constants. The first actual estimate of the number of molecules in 1 c.c. of a gas under standard conditions was made in 1865 by Loschmidt, and from this the number of molecules (atoms) in a gram-molecule (gram-atom) was later evaluated.

Again, from (200), $\frac{1}{2}mC^2=\frac{3}{2}RT$, and substituting this result in equation (197) $p=NRT$. If there is a mixture of gases, then

$$p=(N_1+N_2+ \ . \ . \ .)RT=N_1RT+N_2RT+ \ . \ . \ .,$$

so that the pressure in a mixture of gases is equal to the sum of the pressures exerted separately by the several components of the mixture. This is *Dalton's Law*, and from equations (197) and (200) we see that the pressure of a gas is proportional to its density, provided that the temperature remains unchanged.

It is evident that the various laws, deduced above and confirmed by experiment, are true only within the limits imposed by the assumptions made in the deductions. The most important of these assumptions is that the volume of a molecule is so small, compared with the intermolecular distances, that it may be treated as a point. This is true only for ideal gases, and so the laws will hold for real gases within varying degrees of closeness, which depend on the extent to which the gas approaches the state of a perfect gas. These laws must apply to any medium, since the method by which the expression for the pressure was found, in no way required that the medium should be gaseous. They are found to be true for the osmotic pressure of weak solutions,[1] and the conception of pressure can be extended to the pressure exerted by free electrons moving about in a conducting solid.

The value of C may be calculated from the relation

$$p=\frac{\rho C^2}{3}.$$

For instance, the mass of a litre of hydrogen is 0·08987 gm., at the standard pressure of 76 cm. of mercury and at 0° C., so that

$$p=76 \times 13·59 \times 981=1·01322 \times 10^6 \text{ dynes per sq. cm.}$$

and $\rho=0·00008987$ gm. per c.c. ; thus for hydrogen at 0° C.,

$$C=1·839 \times 10^5 \text{ cm. per second.}$$

Also from the relation

$$C^2=\frac{3RT}{m},$$

$\frac{R}{m}=4·129 \times 10^7$, and from this value of $\frac{R}{m}$ for hydrogen we can calculate its value for any other substance. The mass of the hydrogen atom is $1·673 \times 10^{-24}$ gm.[2] Hence $R=1·381 \times 10^{-16}$ erg per degree, and since the number of molecules in a gram-molecule $=6·023 \times 10^{23}$, the value of R_m is $8·318 \times 10^7$ ergs per degree.

---

[1] See Article 152.
[2] Birge, *Reports on Progress in Physics*, Vol. VIII, 130 (1941).

The quantity $\dfrac{3R}{2}$ has been denoted by α, so that

$$\alpha = \tfrac{3}{2}R = 2 \cdot 072 \times 10^{-16} \text{ erg per degree,}$$

and the kinetic energy of a molecule at $0°$ C. is

$$\alpha T = 2 \cdot 07 \times 10^{-16} \times 273 = 5 \cdot 65 \times 10^{-14} \text{ erg.}$$

130. Maxwell's Law of Distribution of Velocities.—It is evident that even if all the molecules in a given volume actually possessed the same velocity at any initial instant, the collisions occurring would disturb this equal distribution of velocities, and a non-uniform distribution would soon be established. By applying the laws of probability, Maxwell [1] showed that it is possible to calculate the law according to which the velocities of the molecules would be distributed at any temperature.

It is difficult to imagine the motion of a large number of spheres moving about in space, but we may consider the analogous motion in two dimensions, such as a number of billiard balls on a billiard table. The cushions represent the walls of a containing vessel, and the resulting state of motion after the balls have been started at random, with random velocities, will give a representation of what is considered to be the condition of gas molecules. At any instant some of the balls may be brought to rest, while others, as the result of favourable impacts, will possess velocity far in excess of the average velocity of all the balls.

Consider a gas in a state of *thermal equilibrium*, and assume that the molecular collisions do not disturb the density of the gas so that, on an average, it remains constant. In addition, it is usual to assume that the molecules having velocity components lying within any small specified limits are, at every instant throughout the motion of the gas, distributed at random, independently of the positions, or velocities, of the other molecules, provided that two molecules do not occupy the same space. Maxwell has shown that under these conditions the magnitudes of the molecular velocities are distributed according to a law which is independent of the collisions, *i.e.* the law of distribution is not modified by collisions.

Let u, v, w be the velocity components along the x, y, z axes of a molecule moving with velocity q, so that

$$u^2 + v^2 + w^2 = q^2 \qquad . \qquad . \qquad . \qquad (202)$$

Then the probability that any molecule has a component velocity along the x axis intermediate between u and $u + du$ may be stated as $f(u)du$, where $f(u)$ represents some function of u. Similarly, the probability that the component velocities along the y and z axes are between v and $v + dv$, or w and $w + dw$, respectively, is $f(v)dv$, or $f(w)dw$, respectively. These three components are independent, so the probability that they occur simultaneously is given by $f(u) \, f(v) \, f(w) \, du \, dv \, dw$, or, if q is the resultant velocity, by

[1] Maxwell, *Collected Works*, **1**, 380.

$F(q)\ du\ dv\ dw$, or $\phi(q^2)\ du\ dv\ dw$, where $F(q)$ is a function of q and $\phi(q^2)$ a different function of q^2. Hence

$$f(u)\ f(v)\ f(w) = \phi(q^2) = \phi(u^2 + v^2 + w^2). \qquad . \qquad (203)$$

Keeping q constant and differentiating,

$$\frac{f'(u)du}{f(u)} + \frac{f'(v)dv}{f(v)} + \frac{f'(w)dw}{f(w)} = 0, \qquad . \qquad . \qquad (204)$$

where $f'(u)$, *etc.*, represent the first differentials. Differentiating (202), keeping q constant,

$$udu + vdv + wdw = 0, \qquad . \qquad . \qquad (205)$$

and if we multiply (205) by λ and add the results to (204) we obtain

$$\left[\frac{f'(u)}{f(u)} + \lambda u\right]du + \left[\frac{f'(v)}{f(v)} + \lambda v\right]dv + \left[\frac{f'(w)}{f(w)} + \lambda w\right]dw = 0. \quad (206)$$

Every one of these terms is independent of the others, and so

$$\left[\frac{f'(u)}{f(u)} + \lambda u\right]du = 0 \qquad . \qquad . \qquad . \qquad (207)$$

together with similar equations in v and w.

Solving these equations,

$$f(u) = Ke^{-\frac{\lambda u^2}{2}} = Ke^{-hu^2}, \qquad . \qquad . \qquad . \qquad (208)$$

where $h = \dfrac{\lambda}{2}$. Similar expressions hold for $f(v)$ and $f(w)$.

From the definition of probability it follows that

$$\int_{-\infty}^{+\infty} f(u)du = \int_{-\infty}^{+\infty} Ke^{-hu^2}du = 1, \qquad . \qquad . \qquad (209)$$

together with similar expressions in v and w. But

$$\int_{-\infty}^{+\infty} e^{-hu^2}du = \sqrt{\frac{\pi}{h}},$$

so that from (209)

$$K = \sqrt{\frac{h}{\pi}},$$

and thus

$$f(u)\ f(v)\ f(w)\ du\ dv\ dw = \sqrt{\frac{h^3}{\pi^3}} \cdot e^{-h(u^2 + v^2 + w^2)}\ du\ dv\ dw,$$

or, transferring to spherical co-ordinates, the probability of the velocity being between q and $q+dq$ is

$$\sqrt{\frac{h^3}{\pi^3}} \cdot e^{-hq^2} q^2 dq\ \sin\theta d\theta\ d\beta,$$

in which q makes an angle θ with the axis of z and the plane containing q, and the axis of z makes an angle β with the axis of x.

Thus of the N molecules per c.c., the number, dN_q, having a resultant velocity between q and $q+dq$ is

$$dN_q = N \int_{\theta=0}^{\theta=\pi} \int_{\beta=0}^{\beta=2\pi} \sqrt{\frac{h^3}{\pi^3}} e^{-hq^2} q^2 dq \ sin\ \theta d\theta \ d\beta$$

$$= 4N \sqrt{\frac{h^3}{\pi}} e^{-hq^2} q^2 dq. \qquad \qquad (210)$$

Hence the mean, or average, velocity of all the molecules will be the average value of q, and may be denoted by c. It is given by

$$c = \frac{1}{N} \int_0^\infty q \cdot dN_q = \int_0^\infty 4 \sqrt{\frac{h^3}{\pi}} e^{-hq^2} q^3 dq = \frac{2}{\sqrt{\pi h}}. \qquad (211)$$

It is convenient to introduce a velocity C defined as being such that the mean value of c^2 is equal to C^2; for example, C was used in deducing an expression for the gas pressure. The mean kinetic energy of a molecule is then $\frac{1}{2} mC^2$ and

$$C^2 = \frac{1}{N} \int_0^\infty q^2 dN_q = \int_0^\infty 4 \sqrt{\frac{h^3}{\pi}} e^{-hq^2} q^4 dq = \frac{3}{2h} \qquad (212)$$

In terms of C, the average velocity c is given by

$$c = \sqrt{\frac{8}{3\pi}} \cdot C = 0 \cdot 921 C \qquad \qquad (213)$$

The most probable velocity c_0 may be found by differentiating equation (210) with respect to q and equating the result to zero. The result is

$$c_0 = \frac{1}{\sqrt{h}}, \qquad \qquad (214)$$

and

$$\frac{c_0}{C} = \sqrt{\tfrac{2}{3}} \qquad \qquad (215)$$

From equation (208) the number of molecules, N_x, which cross 1 sq. cm. of a surface, perpendicular to the axis of x, in 1 second is

$$N_x = \int_0^\infty u dN_u = \int_0^\infty N \sqrt{\frac{h}{\pi}} u e^{-hu^2} du = \frac{N}{2\sqrt{\pi h}} = \frac{Nc}{4} \qquad (216)$$

Maxwell's deduction of the law for the distribution of velocities is not very satisfactory, because it assumes that the three velocity components are independent. Later he put forward another proof,[1] but it is doubtful whether this second proof is superior to the original one. The values of the molecular velocities are given in Table XIII.

[1] Maxwell, *Collected Works*, 2, 43.

TABLE XIII.—MOLECULAR VELOCITIES [1]

Gas.	C. Root Mean Square Velocity at N.T.P.		c. Average Velocity at N.T.P.	
Hydrogen	18.38×10^4 cm. per sec.		16.93×10^4 cm. per sec.	
Helium	13·11	,, ,,	12·08	,, ,,
Water vapour	6·15	,, ,,	5·65	,, ,,
Neon	5·84	,, ,,	5·38	,, ,,
Carbon monoxide	4·93	,, ,,	4·54	,, ,,
Nitrogen	4·93	,, ,,	4·54	,, ,,
Ethylene	4·93	,, ,,	4·54	,, ,,
Nitric oxide	4·76	,, ,,	4·38	,, ,,
Oxygen	4·61	,, ,,	4·25	,, ,,
Argon	4·13	,, ,,	3·80	,, ,,
Carbon dioxide	3·93	,, ,,	3·62	,, ,,
Nitrous oxide	3·93	,, ,,	3·62	,, ,,
Krypton	2·86	,, ,,	2·63	,, ,,
Xenon	2·28	,, ,,	2·10	,, ,,
Mercury vapour	1·84	,, ,,	1·70	,, ,,
Air	4·85	,, ,,	4·47	,, ,,
Ammonia	6·33	,, ,,	5·82	,, ,,

Table XIV gives the relative distribution of molecular velocities as calculated by Dushman.[2] Under Δx is given the range of velocities in terms of the most probable velocity, whose value is taken as unity, and under Δy the fraction of the total number of molecules which have velocities corresponding to this range. Thus 16·1 per cent. of all the molecules have velocities which range between 0·9 and 1·1 times the most probable velocity at any temperature. Similarly, it follows that 68·4 per cent. of the molecules have velocities ranging between 0·5 and 1·5 times the most probable velocity, while only 3·1 per cent. have velocities that exceed 2·5 times the most probable velocity.

TABLE XIV.—RELATIVE DISTRIBUTION OF MOLECULAR VELOCITIES
(Maxwell's Law)

Δx.	Δy.	Δx.	Δy.
0–0·1	0·001	1·3–1·5	0·112
0·1–0·3	0·021	1·5–1·7	0·078
0·3–0·5	0·063	1·7–1·9	0·058
0·5–0·7	0·112	1·9–2·1	0·034
0·7–0·9	0·149	2·1–2·5	0·030
0·9–1·1	0·161	2·5–3·0	0·008
1·1–1·3	0·150		
0·5–1·5	0·684	0–2·5	0·969

[1] See Dushman, *General Electric Review*, 15, 952, 1042, 1159 (1915); also Jeans' *Dynamical Theory of Gases*.

[2] Dushman, *General Electric Review*, 23, 493 (1920).

131. The Equipartition of Energy.—The total number of independent quantities, which must be known before the configuration and position of any system can be determined, is called the number of *degrees of freedom* of the system. This number depends on the capabilities of motion of the parts of the system. For example, in the case of an atom, which we may regard as a rigid body, its position can be fixed when x, y, z, the co-ordinates of the centre of gravity of the body, and three angles θ, β, ψ, determining the orientation of the body, are given. If we regard the atoms as points, each atom will have three degrees of freedom, corresponding to the x, y, z co-ordinates ; and since the number of degrees of freedom of a complex system is equal to the sum of the numbers of degrees of freedom of the constituent systems, a diatomic molecule must necessarily have *six* degrees of freedom. If the two atoms are, under any conditions, so closely bound together that their distance apart is fixed, the number of degrees of freedom is reduced to *five*. Each molecule will possess an axis of symmetry, namely, the line joining the centres of the two atoms. Let us take any two other axes in the molecule in the plane perpendicular to the axis of symmetry. The kinetic energy, E, is given by

$$2E = m(u^2 + v^2 + w^2) + mk_0{}^2(\omega_1{}^2 + \omega_2{}^2) + mk_1\omega_3{}^2,$$

where k_0, k_0, k_1 are the *radii of gyration* about these two axes and the axis of symmetry, ω_1, ω_2, ω_3 being the components of the *angular velocities* about these three axes.

Intermolecular collisions cannot affect the values of ω_3. This may be ignored in considering energy changes, and the energy which the gas molecules possess is uniformly distributed among the various possible degrees of freedom. This is known as the *Equipartition of Energy theorem.* Thus :

$$\overline{mu^2} = \overline{mv^2} = \overline{mw^2} = \overline{mk_0{}^2\omega_1{}^2} = \overline{mk_0{}^2\omega_2{}^2},$$

where the bar indicates that the average value of the term throughout the gas is to be considered. It may be shown [1] that the value of each of these terms is RT, so that the mean kinetic energy of translation of a molecule is given by

$$\tfrac{1}{2}m(\bar{u}^2 + \bar{v}^2 + \bar{w}^2) = \tfrac{1}{2}mC^2 = \tfrac{3}{2}RT,$$

as stated in (200).

Now if E is the mean energy possessed by each of the molecules in 1 c.c. of gas, the *first law of thermodynamics* may be stated thus :

$$dQ = NdE + pdV,$$

where dV is the change in volume when heat, dQ, is supplied to the gas, *i.e.*

$$dQ = NdE + RNT\frac{dV}{V} \qquad . \qquad . \qquad . \qquad (217)$$

---

[1] Jeans, *Dynamical Theory of Gases*, p. 87.

If C_v is the specific heat of the gas at constant volume,

$$C_v = \frac{1}{Nm}\left(\frac{dQ}{dT}\right)_v = \frac{1}{m}\frac{dE}{dT} \qquad . \qquad . \quad (218)$$

In a similar manner, if C_p is the specific heat of the gas at constant pressure,

$$C_p = \frac{1}{Nm}\left(\frac{dQ}{dT}\right)_p = \frac{1}{m}\frac{dE}{dT} + \frac{R}{m}, \qquad . \qquad . \quad (219)$$

since at constant pressure (217) becomes

$$dQ = NdE + RNdT.$$

For many gases C_v and C_p are approximately independent of the temperature over a large range of pressures and temperatures, so that $\dfrac{dE}{dT}$ is constant, and therefore the mean energy of a molecule of the gas bears a constant ratio to the *translational* energy, the latter being proportional to the absolute temperature. Let us denote this ratio by $(1+\alpha)$. Then

$$E = (1+\alpha)\tfrac{1}{2}mC^2 = (1+\alpha)\tfrac{3}{2}RT, \qquad . \qquad . \quad (220)$$

and

$$\frac{dE}{dT} = \tfrac{3}{2}R(1+\alpha),$$

so that from equations (218) and (219)

$$C_v = \frac{3R}{2m}(1+\alpha),$$

and

$$C_p = \frac{R}{m}[1 + \tfrac{3}{2}(1+\alpha)].$$

Thus γ, the ratio of the specific heats, is given by

$$\gamma = \frac{C_p}{C_v} = 1 + \frac{2}{3(1+\alpha)}. \qquad . \qquad . \qquad . \quad (221)$$

Although we do not possess sufficient knowledge of the molecule's internal structure to evaluate the quantities $\dfrac{dE}{dT}$ and α, we may determine their values to some extent by measuring γ experimentally and using equation (221). For example, in the case of air, experiment shows that γ is almost independent of the temperature and approximately equal to $\tfrac{7}{5}$, so that from equation (221) α is equal to $\tfrac{2}{3}$.

The energy of a molecule having n degrees of freedom, in addition to its translational movements, may be written

$$E = \tfrac{1}{2}m(u^2 + v^2 + w^2) + \tfrac{1}{2}mk_1{}^2\omega_1{}^2 + \cdot \cdot \cdot,$$

where the value of each term on the right-hand side is $\dfrac{RT}{2}$. Hence

$$E = \frac{RT}{2}(3+n),$$

and comparing this result with that given in equation (220) $n=3\alpha$. From this we see that corresponding to $n=0, 1, 2$, *etc.*, $\alpha=0, \frac{1}{3}, \frac{2}{3}$, *etc.*, and from equation (221)

$$\gamma=1+\frac{2}{3+n} \quad . \quad . \quad . \quad . \quad (222)$$

For monatomic gases $\gamma=1\frac{2}{3}$ and $n=0$. There is no molecular energy except that of translation, so that the molecules of these gases are spherical bodies and cannot acquire rotational energy by collision.

There is no gas, apparently, for which $\gamma=1\frac{1}{2}$, *i.e.* $n=1$, but for $n=2, \gamma=1\frac{2}{5}$, and hydrogen, nitrogen, oxygen, *etc.*, have, very approximately, these values for n and γ. We conclude, therefore, that there are *five degrees of freedom* in the *diatomic* molecule, and the structure which our theory indicates is fully confirmed by experiment. In addition to the two terms representing the rotational energy, the atoms are capable of changing their relative distance apart, and this gives rise to another kinetic energy and another potential energy of vibration, the two atoms moving along their line of centres.

For many gases and vapours the value of γ approaches unity, and the molecules of these substances cannot be regarded simply as rigid bodies, since the energy of internal motion is comparable with the energies of translation and rotation.

132. The Mean Free Path.—The average distance traversed by a molecule between successive collisions is termed the *mean free path*, or the mean path of the molecule. When we define the mean free path as the average distance traversed by all the molecules between successive collisions, it is assumed that the molecules actually collide like billiard balls, *i.e.* the molecules are assumed to be rigid elastic spheres possessing definite dimensions and exerting no attractive or repulsive forces on each other. This, however, is certainly not in accordance with the facts. We have every reason to believe that the structure of atoms and molecules is exceedingly complex. It is probably impossible to state definitely what is the diameter of a hydrogen atom or molecule. If we consider the velocity components of the molecules in a given direction, we find that at the end of a certain distance, L, the average value of the velocity components of all these molecules, taken in the same direction, has decreased by a certain amount; in other words, the average number of molecules travelling in the given direction is less after they have traversed the distance L. On this basis the term free path has a physical meaning which is independent of all ideas that we may form of the actual structure of the molecule, or of the nature of the intramolecular forces.

Suppose that the centres of the molecules approach to within an average distance, σ, from each other, where σ is the diameter of a molecule. Let all the molecules except one be at rest, so that the centre of any other molecule cannot approach within the surface of a sphere, of radius σ, which surrounds the moving molecule. This

sphere is known as the *sphere of molecular action*. The volume swept
out per second by the moving molecule is $\pi\sigma^2 C$ where C is its velocity,
and this volume includes the centres of $\pi\sigma^2 NC$ molecules, this
number representing the collisions made by the molecule per second.
Then

$$L = \frac{C}{\pi\sigma^2 CN} = \frac{1}{\pi\sigma^2 N},$$

but $mN = \rho$, so that

$$L = \frac{m}{\pi\sigma^2 \rho}, \qquad . \qquad . \qquad . \qquad . \quad (223)$$

and is inversely proportional to the gas pressure. Its magnitude
under normal pressure and temperature is, approximately, 10^{-5} cm.,
whereas at a pressure of 10^{-4} mm. of mercury, which is about the
degree of vacuum in electric glow lamps, the mean free path for
most gases is 5–10 cm.

This equation has been deduced on the assumption that all the
molecules, except the one projected, are at rest. Let C be the
velocity of the projected molecule A, and C_1 that of all the other
molecules, C_1 remaining constant in magnitude but not in direction,
although its distribution is uniform in all directions. Then the
velocity of A, relative to the molecules which move in directions
inclined at angle θ to the direction of C, is $(C^2 + C_1^2 - 2CC_1 \cos \theta)^{\frac{1}{2}}$,
and since, if N_1 is the number of molecules per c.c. possessing velocity
C_1, the number which move between θ and $\theta + d\theta$ is $\dfrac{N_1 \sin \theta}{2} d\theta$,
the mean relative velocity C_r of all the molecules is

$$C_r = \frac{1}{N_1} \int_0^\pi \frac{N_1 \sin \theta}{2} (C^2 + C_1^2 - 2CC_1 \cos \theta)^{\frac{1}{2}} d\theta,$$

$$= \left[\frac{1}{6CC_1} (C^2 + C_1^2 - 2CC_1 \cos \theta)^{\frac{3}{2}} \right]_0^\pi,$$

and if $C = C_1$, $C_r = \frac{4}{3} C$.

Thus the relative velocity of the projected molecule is greater
than that assumed in deducing equation (223), and as the number
of collisions is increased in the ratio $\dfrac{C_r}{C}$, *i.e.* $\frac{4}{3}$, the mean free path
is decreased in the ratio $\frac{3}{4}$, so that

$$L = \frac{3}{4\pi\sigma^2 N} \qquad . \qquad . \qquad . \qquad . \quad (224)$$

If we take Maxwell's Law for the distribution of velocities into
account, it can be shown [1] that the mean free path becomes

$$L = \frac{1}{\sqrt{2}\pi\sigma^2 N} \qquad . \qquad . \qquad . \qquad . \quad (225)$$

[1] Jeans, *Dynamical Theory of Gases*, p. 37.

Jeans has pointed out that this equation cannot be accurate since it does not take into account the persistence of velocities after collision, and he shows that in the case of two similar molecules, colliding with relative velocities that may vary from 0 to ∞, the average value of the persistence is equal, approximately, to two-fifths of the value when the molecules collide with equal velocities, *i.e.* on an average, the molecules travelling in a given direction will, after collision, have lost three-fifths of their velocity component in that direction. He states that the formula should be

$$L=\frac{1\cdot319}{\sqrt{2}\pi\sigma^2N}. \quad . \quad . \quad . \quad (226)$$

These results are true only for rigid elastic spheres with no intermolecular forces. Assuming the existence of such forces, the effect is to shorten the free path,[1] and under these conditions

$$L=\frac{1\cdot402}{\sqrt{2}\pi\sigma^2N\left(1+\dfrac{K}{T}\right)}, \quad . \quad . \quad (227)$$

where K is a constant for each gas and T is the absolute temperature.

It must be realised that the idea of molecules and atoms being rigid elastic spheres is simply one of convenience and bears no relation to the modern theory of molecular structure. The principle of indefiniteness and the nuclear structure of molecules preclude any definite size, and experiments on the scattering of electrons show that the effective cross-section of atoms and molecules for such scattering varies with the speed of the impinging electrons.

Molecular velocities are distributed according to Maxwell's Law, and the free paths of the molecules also differ from the mean free path, L. The law of distribution may be deduced as follows :

The probability, P_x, that a molecule moving with a velocity c shall describe a free path at least equal to x is $f(x)$, and the probability that it will pass over the path $x+dx$ is, therefore,

$$P_{x+dx}=f(x+dx)=f(x)+f'(x)dx,$$
$$=P_x+\frac{dP_x}{dx}dx.$$

After the molecule has described a distance x, the chance of collision within a further distance dx is $\dfrac{dx}{L}$, and the probability that it will move over the distance dx is

$$1-\frac{dx}{L}=P_{dx}.$$

Now according to the rules of probability $P_{x+dx}=P_x.P_{dx}$, or the probability that the molecule will pass over the distance $x+dx$

[1] Sutherland, *Phil. Mag.*, 36, 507 (1893).

without a collision is equal to the product of the probabilities that it will pass over x and dx without a collision.   Hence

$$P_x P_{dx} = P_x + \frac{dP_x}{dx} dx,$$

$$P_x \left(1 - \frac{dx}{L}\right) = P_x + \frac{dP_x}{dx} dx,$$

or,

$$P_x = Ke^{-\frac{x}{L}},$$

where K is an arbitrary constant.   The probability that the molecule passes over the distance $x=0$ without a collision is unity, so $K=1$ and $P_x = e^{-\frac{x}{L}}$.   Hence the probability that a molecule has a free path lying between the lengths x and $x+dx$ is

$$P_x - P_{x+dx} = \frac{1}{L} e^{-\frac{x}{L}} dx, \qquad . \qquad . \qquad . \qquad (228)$$

which is obtained by differentiating the expression for P_x.

It is clear from the form of this expression that free paths which are many times greater than the mean free path will be extremely rare.   For example, only one in 148 describes a path as great as $5L$.

133. The Coefficient of Viscosity.—A molecule describing a free path of length L is in effect transporting a certain amount of momentum, energy, and mass through this distance L.   If the gas were in a steady state, each such transport would be exactly balanced by an equal and opposite movement in the reverse direction, and the net transport would be nil.   Imagine, however, that this steady state has not been attained, and consider that the gas is moving, in the mass, along the x direction with a velocity V, this velocity being everywhere the same in a plane xy, but varying along the direction of the z axis, increasing as z increases.   The molecules will cross the planes $z=constant$ in both directions, but those which cross the plane $z=z_0$ (Fig. 82) in a downward direction will possess less momentum than that appropriate to the plane $z=z_0$, because they come from a region where the velocity is less than it is at the plane $z=z_0$.   In a similar manner those molecules which cross the plane $z=z_0$, moving upwards, will, on an average, have momentum greater than that possessed by the molecules in the plane $z=z_0$.   Since there is, on the whole, no mass motion along the z axis, the number of molecules which cross this plane per second moving downwards is equal to the number moving upwards which cross the plane in the same time, so that, on the whole, there is a net gain of upward momentum, or an upward transport of momentum.

Consider a molecule meeting the plane $z=z_0$ in Q, having previously come from a collision at P, so that the z co-ordinate of P is $z_0 - L \cos \theta$, where θ is the angle that PQ makes with the z axis.

If the velocity gradient of the gas motion is uniform, we may state that

$$U=Az, \text{ and } U_0=Az_0,$$

where A is a constant, and the velocity parallel to the x axis, which the molecule possessed when at P, is

$$u+(z_0-L \cos \theta)A,$$

where u is the velocity along the x axis due to the thermal agitation, and may be neglected since the transfer of momentum due to thermal

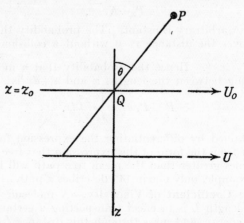

FIG. 82.—COEFFICIENT OF VISCOSITY. THERMAL CONDUCTIVITY.

agitation is, on the whole, zero. Thus the useful momentum, parallel to the x axis, which is transferred across the plane $z=z_0$ by the molecule, is

$$m\left(z_0-L \cos \theta\right)\frac{dU}{dz},$$

since

$$A=\frac{U}{z}=\frac{dU}{dz}.$$

If we suppose that the molecules possess an average velocity of agitation equal to c, then we have shown in equation (196) that the number of molecules, whose directions make angles with the z axis comprised between the limits θ and $\theta+d\theta$, which cross per sec. each sq. cm. of a plane xy is

$$\tfrac{1}{2}Nc \cos \theta \sin \theta d\theta,$$

so that the useful momentum transported per sec. per sq. cm. of plane $z=z_0$ by molecules coming from the plane $z=z_0-L \cos \theta$ is

$$\int_0^\pi \frac{m}{2}(z_0-L \cos \theta)Nc \cos \theta \sin \theta d\theta \frac{dU}{dz}=-\frac{NmcL}{3}\frac{dU}{dz}.$$

But if we have a viscous fluid, of coefficient of viscosity η, moving with the velocity of the gas, the viscous drag per unit area of the plane $z=z_0$ in the direction of the x axis is

$$\eta \frac{dU}{dz},$$

and since the rate of change of momentum is force, we have

$$\eta = \frac{NmcL}{3} = \frac{\rho cL}{3} \qquad . \quad . \quad . \quad (229)$$

The gas behaves exactly like a viscous fluid.

Chapman,[1] following Maxwell's method, arrives at the formula

$$\eta = \frac{0{\cdot}491mc}{\sqrt{2\pi\sigma^2}}; \qquad . \quad . \quad . \quad (230)$$

in a later paper [2] he corrects the factor 0·491 to 0·499.

Theoretically η is independent of the density of the gas, when the molecules are assumed to be elastic spheres, and since L, to a first approximation, is inversely proportional to the number of molecules per c.c., it is evident that, whatever structure we assume for the molecules of the gas, η will be independent of N. We thus obtain *Maxwell's Law* that *the coefficient of viscosity of a gas is independent of its density.* This law is by no means completely confirmed by experiment. For certain gases, such as carbon dioxide, it fails completely at high pressures, and there is a departure from the law at very low pressures when the free path becomes comparable with, or even greater than, the dimensions of the vessel in which the experiment is being conducted. In this case the mean free path is limited by the size of the apparatus and cannot exceed some value, say L_0. Then η cannot be greater than $\frac{1}{3}\rho cL_0$ and tends to zero with zero value of ρ. This has been confirmed experimentally.

If we consider equation (229) and remember that c is proportional to the square root of the absolute temperature, it is evident that η should vary in a similar way, but in practice it varies to a greater extent than the square root of the absolute temperature. This is due to the size of the spheres *decreasing* as the mean molecular velocity, *i.e.* as the temperature, *increases*. Thus η depends on the temperature both through c and σ in equation (230). If we assume that the law of force between two molecules, whose centres are distant r apart, is of the form $\dfrac{\mu}{r}$, then it can be shown that $\dfrac{1}{\sigma^2}$ is proportional to $T^{\frac{2}{s-1}}$, and from equation (230) η will vary as T^n where

$$n = \tfrac{1}{2} + \frac{2}{s-1}.$$

[1] Chapman, *Phil. Trans.*, A, **211**, 433 (1911).
[2] *Idem.*, *Proc. Roy. Soc.*, A, **93**, 1 (1916).

For many gases we may say, therefore, that

$$\eta = \eta_0 \left(\frac{T}{273}\right)^n,$$

where n is given by

$$2n = \frac{s+3}{s-1}.$$

Sutherland [1] assumed that

$$\sigma^2 = \sigma_\infty{}^2 \left(1 + \frac{K}{T}\right), \quad . \quad . \quad . \quad (231)$$

K, σ_∞ being constants, σ_∞ being the value of σ when $T = \infty$, and K is the temperature at which $\sigma^2 = 2\sigma_\infty{}^2$. Hence if L_1 and L_2 are the mean free paths at temperatures T and $273°$ absolute, from equation (226),

$$\frac{L_1}{L_2} = \frac{\sigma_{273}{}^2}{\sigma_T^2} = \frac{1 + \dfrac{K}{273}}{1 + \dfrac{K}{T}},$$

and

$$\frac{\eta}{\eta_0} = \frac{(cL_1)_T}{(cL_2)_{273}} = \left(\frac{T}{273}\right)^{\frac{3}{2}} \cdot \frac{1 + \dfrac{K}{273}}{1 + \dfrac{K}{T}},$$

or,

$$\frac{\eta}{\eta_0} = \left(\frac{T}{273}\right)^{\frac{3}{2}} \cdot \frac{K+273}{K+T}, \quad . \quad . \quad . \quad (232)$$

which is *Sutherland's formula* for the viscosity of a gas at any temperature.

Since the value of η can be determined experimentally, the value of σ can be calculated by means of equation (230). There is good agreement between the values for the molecular diameter calculated in this manner and those obtained by other methods.

134. Thermal Conductivity.—The flow of heat is directly connected with the molecular motions, and a theory of thermal conduction may be deduced in the same way as that employed for viscosity. As the molecules move from places of higher to places of lower temperature, they lose heat energy at the expense of their kinetic energy, which is converted into potential energy of attraction, brought about by passing into denser layers. Thus, in the case of a gas in which a temperature gradient exists, there is a continual passage of the faster moving molecules from the hot side across any plane to the colder side.

[1] Sutherland, *Phil. Mag.*, 5, **36**, 507 (1893).

Let E denote the mean energy of a molecule at P (Fig. 82), where, as before, the co-ordinate of P is $z_0 - L \cos \theta$. The mean energy of the molecules arriving at the plane $z = z_0$, and originating from the gas layer corresponding to P, is

$$E - L \cos \theta . \frac{\partial E}{\partial z},$$

where $\frac{\partial E}{\partial z}$ is the energy gradient along the z axis. As before, the number of molecules which cross unit area of the plane $z = z_0$ in a direction making an angle between θ and $\theta + d\theta$ with the z axis, per second is

$$\tfrac{1}{2} Nc \cos \theta \sin \theta d\theta,$$

and the total energy flow across this unit area per second is

$$\int_{\theta=0}^{\theta=\pi} \left(E - L \cos \theta \frac{\partial E}{\partial z} \right) \frac{Nc}{2} \cos \theta \sin \theta d\theta = -\frac{NcL}{3} \frac{\partial E}{\partial z},$$

the negative sign denoting that the energy flow is in the direction in which z decreases. The rate of flow of heat across unit area is $-k \frac{\partial T}{\partial z}$, where k is the thermal conductivity and $\frac{\partial T}{\partial z}$ the temperature gradient, so that

$$k \frac{\partial T}{\partial z} = \frac{NcL}{3} . \frac{\partial E}{\partial z} = \frac{NcL}{3} . \frac{\partial E}{\partial T} . \frac{\partial T}{\partial z}.$$

But from (218)

$$\frac{\partial E}{\partial T} = mC_v.$$

Hence

$$k = \frac{NcLm}{3} C_v,$$

and from (229)

$$k = \eta C_v. \qquad . \qquad . \qquad . \qquad . \quad (233)$$

If the molecules are treated as elastic spheres, it may be shown that the relation between k and η is

$$k = \varepsilon \eta C_v,$$

where $\varepsilon = 1 \cdot 395$. Chapman[1] found ε to be $2 \cdot 500$.

Comparing the calculated and experimental values of $\frac{k}{\eta C_v}$, there does not appear to be uniformity in the results. The two values agree for monatomic gases, but show poor agreement for gases in which the molecules are of the most complex structure, such as ethylene, carbon dioxide, etc.

[1] Chapman, *Phil. Trans.*, A, **211**, 433 (1911).

135. Thermal Transpiration.

—If two vessels, containing gas at low pressure and at different temperatures, are joined by means of capillary tubing, there is a flow of gas from the colder to the hotter chamber, and this flow continues until a certain pressure difference, depending on the temperature difference, is established. This phenomenon is known as *thermal transpiration* and was discovered by Osborne Reynolds,[1] who used apparatus similar to that shown in Fig. 83. Two chambers (1) and (2) were separated by means of a plate of porous material, and they could be maintained at different temperatures by passing through the jackets, C and D, water and steam, respectively. A mercury manometer indicated

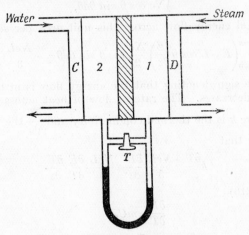

FIG. 83.—THERMAL TRANSPIRATION.

the pressure difference in the two compartments (1) and (2), and by means of the tap T the pressures could be equalised. With T closed, the pressure in (1) gradually rises as the gas passes from (2) to (1) through the porous material. When the mean free path of the gas molecule is large compared with the size of the pores, the final pressures in the two chambers are directly proportional to the square root of the absolute temperatures, and this result is independent of the nature of the gas. A simple explanation of this is as follows :

Let N_1 be the number of molecules per c.c., C_1 the square root of the mean squares of their velocities, T_1 the absolute temperature, in compartment (1), and let similar symbols with the suffix 2 refer to the other compartment. Then, if m is the mass of each

[1] Osborne Reynolds, *ibid.*, A, **170**, 727 (1879).

molecule and S the area of an orifice, the mass of gas passing normally through the orifice per second from (1) to (2) is $\dfrac{N_1C_1mS}{6}$, and similarly from (2) to (1) $\dfrac{N_2C_2mS}{6}$, so that equilibrium is established when

$$\frac{N_1C_1mS}{6}=\frac{N_2C_2mS}{6}.$$

But if p_1 and p_2 are the final pressures when equilibrium is attained,

$$\frac{p_1}{p_2}=\frac{N_1mC_1{}^2}{N_2mC_2{}^2}=\frac{C_1}{C_2}=\sqrt{\frac{T_1}{T_2}}, \qquad . \qquad . \qquad . \qquad (234)$$

and the same formula holds when the two compartments are connected by means of a fine bore tube along which a temperature gradient is maintained. Experiment shows that when the diameter of this tube is large compared with the mean free path, *i.e.* at high pressures, two currents of gas pass along the tube. The outer layers move from the cold to the warm end, and the central layers move in the opposite direction. When the diameter is small in comparison with the mean free path, what is termed *molecular flow* occurs, and there is no fluid flow of the gas layers.

The simple theory given above does not hold at higher pressures.[1] Thus, consider an area of 1 sq. cm. in a section perpendicular to the length of the tube along which a temperature gradient, $\dfrac{\partial T}{\partial x}$, is maintained. If all the molecules at this section have the same average velocity c, and we consider another section distant $L \cos \theta$ away, towards the hot end, the velocity of the molecules coming from this second section, and moving in a direction θ to the axis of the tube is $c+\dfrac{\partial c}{\partial x}L \cos \theta$. Thus we may take the average velocity of all the molecules arriving at the unit area, and coming from the hot end of the tube, to be $c+\dfrac{L}{2}\cdot\dfrac{\partial c}{\partial x}$, or we may assume that, on an average, the molecules arriving at the area are those which come from a distance $\dfrac{L}{2}$ away from the area. We have shown previously, equation (216), that the number of molecules which cross 1 sq. cm. of surface perpendicular to the x axis is $\dfrac{Nc}{4}$, so that the number crossing the unit area under consideration per second is

$$\frac{Nc}{4}+\frac{\partial}{\partial x}\left(\frac{Nc}{4}\right)\frac{L}{2}, \text{ approximately.}$$

[1] See West, *Proc. Phys. Soc.*, **31**, 278 (1919). The treatment follows that given by West.

Hence the total mass of gas flowing per second through this unit area from the hot to the cold side is

$$\frac{m}{4}\left[Nc+\frac{LN}{2}\frac{\partial c}{\partial x}+\frac{Lc}{2}\frac{\partial N}{\partial x}\right].$$

Similarly, the total mass flowing from the cold to the hot side is

$$\frac{m}{4}\left[Nc-\frac{LN}{2}\frac{\partial c}{\partial x}-\frac{Lc}{2}\frac{\partial N}{\partial x}\right],$$

and the resultant flow is obtained by adding these masses together, i.e.

$$\frac{mNLc}{4}\left[\frac{1}{N}\frac{\partial N}{\partial x}+\frac{1}{c}\frac{\partial c}{\partial x}\right].$$

But

$$p=\frac{mNC^2}{3}=\frac{\pi mNc^2}{8},$$

and

$$\frac{\partial p}{\partial x}=\frac{\pi}{8}mc^2\frac{\partial N}{\partial x}+\frac{\pi}{4}Nmc\frac{\partial c}{\partial x}$$

$$=p\left[\frac{1}{N}\frac{\partial N}{\partial x}+\frac{2}{c}\frac{\partial c}{\partial x}\right].$$

Taking

$$\eta=0{\cdot}31mNLc,$$

the mass of gas moving through the tube, of radius r, per second is

$$\frac{\pi r^2}{4}\cdot\frac{\eta}{0{\cdot}31}\left[\frac{1}{p}\frac{\partial p}{\partial x}-\frac{1}{c}\frac{\partial c}{\partial x}\right],$$

and since c^2 is proportional to T, this mass becomes

$$\frac{\pi r^2\eta}{1{\cdot}24}\left[\frac{1}{p}\frac{\partial p}{\partial x}-\frac{1}{2T}\frac{\partial T}{\partial x}\right] \qquad . \qquad . \qquad . \quad (235)$$

This flow will continue until a sufficient pressure is developed on the hot side to cause an equal flow of gas in the reverse direction. The mass of gas discharged from a tube by a small pressure gradient is, according to Poiseuille,[1]

$$\frac{\pi}{8}\cdot\frac{\rho_1 pr^4}{\eta}\cdot\frac{\partial p}{\partial x}, \qquad . \qquad . \qquad . \quad (236)$$

where ρ_1 is the density of the gas at $T°$ and under a pressure of 1 dyne per sq. cm. This formula takes no account of slip which occurs at the surface of the tube.

Now in deducing equation (235) we assumed that all the molecules possessed the same velocity, but it is more accurate to use

[1] See Article 123.

Maxwell's distribution law, so that the mass of gas flowing across the section is

$$\frac{3\pi}{8} \cdot \frac{\pi r^2 \eta}{1 \cdot 24} \left[\frac{1}{p} \frac{\partial p}{\partial x} - \frac{1}{2T} \frac{\partial T}{\partial x} \right],$$

and equating this to expression (236),

$$-2 \cdot 98 r^2 \eta \left[\frac{1}{p} \frac{\partial p}{\partial x} - \frac{1}{2T} \frac{\partial T}{\partial x} \right] = \frac{\pi}{8} \frac{\rho_1 p r^4}{\eta} \frac{\partial p}{\partial x},$$

the negative sign being used as the flows are in opposite directions. Whence

$$\frac{\partial p}{\partial T} = \frac{\eta^2}{\dfrac{2\eta^2 T}{p} + 65\rho_0 p r^2}, \qquad . \qquad . \qquad . \qquad (237)$$

where ρ_0 is the density of the gas at $0°$ C. under a pressure of 1 dyne per sq. cm.

If p is very small, this reduces to

$$\frac{\partial p}{\partial T} = \frac{p}{2T},$$

i.e.

$$p \propto \sqrt{T},$$

which agrees with equation (234), so that the thermal transpiration formula (235) is true for high and low gas pressures. It also appears to hold at intermediate pressures. At high pressures $\dfrac{\partial p}{\partial T}$ becomes inversely proportional to the pressure, and is dependent on the nature of the gas. The pressure difference rises less rapidly and eventually reaches a maximum. It then begins to fall off and finally diminishes inversely as the pressure.

136. The Flow of Gases at Low Pressures.—If the temperature is maintained constant, the rate of flow of gases through narrow tubes is governed by Poiseuille's Law at high and moderate pressures, and the rate is limited by the collision frequency between molecules. At very low pressures, where the value of the mean free path is greater than the radius of the tube, the intermolecular collisions become less numerous than the collisions of the molecules with the containing walls, and the term *molecular flow* was suggested by Knudsen[1] to designate the condition of gases flowing through tubes at such low pressures. At this stage the coefficient of viscosity loses all significance, and the flow is governed by the collisions with the wall of the tube.

Knudsen assumes that any plane surface, no matter how smooth it may appear, contains, in reality, projections which are due, probably, to one or more atoms being piled above the surrounding atoms,

[1] Knudsen, *Ann. d. Phys.*, **28**, 75 (1908); **28**, 999 (1909).

and these projections of molecular dimensions are irregularly distributed over the surface. Consequently, a gas molecule on striking the surface is repelled in a direction which is totally independent of the direction of incidence, and the distribution of directions of an infinitely large number of molecules after reflection from a surface follows the cosine law which holds for the reflection of light from an illuminated surface.

Kundt and Warburg [1] found, at these very low pressures, there was distinct evidence that the gas molecules " slipped over " boundary surfaces, so that the apparent viscosity was decreased. The amount of this slip increased as the pressure was lowered, varying inversely as the pressure at the lowest pressures. If we denote the coefficient of slip by δ, the tangential force per sq. cm., or the amount of momentum, μ, transferred per second by the molecules striking unit area of the boundary surface, supposed at rest, is

$$\mu = \frac{\eta U}{d + 2\delta},$$

where $\frac{U}{d}$ is the velocity gradient and η the coefficient of viscosity. Since at very low pressures δ is inversely proportional to the pressure, we may write

$$\delta = bL,$$

where b is a constant. Hence, neglecting d compared with L,

$$\mu = \frac{\eta U}{2bL},$$

but from equations (199), (200), (223), and (229)

$$\frac{\eta}{L} = \frac{p}{3} \sqrt{\frac{8M}{\pi R_m T}},$$

where M is the molecular weight of the gas in grams, so that

$$\mu = \frac{2pU}{3b} \sqrt{\frac{M}{2\pi R_m T}}.$$

It has been found that equation (229) is only approximately true, and that a better representation is

$$\eta = 0.35 \rho c L.$$

If we use this value for η,

$$\mu = \frac{2 \times 0.35}{b} pU \sqrt{\frac{M}{2\pi R_m T}} \quad . \quad . \quad . \quad (238)$$

Neglecting the number of intermolecular collisions, we may consider that U is the velocity of flow of the gas as a whole along the tube, so that the mass flowing through per second is given by

$$Q = \pi r^2 \rho U, \quad . \quad . \quad . \quad (239)$$

[1] Kundt and Warburg, *Pogg. Ann.*, 155, 340 (1875).

where r is the radius of the tube. If l is its length, p_1 and p_2 the pressures at its ends, then the condition for steady flow is that

$$\mu.2\pi rl=[p_1-p_2]\pi r^2, \qquad . \qquad . \qquad . \qquad (240)$$

and from equations (238), (239), and (240)

$$Q=\frac{\pi r^3\rho b}{1\cdot4lp}[p_1-p_2]\sqrt{\frac{2\pi R_mT}{M}},$$

but

$$\frac{p}{\rho}=\frac{R_mT}{M},$$

so

$$Q=\frac{\pi r^3b}{1\cdot4l}[p_1-p_2]\sqrt{\frac{2\pi M}{R_mT}} \qquad . \qquad . \qquad . \qquad (241)$$

All experimenters are agreed that the exact value of b must depend upon the ratio of the number of molecules reflected according to the laws of reflection to the number striking the surface. Knudsen assumes that, in general, this ratio is practically zero, or the momentum of all the molecules striking a surface is almost completely transferred to the surface. On this assumption he derives the relation $b=\frac{2\cdot88}{\pi}$, and so $\delta=0\cdot917L$.

The expression (241) for the rate of flow of a gas along a tube at very low pressures agrees well with experimental results. As the rate varies as r^3, great resistance to flow is exerted by narrow bore tubes. This is a point to be considered when modern high-speed pumps are exhausting at very low pressures. The rate of flow along the tube connecting the pump to the vessel being exhausted is governed by equation (241), and to use the pump most efficiently it should be joined to the apparatus by tubes which are as short and wide as possible. It is more important that the tube should be wide than short.

137. Flow of Gas at Very Low Pressures through a Hole in a Thin Plate.—It is sometimes important to calculate the amount of gas flowing through a hole in a thin plate when the diameter of the hole is small compared with the mean free path of the molecules. If N_1 and N_2 are the numbers of molecules per c.c. on the two sides of the plate, p_1, p_2, and ρ_1, ρ_2, the corresponding pressures and densities, the resultant mass of gas which passes through 1 sq. cm. per sec. is equal to the difference between the masses which cross both ways, and is given from equation (216) by

$$\frac{N_1cm}{4}-\frac{N_2cm}{4}=\frac{c}{4}(\rho_1-\rho_2),$$

and from equations (213), (200), (197) this is equal to

$$[p_1-p_2]\sqrt{\frac{N_mm}{2\pi R_mT}} \qquad . \qquad . \qquad . \qquad (242)$$

The vapour pressure of highly refractory metals may be determined by means of this formula. Egerton [1] has measured the vapour pressures of zinc, cadmium, and lead, the metals being contained in a small pot provided with a hole of known area. After weighing the pot, it was placed in a silica tube within which a high vacuum was maintained ($p_2=0$), and the tube was inserted in a hole in a large block of copper maintained at a constant temperature. The pot was again weighed at the completion of the experiment, and the loss in weight gave the amount of vapour that had escaped from the orifice. Thus, from equation (242), p_1 could be calculated, $N_m m$ being the molecular weight of the element used. A correction must be applied for the number of molecules that return from the far side, through the hole, to the space occupied by the vapour in equilibrium with the metal.

This formula has also been used by Langmuir [2] to measure the rates at which highly refractory metals evaporate. If the vapour pressure of any substance does not exceed 1 mm. of mercury, the actual evaporation rate is independent of the pressure around it, or, in other words, the evaporation in a high vacuum takes place at the same rate as it does in the presence of the saturated vapour, so that equilibrium is a balance between the evaporation and condensation rates. Now the rate at which the vapour condenses on the metal cannot exceed the rate at which it comes into contact with the metal, and the latter rate is given by equation (242), remembering that p_2 is zero. If it is assumed that every atom of vapour condenses on striking the metal, then this equation represents the relation between the vapour pressure and the rate of evaporation in a vacuum. If, however, a certain proportion, α, of the atoms of vapour is reflected from the surface, then the vapour pressure will be greater than that calculated in the ratio $1 : 1-\alpha$. There are good reasons for believing that this reflection from the surface is negligible.

At the equilibrium stage as many atoms evaporate per second per sq. cm. of surface as condense, and, consequently, equation (242) gives a measure of the evaporation rate at a temperature T. By observing the loss in weight per second of a tungsten filament, it is possible to calculate the vapour pressure of tungsten at this temperature. The filaments are weighed before and after evaporation, and the temperature is determined by means of an optical pyrometer.

138. Radiometer Phenomena.—At very low gas pressures forces known as *radiometric forces* are exerted between two surfaces which are situated close together, the surfaces being maintained at different temperatures. One of the first instruments used for detecting these forces was the radiometer devised by Sir William Crookes. It consists of a glass bulb in which a vane is mounted on a vertical axis. The vane has four arms of aluminium wire to which are attached four small thin mica plates, coated on one side with lamp-

[1] Egerton, *Proc. Roy. Soc.*, A, **103**, 469 (1923).
[2] Langmuir, *Phys. Zeits.*, **14**, 273 (1913).

black. These plates are set so that their planes are parallel to the axis. If a source of heat is brought near the bulb, and the degree of rarefaction inside is correct, the vane rotates. At extremely low pressures the rotation practically ceases. There is a mechanical force exerted between two surfaces maintained at different temperatures, the molecules striking the hotter surface rebounding with a higher average kinetic energy than those which strike the surface at the lower temperature. In the radiometer the blackened surfaces absorb heat from the heat source, and the molecules rebounding from these surfaces are at a higher temperature, or, more strictly, possess greater kinetic energy than those impinging against the other faces, or the walls of the containing vessel. Consequently, momentum is imparted to the vanes and they rotate.

139. The Virial Theorem.—A real gas will differ from the ideal or perfect, gas which was considered in Article 129 in at least two respects. The molecules which were treated as points must have size and shape, and the forces of cohesion are not negligible in the real gas. Thus the various equations deduced in that section, which give the pressure accurately in the case of an ideal gas, only hold approximately for a real gas. Clausius attempted to calculate the relation between pressure, volume, and temperature in an imperfect gas by means of the *Virial Theorem*.

Let x, y, z be the co-ordinates of the position of a molecule, m its mass, r the distance it is away from the origin, and c its resultant velocity. Let X, Y, Z be the components of the external forces acting on the molecule. Since

$$\frac{d^2}{dt^2}(x^2) = 2x\frac{d^2x}{dt^2} + 2\left(\frac{dx}{dt}\right)^2,$$

and

$$m\frac{d^2x}{dt^2} = X,$$

$$\tfrac{1}{2}Xx = \frac{m}{4}\frac{d^2}{dt^2}(x^2) - \frac{m}{2}\left(\frac{dx}{dt}\right)^2.$$

If we add to this equation the two analogous relations relative to the other axes of co-ordinates, then

$$\tfrac{1}{2}[Xx + Yy + Zz] = \frac{m}{4}\frac{d^2}{dt^2}(r^2) - \frac{mc^2}{2} \qquad . \qquad . \quad (243)$$

Taking the mean value of the integral of $\dfrac{m}{4}\dfrac{d^2}{dt^2}(r^2)$ over a period of time t,

$$\frac{m}{4t}\int_0^t \frac{d^2}{dt^2}(r^2)dt = \frac{m}{4t}\left[\left(\frac{dr^2}{dt}\right)_t - \left(\frac{dr^2}{dt}\right)_0\right].$$

The co-ordinates and velocities of the molecules are finite, so that $\left(\dfrac{dr^2}{dt}\right)_t$ and $\left(\dfrac{dr^2}{dt}\right)_0$ are both finite, and if t increases indefinitely,

$$\frac{m}{4t}\int_0^t \frac{d^2}{dt^2}(r^2)dt=0,$$

so that integrating equation (243) and dividing the result by t,

$$\tfrac{1}{2}[\overline{Xx}+\overline{Yy}+\overline{Zz}]+\frac{mC^2}{2}=0, \qquad . \qquad . \qquad (244)$$

where the bars represent the average values, and, summing up for all molecules,

$$\tfrac{1}{2}\Sigma[\overline{Xx}+\overline{Yy}+\overline{Zz}]+E=0, \qquad . \qquad . \qquad (245)$$

E being the steady average value of the kinetic energy.

The expression $\tfrac{1}{2}\Sigma[\overline{Xx}+\overline{Yy}+\overline{Zz}]$ has been called by Clausius the *Virial* of the forces acting upon the gas, and equation (245) is known as the *Virial Theorem*.

140. The Equation of State.—If a uniform pressure, p, acts on the boundary surface enclosing a volume, V, of gas, and we consider an area dS whose normal is inclined at an angle θ with the x axis, then

$$X=-pdS\,.\,cos\,\theta,$$

and

$$\Sigma\overline{Xx}=-\Sigma pdS\,.\,x\,cos\,\theta=-p\Sigma dV=-pV,$$

where dV is an elementary volume of length x along the x axis and of cross-section $dS\,.\,cos\,\theta$. Hence from (244)

$$3pV=mNVC^2, \qquad . \qquad . \qquad (246)$$

or,

$$p=\frac{\rho C^2}{3},$$

where N is the number of molecules per c.c. This is the law for perfect gases.

If the gas is not a perfect one, we must take into account the intermolecular forces. We suppose that the force between two molecules distant r apart is one of repulsion represented by $f(r)$. Let the centres of the two molecules be at x, y, z, and x_1, y_1, z_1, and if X, Y, Z, and X_1, Y_1, Z_1 are the components of the forces acting on them,

$$X=f(r)\frac{x-x_1}{r}, \qquad X_1=f(r)\frac{x_1-x}{r}.$$

The contribution to $\Sigma\overline{Xx}$ made by these two forces is

$$Xx+X_1x_1=\frac{f(r)}{r}[x-x_1]^2.$$

Hence the contribution they make to $\Sigma[\overline{Xx}+\overline{Yy}+\overline{Zz}]$ is

$$\Sigma\left\{\frac{f(r)}{r}\left([x-x_1]^2+[y-y_1]^2+[z-z_1]^2\right)\right\}=\Sigma rf(r),$$

where the summation extends over all pairs of molecules. Thus equation (244) together with (246) gives us

$$\frac{3pV}{2}+\tfrac{1}{2}\Sigma rf(r)=\tfrac{1}{2}\Sigma mC^2.$$

In the summation the force between two particles is to be reckoned once only, and the forces accounted for in the second term are, of course, to be excluded in the third term. In the present application we will suppose all the mutual forces accounted for in the second term. For one particle in the interior, the total of the mutual forces acting upon it is

$$\tfrac{1}{2}\cdot4\pi\int_0^\infty rf(r)r^2dr,$$

and integrating by parts we have, writing $-d[\phi(r)]$ for $f(r)dr$,

$$-2\pi\left[\left\{r^3\phi(r)\right\}_0^\infty-3\int_0^\infty\phi(r)r^2dr\right]=6\pi\int_0^\infty r^2\phi(r)dr,$$

since the first term is zero at both limits. If now we write

$$r\phi(r)dr=-d[\psi(r)],$$

this becomes

$$-6\pi\int_0^\infty rd[\psi(r)],$$

and, integrating by parts,

$$-6\pi\left[\left\{r\psi(r)\right\}_0^\infty-\int_0^\infty\psi(r)dr\right]=3K,$$

from equation (169), since again the first term is zero at both limits.

The summation extended over the whole volume gives $3KV$, but this must be halved, otherwise each force will be reckoned twice, Hence

$$\frac{3pV}{2}+\frac{3KV}{2}=\tfrac{1}{2}\Sigma mC^2,$$

or,

$$[p+K]V=\tfrac{1}{3}\Sigma mC^2,$$

where K is the intrinsic pressure. The latter is proportional to ρ^2, ρ being the density of the gas, and so, since ρ is proportional to $\dfrac{1}{V}$,

$$\left(p+\frac{a}{V^2}\right)V=\tfrac{1}{3}\Sigma mC^2, \qquad . \qquad . \qquad . \quad (247)$$

where a is a constant and we have supposed the particles to be infinitely small.

It is now necessary to consider the effect on the virial of the finite, though small, size of the molecules. Van der Waals [1] showed that in this case the virial of the repulsive forces at impact gives

$$p(V-b)=\tfrac{1}{3}\Sigma mC^2, \qquad . \qquad . \qquad . \quad (248)$$

where for hard spherical masses the value of b is four times the total volumes of the spheres. If the cohesive force be of the character supposed, it exercises no influence upon any particle in the interior and is completely accounted for by the addition to p of $\dfrac{a}{V^2}$, so that as equation (248) is correct when there is no cohesive force, the effect of such is properly represented by

$$\left(p+\frac{a}{V^2}\right)(V-b)=\tfrac{1}{3}\Sigma mC^2,$$

i.e.

$$\left(p+\frac{a}{V^2}\right)(V-b)=nRT, \qquad . \qquad . \quad (249)$$

n being the total number of molecules in the volume V. This is *Van der Waals' equation* connecting p, V, and T.

This equation may be deduced, without using the virial theorem, in the following manner : As the centres of the molecules cannot approach closer than the molecular diameter σ, we may imagine each molecule to be surrounded by the sphere of influence of radius σ, such that the centre of no other molecule may penetrate it. Hence if V is the total volume of the gas, and we consider n to be the total number of molecules in this volume, $(n-1)\tfrac{4}{3}\pi\sigma^3$ is excluded for the centres of the other molecules, *i.e.* the actual volume free from the spheres of influence is $V-\tfrac{4}{3}\pi n\sigma^3$, since n is large compared with unity. Thus the real molecular density is n_1, where

$$n_1=\frac{n}{V-\tfrac{4}{3}\pi n\sigma^3} \cdot \qquad . \qquad . \qquad . \quad (250)$$

When we consider a gas enclosed within a vessel, the centres of the molecules may approach to within a distance $\dfrac{\sigma}{2}$ from the walls, but if a molecule is at a distance σ from the wall, its sphere of influence extends to the wall, and the centre of no molecule can lie within the hemisphere $\tfrac{2}{3}\pi\sigma^3$. Thus, if dV is a volume taken in the vicinity of the walls of the containing vessel, $n_1 \cdot \tfrac{2}{3}\pi\sigma^3$ is the fraction of this volume per c.c. which is not available for the centres of any other

[1] Van der Waals, *Physical Memoirs* (1890).

molecules. So that if dV_1 is the actual amount of dV existing as free space,

$$\frac{dV - dV_1}{dV} = \frac{n_1 \cdot \frac{2}{3}\pi\sigma^3}{1},$$

or,

$$dV_1 = dV(1 - \frac{2}{3}\pi\sigma^3 n_1).$$

Hence from equation (250) $dV_1 = dV\left(1 - \frac{\frac{2}{3}\pi\sigma^3 n}{V}\right)$, approximately.

The actual number of molecules contained in the volume dV is $n_1 dV_1$, where

$$n_1 dV_1 = \frac{n\left(1 - \frac{\frac{2}{3}\pi\sigma^3 n}{V}\right)dV}{V - \frac{4}{3}\pi\sigma^3 n} = \frac{ndV}{V\left(1 - \frac{2}{3}\frac{\pi\sigma^3 n}{V}\right)}, \text{ approximately.}$$

If the molecules were considered as points, this number would be

$$\frac{ndV}{V},$$

so that the effect of the finite size of the molecules is to diminish the volume by $\frac{2}{3}\pi\sigma^3 n$. Hence the gas equation becomes

$$p(V - b) = nRT,$$

where $b = \frac{2}{3}\pi\sigma^3 n$, and represents a volume *four times* as large as the total volume of the molecules present in the volume, V, of gas considered.

When we consider the intermolecular forces between the molecules, the mean effect within the interior of the gas is obviously zero, but for those molecules near the boundary walls of the containing vessel, the resultant internal force is directed towards the interior, and this internal pressure supplements the ordinary pressure. The former is proportional to the number of molecules per c.c. near the boundary surface and to the number per c.c. within the gas, so that the force is proportional to n^2, or it is $\frac{a}{V^2}$ where a is a constant. Van der Waals' equation of state thus reduces to

$$\left(p + \frac{a}{V^2}\right)(V - b) = nRT. \qquad . \qquad . \qquad . \qquad (251)$$

It was proposed to represent by means of it the behaviour of carbon dioxide, but the experimental results for other gases do not agree with the equation. It does, however, represent the isotherms of fluids, and so is a confirmation of the kinetic theory of fluids.

The internal pressure term, $\frac{a}{V^2}$, corresponds to molecular attraction, which varies inversely as the fourth power of the distance between the molecules. Thus, suppose that they are arranged in rows at intervals of l. The attraction which the molecules in one-half of a row exert on those in the other half is $\dfrac{k}{l^d}$, where k is a constant. If we consider a cube of 1 cm. edge, each half of the cube contains $\dfrac{1}{l^2}$ rows, and the total force exerted between the molecules in the two halves will be

$$\frac{1}{l^2} \cdot \frac{k}{l^d} = \frac{k}{l^{d+2}},$$

but

$$n = \frac{1}{l^3} = \frac{\rho}{m},$$

and the internal pressure is, therefore,

$$k\left(\frac{\rho}{m}\right)^{\frac{d+2}{3}} = \frac{k_1}{V^{\frac{d+2}{3}}},$$

where k_1 is a constant.

Thus

$$\frac{a}{V^2} = \frac{k_1}{V^{\frac{d+2}{3}}},$$

i.e.

$$2 = \frac{d+2}{3}, \quad \text{or} \quad d = 4,$$

and the molecular force of attraction varies inversely as the fourth power of the distance between the molecules.

141. Size of the Molecules.—Although it is incorrect to assume that an atom is an impenetrable elastic volume of constant magnitude, there is a certain volume associated with each molecule through which the centre of another molecule cannot pass. The magnitude of the volume depends upon external conditions, *i.e.* the forces exerted when the molecules approach. Two molecules approach each other until their translational kinetic energy is completely transformed into potential energy of repulsion, so that a nearer approach must take place with a rise in temperature, which corresponds to an increase in kinetic energy. Hence the molecular volume decreases at higher temperatures.

The apparent volume, therefore, is caused by repulsive forces between molecules, but the real volume will be less than this. At the absolute zero of temperature there is no translational energy, and the molecule will take up positions where the forces of attraction and repulsion, acting on it, balance. In this case the real and apparent volumes are equal, and the apparent volume is likely to be greater at the zero than at any other temperature, because the velocity of approach is likely to make the molecules approach closer in opposition to their repulsion than otherwise, so that this volume is a superior limit of the apparent molecular volume for temperatures above the absolute zero.

The diameter, σ, of a molecule may be determined from b, the constant in Van der Waals' equation (251) :—

$$\left(p+\frac{a}{V^2}\right)(V-b)=nRT,$$

from which we have, at constant volume,

$$\frac{1}{p}\left(\frac{dp}{dT}\right)_v=\frac{1}{T}\left(1+\frac{a}{pV^2}\right), \qquad . \qquad . \qquad . \qquad (252)$$

which is the pressure coefficient of the gas at constant volume, and may be determined by experiment. Thus if T, p, and V are known, a may be calculated.

At constant pressure we have, neglecting small terms,

$$\frac{1}{V}\left(\frac{dV}{dT}\right)_p=\frac{1}{T}\left(1+\frac{2a}{pV^2}-\frac{b}{V}\right), \qquad . \qquad . \qquad (253)$$

and this is the coefficient of expansion at constant volume, and may be measured experimentally. Hence, if a is known from above, b may be determined, and σ found from the relation $b=\frac{2}{3}\pi n\sigma^3$.

The value of σ may also be calculated from the known mean free paths with the help of equation (226), taking $N=2\cdot705\times10^{19}$, but, in general, the results for σ obtained by this method are larger than those given from Van der Waals' constants. It should be noted that the latter method gives the true volume, whereas in the free path measurements we obtain the cross-section, so that the two sets of values found for σ may be interpreted as indicating that the molecules are not really spherical in shape. For hydrogen and helium the results are concordant, and we assume that the molecules in these gases are spherical. It must be remembered that the apparent, or effective size, is being measured by these methods.

Since the value of η, the coefficient of viscosity, can be determined experimentally, σ may be found with the aid of equation (230). The size of the molecules decreases as the mean molecular velocity increases and, therefore, as the temperature rises, but from Sutherland's formula (231) the value of σ_∞, the diameter of the hard kernel, may be determined.

There appears now to be no doubt that, in the case of monatomic gases, the atoms, when in thermal agitation, behave like hard spheres which exert mutual attraction on one another. When we come to consider the case of diatomic molecules—as, for example, in chlorine gas—we are met by the difficulty that we are no longer entitled to regard the molecule as a sphere. The viscosity formula, however, gives a means of calculating $\pi\sigma^2$, which is the area presented as a target by the molecule to other molecules approaching it from all directions. Thus Rankine [1] obtained the mean target areas for carbon dioxide and nitrous oxide, $0\cdot870\times10^{-15}$ cm. and $0\cdot867\times10^{-15}$ cm., respectively, so that within the limits of experimental error, the molecules of these two gases behave, in the gaseous state, as though they were of identical size and shape. This identity is attributed by Langmuir [2] to the arrangement of the external electrons being the same in the molecules of the two gases.

The molecular radius may also be estimated for a gas from its density in the liquid state. Thus if 1 c.c. of gas is condensed to the liquid condition and the molecules, supposed to be hard spheres, are packed as closely as possible, they would occupy a volume

$$\frac{N\sigma^3}{\sqrt{2}},$$

since, with closest packing, the molecules are associated in triangular pyramidal piles and, if the base of such a pyramid is an equilateral triangle having m molecules in each side, the total number in the pile is

$$\Sigma m + \Sigma(m-1) + \ldots + (2+1) + 1,$$

or,

$$(\Sigma m^2 + \Sigma m)/2 = m(m+1)(m+2)/6 = m^3/6,$$

when m is large.

The volume of the pyramid is

$$V = m^3\sigma^3/6\sqrt{2}.$$

But $m^3/6 = N$, the number of molecules in 1 c.c. of the gas, and hence

$$V = N\sigma^3/\sqrt{2}.$$

If the density of the gas is δ, and that of the resulting liquid Δ, the volume of the liquid is $\frac{\delta}{\Delta}$, and

$$\frac{\delta}{\Delta} = \frac{N\sigma^3}{\sqrt{2}},$$

so that σ may be found, if N is known. The general agreement between the values of σ calculated in this way, and those obtained by the previous methods is fairly satisfactory.

Values for the diameters of molecules together with the mean free path values are given in Table XV. These have been taken from Jeans' *Dynamical Theory of Gases* and Kaye and Laby's Tables. These experimenters take $N = 2\cdot75\times10^{19}$, whereas in Table XV the results are calculated for $N = 2\cdot705\times10^{19}$.

[1] Rankine, *Proc. Roy. Soc.*, A, 98, 373 (1920).
[2] Langmuir, *Journ. Amer. Chem. Soc.*, 41, 868 (1919).

TABLE XV.—SIZE AND FREE PATHS OF MOLECULES

The molecular diameters are calculated by means of the following formulæ :—

1. Viscosity :

$$\eta = 0\cdot499\frac{mc}{\sqrt{2}\pi\sigma^2}, \text{ or } \sigma^2 = \frac{0\cdot499}{\pi\sqrt{2}}\cdot\frac{\rho c}{N\eta}.$$

2. Van der Waals' constant :

$$b = \tfrac{2}{3}\pi N\sigma^3.$$

3. Density of liquids :

$$\frac{\delta}{\varDelta} = \frac{N\sigma^3}{\sqrt{2}}.$$

Gas.	Mean Free Path, L, at N.T.P.	Molecular Diameter σ deduced from		
		η.	b.	$\frac{\delta}{\varDelta}$ (Upper Limit).
Hydrogen .	$11\cdot6 \times 10^{-6}$ cm.	$2\cdot70 \times 10^{-8}$ cm.	$2\cdot53 \times 10^{-8}$ cm.	$3\cdot94 \times 10^{-8}$ cm.
Helium . .	$17\cdot1$,,	$2\cdot18$,,	$1\cdot97$,,	$4\cdot0$,,
Water vapour .	$4\cdot0$,,	$4\cdot58$,,		$3\cdot76$,,
Carbon mon- oxide .	$5\cdot8$,,	$3\cdot81$,,	..	$4\cdot24$,,
Ethylene .	$2\cdot7$,,	$5\cdot57$,,	..	$5\cdot37$,,
Nitrogen. .	$5\cdot7$,,	$3\cdot79$,,	$3\cdot56$,,	$3\cdot98$,,
Air . .	$5\cdot9$,,	$[3\cdot75]$,,	$3\cdot32$,,	..
Nitric oxide .	$5\cdot9$,,	$3\cdot75$,,	..	..
Oxygen . .	$6\cdot3$,,	$3\cdot65$,,	$2\cdot91$,,	$3\cdot72$,,
Argon . .	$6\cdot3$,,	$3\cdot67$,,	$2\cdot87$,,	$4\cdot04$,,
Carbon dioxide	$4\cdot0$,,	$4\cdot58$,,	$3\cdot42$,,	$4\cdot06$,,
Nitrous oxide .	$3\cdot9$,,	$4\cdot64$,,	..	$4\cdot65$,,
Methyl chloride	$2\cdot6$,,	$5\cdot67$,,	..	$4\cdot93$,,
Ethyl chloride .	$2\cdot2$,,	$6\cdot17$,,	..	$5\cdot31$,,
Chlorine . .	$2\cdot9$,,	$5\cdot41$,,	..	$4\cdot63$,,
Benzene . .	$1\cdot5$,,	$7\cdot50$,,	..	$5\cdot87$,,
Krypton. .	$4\cdot9$,,	$4\cdot13$,,	$3\cdot16$,,	$4\cdot46$,,
Xenon . .	$3\cdot5$,,	$4\cdot88$,,	$3\cdot45$,,	$4\cdot50$,,

If e be the charge of electricity carried by the hydrogen atom in electrolysis, and N_m the number of atoms in 1 gram-molecule of hydrogen, it is known from experiments on the electrolysis of solutions that

$$N_m e = 9647 \text{ electro-magnetic units.}$$

The value of e is $4\cdot802 \times 10^{-10}$ electrostatic unit so that $N_m = 6\cdot023 \times 10^{23}$.

The absolute mass of a hydrogen atom is equal to $\frac{1}{N_m}$, hence it is $1\cdot673 \times 10^{-24}$ gm. As the density of hydrogen is $8\cdot987 \times 10^{-5}$ gm. per c.c., $N = 2\cdot687 \times 10^{19}$ per c.c.

Chapman [1] obtained a general expression for the velocity distribution function of a gas in which the mean velocity and temperature vary from point to point, the molecules possessing spherical symmetry, and the state being such that the molecular paths are sensibly

[1] Chapman, *Phil. Trans.*, **216**, 379 (1916).

rectilinear for the greater part of the time between successive collisions. In addition, the duration of a collision is assumed to be small, compared with the time between successive collisions, and the mean free path is small compared with the space variation of pressure, density, and temperature. The formulæ obtained have been worked out in detail for three special types of molecules : (a) point centres of force varying as the inverse nth power of the distance, (b) rigid elastic spheres, (c) rigid elastic attracting spheres. The diameters of the molecules calculated on the hypothesis that they attract one another (Table XVI) are less than those calculated on the hypothesis that no such forces exist (Table XV), the apparent size in the latter case including part of the extension of the field of force of the molecule. The results differ to a slight extent from those calculated by Chapman himself, owing to the adoption in the present calculation of Millikan's value $2 \cdot 705 \times 10^{19}$ for the number of molecules per c.c. at S.T.P. The values of the diameters calculated from the constant b of Van der Waals' Law are also given for comparison. The agreement between the two sets of values is in most cases remarkable, and the table as a whole is a testimony to the close numerical accuracy now attained by the kinetic theory ; where there is disagreement in the table, there is, in most cases, uncertainty as to the data.

While exact agreement may be expected only for monatomic gases, the values for diatomic gases show that the theory gives a mean diameter in the case of other gases which agrees with that found from values of b (see Table XVI).

Bragg [1] has estimated the dimensions of certain atoms from X-ray measurements. He regards his values as measures of the diameters of the outer electron shells of the respective atoms, and comparing his results with the values obtained from the kinetic theory, it is

TABLE XVI.—MOLECULAR DIAMETERS FOR ATTRACTING SPHERES

Gas.	σ measured from	
	η.	b.
Argon . . .	$2 \cdot 87 \times 10^{-8}$ cm.	$2 \cdot 87 \times 10^{-8}$ cm.
Krypton . .	3·15 ,,	3·16 ,,
Xenon . . .	3·50 ,,	3·45 ,,
Helium . . .	1·91 ,,	1·97 ,,
Oxygen . . .	2·96 ,,	2·91 ,,
Hydrogen . .	2·38 ,,	2·53 ,,
Nitrogen . .	3·13 ,,	$\begin{cases} 3 \cdot 56 \ ,, \\ 3 \cdot 10 \ ,, \end{cases}$
Air . . .	3·11 ,,	3·32 ,,
Carbon dioxide .	$\begin{cases} 3 \cdot 23 \ ,, \\ 3 \cdot 30 \ ,, \end{cases}$	3·22 ,, 3·42 ,,

[1] Bragg, *Phil. Mag.*, **40**, 169 (1920) ; **2**, 258 (1926).

seen that, from the latter theory, the moving atoms of a gas do not approach so closely during an encounter that even the outer electrons intermingle. The atom, in so far as collision is concerned, is to be regarded as a hard elastic sphere of radius $\frac{\sigma}{2}$, which is quite definitely greater than the distance d between the centre of the atom and its outer electrons. The ratios in column 4, Table XVII, show that the relation between these two radii is not one of strict proportionality, but depends on the particular type of atom. For further details the reader is advised to consult Bragg's papers.

TABLE XVII.—MOLECULAR DIAMETERS (BRAGG)

Gas.	Molecular Diameter.		
	From Crystal Measurements. $2d$.	From Viscosity Measurements. σ.	Ratio $\frac{2d}{\sigma}$.
Neon . .	$1 \cdot 30 \times 10^{-8}$ cm.	$2 \cdot 35 \times 10^{-8}$ cm.	0·553
Argon . .	2·05 ,,	2·87 ,,	0·714
Krypton . .	2·35 ,,	3·15 ,,	0·746
Xenon . .	2·70 ,,	3·50 ,,	0·771

EXAMPLES

1. Show that the average kinetic energy of translation of the gas molecules in a given volume is three-quarters that of the molecules which collide during some period of the time with the wall of the containing vessel.

2. Assuming the Maxwellian distribution of velocities among the molecules of a gas, find the relation between the mean velocity, c, the mean square velocity, C, and the most probable velocity, c_0.

$$[c/C = \sqrt{8/3\pi} \; ; \quad c_0/C = \sqrt{2/3}.]$$

3. If the molecules of a gas are considered to be hard elastic spheres, of mass m and diameter σ, show that the total number of collisions per unit volume per unit time between the molecules which are moving with relative velocity between v and $v+dv$ is

$$\rho^2\sigma^2[\pi m^3/16R^3T^3]^{\frac{1}{2}}e^{-mv^2/4RT}v^3dv,$$

where T is the temperature, ρ the molecular density, and R is the universal gas constant.

4. The ratio of the principal specific heats of helium is 1·66, the value for air is 1·40, that for sulphur dioxide is 1·29, and that for ethyl ether is 1·024. How do you account for these values?

5. Assuming the density of hydrogen to be 0·089 gm. per litre, find the mean square velocity of hydrogen molecules at standard temperature and pressure. [$1 \cdot 7 \times 10^5$ cm. per sec.]

6. Assuming the ordinary values of such physical constants as you require, calculate the intrinsic energy of air at 15° C. and 75 cm. pressure.

$[2 \cdot 02 \times 10^9$ ergs per gm.$]$

7. Determine the mean free path and collision frequency for air molecules at standard temperature and pressure, given that the viscosity is $1 \cdot 7 \times 10^{-4}$ C.G.S. units and the density $1 \cdot 29$ gm. per litre.

$[8 \cdot 2 \times 10^{-6}$ cm. ; $5 \cdot 9 \times 10^9.]$

8. Calculate the molecular diameter, the total number of molecules per c.c. and the mass of a molecule of oxygen. Density of oxygen gas is $1 \cdot 43$ gm. per litre ; density of liquid oxygen $1 \cdot 24$ gm. per c.c. ; mean free path of the molecules $6 \cdot 3 \times 10^{-6}$ cm.

$[4 \cdot 6 \times 10^{-8}$ cm. ; $4 \cdot 9 \times 10^{19}$; $2 \cdot 9 \times 10^{-23}$ gm.$]$

9. Show that the constant b in Van der Waal's equation represents approximately four times the proper volume of the molecules of the fluid.

CHAPTER IX

FOURIER'S THEOREM AND FOURIER SERIES

142. Fourier's Theorem.—The composition of simple harmonic vibrations of commensurate periods may result in periodic motions of various characters, and they may be studied by means of an important theorem, introduced by Fourier in his renowned *Analytical Theory of Heat*. It may be formally enunciated as follows :—

Any finite periodic motion may be produced by a suitable combination of commensurate simple harmonic motions of suitable amplitudes and phases.

The theorem also shows how to determine the amplitudes and phases of the components required to produce any given resultant. In other words, it shows how to analyse any given periodic motion, however complicated, into the simple harmonic components of which it may be conceived to be compounded.

Analytically, the theorem may be expressed thus : If $y=f(x)$ is any continuous function of the independent variable, x, between the limits $x=0$ and $x=2\pi$, then, also between these limits,

$$f(x)=A_0+A_1 \cos x+A_2 \cos 2x+ \ldots +A_n \cos nx+ \ldots$$
$$+B_1 \sin x+B_2 \sin 2x+ \ldots +B_n \sin nx+ \ldots \quad (254)$$

A rigid proof of this is beyond the scope of this book, but the possibility of the expansion—which at first acquaintance seems to be very limited—is illustrated by the following argument.

Let (x_1y_1), (x_2y_2), (x_3y_3) be any three pairs of conjugate values in the equation $y=f(x)$, then, substituting these values in

$$y=A_0+A_1 \cos x+B_1 \sin x,$$

we have

$$y_1=A_0+A_1 \cos x_1+B_1 \sin x_1,$$
$$y_2=A_0+A_1 \cos x_2+B_1 \sin x_2,$$
$$y_3=A_0+A_1 \cos x_3+B_1 \sin x_3,$$

and these equations may be solved for A_0, A_1, and B_1. We thus compel coincidence of these two equations in the three selected places. Similarly, the two equations

$$y=f(x),$$

and

$$y=A_0+A_1 \cos x+ \ldots +A_n \cos nx+B_1 \sin x+ \ldots +B_n \sin nx,$$

may be made to coincide in $(2n+1)$ selected places. If n be made infinitely great, the two equations agree at an infinity of values and this suggests the possibility of a point-by-point agreement.

The series resulting from such an analysis of a given function all come within the scope of the full expansion given in equation (254) and are called *Fourier series*.

143. Evaluation of the Coefficients.—If each term of the right-hand side of equation (254) is multiplied by dx and integrated, we have

$$\int f(x)dx = A_0\int dx + A_1\int \cos x.dx + \ldots + A_n\int \cos nx.dx + \ldots$$

$$+ B_1\int \sin x.dx + \ldots + B_n\int \sin nx.dx + \ldots$$

and every term, except the first, disappears for the limits 0 and 2π, giving

$$\int_0^{2\pi} f(x)dx = 2\pi A_0 \quad \text{or} \quad A_0 = \frac{1}{2\pi}\int_0^{2\pi} f(x)dx \qquad . \quad (255)$$

Now multiply each side of equation (254) by $\cos nx.dx$ and integrate. Thus

$$\int f(x) \cos nx.dx = A_0\int \cos nx.dx + A_1\int \cos x \cos nx.dx + \ldots$$

$$+ A_n\int \cos^2 nx.dx + \ldots + A_m\int \cos mx \cos nx.dx + \ldots$$

$$+ B_1\int \sin x \cos nx.dx + \ldots + B_n\int \sin nx \cos nx.dx + \ldots$$

$$+ B_m\int \sin mx \cos nx.dx + \ldots$$

On integrating from 0 to 2π, each of the integrals on the right-hand side is zero except

$$A_n\int_0^{2\pi} \cos^2 nx.dx = \tfrac{1}{2}A_n\int_0^{2\pi}(1 + \cos 2nx)dx = \pi A_n,$$

and thus

$$A_n = \frac{1}{\pi}\int_0^{2\pi} f(x) \cos nx.dx \qquad . \qquad . \qquad . \quad (256)$$

Similarly, by multiplying both sides of equation (254) by $\sin nx.dx$ and integrating from 0 to 2π, we have

$$B_n = \frac{1}{\pi}\int_0^{2\pi} f(x) \sin nx.dx \qquad . \qquad . \qquad . \quad (257)$$

Thus the theorem may be written in the form :—

$$f(x) = \frac{1}{2\pi}\int_0^{2\pi} f(x)dx + \sum_{n=1}^{n=\infty} \frac{\cos nx}{\pi}\int_0^{2\pi} f(x) \cos nx.dx$$

$$+ \sum_{n=1}^{n=\infty} \frac{\sin nx}{\pi}\int_0^{2\pi} f(x) \sin nx.dx \qquad . \quad (258)$$

Before developing the theorem to make it applicable outside the narrow limitations of the range 0 to 2π, it will be useful to point out three special features of the coincidence which has been assumed between the arbitrary function $f(x)$ and the corresponding Fourier expansion.

(i) At a discontinuity in $f(x)$ between 0 and 2π, the series gives the mean value of $f(x)$ on the two sides of the discontinuity.

(ii) At 0 and 2π, the value of the series is again the mean of the values of $f(x)$ at each of these points.

(iii) It is not necessary that $f(x)$ should have the same mathematical form throughout the range 0 and 2π. If it has different values, then, in the integration, each must be integrated between its own limits. Thus if $y = f_1(x)$ from 0 to l and $y = f_2(x)$ from l to 2π, we have

$$A_0 = \frac{1}{2\pi} \left[\int_0^l f_1(x)dx + \int_l^{2\pi} f_2(x)dx \right],$$

and similarly for A_n and B_n.

144. Example of a Fourier Expansion.—Let $y = x$ from $x = 0$ to $x = 2\pi$, *i.e.* $f(x) = x$ and

$$A_0 = \frac{1}{2\pi} \int_0^{2\pi} x \, . \, dx = \pi,$$

$$A_n = \frac{1}{\pi} \int_0^{2\pi} x \cos nx \, . \, dx = \frac{1}{n\pi} \int_0^{2\pi} x \, . \, d(\sin nx).$$

Integrating by parts,

$$A_n = \frac{1}{n\pi} \left[\left(x \sin nx \right)_0^{2\pi} - \int_0^{2\pi} \sin nx \, . \, dx \right],$$

and both these terms disappear when the limits are applied. Thus there are no cosine terms in the expansion. Also

$$B_n = \frac{1}{\pi} \int_0^{2\pi} x \sin nx \, . \, dx = -\frac{1}{n\pi} \left[\left(x \cos nx \right)_0^{2\pi} - \int_0^{2\pi} \cos nx \, . \, dx \right] = -\frac{2}{n},$$

and thus we have

$$y = x = \pi - 2[\sin x + \tfrac{1}{2} \sin 2x + \tfrac{1}{3} \sin 3x + \, . \, . \, .].$$

It is interesting and instructive to see how a few of the terms of this series combine graphically to approximate to the straight line $y = x$. Fig. 84 shows the result of graphing,

(a) $y = \pi - 2 \sin x$,
(b) $y = \pi - 2 \sin x - \sin 2x$,
(c) $y = \pi - 2 \sin x - \sin 2x - \tfrac{2}{3} \sin 3x$.

It will be seen that a gradual approach to the line $y = x$ is obtained as the number of terms increases. This example, however, is not very rapidly convergent, and in many cases terms beyond the first three, or four, produce only a small effect.

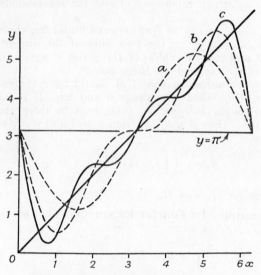

Fig. 84.—Fourier Expansion of $y=x$.

145. Extension of the Range.—In practical cases the function to be analysed rarely recurs at intervals of 2π, so it is necessary, in order to give the analysis a desirable flexibility, to develop the expansion to cover the more generalised range from 0 to, say, $2l$.

Let a quantity z be defined by $z=\dfrac{xl}{\pi}$, so that $dx=\dfrac{\pi}{l}dz$, and at $x=0$, $z=0$; at $x=2\pi$, $z=2l$. Also $f(x)=\phi(z)$.

Substituting for $f(x)$, x and dx in the generalised expansion (258) we have

$$\phi(z)=\frac{1}{2\pi}\int_0^{2l}\phi(z)\frac{\pi}{l}dz+\sum_{n=1}^{n=\infty}\frac{1}{\pi}\cos\frac{n\pi z}{l}\int_0^{2l}\phi(z)\frac{\pi}{l}\cos\frac{n\pi z}{l}dz$$

$$+\sum_{n=1}^{n=\infty}\frac{1}{\pi}\sin\frac{n\pi z}{l}\int_0^{2l}\phi(z)\frac{\pi}{l}\sin\frac{n\pi z}{l}dz$$

$$=\frac{1}{2l}\int_0^{2l}\phi(z)dz+\sum_{n=1}^{n=\infty}\frac{1}{l}\cos\frac{n\pi z}{l}\int_0^{2l}\phi(z)\cos\frac{n\pi z}{l}dz$$

$$+\sum_{n=1}^{n=\infty}\frac{1}{l}\sin\frac{n\pi z}{l}\int_0^{2l}\phi(z)\sin\frac{n\pi z}{l}dz.$$

If, now, z is identified with the independent variable x, and $\phi(z)$ with the arbitrary function $f(x)$, then, over the range $x=0$ to $x=2l$,

$$f(x)=\frac{1}{2l}\int_0^{2l} f(x)dx + \sum_{n=1}^{n=\infty} \frac{1}{l} \cos \frac{n\pi x}{l} \int_0^{2l} f(x) \cos \frac{n\pi x}{l} dx$$

$$+ \sum_{n=1}^{n=\infty} \frac{1}{l} \sin \frac{n\pi x}{l} \int_0^{2l} f(x) \sin \frac{n\pi x}{l} dx \quad . \quad (259)$$

146. Displacement Curves.—Let $x=t$. Then $y=f(t)$ is the displacement curve of any vibrating system, and the range is from 0 to the periodic time t_0. If we put $\frac{2\pi}{t_0}=\omega$, the expansion (259) is changed by the substitution of t_0 for $2l$, and $\omega=\frac{2\pi}{t_0}$ for $\frac{2\pi}{2l}$, or $\frac{\pi}{l}$, and becomes

$$(t)=\frac{1}{t_0}\int_0^{t_0} f(t)dt + \sum_{n=1}^{n=\infty} \frac{2}{t_0} \cos n\omega t \int_0^{t_0} f(t) \cos n\omega t . dt$$

$$+ \sum_{n=1}^{n=\infty} \frac{2}{t_0} \sin n\omega t \int_0^{t_0} f(t) \sin n\omega t . dt \quad . \quad (260)$$

But we may write

$$A_1 \cos \omega t + B_1 \sin \omega t = C_1 \cos (\omega t - \delta_1),$$

where $C_1=\sqrt{A_1{}^2+B_1{}^2}$ and $\tan \delta_1=\frac{B_1}{A_1}$, and the analysis of the displacement curve may be written in the following form :—

$$f(t)=C_0+C_1 \cos (\omega t - \delta_1) + \ldots + C_n \cos (n\omega t - \delta_n) + \ldots, \text{ etc.,} \quad (261)$$

where

$$C_0=A_0 ; \qquad C_1=\sqrt{A_1{}^2+B_1{}^2} ; \qquad C_n=\sqrt{A_n{}^2+B_n{}^2},$$

and

$$\tan \delta_1=\frac{B_1}{A_1} ; \qquad \tan \delta_n=\frac{B_n}{A_n}.$$

In equation (261) C_2, etc., give the amplitudes of the harmonic overtones present, and δ_2, δ_3, etc., the phases.

147. Partial Fourier Series.—In analysing the function $y=x$ it was noted that the expansion contains no cosine terms. Similarly, an expansion may have no sine terms. Such expansions are called *partial Fourier series*, and their occurrence may be foreseen by an examination of the type of symmetry shown by the graph of the function to be analysed. For example,

$$\cos n\omega t = \cos (2n\pi - n\omega t) = \cos n\omega (t_0 - t),$$

and the curve

$$A_0 + A_1 \cos \omega t + \ldots + A_n \cos n\omega t + \ldots \quad . \quad (262)$$

must be symmetrical about the *middle ordinate* of the range, *i.e.*
ordinates equidistant from $t=\dfrac{t_0}{2}$ are *equal and of the same sign*. Conversely, if this type of symmetry exists in the displacement curve, it
may be assumed that expression (262) is its Fourier expansion. This
is illustrated in Fig. 85 (*a*), which would yield such an expansion.

Also, since

$$sin\ n\omega t=-sin\ (2n\pi-n\omega t)=-sin\ (t_0-t),$$

the curve

$$B_1\ sin\ \omega t+\ .\ .\ .\ +B_n\ sin\ n\omega t+\ .\ .\ .\qquad .\quad (263)$$

is symmetrical about the *middle point* of the range, *i.e.* ordinates
equidistant from $t=\dfrac{t_0}{2}$ are of *equal* magnitude but are *opposite in*
sign. For a curve yielding the series (263) as its expansion, see
Fig. 85 (*b*).

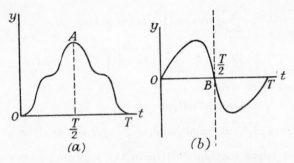

FIG. 85.—SYMMETRY OF PARTIAL FOURIER SERIES.

148. Analysis into Partial Fourier Series.—If the function
$f(x)$ to be analysed is given between the limits $x=0$ and $x=l$, then
its expansion into a Fourier series may be made in different ways,
according to the type of symmetry it is assumed to have beyond
this range. In the first place it may be assumed to have the same
form from l to $2l$, from $2l$ to $3l$, *etc.*, *i.e.* the given value $f(x)$ occurs
periodically at intervals of l. This makes 0 to l the whole range,
and the full series occurs in the expansion, while the coefficients
have the values,

$$A_0=\frac{1}{l}\int_0^l f(x)dx,\qquad A_n=\frac{2}{l}\int_0^l f(x)\ cos\ \frac{2n\pi x}{l}dx,$$

$$B_n=\frac{2}{l}\int_0^l f(x)\ sin\ \frac{2n\pi x}{l}dx\qquad .\quad (264)$$

Secondly, it may be assumed that l is half the range, and that the
graph is symmetrical about the ordinate $x=l$, *i.e.* it may resemble

the curve in Fig. 85 (*a*), where *OA* represents graphically the given function. In this case the expansion is given by a *half-range cosine series* of the form expressed by (262), *i.e.*

$$y = f(x) = A_0 + A_1 \cos \frac{\pi x}{l} + \ldots + A_n \cos \frac{n \pi x}{l} + \ldots , \quad (265)$$

where

$$\left. \begin{array}{l} A_0 = \dfrac{1}{2l} \displaystyle\int_0^{2l} f(x) dx = \dfrac{1}{l} \displaystyle\int_0^l f(x) dx, \\[2mm] A_n = \dfrac{1}{l} \displaystyle\int_0^{2l} f(x) \cos \dfrac{n \pi x}{l} dx = \dfrac{2}{l} \displaystyle\int_0^l f(x) \cos \dfrac{n \pi x}{l} dx. \end{array} \right\} \quad (266)$$

The second formulæ follow because the integrals have the same values in the two halves of the range.

Finally, we may suppose that *l* is half the range and the curve is symmetrical about the middle point $y = 0$, $x = l$; thus it is of the type Fig. 85 (*b*), where *OB* is the given function. The expansion then becomes a *half-range sine series*, similar to (263),

$$y = f(x) = B_1 \sin \frac{\pi x}{l} + \ldots + B_n \sin \frac{n \pi x}{l} + , \ldots \quad (267)$$

where

$$B_n = \frac{1}{l} \int_0^{2l} f(x) \sin \frac{n \pi x}{l} dx = \frac{2}{l} \int_0^l f(x) \sin \frac{n \pi x}{l} dx \quad (268)$$

It is, of course, the second formula in each of the equations (266) and (268) which is used in the calculations of the coefficients, since, over this range of values of x, $f(x)$ has the value given.

149. Fourier Series as the Solution of an Important Type of Differential Equation.—The discussion of an important type of differential equation, which is of special importance in problems of heat and diffusion, has been introduced at this stage because its solution involves series of the Fourier type. The equation is

$$\frac{\partial c}{\partial t} = k \frac{\partial^2 c}{\partial x^2} \quad \cdot \quad \cdot \quad \cdot \quad \cdot \quad (269)$$

A solution of the form $c = B e^{Rt} \sin mx$ may be tried. If this is substituted in equation (269) it gives $R = -m^2 k$, and a similar result is obtained by putting $c = A e^{Rt} \cos mx$. Thus the solution may be written

$$c = A_0 + B_0 x + A_1 e^{-m_1^2 kt} \cos m_1 x + A_2 e^{-m_2^2 kt} \cos m_2 x + \ldots$$
$$+ A_n e^{-m_n^2 kt} \cos m_n x + \ldots + B_1 e^{-m_1^2 kt} \sin m_1 x$$
$$+ B_2 e^{-m_2^2 kt} \sin m_2 x + \ldots + B_n e^{-m_n^2 kt} \sin m_n x + \ldots \quad (270)$$

where $A_0, A_1, \ldots, B_1, \ldots, m_1$, etc., have values which will be determined by the initial conditions.

If when $t = 0$, c is given for some range of x from 0 to l, say, by $c = f(x)$, then equation (270) reduces to

$$f(x) = A_0 + B_0 x + A_1 \cos m_1 x + \ldots + A_n \cos m_n x + \ldots + B_1 \sin m_1 x$$
$$+ \ldots + B_n \sin m_n x + \ldots \quad (271)$$

But it has already been shown that $f(x)$ may be expanded into different Fourier series over the range $x=0$ to $x=l$. The choice of the appropriate form will depend on boundary and final conditions, but equation (271) will, in all cases, reduce to one of the expansions described in the previous article, and the coefficients of equation (271), and thus of (270), will be given by the appropriate coefficient given in equations (264), (266), and (268). In addition, the m's now take the values of (259) without loss of generality. It will be seen that, beyond the present simplification, each problem must be considered individually, since the final form of the solution depends so much on the special conditions. A complete example is discussed in Article 160, while applications are also made in Article 209.

EXAMPLES

1. Show that if a periodic function is displaced by half the range and the new function is added to the first, the result gives twice the sum of the independent term and even harmonics ; when the second is subtracted from the first, the result is twice the sum of the odd harmonics.

2. Prove that the root mean square value of a periodic function is equal to $[A_0{}^2+\frac{1}{2}(\Sigma A^2+\Sigma B^2)]^{\frac{1}{2}}$ where A_0, A, and B are the usual Fourier coefficients.

3. An alternating electromotive force of sine form is applied to a full-wave rectifier. Obtain an expression for the rectified current in harmonic series.
$$[(4A/\pi)\{\tfrac{1}{2}-(cos\ 2\omega t)/3-(cos\ 4\omega t)/15-(cos\ 6\omega t)/35-\ \ldots\}.]$$

4. Find a harmonic series which will represent the current in a circuit consisting of a diode valve of impedance R to which an alternating E.M.F. $E\ sin\ \omega t$ is applied.
$$[C=(E/2\pi R)\{2+\pi\ sin\ \omega t-4[(cos\ 2\omega t)/3+(cos\ 4\omega t)/15+\ \ldots]\}.]$$

5. A quantity y has the value a from $x=0$ to $x=\pi$ and $-a$ from $x=\pi$ to $x=2\pi$. Express y as a Fourier expression in x.
$$[(4a/\pi)\{sin\ x+(sin\ 3x)/3+(sin\ 5x)/5+\ \ldots\}.]$$

6. If $y=x^2$ over the range $x=0$ to $x=l$, find a full Fourier expansion for y for points inside these limits.
$$[l^2/3+(l^2/\pi^2)\{cos\ \beta x+(cos\ 2\beta x)/4+\ \ldots\}$$
$$-(l^2/\pi)\{sin\ \beta x+(sin\ 2\beta x)/2+\ \ldots\}].\quad (\beta=\pi/l).$$

7. Express x^2 from $x=0$ to $x=l$ as a cosine series.
$$[l^2/3-(4l^2/\pi^2)\{cos\ \beta x-(cos\ 2\beta x)/4+(cos\ 3\beta x)/9-\ \ldots\}].\quad (\beta=\pi/l).$$

8. A displacement curve has the following shape : $y=4at/T$ from $t=0$ to $T/4$, $y=2a-4at/T$ from $t=T/4$ to $3T/4$, $y=4at/T-4a$ from $t=3T/4$ to T. Find the amplitude of the fundamental and of the first two harmonics.
$$[8a/\pi^2\ ;\ \ 8a/9\pi^2\ ;\ \ 8a/25\pi^2.]$$

9. A condenser is charged rapidly and then discharged through a high resistance at equal intervals of T sec., so that the current, y, it supplies is given from 0 to T by $log\ y=log\ B-kt$. Show, by a Fourier analysis, that the amplitude of the harmonic of period T/n is $2B(1-e^{-kt})/T\ \sqrt{(k^2+n^2\omega^2)}$ where $\omega T=2\pi$.

10. A metal bar at temperature 0° C., and of length l, thermal conductivity k, density d and specific heat s has one end suddenly raised to, and maintained at, T° C., while the other is maintained at 0° C. If no heat can flow through the sides of the bar, find an expression for the temperature at any point distant x from the cold end at any time t.

$[Tx/l - (2T/\pi l)\{e^{\alpha t} \sin \beta x - (e^{4\alpha t} \sin 2\beta x)/2 + (e^{9\alpha t} \sin 3\beta x)/3 + \ldots \}.]$

$(\beta = \pi/l; \quad \alpha = -k\beta^2/ds.)$

CHAPTER X

OSMOSIS AND DIFFUSION

150. Osmosis.—A bladder full of alcohol becomes distended when immersed in water, but if the bladder contains water and is immersed in alcohol, it shrinks. This is explained by the fact that the membrane is permeable by water but not by alcohol, so that the passage of the former through its walls is not compensated by a reciprocal movement of the latter. The bladder thus has a property of selective transmission, and its action may be compared to that of a sieve whose meshes are sufficiently coarse to allow small particles to pass through while rejecting others of greater size. Such a membrane is said to be *semi-permeable*, and this process of preferential transmission, which is called *osmosis*, has an important part in many organic functions both animal and vegetable.

Different semi-permeable membranes vary in their characteristic demarcation between transmitted and rejected substances. Thus, a colloidal film such as a piece of bladder is traversed by crystalloids as well as by water, but colloids are not transmitted. This peculiar property was utilised by Graham for the separation of crystalloids from colloids and is termed *dialysis*. Other membranes differentiate between classes of crystalloids, while others are permeable practically only by water. Thus the type of separation desired, or the special kind of osmotic action to be studied, needs a particular selection of the semi-permeable membrane to be used. One, which was of great service in the early study of osmotic laws, is caused by the interaction of copper sulphate and potassium ferrocyanide. The precipitated cupric ferrocyanide is permeable by water but not by sugar. The film is mechanically weak, but if a porous pot containing copper sulphate stands in a solution of potassium ferrocyanide, the chemical action and precipitation occur in the pores of the vessel and thus the film receives the necessary support.

151. Osmotic Pressure.—If a porous pot impregnated by the membrane described above contains a sugar solution and is immersed in water, the selective transmission causes an accumulation of water inside the vessel, with a consequent rise in the level of its liquid. The process ceases when a definite excess pressure is thereby produced. This pressure, which is called the *osmotic pressure*, clearly equals the difference of pressure which must initially be present on the solution side of the membrane if no osmotic action is to result. The experiment may be explained in terms of molecular motion. The walls of the membrane are continually receiving impacts from the water molecules on one side and from a mixture of water and

286

sugar molecules on the other. Since the sugar is refused transmission there will be an initial excess inflow of water. The accumulating excess pressure inside the vessel assists the escape of water from the inside and tends to lessen the inflow. When a state of dynamic equilibrium is reached, the exchange of molecules is balanced and the rise of pressure ceases. It is to be expected that the osmotic pressure will increase with an increasing strength of original sugar solution, or, in a more general case, with greater difference in the concentrations on the two sides of the membrane, since the pressure results from the presence of the sugar particles among the bombarding molecules. If the concentration is the same on both sides of the membrane, there is obviously no osmotic pressure.

The mechanism of the passage of a liquid through a membrane is not fully understood. It may be, as the previous analogy suggests, a purely physical process dependent on the relative sizes of the molecules in the solution and the pores of the membrane. On the other hand, it is possible that loose chemical compounds are formed between the membrane and the solvent, and that these compounds, gradually saturating the membrane, decompose on its other side where the concentration of the solvent is less. Another possible explanation depends upon the difference in surface tension which may exist between the membrane and the solution, or solvent. The surface tension of salt solutions is different from that of pure water, and the surface energy of a solid in contact with a solution is less than with pure water, so that the layer of liquid in contact with the solid will become richer in salt than the bulk of the solution.[1] As the solution flows through the capillary tubes, the salt will collect along the walls and the faster-moving central regions will have a diminished concentration. The effect is that the liquid finally comes through as pure water. Similar considerations may explain the behaviour of semi-permeable membranes in which the pores act as capillaries.

The expression " osmotic pressure of a solution " is, speaking strictly, incorrect, inasmuch as a solution does not of itself possess any osmotic pressure, and the term is used somewhat loosely to denote the hydrostatic or mechanical pressure which would be produced if the solution were separated from the pure solvent by a membrane permeable only by the latter. A realisation that osmotic pressure is produced by osmosis and not *vice versa* will prevent the common confusion which gives rise to the idea that osmotic pressure acts in an unusual manner, by causing a movement from a lower to a higher pressure level.

152. The Laws of Osmosis.—The main quantitative features of osmosis were discovered by Pfeffer. Investigating the connection between osmotic pressure and solution strength, he found that the relation for non-electrolytic solutions was one of direct proportion-

---

[1] See Gibbs' Theorem, Article 101, Chapter VI.

ality, so that, if P is the osmotic pressure of a solution of concentration c gram-molecules per c.c., the law may be written

$$P \propto c.$$

He also found that, at least approximately, the osmotic pressure P is proportional, for a given solution of constant strength, to the absolute temperature, or

$$P \propto T.$$

If these laws are combined and if, instead of considering c the concentration, we use the volume V of solution, which contains 1 gram molecule of solute, then, since $c = \dfrac{1}{V}$,

$$PV = RT, \qquad . \qquad . \qquad . \qquad . \qquad (272)$$

where R is a constant.

With electrolytic solutions the results, as would be expected, are more complicated, owing to the dissociation which accompanies solution in such cases. With very dilute solutions, in which dissociation is practically complete, the osmotic pressures are nearly double those given by equation (272), while very strong solutions approximate in effect more closely to the formula. This difference between electrolytic and non-conducting liquids is quite general and applies in all the other results of osmosis.

Van 't Hoff propounded the kinetic theory of solutions and deduced, on thermodynamical grounds, that $P \propto T$ if the solution is so dilute that the heat effect of further dilution is negligible. The formula $PV = RT$ was put forward by Van 't Hoff only for solutions of infinite dilution, and consideration of the factors influencing the departure of gases from Charles' and Boyle's Laws will lead to the anticipation that, for any except dilute solutions, the simple van 't Hoff relation will err to a degree which becomes more marked with increasing concentrations.

An outline of Van 't Hoff's method is given below. Consider an involatile liquid solvent whose volume, at constant temperature, is unaltered by a dissolved gas. Commencing with a volume v of gas under pressure p_0 and with a volume V of liquid just sufficient to dissolve the gas under the same pressure, allow the gas to expand until its rarity is such that no sensible dissipation of energy occurs when contact with the liquid is established. The gas is then compressed until, just as it disappears through solution under rising pressure, the pressure rises to p_0. The operation must be conducted at constant temperature and so slowly that the condition never deviates sensibly from that of equilibrium. The process is accordingly reversible.

Imagine that the liquid and gas are confined under a piston in a cylinder of unit cross-section. During the first stage—that of expansion—contact is prevented by a partition inserted at the liquid surface. Let the distance of the piston from this partition be x, so that initially, $x=v$. At any further stage the pressure p is given by $p=\dfrac{p_0 v}{x}$, so that the work done during expansion is

$$p_0 v \int_v^x \frac{dx}{x}=p_0 v \log \frac{x}{v}, \qquad . \qquad . \qquad . \qquad (273)$$

where x is large compared with v. During condensation the partition is removed and the pressure upon the piston is less than before, because the gas which was previously confined to the space x is now partly in solution. If α denotes the solubility, the available volume is practically increased in the ratio $\dfrac{x}{x+\alpha V}$ so that the pressure on the piston in the position x is

$$p=\frac{p_0 v}{x+\alpha V},$$

and the work required to be done during the compression is

$$p_0 v \int_0^x \frac{dx}{x+\alpha V}=p_0 v \log \frac{x+\alpha V}{\alpha V}. \qquad . \qquad . \qquad (274)$$

By supposition the quantity of liquid is such as to be just capable of dissolving the gas, and so $\alpha V=v$. Hence the total work lost during both operations is the difference between (274) and (273), *i.e.*

$$p_0 v \left[\log \frac{\alpha V+x}{\alpha V}-\log \frac{x}{\alpha V} \right]=p_0 v \log \frac{\alpha V+x}{x},$$

and, as x is indefinitely great, this is equal to zero, so that, on the whole, no gain or loss of work results from passing reversibly from the initial to the final state of things.

Now introduce a semi-permeable membrane, permeable to gas but not to liquid, just under the piston which rests at the liquid surface. A second membrane, permeable to liquid but not to gas, is substituted, as a piston, for the bottom of the cylinder and may be " backed " upon its lower side by pure solvent. Arrange the motions of the two pistons so that, as the upper one is raised through the volume v and the lower one through V, the gas is expelled, the pressure of the gas remaining at p_0. The liquid which has not yet been expelled retains a constant strength and, therefore, a constant osmotic pressure P. When the expulsion is complete, the work done on the lower piston is PV and that recovered from the gas is $p_0 v$, so that $PV-p_0 v$ is the net work done. Since the whole experiment is reversible, and since the whole cycle has been conducted at constant temperature, it follows from the second law of thermodynamics that no energy is lost, or gained, during the cycle, and so

$$PV = p_0 v.$$

The osmotic pressure is thus determined, and it is evident that its value is that of the pressure which the gas, as a gas, would exert in the space V.

From this follows the formal extension of Avogadro's Law to the osmotic pressure of dissolved gases, and thence, by a natural hypothesis, to the osmotic pressures of other dissolved substances, even although they may not be capable of existing in the gaseous condition. Thus the constant R of equation (272) is the same as the universal gas constant.

To deduce the relation between osmotic pressure and temperature consider the first law of thermodynamics,

$$dE = dH + dW,$$

where E is the internal energy of a system, H the heat given to, and W the work done on, the system. Also $d\phi = \dfrac{dH}{T}$, where $d\phi$ is the change of entropy and T is the absolute temperature, so that

$$dE = T d\phi + dW, \qquad . \qquad . \qquad . \qquad (275)$$

and, writing ψ for $E - T\phi$,

$$d\psi = dE - T d\phi - \phi dT,$$

or, from equation (275),

$$d\psi = -\phi dT + dW,$$

i.e.

$$\phi = -\frac{d\psi}{dT},$$

if no work is done. Hence

$$\psi = E + T\frac{d\psi}{dT}.$$

This is termed the *equation of free energy*.

In the case of osmotic pressure the free energy is the work obtainable by a reversible and isothermal process, and is equal to $-Pv$, P being the osmotic pressure and v the increase in volume of a solution when the solvent is added, isothermally and reversibly, through a semi-permeable membrane, so that, assuming no change in E—*i.e* no heat of dilution—during the process,

$$Pv = T\frac{\partial}{\partial T}(Pv).$$

Neglecting any change of volume with temperature,

$$P = T\frac{\partial P}{\partial T},$$

which gives a relation between the osmotic pressure and the temperature. This is only true if there is no heat of solution, *i.e.* for very weak solutions. Hence

$$\frac{\partial P}{P} = \frac{\partial T}{T},$$

or
$$\log P = \log T + constant,$$

i.e.
$$P = RT,$$

where R is the integration constant. This shows that the osmotic pressure is proportional to the thermodynamic temperature.

153. Vapour Pressure—The vapour pressure of a solution is less than that of the solvent alone, and the difference may be investigated by the following simple, though approximate, method. In

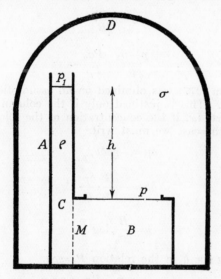

FIG. 86.—VAPOUR PRESSURE OF A SOLUTION.

Fig. 86, A is a vessel divided into two parts, B and C, by a semi-permeable membrane M. The former contains pure solvent and the vapour pressure over it is p, while C contains the solution whose vapour pressure is p_1. The whole is enclosed by an outer vessel D containing, in addition to the liquids, only the vapour whose density is σ. Owing to osmosis the level in C will be higher by an amount h than that in B, the difference in pressure on the two sides of M being P, the osmotic pressure of the solution. By equating this to the hydrostatic pressure difference we have

$$P = p_1 + g\rho h - p, \qquad . \qquad . \qquad . \qquad (276)$$

where ρ is the density of the solution. But p and p_1 are pressures at a difference of level h in the vapour whose density σ is supposed constant. Then

$$p = p_1 + g\sigma h \quad . \quad . \quad . \quad . \quad (277)$$

Eliminating gh between (276) and (277), we have

$$\frac{p - p_1}{\sigma} = \frac{P + p - p_1}{\rho},$$

or,

$$p - p_1 = \frac{P\sigma}{\rho - \sigma}.$$

Here σ is the vapour density under its own pressure. If σ_0 is the density under the standard atmospheric pressure B,

$$\sigma = \sigma_0 \frac{p}{B},$$

and

$$\frac{p - p_1}{p} = \frac{P\sigma_0}{B\rho} \quad . \quad . \quad . \quad . \quad (278)$$

The equation (277) was obtained on an assumption of uniform vapour density. This is justified only if the column of vapour of height h is short, *i.e.* if the concentration of the solution is small. If this is not the case we must write

$$\delta p = -g\sigma\delta h,$$

so that

$$\delta h = -\frac{B}{g\sigma_0} \cdot \frac{\delta p}{p}.$$

Integrating,

$$h = \frac{B}{g\sigma_0} \cdot \log \frac{p}{p_1},$$

or, substituting for h in the relation $P = g\rho h$,

$$\log \frac{p}{p_1} = \frac{P\sigma_0}{B\rho} \quad . \quad . \quad . \quad . \quad (279)$$

This gives a necessary relation between the osmotic pressure and the lowering of the vapour pressure of any solution, and is independent of any assumption as to the physical nature of osmotic pressure. Let us transform this equation into a form which gives the concentration of the solution in terms of the ratio of the number of molecules of dissolved substance to the number of molecules of solvent. If one gram-molecule of the solute occupies a volume v_0 in the solution or in gaseous form at a pressure B, then the osmotic pressure for a concentration n_0 gram-molecule in a volume v is

$$P = \frac{Bv_0 n_0}{v}.$$

The mass of solvent is nM where n is the number of gram-molecules of solvent and M its molecular weight. Hence

$$v = \frac{nM}{\rho},$$

so that

$$P = \frac{Bv_0 n_0 \rho}{nM},$$

and $\sigma_0 = \dfrac{M}{v_0}$, assuming that the molecular weight is the same in the liquid and vapour states. Substituting in equation (279)

$$\log \frac{p}{p_1} = \frac{Bv_0 n_0 \rho}{nMB\rho} \cdot \frac{M}{v_0} = \frac{n_0}{n}.$$

This is independent of the temperature, so that the relative lowering of the vapour pressure should be independent of the temperature, if no molecular change takes place in the nature of the vapour.

154. Boiling-point.—The boiling-point of a liquid is that temperature at which its vapour pressure equals the external pressure. Thus, if we have a pure solvent and a solution both at the temperature of the boiling-point of the former, the vapour pressures will be respectively equal to, and less than, the external pressure, since the vapour pressure of the solution is less than that of the solvent. It will be necessary to raise the temperature of the solution still more before it boils, *i.e.* before equality between its vapour pressure and the external pressure is reached. This elevation of the boiling-point may be evaluated as follows : Fig. 87 represents a closed vessel divided into compartments A and B by a semi-permeable membrane. The upper half of each chamber contains only the vapour of the solvent, while A has also a quantity of solution at a temperature $T + dT$, and B a quantity of solvent at a temperature T. If these are temperatures at which the vapour pressures are equal, they represent corresponding boiling-points for an equal external pressure. Now suppose the following cycle of operations to be performed :—

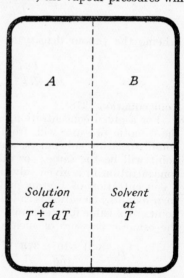

A   *B*

Solution at $T \pm dT$ *Solvent at T*

Fig. 87.—Boiling-point and Freezing-point of a Solution.

(i) Force v c.c. of solvent from B to A against the osmotic pressure P. The work done will be Pv ergs.

(ii) Evaporate this amount of liquid in A. The heat absorbed in this process is $\rho v L_1$ ergs, where ρ is the liquid density and L_1 its latent heat—expressed in work units—at the temperature $T+dT$.

(iii) Transfer the vapour formed from A to B. Since there is equality of pressure on both sides of the membrane above the liquids, this involves no expenditure of work.

(iv) Condense the vapour in B. The heat given out will be $\rho v L$ ergs, where L is the latent heat at the temperature T.

This cycle is reversible and, applying the two fundamental laws of thermodynamics, we have

$$\frac{\rho v L}{T}=\frac{\rho v L_1}{T+dT}=\frac{Pv}{dT},$$

or,

$$dT=\frac{PT}{\rho L} \quad . \quad . \quad . \quad . \quad (280)$$

But since $P=\dfrac{RT}{v_1}$, where $v_1 = $ volume of 1 gm. of vapour at a pressure P and R is the constant per gm. of vapour,

$$\frac{LdT}{RT^2}=\frac{1}{\rho v_1}=\frac{\sigma}{\rho},$$

σ being the vapour density at a pressure P, so that $\sigma=\dfrac{P\sigma_0}{B}$ and

$$\frac{LdT}{RT^2}=\frac{P\sigma_0}{B\rho}=\frac{p-p_1}{p}$$

from equation (278).

For a given concentration, measured in gram-molecules per c.c., the osmotic pressure will, from equation (272), be the same for all non-dissociating substances, and thus the elevation of the boiling-point will be the same; or all solutions with the same molecular concentration in a given solvent have the same boiling-point. For a concentration of 1 gram-molecule per 100 grams of solvent the corresponding elevation is called the *molecular elevation* of the boiling-point. Its value for water may be calculated as follows : At 100° C. the osmotic pressure of such a solution is, from equation (280),

$$P=\frac{8\cdot31\times10^7\times373}{100}=3\cdot10\times10^8 \text{ dynes per sq. cm.,}$$

and

$$dT=\frac{3\cdot10\times10^8\times373}{0\cdot96\times537\times4\cdot2\times10^7}=5\cdot34° \text{ C.}$$

The boiling-points deduced in this way agree extremely well with experiment, and this fact may be regarded as strong evidence in favour of the theory of osmotic pressure.

155. Freezing-point.—In a somewhat similar manner the depression of the freezing-point of a solution below that of the pure solvent may be deduced.   In Fig. 87 let T and $T-dT$ represent corresponding freezing-points, and suppose that a cycle is performed as follows :—

(i) Force v c.c. of solvent from B to A.   The work done is again Pv.

(ii) Freeze this quantity of liquid in A ; the heat liberated is $\rho v L_1$, where L_1 is the latent heat of solidification at the temperature $T-dT$.

(iii) Transfer the solid from A to B.

(iv) Allow it to melt and absorb heat equal to $\rho v L$, where L is the latent heat of fusion at the temperature T.

Then we have

$$\frac{\rho v L_1}{T-dT}=\frac{\rho v L}{T}=\frac{Pv}{dT},$$

or,

$$dT=\frac{PT}{\rho L} \quad . \quad . \quad . \quad . \quad (281)$$

The *molecular depression* of the freezing-point of water is given by

$$P=\frac{8{\cdot}31\times10^7\times273}{100}=2{\cdot}27\times10^8 \text{ dynes per sq. cm.}$$

$$dT=\frac{2{\cdot}27\times10^8\times273}{80\times4{\cdot}2\times10^7}=18{\cdot}4° \text{ C.}$$

This expression, also, has been verified.

156. Osmotic Pressure of Electrolytes.—In solutions of electrolytes the osmotic pressure and its correlated effects are abnormally great.   Organic solutes dissolved in water give osmotic effects which agree with van 't Hoff's theory, these effects depending on the number and not on the nature of the dissolved molecules.   When experiments yield abnormally low values, it follows that the number of solute particles is less than that indicated by the chemical formula, and it is natural to suppose that aggregation has occurred. When, on the other hand, unusually large values are obtained for solutions of electrolytes, it is necessary to infer that some of the molecules have dissociated, and the degree of dissociation may be determined by the measurement of the osmotic pressure effects. The depression of the freezing-point has been more thoroughly investigated than the other properties.   If, for example, in a certain solution m_0 inactive and m active molecules exist, each of the latter giving α ions, the total osmotic pressure produced will be proportional to $m_0+\alpha m$, whereas the normal osmotic pressure would be proportional to m_0+m.   By measuring the electrical conductivity we can find the fraction of the molecules which, at any moment, is active. Let us call this β. Then, as shown by Arrhenius,

$$\beta = \frac{m}{m_0 + m},$$

so that, if the ratio of the actual osmotic pressure to the normal value is called i,

$$i = \frac{m_0 + \alpha m}{m_0 + m} = 1 + (\alpha - 1)\beta.$$

The same ratio could also be found by direct experiment on the depression of the freezing-point, for we know the normal value from van 't Hoff's theory, and if dT be the observed depression for a solution with 1 gram equivalent per litre,

$$i = \frac{dT}{1 \cdot 84},$$

since $1 \cdot 84$ is the calculated depression for such a solution in water. We can thus compare the value of i, as directly determined by observations on the freezing-point, with its value calculated from conductivity experiments.

Thus there are two relations involved in the dissociation theory. Firstly, the number of ions into which a molecule must dissociate in order to explain its electrical behaviour, when completely dissociated in a very dilute solution, should be the same as the number required to give its observed osmotic pressure. Secondly, in dilute solutions of simple salts the abnormally great osmotic pressure should diminish with the coefficient of electric ionisation. The experimental evidence on the whole supports Arrhenius' theory. The observed depressions never appreciably exceed the theoretical values, and the discrepancies in the other direction are readily explained by incomplete ionisation.

When we consider the second relation indicated by Arrhenius, that the coefficient of ionisation, measured electrically, should agree with its value calculated from osmotic pressure effects, this relation cannot hold for concentrated solutions, since the thermodynamic theory of osmotic pressure is valid only when the solute particles are beyond each other's sphere of influence. Nevertheless, experiments on these lines are of great interest, for confirmation of the relation for dilute aqueous solutions of simple salts would be reliable evidence that the Arrhenius theory gives, in such simple cases, a complete explanation of the phenomena. The amount of divergence in other cases would supply useful indications of the nature and amount of the disturbing influences. In general, the experimental results indicate that the relation holds only at great dilution even with such simple salts as potassium chloride.

157. Measurement of Osmotic Pressure.—The measurements made by Pfeffer were too few in number and insufficient in accuracy to give a satisfactory test of the theory of osmosis. Determinations may be made using indirect means such as by measurements on vapour pressures, freezing-points, and boiling-points, but the best results are obtained by a modification of Pfeffer's method in which special care is taken in the manufacture of the porous pot and in the deposition of the chemical membrane. For concentrated solutions, again, the high pressures involved necessitate extreme accuracy in mechanical detail, particularly in the method of attaching the manometer which measures the pressure. By reason of the extent and thoroughness which H. N. Morse [1] and his co-workers applied to their measurements, these may be taken as typical of later experiments with concentrated solutions. This work occupied Morse for many years. One of the early difficulties was the method of manufacturing vessels which possessed the essential qualities of uniform strength and porosity, combined with a texture so fine that the membrane was deposited on the inner wall. Finally, a mixture of clays was discovered such that, on sifting, kneading, pressing, and baking in an electric furnace, practical uniformity in these qualities was obtained. The membrane was of copper ferrocyanide, but Pfeffer's method of preparation yielded films of insufficient strength to sustain the high pressures used. Ultimately it was found that, by electric endosmose, membranes of much greater mechanical strength could be obtained. The manometers used were closed U-tubes containing nitrogen and carefully calibrated. Many different types of attachment between cell and manometer were tried. An example of one of the later developments is shown in Fig. 88. The pot A receives the conical glass bulb B attached to the tube C, and good contact is maintained by means of the nuts H, J

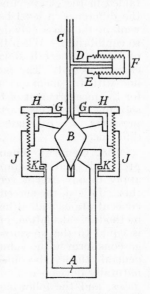

FIG. 88.—MORSE'S APPARATUS FOR THE MEASUREMENT OF OSMOTIC PRESSURES.

which act on the collar G and the packing ring K. The collar is sealed on to B by cement, and the side tube D is cemented to a threaded brass tube E which is closed by the nut F. The latter permits the pressure on the solution to be raised to prevent osmosis. Thus the pressure given by a manometer attached to C is the osmotic pressure. Readings were taken to 80° C. under thermostatic control, and pressures as high as 30 atmospheres were employed.

Most osmometers—instruments for measuring osmotic pressure—utilise the manometer, or gauge method, for the measurement of the pressure difference, but osmotic balances are more sensitive.[2]

[1] Morse, *Amer. Chem. Journ.* (1901–12).
[2] See Svedberg, *Nature*, **153**, 523 (1944).

In such a balance one of the scale pans is removed and on the floor of the balance case is fixed a stand with an adjustable platform carrying a glass cylinder filled with solvent. The lower part of the osmotic cell is conical in shape and the semi-permeable membrane is attached to its base—the membrane itself acting as a packing material against leakage. The upper half of the cell is a glass tube and the whole is suspended from the balance arm. The osmotic cell and part of the glass tube is filled with solution and suspended from the balance in such a way that it dips into the solvent contained in the glass cylinder. By means of the adjustable platform the difference in level between the solution in the cell and the solvent in the glass cylinder can be varied. The balance is adjusted to equilibrium. When the weight of the cell increases, due to inflow of solvent, the cell sinks until the buoyancy compensates the increased weight. The position, when the meniscus in the cell is in line with the meniscus in the cylinder, is taken as reference point for the measurement of the difference in levels between solution and solvent. From this starting position all level differences, *i.e.* osmotic pressures, are calculated by means of the corresponding weight differences.

158. General Theory of Solutions.—It has been stated previously that the simple $PV=RT$ relation cannot be expected to apply to any except very dilute solutions, and experiments verify this. Indeed, the agreement is close only for a very limited range of concentrations and, although this range may be extended by Morse's method of calculation, on the assumption that the osmotic pressure is equal to the pressure which would be exerted by the solute in gaseous form in the volume occupied by the solvent at 4° C., a more general theory becomes essential. Attempts in this direction naturally developed along the lines of Van der Waals' equation for gases, and the following have been suggested :—

$$\left(\frac{A}{V}+P+\frac{a}{V^2}\right)(V-b)=RT, \quad . \qquad . \qquad . \quad (282)$$

$$\left(\frac{A}{V}+P-\frac{a}{V^2}\right)(V-b)=RT, \quad . \qquad . \qquad . \quad (283)$$

where $\frac{a}{V^2}$ and $\frac{A}{V}$ are the correcting factors for the attraction between solute molecules, and between solute and solvent, respectively. In equation (282) V is the volume of *solvent* containing 1 gram-molecule of solute, while in equation (283) it is the corresponding *solution* volume. An objection to these equations and the many possible similar empirical forms is, as was pointed out by Callendar,[1] that the constants involved cannot be connected with the other properties of the solutions.

[1] Callendar, *Proc. Roy. Soc.*, A, **80**, 466 (1908) ; *Proc. Roy. Inst.*, **19**, 485 (1911).

It is natural to expect that a general osmotic equation will be much more complicated than that of a gas, but Sackur [1] and Porter [2] have shown that a simple formula of the type

$$P(V-b)=RT$$

represents the facts over a large range of concentrations. In this equation V is the volume of solution containing 1 gram-molecule, while the quantity b varies with temperature. Owing to hydration it is a value larger than the volume of the 1 gram-molecule of solute, its variation with temperature being attributed to a corresponding change in the degree of hydration.

Thermodynamical principles may also be applied to a solution if certain simplifying assumptions are made. The results of this process will, of course, be valuable and applicable to experimental facts only to the degree to which actual solutions fulfil the assumed conditions. For instance, if the solutions are such that the components are neither associated nor dissociated, intermix without change of volume or heat effect, and do not interact, then the resultant equation [3] is

$$P=\frac{RT}{V}[-\log(1-x)]-\tfrac{1}{2}\beta P^2,$$

where V is the molecular volume of the solvent under standard pressure conditions, x is the ratio of the number of molecules of the solute to the total number present, and β is the compressibility. If, further, $\tfrac{1}{2}\beta P^2$ is negligibly small—as it will be except at very high pressures—then, by expending the right-hand side,

$$P=\frac{RT}{V}\left(x+\frac{x^2}{2}+\frac{x^3}{3}+\ \ldots\right). \qquad . \qquad . \qquad (284)$$

Unfortunately, the experimental verification of this result is not easy, but considerable information can be obtained from vapour pressure, freezing-point, and boiling-point determinations. It is therefore necessary to obtain more exact relations between these quantities and the osmotic pressure.

Equations connecting osmotic pressure and vapour pressure differ in their complexity according to the number of factors which are taken into account. One, due to Spens,[4] has the simple form,

$$\log\frac{p}{p_1}=\frac{Pv_1}{s_0 p_1}, \qquad . \qquad . \qquad . \qquad (285)$$

where v_1 is the increase in the volume of a large amount of solution when unit mass of the solvent is added, and s_0 is the specific volume of the vapour, p and p_1 being the vapour pressures of the solvent

[1] Sackur, *Zeits. Phys. Chem.*, 70, 447 (1909) ; *Zeits. Elektroch.*, 18, 641 (1912).
[2] Porter, *Trans. Far. Soc.*, 13, 119 (1917).
[3] See Findlay, *Osmotic Pressure*, p. 55 (1919).
[4] Spens, *Proc. Roy. Soc.*, A, 77, 234 (1906).

and solution respectively. A more general and more complicated equation was obtained by Porter.[1]

In considering the connection between osmotic pressure and freezing-point it is necessary to remember that, since the freezing-point varies with the concentration, in order to associate the osmotic pressure with the concentration alone, its variation with temperature must be known, and this implies a knowledge of the heat of dilution. Callendar [2] states that the vapour pressure and the temperature of water are related according to the equation,

$$\log \frac{p}{p_0} = \frac{2 \cdot 64 \Delta T}{T} + 4 \cdot 71 \left(\frac{\Delta T}{T} + \frac{T_0}{T} \log \frac{T}{T_0} \right),$$

where p and p_0 are the vapour pressures in the liquid and solid phases, T and T_0 are the absolute temperatures ($T_0 = 273$) and $\Delta T = T_0 - T$. This equation may be reduced without great loss of accuracy to

$$\log \frac{p}{p_0} = 2 \cdot 64 \frac{\Delta T}{T_0},$$

and if the vapour pressure p_0 of ice at the freezing-point T is substituted in equation (285), the required connection between P and T is obtained.

The relations between boiling-point and osmotic pressure may be obtained in a similar manner,[2] but they are difficult to verify owing to the lack of sufficient data.

These indirect methods of testing the general equation (284) have shown that it represents the temperature law of osmotic pressure variation over a large range of concentrations and temperatures with considerable accuracy, and, in spite of much criticism, the kinetic theory of osmotic pressure still remains the only one which gives values agreeing with experience. As was emphasised by Porter [3] in an admirable review of the question, any alternative theory, in addition to giving a more exact representation of facts, must overcome the difficulty of explaining away the results which it is reasonable to expect from the known molecular agitations of solutions.

159. Diffusion.—Closely connected with osmosis is the phenomenon of *diffusion*. If two fluids in contact are able to mix in any proportions they will do so spontaneously until a uniform mixture is produced. The process by which the intermixture is brought about is called *diffusion* and is due to the migratory movements which characterise fluids. Diffusion is rapid in gases, comparatively slow in liquids, but in both cases the rapidity of movement depends on the rate of change of density at the place considered. It continues in opposition to gravity, and thus is not a buoyancy effect. This may be shown by superposing a layer of water on, say, a copper sulphate solution. If this is done with sufficient care to avoid cur-

[1] Porter, *Proc. Roy. Soc.*, A, **79**, 519 (1907); A, **80**, 427 (1908).
[2] Callendar, *ibid.*, A, **80**, 466 (1908).
[3] Porter, *Trans. Far. Soc.*, **13**, 119 (1917).

rents in the liquids, the line of demarcation is sharp between the blue solution and the colourless water. After a time the blue coloration will be found to have spread upwards, and a gradual change in the depth of tint will be seen to extend throughout the whole liquid. After a considerable time the mixture will become very nearly uniform.

160. Fick's Law.—The interdiffusion of liquids was studied by Graham, who used a wide-necked bottle nearly filled with a salt solution. The bottle was placed in another vessel containing water, which was made to extend into the bottle by carefully squeezing out a sponge, saturated with water, on to a cork floating in the solution. In this way a column of water was superposed on the liquid, and after the lapse of some days the amount of salt which had diffused into the water was measured. Graham's experiments showed that the rate of diffusion of aqueous solutions depended on the type of salt used, increased with greater strength and also with the temperature. These results were given in a simple mathematical form by Fick, known as *Fick's Law*, which may be stated as follows : Imagine a plane drawn in the liquid along the direction of constant density. Then, if the concentration gradient—or change of concentration with distance—measured at right angles to this plane is $\frac{\partial c}{\partial x}$, the mass of dissolved substance crossing unit area of the plane per second is equal to $k\frac{\partial c}{\partial x}$, where k is a constant called the *coefficient of diffusion* of the dissolved substance.

If two such planes A, B are separated by a distance δx and each has unit area, then, if the concentration at A at any time t is c, that at B will be $c - \frac{\partial c}{\partial x}\delta x$. The inflow of dissolved substance at A in time δt will be $k\frac{\partial c}{\partial x}\delta t$, while the outflow from B will be

$$k\frac{\partial c}{\partial x}\delta t - k\frac{\partial^2 c}{\partial x^2}\delta x \delta t.$$

Thus the space between A and B has a net gain of $k\frac{\partial^2 c}{\partial x^2}\delta x$ gm. per sec. Since the volume enclosed is δx, the change of concentration is $k\frac{\partial^2 c}{\partial x^2}\delta t$, or the rate of change of concentration is given by

$$\frac{\partial c}{\partial t} = k\frac{\partial^2 c}{\partial x^2} \qquad . \qquad . \qquad . \qquad (286)$$

This is the general equation governing the process of diffusion, and suffices to solve any problem when the initial conditions are given. As is shown in Chapter IX, the solution to equation (286) is a Fourier expansion whose form depends on these initial conditions.

As an example consider the following problem. A solution of strength c_0 occupies a length l of a cylindrical vessel and has a length l_1 of solvent superposed on it. The concentration c at any point in the vessel at any subsequent time may be found as follows :—

A solution of equation (286) which satisfies the initial conditions is

$$c = A_0 + A_1 e^{-km_1^2 t} \cos m_1 x + A_2 e^{-km_2^2 t} \cos m_2 x + \ldots \quad (287)$$

in which, when $t=0$, $c=c_0$ from $x=0$ to $x=l$, and, when $t=\infty$, $c = \dfrac{c_0 l}{l+l_1}$ for the same range of x. When $t=\infty$, equation (287) reduces to $c=A_0$. Hence

$$A_0 = c_0 \frac{l}{l+l_1} \quad . \quad . \quad . \quad . \quad (288)$$

But $f(x)$ may be expanded into a half-range cosine series by the usual formula :—

$$f(x) = A_0 + A_1 \cos \frac{\pi x}{l+l_1} + A_2 \cos \frac{2\pi x}{l+l_1} + \ldots$$

where

$$A_n = \frac{2}{l+l_1} \int_0^{l+l_1} f(x) \cos \frac{n\pi x}{l+l_1} dx = \frac{2c_0}{l+l_1} \int_0^l \cos \frac{n\pi x}{l+l_1} dx$$

$$A_n = \frac{2c_0}{n\pi} \sin \frac{n\pi l}{l+l_1},$$

where $n=1, 2, 3$, etc. Thus

$$c = \frac{c_0 l}{l+l_1} + \frac{2c_0}{\pi} \sum \frac{1}{n} \sin \frac{n\pi l}{l+l_1} e^{-kat} \cos \frac{n\pi x}{l+l_1},$$

in which $a = \left(\dfrac{n\pi}{l+l_1} \right)^2$.

161. Coefficient of Diffusion.—We have seen that by applying Fourier's theorem it is possible to deduce, in a form containing k, the concentration at a given point at any time subsequent to a given distribution of strengths. Thus, if the variation at some point is measured from time to time, it will be possible to evaluate the coefficient of diffusion. It must, however, be possible to determine the concentration without causing a disturbance of the liquid. In Kelvin's method this was done very simply by noting the position of a series of glass beads of varying densities placed in the liquid, so that the density distribution could be noted throughout the experiment. Other methods which have been used with differing degrees of success are measurements of refractive indices, rotations of polarised light for sugar solutions, and contact potential differences. More recently the optical methods have been extended so as to be available in a greater variety of cases and to give much greater accuracy in working. For example, Littlewood [1] describes a method of determining concentrations to within about 0·05 gm. per

[1] Littlewood, *Proc. Phys. Soc.*, **34**, 71 (1922).

litre at any point and time during diffusion. His method depends on the bending of rays of light incident at nearly grazing angles on the top surface. Owing to the changing density with depth, the ray is bent into an arc and the total deviation depends only on the refractive indices at the points of entrance into, and exit from, the solution. If V is the velocity of light in the medium at the point of entry, the distance travelled by the ray in a time δt is $y = V\delta t$, while the distance travelled by a ray which enters at a distance δl below the first is

$$y_1 = \left(V + \frac{dV}{dl}.\delta l\right)\delta t.$$

Thus the wave front, and hence the ray direction, is turned through an angle ψ given by

$$tan\ \psi = -\frac{dV}{dl}\delta t = -\frac{y}{V}\frac{dV}{dl}.$$

When $y = a$, the width of the vessel,

$$tan\ \psi = -\frac{a}{V}\frac{dV}{dl},$$

and ψ is the angle of incidence on the far side of the vessel. Thus α, the angle of deviation on emergence, is given by $sin\ \alpha = \mu\ sin\ \psi$ and, since μV is constant,

$$sin\ \alpha = a\frac{d\mu}{dl}.$$

Thus the change in deviation for a given angle of incidence depends on the difference in concentration at the various points of emergence at the side of the vessel when the incident ray is displaced laterally. This difference was measured, in Littlewood's experiments, by a tilting mirror device, which indicated changes of the order of one minute of arc. From these measurements of the change in concentration with depth, obtained from time to time, all the necessary data for a calculation of the coefficient of diffusion are known.

Later, Clack,[1] by a somewhat similar method which was capable of measuring concentrations at points fairly close together, was enabled to make a much more detailed investigation of the change in diffusion coefficient with concentration. He produced a definite concentration gradient from practically zero strength to saturation in a vertical diffusion cell. When steady conditions were reached, the change of refractive index with depth was measured, as in Littlewood's experiments, from the deviation of a ray, in this case initially horizontal, as it penetrated layers of increasing density. The method of measurement was different, however, and depended on the vertical displacement of the central fringe in the interference pattern produced by two narrow and near horizontal slits illuminated by mercury green light. To connect the change of refractive index with concentration, a Rayleigh refractometer was used, and a com-

[1] Clack, *Proc. Phys. Soc.*, 36, 313 (1924).

bination of these results determined the distribution of concentration with depth. In addition, the quantity of solute diffusing through the cell when steady conditions were established was measured by chemical analysis or by drying and weighing.

If the diffusion coefficient is assumed to be independent of the concentration gradient then, on steady conditions being reached, and the diffusion cell having a constant cross-sectional area, the gradient of concentration would be constant, and no detailed examination would be required. Clack's experiments showed a varying gradient, even under steady conditions, from top to bottom of the cell and this enabled the variation of k with c to be found. The theory of this more general form of dynamic equilibrium was given by Clack in an earlier paper [1] in the form:—

$$k = \frac{i}{A(1-\delta)} \frac{dl}{dc} \frac{d-c-c\delta}{d-c},$$

in which i is the net change in the mass of the cell contents per second, A is the cross-sectional area of the diffusion cell, c is the concentration in gm. per c.c. at a distance l from the top, d is the density at the same point, and δ is the ratio of the mass of water entering the top of the cell per second to the mass of salt leaving per second. The gradient $\dfrac{dl}{dc}$ was given, as already explained, by the product $\dfrac{dl}{d\mu} \cdot \dfrac{d\mu}{dc}$ in which $\dfrac{dl}{d\mu}$ was obtained by the fringe measurements and $\dfrac{d\mu}{dc}$ by the refractometer readings.

The greatest difficulty in such experiments is the great time needed to set up, and subsequently to measure changes in concentration of solutions in the usual large-size vessels, during which time it is necessary to avoid mechanical and thermal disturbances. It is pointed out by Furth [2] that if the linear dimensions are reduced by a factor n, the time needed will be reduced by the factor n^2. The consequent small-scale instrument which incorporates collimator, diffusion cell, and observing microscope he calls a microdiffusiometer. Two different methods of following the level of some selected concentration are utilised. The first applies when considerable coloration effects accompany changes in solution strength, and in essence the level of a fixed colour shade is observed against the time in terms of eyepiece micrometer divisions. In the second method, applicable to transparent colourless solutions, the image is the shadow region produced by total internal reflection, and thus correlates the diffusion current with the time by means of the refractive index.

These investigations, which were made with sodium chloride,

[1] Clack, *Proc. Phys. Soc.*, **29**, 51 (1916).
[2] Furth, R., *Physik. Z.*, **26**, 719 (1925); *Zeits. f. Phys.*, **91**, 609 (1934); *Jour. Sci. Instr.*, **22**, 61 (1945).

potassium chloride, and potassium nitrate solutions, showed that in each case, with gradually increasing strength, the coefficient of diffusion reached a minimum value—in the first two cases with comparatively dilute solutions—and then increased in a practically linear form. This agrees with the conclusions arrived at by Arrhenius from his theory of ionic dissociation. He concluded that the coefficient should, with increasing concentration, at first fall to a minimum on account of decreasing dissociation, and later, with more concentrated solutions, it should increase because of intermolecular attractions.

162. Diffusion and Osmotic Pressure.—If the concentration of different parts of a solution is non-uniform, the osmotic pressure also varies, and by imagining the parts of the solution to be separated by ideal semi-permeable membranes, we see that the osmotic pressure is the force per unit area which must be applied by the diaphragm to the dissolved molecules in bulk to prevent their diffusion. Consider a vertical cylinder with a solution of a non-electrolyte in the lower portion and water above ; the dissolved substance gradually makes its way upwards and finally a uniform solution results. Let the osmotic pressure at a height x in the cylinder be P, so that, if A is the cross-section, the substance in the layer whose volume is $A\delta x$ is under the action of a force $A\delta P$. If c is the concentration in gram-molecules per c.c., the force acting in the x direction on each gram-molecule in the layer due to this force is

$$-\frac{A\delta P}{cA\delta x} = -\frac{1}{c} \cdot \frac{dP}{dx}.$$

Let F be the force required to drive 1 gram-molecule through the solution with a velocity of 1 cm. per sec., so that, if the drift velocity is constant, F must be equal to the viscous drag on the gram-molecule. Hence the velocity acquired is

$$-\frac{1}{cF} \cdot \frac{dP}{dx},$$

and if δN is the number of gram-molecules which pass across each layer in a time δt,

$$\delta N = -\frac{1}{cF} \cdot \frac{dP}{dx} Ac\delta t = -\frac{A}{F} \cdot \frac{dP}{dx} \delta t.$$

For dilute solutions, $P = cRT$ and

$$\delta N = -\frac{RT}{F} A \frac{dc}{dx} \delta t.$$

But, by Fick's Law,

$$\delta N = -kA\frac{dc}{dx}\delta t, \quad \cdot \quad \cdot \quad \cdot \quad \cdot \quad (289)$$

so that k, the diffusion coefficient, corresponds to the factor $\dfrac{RT}{F}$.

Owing to the slow rate of diffusion, the day instead of the second has been adopted as the unit of time for practical work. The force required to drive 1 gram-molecule through the solution with a velocity of 1 cm. per sec. is

$$F = -\frac{RT}{\delta N}A\frac{dc}{dx}\delta t = \frac{86400RT}{k},$$

and if k is known, we can calculate the force required to produce unit velocity. For example, k for formic acid at $0°$ C. is 0.472, and the force required to drive 1 gram-molecule through water with a velocity of 1 cm. per sec. is equal to 4.34×10^{12} gm. weight.

163. Diffusion of Electrolytes.—Consider the solution of a single electrolyte containing two monovalent ions. Let u and v be the velocities of the cations and anions, respectively, when subjected to unit force. The velocities in the present case will be $-\frac{u}{c}\cdot\frac{dP}{dx}$ and $-\frac{v}{c}\cdot\frac{dP}{dx}$, and the amounts of each passing any cross-section of the cylinder in time δt are

$$-uA\frac{dP}{dx}\delta t \quad \text{and} \quad -vA\frac{dP}{dx}\delta t.$$

If u is different from v, a potential difference is set up and the force on a gram-equivalent of an ion carrying a charge e is $e\frac{dE}{dx}$, so that the numbers of the two ions which would cross a section in time δt under the action of this force alone are

$$-uAce\frac{dE}{dx}\delta t \quad \text{and} \quad +vAce\frac{dE}{dx}\delta t,$$

and the total number of gram-equivalents which diffuse in a given time under the influence of both the osmotic and electric forces must be equal. Hence

$$\delta N = -uA\delta t\left(\frac{dP}{dx}+ce\frac{dE}{dx}\right) = -vA\delta t\left(\frac{dP}{dx}-ce\frac{dE}{dx}\right),$$

i.e.

$$\delta N = -\frac{2uv}{u+v}A\frac{dP}{dx}\delta t,$$

but since $P=cRT$ and, from equation (289), $\delta N = -kA\frac{dc}{dx}\delta t,$

$$k = \frac{2uv}{u+v}RT.$$

Thus, if u and v are known—and they may be calculated from the migration of the ions—k can be determined. For example, with hydrochloric acid the velocity of the hydrogen ion under a gradient of 1 volt per cm. is $0\cdot0032$ cm. per sec., and

$$u=\frac{0\cdot0032\times10^{-8}}{9647}=3\cdot32\times10^{-15} \text{ cm. per sec.,}$$

the charge being 9647 absolute units, and 1 volt is 10^8 absolute units. For the chlorine ion

$$v=7\cdot15\times10^{-16} \text{ cm. per sec.,}$$

and thus

$$k=\frac{2uv}{u+v}RT=2\cdot30.$$

This agrees well with the experimental value $2\cdot30$ obtained by Scheffer.

164. Diffusion in Gases.—It has already been mentioned that the interdiffusion of gases is much more rapid than that of liquids, and that in both cases the rapidity of movement depends on the density gradient. A law of the same form as Fick's Law for liquids applies to gaseous diffusion. Consider two gases A and B, and suppose that the density gradient of one, say A, at a given point is $\frac{d\rho}{dx}$, then the mass of gas A passing per second through each square centimetre of the plane is $k\frac{d\rho}{dx}$, where k is a constant which depends on the nature of the two gases and is called their *coefficient of interdiffusion*. It has generally been supposed in experiments on gaseous diffusion that k is independent of the proportions of the gases, but this is probably only approximately true. The measurement of k is not easy owing to the difficulty of setting up an initial known distribution of the two gases. Loschmidt and Obermayer used a long cylinder divided, by a disc, into two parts, in the lower of which the denser gas was placed, and then the diaphragm was carefully removed to avoid setting up currents. The disc was subsequently replaced, and an analysis of the proportions of the gases in the two parts gave a measure of their interdiffusivity. These observers agreed fairly well in their results, and measurements made by Waitz, on the diffusion of carbon dioxide into air, verified their values for these gases. Waitz used a Jamin interferometer to estimate the proportions of gas at any place from time to time by a measurement of the refractive index. His method was superior to that of the previous experimenters and enabled him to decide that k varied, to some extent, with the proportions of the gases present.

The theoretical calculation of the total quantity of either of the components, which has crossed over into the other compartment in a given time, can be illustrated by taking the case where the diaphragm divides the cylinder into two equal portions. Then, if the total length of the cylinder is $2l$, its cross-section is A, and the initial density of the denser component in the lower compartment is ρ_0, the subsequent distribution of density ρ with distance x from the bottom at time t is given by

$$\rho=\frac{\rho_0}{2}+\frac{2\rho_0}{\pi}\left[e^{-kt\left(\frac{\pi}{2l}\right)^2}\cos\frac{\pi x}{2l}-\tfrac{1}{3}e^{-9kt\left(\frac{\pi}{2l}\right)^2}\cos\frac{3\pi x}{2l}+\ \ldots\ \right].$$

Thus

$$-\frac{\partial\rho}{\partial x}=\frac{2\rho_0}{\pi}\left[e^{-kt\left(\frac{\pi}{2l}\right)^2}\frac{\pi}{2l}\sin\frac{\pi x}{2l}-e^{-9kt\left(\frac{\pi}{2l}\right)^2}\frac{\pi}{2l}\cdot\sin\frac{3\pi x}{2l}+\ \ldots\ \right].$$

At $x=l$

$$-\frac{\partial\rho}{\partial x}=\frac{\rho_0}{l}\left[e^{-kt\left(\frac{\pi}{2l}\right)^2}+e^{-9kt\left(\frac{\pi}{2l}\right)^2}+e^{-25kt\left(\frac{\pi}{2l}\right)^2}+\ \ldots\ \right].$$

In time ∂t the mass diffusing past this plane is $k\dfrac{\partial\rho}{\partial x}A\partial t$, or

$$-kA\frac{\rho_0}{l}\left[e^{-kt\left(\frac{\pi}{2l}\right)^2}+e^{-9kt\left(\frac{\pi}{2l}\right)^2}+\ \ldots\ \right]\partial t,$$

and in time t the total mass which has entered the upper half is

$$M=\frac{kA\rho_0}{l}\left[\frac{4l^2}{k\pi^2}\left(1-e^{-kt\left(\frac{\pi}{2l}\right)^2}\right)+\frac{4l^2}{9k\pi^2}\left(1-e^{-9kt\left(\frac{\pi}{2l}\right)^2}\right)+\ \ldots\ \right],$$

or,

$$M=\frac{4lA\rho_0}{\pi^2}\left[1+\frac{1}{9}+\frac{1}{25}+\ \ldots\ \right]-\frac{4lA\rho_0}{\pi^2}\cdot e^{-kt\left(\frac{\pi}{2l}\right)^2},$$

since after any appreciable time only the first exponential term will be significant. Thus

$$M=\frac{4lA\rho_0}{\pi^2}\cdot\frac{\pi^2}{8}-\frac{4lA\rho_0}{\pi^2}e^{-kt\left(\frac{\pi}{2l}\right)^2},$$

or,

$$k=-\frac{4l^2}{\pi^2t}\log\left[\frac{\pi^2}{4A l\rho_0}\left(\frac{M_0}{2}-M\right)\right],$$

M_0 being the original mass of that component.
Finally

$$k=-\frac{4l^2}{\pi^2t}\log\left[\frac{\pi^2}{8}\left(1-\frac{2M}{M_0}\right)\right].$$

As an example k for carbon dioxide is about $0\cdot14$, and thus the time for $M=\dfrac{M_0}{4}$ and $l=50$ is $t=58$ minutes, or for hydrogen to air $k=0\cdot63$ and $t=13$ minutes. It will thus be seen that, if at the commencement there had been a mixture of hydrogen and carbon dioxide in the lower chamber, there would be a rapid separation of the constituents as a result of their different rates of diffusion. This process of differential diffusion has been used to separate radioactive substances.

As with liquids, the interdiffusion of gases increases with temperature, but to a much greater degree. The experiments of Loschmidt and Obermayer showed that, if the law of temperature is expressed in the form $k_1 = kT^n$, where T is the absolute temperature, then n has a value intermediate between 1·75 and 2. With gases the pressure also affects the process of diffusion, k being inversely proportional to the combined pressure of the mixed gases.

165. Diffusion and the Kinetic Theory of Fluids.—The tendency towards uniformity shown by a mixture of substances which are non-uniformly distributed is a consequence of the translational motion of the molecules, and it should therefore be possible to connect diffusion phenomena with other deductions from the kinetic theory of fluids. Consider a mixture whose components may be represented by (1) and (2). Migration of the (1) molecules will

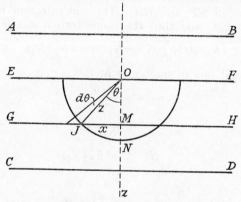

Fig. 89.—Diffusion and the Kinetic Theory.

occur in the direction of decreasing concentration, and, on the whole, the molecules (2) will migrate in the opposite direction, *i.e.* in their own direction of decreasing concentration, so that if n_1 denotes the number of molecules (1) which, on the average, travel across 1 sq. cm. per sec., and $\frac{d}{dz}(N_1)$ the concentration gradient,

$$n_1 = k_1 \frac{d}{dz}(N_1),$$

where k_1, the coefficient of diffusion of the molecules (1), depends on the density of the mixture, the ratio of the masses of the constituents, and the concentration gradient at the point considered.

The path of a given molecule is zigzag in character on account of the interaction between the molecules and may be termed the diffusion free path, while the average distance traversed between successive collisions is the mean free path. Suppose the motion of the (1) molecules is towards the plane CD (Fig. 89), and the molecules (2) move towards AB. The Oz axis is at right angles to AB, and if, with centre O and any radius z, a semicircle is described to cut GH in J, then $OJ=ON=z$. Let $MJ=x$ and the angle $JOM=\theta$. The proportion of the molecules n_1 moving between angles θ and $\theta+d\theta$ with the normal is

$$n_1\frac{2\pi xz d\theta}{2\pi z^2}=n_1\ sin\ \theta d\theta,$$

since $x=z\ sin\ \theta$, and the number of these whose paths lie between z and $z+dz$ is, from (228),

$$n=n_1\ sin\ \theta d\theta\frac{z}{L_1^2}e^{-\frac{z}{L_1}}dz,\quad .\quad .\quad .\quad (290)$$

where L_1 is the mean free path of the molecules (1). A corresponding number n' will proceed in the opposite direction starting from GH, and these two numbers will be respectively proportional to the concentrations in EF and GH. The concentration in EF is N_1 molecules per c.c., and thus the concentration in GH is

$$N_1-OM\frac{d}{dz}(N_1)=N_1-z\ cos\ \theta\frac{d}{dz}(N_1).$$

Hence the total loss of molecules in EF is

$$n-n'=\frac{n-n'}{n}n,$$

and since

$$\frac{n}{n'}=\frac{N_1}{N_1-z\ cos\ \theta\frac{d}{dz}(N_1)},$$

or,

$$\frac{n-n'}{n}=\frac{z\ cos\ \theta\frac{d}{dz}(N_1)}{N_1},$$

the loss is, from equation (290),

$$\frac{z\ cos\ \theta\frac{d}{dz}(N_1)}{N_1}n_1\ sin\ \theta d\theta\frac{z}{L_1^2}e^{-\frac{z}{L_1}}dz.$$

The total loss is obtained by integrating this expression from 0 to ∞ for z, and from 0 to $\frac{\pi}{2}$ for θ, and gives

$$\frac{n_1L_1}{N_1}.\frac{d}{dz}(N_1)\quad .\quad .\quad .\quad .\quad (291)$$

In the same way the gain of molecules (2) in the plane EF is given by

$$\frac{n_2L_2}{N_2}.\frac{d}{dz}(N_2),\quad .\quad .\quad .\quad .\quad (292)$$

where L_2 is the mean free path of the molecules (2), the gradient being measured along the direction of decrease in concentration of molecules (2). Thus the total loss of molecules, irrespective of kind, is

$$\frac{n_1 L_1}{N_1}\cdot\frac{d}{dz}(N_1)-\frac{n_2 L_2}{N_2}\cdot\frac{d}{dz}(N_2), \qquad . \qquad . \qquad . \qquad (293)$$

and this represents the gain immediately below EF. The space which these molecules previously occupied in EF must be filled by a transportation in the opposite direction of a volume V of the mixture, and thus EF regains a number $N_1 V$ of molecules (1) and $N_2 V$ of molecules (2). The net loss of the former kind from the plane EF is consequently equal to

$$\frac{n_1}{N_1}L_1\frac{d}{dz}(N_1)-VN_1. \qquad . \qquad . \qquad . \qquad (294)$$

If each molecule (1) occupies a volume V_1 and each molecule (2) a volume V_2, then the total volume evacuated by the escaping molecules of both sorts is

$$\frac{n_1}{N_1}L_1 V_1\frac{d}{dz}(N_1)-\frac{n_2}{N_2}L_2 V_2\frac{d}{dz}(N_2),$$

and this is equal to V. Thus, from expression (294), the net loss of molecules (1) from EF is given by

$$\frac{n_1}{N_1}L_1\frac{d}{dz}(N_1)-N_1\left[\frac{n_1}{N_1}L_1 V_1\frac{d}{dz}(N_1)-\frac{n_2}{N_2}L_2 V_2\frac{d}{dz}(N_2)\right]$$

$$=n_1 L_1\left[\frac{1}{N_1}-V_1\right]\frac{d}{dz}(N_1)+n_2 L_2 V_2\frac{N_1}{N_2}\frac{d}{dz}(N_2).$$

But $N_1 V_1+N_2 V_2=1$ c.c. ; thus $\dfrac{1}{N_1}-V_1=\dfrac{N_2}{N_1}V_2$ and the total loss of molecules (1) from EF per second is d_1, where

$$d_1=V_2\left[\frac{N_2}{N_1}n_1 L_1\frac{d}{dz}(N_1)+\frac{N_1}{N_2}n_2 L_2\frac{d}{dz}(N_2)\right]. \qquad . \qquad (295)$$

This expression represents the net rate of diffusion. A similar expression for the net rate of diffusion, d_2, of the (2) molecules is obtained by an interchange of suffixes, and it is readily seen that

$$\frac{d_1}{d_2}=\frac{V_2}{V_1} \quad \text{or} \quad d_1 V_1=d_2 V_2 \qquad . \qquad . \qquad . \qquad (296)$$

In the case of gases $V_1=V_2$, and thus $d_1=d_2$. Since, also, the pressure is everywhere the same, N_1+N_2 is constant. Thus we have, putting $\dfrac{d}{dz}(N_1)=\dfrac{d}{dz}(N_2)$ and $V_1=\dfrac{1}{N_1+N_2}$,

$$d_1=\frac{1}{N_1+N_2}\left[n_1 L_1\frac{N_2}{N_1}+n_2 L_2\frac{N_1}{N_2}\right]\frac{d}{dz}(N_1) \qquad . \qquad . \qquad (297)$$

If the concentration of the first set of molecules in the mixture is very small, then (295) or (297) becomes

$$d_1 = \frac{n_1}{N_1} L_1 \frac{d}{dz}(N_1),$$

and so the coefficient of diffusion k_1 is

$$k_1 = \frac{n_1}{N_1} L_1 \quad . \qquad . \qquad . \qquad . \qquad (298)$$

Now consider a semi-permeable membrane impervious to the molecules (1) placed across the direction of diffusion. The particles (1) will exert a pressure upon the membrane in their direction of diffusion, and this pressure will be equal to the difference between the osmotic pressures on the two sides of the membrane. Thus we may regard each c.c. of the molecules (1) as being under a force equal to the osmotic pressure difference acting on opposite sides of the unit cube. This force is exerted in giving motion to the particles to overcome the viscous drag of the medium. If, as before, d_1 is the number of molecules (1) diffusing across 1 sq. cm. per sec.,

$$d_1 = N_1 v_1,$$

where v_1 is the average velocity of the (1) molecules as they move against the concentration gradient. If v_1' is the coefficient of mobility of the particles (1), and $\frac{d}{dz}(P_1)$ is the osmotic pressure gradient,

$$v_1 = \frac{v_1'}{N_1} \cdot \frac{d}{dz}(P_1),$$

since the velocity is inversely proportional to the concentration of the molecules. Hence

$$d_1 = v_1' \frac{d}{dz}(P_1) \quad . \qquad . \qquad . \qquad . \qquad (299)$$

and, similarly, for the other set of particles,

$$d_2 = v_2' \frac{d}{dz}(P_2) \quad . \qquad . \qquad . \qquad . \qquad (300)$$

But, from equation (296), $d_1 V_1 = d_2 V_2$, and thus

$$V_2 v_2' \frac{d}{dz}(P_2) = V_1 v_1' \frac{d}{dz}(P_1).$$

Let the concentration of the (1) molecules be small, so that their osmotic pressure obeys the ordinary gas law, *i.e.* $P_1 = \frac{RTN_1}{N}$. Thus

$$\frac{d}{dz}(P_1) = \frac{RT}{N} \cdot \frac{d}{dz}(N_1),$$

and hence

$$d_1 = v_1' \frac{RT}{N} \cdot \frac{d}{dz}(N_1).$$

The diffusion coefficient k_1 is given by

$$k_1 = \frac{v_1' RT}{N} \qquad \cdot \qquad \cdot \qquad \cdot \qquad \cdot \qquad (301)$$

If this is equated to the value given in equation (298), we have

$$v_1' \frac{RT}{N} = \frac{n_1}{N_1} L_1.$$

But the number of molecules crossing 1 sq. cm. per sec. is given by

$$n_1 = \frac{v_1 N_1}{3},$$

and $v_1 t_1 = L_1$ where t_1 is the time taken for the molecule to travel a distance L_1. Hence

$$3 v_1' \frac{RT}{N} = L_1 v_1 = \frac{L_1^2}{t_1}, \qquad \cdot \qquad \cdot \qquad \cdot \qquad (302)$$

so that, if L_1 and t_1 can be measured, v_1' the mobility may be determined. This is of special importance in the case of particles of sufficient size to undergo Brownian motion.

166. Brownian Motion in Liquids.—If the molecules of a liquid were of sufficient size to be visible to the eye it would be possible to detect the zigzag motion which results from molecular collisions. The foregoing results are true, however, for atomic or molecular aggregates such as are obtained in colloidal suspensions, since, although the mass would be struck by a large number of molecules on all sides at a given instant, the impacts would not necessarily be uniformly distributed, and the motion of the colloidal particle would have the characteristics already discussed. The corresponding movements would be relatively slow, and thus it should be possible to observe them under suitable conditions and to verify the most important deductions from the kinetic theory. This observation was first made by Brown, who used a suspension of plant pollen in water. Although no special type of microscope is necessary, the method of illumination is important and, in the ultramicroscope now generally used in studying the *Brownian motion*, the beam is sent through the liquid in a direction perpendicular to the microscope axis, and the particles are seen by means of the light which they scatter into the instrument. The beam must be very intense and the thickness of liquid traversed must be small, otherwise its absorption effect will interfere seriously with observations. By this means the movements of a particle of diameter 6×10^{-7} cm. may be followed.

The absolute motion of the particles is difficult to observe in detail, but this difficulty has been overcome by the application of the cinematograph to the microscope. Direct observation through a microscope gives an impression of a trembling motion rather than a vibration or simple progression, and the particles pursue an irregular zigzag course in all directions in space as if they were subjected to accidental collisions.

167. Einstein's Equation.—If it can be assumed that the mean kinetic energy of a suspended particle is the same as that of a gas molecule at the same temperature it is possible to connect the observed mean free path with the constants of the gas equation. This was done by Einstein,[1] but a simpler means of deriving Einstein's result has been given by Langevin [2] as follows :—

From the kinetic theory of gases $PV = \frac{1}{3}Nmv^2 = RT$. Representing the average kinetic energy of each molecule by E,

$$E = \frac{1}{2}mv^2 = \frac{3}{2}\frac{RT}{N} \qquad . \qquad . \qquad . \qquad (303)$$

From the principle of the equipartition of energy $\frac{E}{3}$ is the kinetic energy due to motion along one, say the x, direction. This energy is due to molecular impacts, and the equation of motion of a particle is

$$m\frac{d^2x}{dt^2} + \delta\frac{dx}{dt} + X = 0,$$

where X is the force produced by molecular bombardment and δ is the damping coefficient due to viscosity. Multiplying throughout by x and remembering that

$$x\frac{d^2x}{dt^2} = \frac{1}{2}\frac{d^2}{dt^2}(x^2) - \left(\frac{dx}{dt}\right)^2,$$

we have

$$\frac{m}{2}\cdot\frac{d^2}{dt^2}(x^2) - m\left(\frac{dx}{dt}\right)^2 + \frac{\delta}{2}\cdot\frac{d}{dt}(x^2) + Xx = 0.$$

If this equation is applied to a large number of particles of the same size and the mean result is taken, then the average value of Xx is zero, since X will, on the average, have equal numbers of positive and negative values. In addition, the average value of $m\left(\frac{dx}{dt}\right)^2 = \frac{RT}{N}$ from equation (303). Hence

$$\frac{m}{2}\cdot\frac{d\alpha}{dt} - \frac{RT}{N} + \frac{\delta\alpha}{2} = 0, \qquad . \qquad . \qquad . \qquad (304)$$

where α is the mean value of $\frac{d}{dt}(x^2)$. By integrating this we obtain

$$\alpha = \frac{2RT}{N\delta} + Ae^{-\frac{t\delta}{m}}, \qquad . \qquad . \qquad . \qquad (305)$$

where A is the integration constant.

From Stokes' Law the value of δ is $6\pi r\eta$, where r is the radius of

[1] Einstein, *Ann. der Physik.*, **17**, 4, 549 (1905) ; *Zeits. f. Elektroch.*, **14**, 235 (1908).

[2] Langevin, *Comptes Rendus*, **146**, 530 (1908).

the particle, and its value for the type of particle considered here is less than 10^{-4} cm. If the density of the particles is taken as unity,

$$\frac{m}{\delta} = \frac{\frac{4}{3}\pi(10^{-4})^3}{6\pi \times 0 \cdot 00018 \times 10^{-4}} = 10^{-5}.$$

Even for air $Ae^{-\frac{t\delta}{m}}$ approaches zero for any appreciable value of t. Hence equation (305) becomes

$$\frac{d}{dt}(x^2) = \frac{2RT,}{N\delta} \qquad . \qquad . \qquad . \qquad . \qquad (306)$$

and, by integration,

$$(x^2)_0 = \frac{2RT}{N\delta} t_0 = \frac{RT}{N} \cdot \frac{t_0}{3\pi r\eta}, \qquad . \qquad . \qquad . \qquad (307)$$

where $(x^2)_0$ denotes the mean value of the squared displacements corresponding to the period t_0. This result gives the average of the squares of the displacements for a large number of similar particles in the time t_0, or for the same particle observed through several intervals of time. We should not expect very exact correspondence between this theoretical formula and observation, because it is difficult to gauge the importance attaching to the assumptions, (a) that the particles may be regarded as rigid spheres, and (b) that surface tension forces may be neglected. Nevertheless, the tests which have been made justify the formula as regards its dependence on temperature, time, viscosity, and particle radius.

168. Brownian Motion of Rotation.—From kinetic theory considerations the rotational energy of suspended particles will, on the average, be the same as the mean translational energy, and Einstein [1] deduced an expression for the mean square of the rotational angle θ in a time t_0 in the form :—

$$(\theta^2)_0 = \frac{RT}{N} \cdot \frac{t_0}{4\pi\eta r^3} \qquad . \qquad . \qquad . \qquad (308)$$

169. Determination of Avogadro's Number N.—Some of the earlier experimental results did not agree well with equation (307), probably because the times during which observations were made were not long enough, and also because the colloidal particles employed were not all spherical. Experiments by Nordlund,[2] who obtained the particles by sparking between mercury electrodes in water, confirm Einstein's equation, and Millikan [3] has verified the equation for Brownian motion in gases. Westgren,[4] by means of a large number of measurements on colloidal gold, silver, and selenium particles of diameters from 6·5 to 13×10^{-6} cm., obtained a result—which he considered to be correct to $\frac{1}{2}$ per cent.—for N, given by

$$N = (6 \cdot 05 \pm 0 \cdot 03) \times 10^{23}.$$

[1] Einstein, *loc. cit.*
[2] Nordlund, *Zeits. Phys. Chem.*, **87**, 40 (1914).
[3] Millikan, *Phys. Rev.*, **32**, 349 (1911).
[4] Westgren, *Zeits. Phys. Chem.*, **92**, 750 (1918).

Perrin [1] tested Einstein's equation by measuring the displacements of a large number of granules in an emulsion. These displacements may be plotted and, if r represents any one displacement whose co-ordinates along two perpendicular axes are x and y,

$$\Sigma(r^2)_0 = \Sigma(x^2)_0 + \Sigma(y^2)_0,$$

but since the displacements will be in all directions, $\Sigma(x^2)_0 = \Sigma(y^2)_0$, and thus

$$\Sigma(x^2)_0 = \tfrac{1}{2}\Sigma(r^2)_0.$$

Substituting this result in (307) and knowing the other quantities occurring in it, Avogadro's number, N, may be calculated. Perrin obtained the value

$$N = 6\cdot82 \times 10^{23},$$

while Nordlund's result was

$$N = 5\cdot91 \times 10^{23}.$$

Perrin [1] also tested Einstein's equation for the rotation angle by observing the time of rotation of comparatively large grains of mastic which could be seen in the microscope. The period was determined by noting the intervals between the successive appearances of certain defects in the particle surface. His results confirmed the theoretical equation.

In another series of experiments Perrin [2] determined the value of N directly, by counting the number of particles in a dilute colloidal solution. The action of gravity causes a decrease in concentration with increasing height, and, in a state of kinetic equilibrium, the distribution of the particles with depth is similar to the variation of gas density with height, since the osmotic pressure which the particles exert obeys the gas laws. Hence

$$dP = Fdh,$$

where dP is the osmotic pressure difference in a vertical distance dh, and F is the force of gravity acting on the particles in 1 c.c. But

$$F = V_c(\rho - \rho_0)gn,$$

where V_c is the volume of one particle, n is the number of particles per c.c., ρ and ρ_0 are the densities of the particles and liquid respectively. Hence, since the osmotic pressure P is given by $P = \dfrac{RT}{N}n$,

$$\frac{RT}{N}dn = V_c(\rho - \rho_0)gndh, \qquad . \qquad . \qquad . \quad (309)$$

and

$$\log \frac{n_1}{n_0} = \frac{N}{RT}V_c(\rho - \rho_0)g(h_1 - h_0), \qquad . \qquad . \quad (310)$$

where n_1 and n_0 denote the concentrations at distances h_1 and h_0 from the surface.

To test this relation a cylindrical column, $0\cdot1$ mm. in height, was

[1] Perrin, *Comptes Rendus*, **146**, 967 (1908); **147**, 475, 530 (1908).
[2] Perrin, *loc. cit.*

viewed under a microscope which could be focused at different levels. When the liquid was first placed in the vessel, the particle distribution was apparently uniform, but after a few minutes it was evident that the concentration increased with depth, and soon a final state was reached which was the same at the end of fifteen days as after only about three hours. In a typical experiment with gamboge particles of $2 \cdot 12 \times 10^{-5}$ cm. diameter, Perrin found at four depths differing successively by 3×10^{-3} cm. the numbers were proportional to 12, 22·6, 47, and 100. Altogether in a single experiment some 13,000 particles were observed, and in this way the values of n_1 and n_0 were determined.

The density of the particles was measured by two methods. In the first it was taken to be the same as that of the substance in the undivided state, and in the second a known volume V of solution was evaporated and the residue m_3 weighed. Then, if m_1 and m_2 are the masses of a volume V of water and emulsion respectively, and d is the density of water at the temperature of the experiment $V = \dfrac{m_1}{d}$, and $\dfrac{m_2 - m_3}{d}$ is the volume of the water present in a volume V of emulsion. Hence the actual volume V_1 occupied by the particles is

$$V_1 = \frac{m_1}{d} - \frac{m_2 - m_3}{d},$$

and their density ρ is given by

$$\rho = \frac{m_3}{V_1} = \frac{m_3 d}{m_1 - m_2 + m_3}.$$

The volume V_c of one of the particles may be found in three ways : (a) if the number of particles in the volume V of the emulsion is counted, then V_c is the ratio of V_1 to this number ; (b) the steady rate of fall v under gravity may be observed by means of the microscope, and r may be found from Stokes' equation,

$$6\pi\eta r v = \tfrac{4}{3}\pi r^3 (\rho - \rho_0) g.$$

Thus V_c may be calculated ; and (c), if the emulsion is slightly acidified with hydrochloric acid, the particles gather on the walls of the vessel in strings, and a measurement of the length of one of these, together with the number of particles constituting the string, is sufficient to determine r. These three methods yielded concordant results, such as $0 \cdot 46\mu$, $0 \cdot 455\mu$, $0 \cdot 45\mu$, and from them Perrin obtained the value

$$N = 7 \cdot 05 \times 10^{23}.$$

The coefficient of diffusion is, from equation (301), given by $\dfrac{v_1' R T}{N}$ where v_1', the mobility, is the actual average velocity of the particles under unit force, so that

$$v_1 = v_1' F,$$

where v_1 is the velocity under a force F. According to Stokes' Law $F = 6\pi\eta r v_1$, and thus the coefficient of diffusion is

$$k = \frac{1}{6\pi r \eta} \cdot \frac{RT}{N} \quad . \quad . \quad . \quad . \quad (311)$$

In Perrin's experiments k was determined by suspending the particles in pure glycerine in which they possess the property of sticking to the glass walls of the containing vessel when they strike during their kinetic motion. By counting the number of granules which adhere to a given area in a measured time-interval after the steady distribution stage has been reached, the coefficient of diffusion perpendicular to that area is determined, and from equation (311) N may be calculated. This method yielded results in accord with other determinations.

In his experiments Perrin used emulsions of gamboge and gum mastic. The gamboge is made by desiccating the milk secreted by a gutteriferous plant; a part of the dry residue is rubbed under distilled water, and the gamboge dissolves, giving a yellow solution containing spherical particles of various microscopic and ultramicroscopic sizes. Those which were used in the above experiments were large compared with the particles of ordinary colloidal solutions, and observations were confined to very small depths. The difficulty of applying a concentration gradient similar to that of the atmosphere to these particles is that, with the rate of increase observed by Perrin over a depth of 0·1 mm., the concentration at a depth of, say, 1 cm. would be enormous. Burton [1] ascribes this discrepancy to the fact that the particles are charged, and, consequently, exert a mutual repulsion. He suggests that the charge on the particles will exert a force on unit charge equal to Ane, where A is a constant and e is the charge on each particle. Consequently the total force on a layer of particles in the thickness dh will be $Ane . ne . dh = An^2e^2 dh$, and Perrin's equation (309) is modified to

$$\frac{RT}{N} dn + An^2 e^2 dh = V_c(\rho - \rho_0) gn . dh.$$

Porter and Hedges [2] point out that the colloidal solution does not, in fact, contain charges all of one sign, but is electrically neutral as a whole. They state that the extension of Perrin's treatment to great depths is possible only if we replace the simple Van 't Hoff formula $PV = RT$, obtained for dilute solutions, by the osmotic law for concentrated solutions, such as the Sackur-Porter relation (Article 158),

$$P(V - b) = RT, \quad \text{or} \quad P = \frac{RTn}{N(1 - b_1 n)}.$$

We thus see that the application of kinetic theory principles to these colloidal suspensions yields results which are in agreement with one another and with determinations of Avogadro's number

[1] Burton, *Proc. Roy. Soc.*, A, **100**, 705 (1922).
[2] Porter and Hedges, *Trans. Far. Soc.*, **18**, 1 (1922).

by entirely different means.   In particular, the velocity distribution and the partition of energy among the particles agree with the Maxwellian laws, while the study of the Brownian motion has given much reliable information concerning the fundamental quantities of molecular theory, and thus has confirmed the hypotheses upon which it is based.

170. Brownian Motion in Gases.—The Brownian movements of particles suspended in gases were studied much later than those in liquids.   Ehrenhaft [1] was the first to carry out direct measurements, and he found that, as predicted by theory, there is a much greater activity in gases than in liquids.   At the same time the action of gravity is much more apparent, and true Brownian movements are masked to some extent by convection currents.   For heavier particles the velocity due to gravity completely hides that due to molecular collisions, while for very small particles which are near the limit of the ultra-microscope (10^{-7} cm.) the reverse is true. De Broglie,[2] one of the earliest experimenters to make a quantitative study with gases, drew the metallic dust arising from the condensation of the vapours, produced by an electric arc struck between metal electrodes, into a glass box, and examined the particles, which were rendered visible by a beam of light passing horizontally through the box.   He found that, when a potential difference was established between two plates in the box, some of the particles approached one plate and some the other.   Later he used minute water drops condensed on tobacco smoke, and determined the rate at which these droplets moved in a horizontal electric field.   The Brownian movement in air is about eight times more vigorous than in water, and by reducing the gas pressure, this movement may be increased to two hundred times that of the liquid.   If the particles were uncharged, Einstein's equation was verified, and the value of N obtained was in good agreement with that deduced from other experiments.   De Broglie used the equation $Fe = v\delta$, where F is the electric field, e the charge on the particle, v the velocity, and δ the damping factor.   He then measured $(x^2)_0$, and since, from (307),

$$(x^2)_0 = \frac{2RT}{N\delta}t,$$

δ may be eliminated from the two equations.   Assuming Perrin's value for N, he calculated e, the charge on the particle.   These experiments are important, because no assumption is made that the particles are alike in size, that they have the same charge, or that Stokes' Law is obeyed.

The most important experiments on the Brownian motion in gases have been made by Millikan,[3] who used minute oil drops formed by blowing, with a simple atomiser, an oil spray into the chamber.

[1] Ehrenhaft, *Phys. Zeits.*, **10**, 308 (1909).
[2] De Broglie, *Comptes Rendus*, **148** 1163 (1909).
[3] Millikan, *Phys. Rev.*, **32**, 349 (1911).

These drops, having a radius of 10^{-4} cm., moved between horizontal plates across which an electric field was maintained. The illuminated drops were observed through a microscope while, under the action of gravity, they moved slowly downwards. During their motion they collect ions present in the chamber and, with the aid of the electric field, a particular particle could be suspended under observation for a long period, and as many displacements as desired could be measured for this particle, instead of assuming exact similarity among the various particles. The gravitational drift velocity v_1 was then observed, and also the velocity v_2 when an electric force X acted against gravity. Then, if m is the mass of the drop,

$$\frac{mg}{Xe-mg}=\frac{v_1}{v_2},$$

or,

$$e=\frac{mg(v_1+v_2)}{Xv_1},$$

and since $mg=v_1\delta$,

$$e=\frac{\delta}{X}(v_1+v_2).$$

Combining this equation with the Einstein relation (307), we have

$$(x^2)_0=\frac{2RT}{N}\cdot\frac{v_1+v_2}{Xe}t,$$

so that the product Ne could be obtained without reference to the size of the particle or the resistance of the medium.

The value of Ne obtained was $2\cdot88\times10^{14}$ electrostatic units as compared with $2\cdot896\times10^{14}$ obtained from electrolysis. This confirms Einstein's assumption that a particle in a gas, whatever its size, moves with a mean translational energy which is a universal constant dependent only on temperature. Similar tests made by Weiss [1] with silver particles and by Eyring [2] with oil drops in hydrogen gave similar results for Ne, and these agreements furnish additional confirmation of the kinetic and atomic hypotheses of matter.

Recent experimental values of Avogadro's number rest on the fact that X-ray wave lengths may be determined directly by means of ruled diffraction gratings. Bragg's law relates the wave length with the lattice constant of a crystal, e.g. rock-salt, so that the latter can be accurately determined in terms of the molecular weight of rock-salt, its density and Avogadro's number. The result is $N=(6\cdot023\pm0\cdot03)\times10^{23}$.

Bond [3] devised a method of calculating the charge e on an elec-

[1] Weiss, *Phys. Zeits.*, **12**, 630 (1911).
[2] Eyring, *Phys. Rev.*, **5**, 412 (1915).
[3] Bond, *Phil. Mag.*, **10**, 994 (1930); **12**, 632 (1931).

tron and hence N from the various methods of determining Planck's constant. The value he obtains is $N = (6 \cdot 054 \pm 0 \cdot 03) \times 10^{23}$ which Birge [1] corrected to $N = (6 \cdot 062 \pm 0 \cdot 03) \times 10^{23}$.

It is instructive to compare the values of N, the number of molecules in a gram-molecule of a substance, and n, the number of molecules in 1 c.c. of a gas at S.T.P., obtained by these and other methods.

TABLE XVIII.—VALUES OBTAINED FOR N AND n

Experimenter.	Method.	$N \times 10^{-23}$.	$n \times 10^{-19}$.
Maxwell . .	Mean free path and density of mercury	4·5	2·0
,, . .	Kinetic theory of gases . .	4·27	1·9
Van der Waals .	Value of " b " for oxygen and nitrogen	4·5	2·0
Meyer . .	Kinetic theory of gases . .	13·8	6·1
Einstein . .	Diffusion coefficient . . .	4·0–9·0	1·8–4·0
Millikan . .	Fall of an ion in an electric field	6·23	2·8
,, . .	Recalculated	6·18	2·77
Perrin . .	Brownian rotational movement .	6·5	2·9
,, . .	Brownian motion in liquids .	7·15	3·2
,, . .	Distribution of colloidal particles	6·82	3·2
Chaudesaignes .	Brownian motion in liquids .	6·4	2·9
Ehrenhaft . .	,, ,, in gases .	6·3	2·8
de Broglie . .	,, ,, ,, .	6·43	2·9
Hopper and Laby	Oil drop	6·023	2·687
Birge, 1941 . .	X-ray data	6·023	2·687

EXAMPLES

1. 10 gm. of sugar of molecular weight 360 is dissolved in 1 litre of water, the temperature being 15° C. If the gas constant per gram-molecule is $8 \cdot 26 \times 10^7$, calculate the osmotic pressure of the solution.
$\qquad$ [$6 \cdot 61 \times 10^5$ dynes per sq. cm.]

2. The sugar solution in the previous question has a density of 1·006 gm. per c.c., and the density of hydrogen at standard pressure and temperature is $8 \cdot 98 \times 10^{-5}$ gm. per c.c., while the saturation pressure of water vapour at 15° C. is 1·200 cm. of mercury. Calculate the amount by which the vapour pressure over the sugar solution falls below that over a pure water surface. [6×10^{-4} cm. of mercury.]

3. Calculate (a) the boiling-point under normal pressure, (b) the freezing-point of the solution in the previous question if the density of water is 1·00 gm. per c.c. at 0° C. and 0·958 at 100° C., the latent heat of steam at 100° C. is 540 cals. and the latent heat of ice is 80·0 cals. Take J as $4 \cdot 18 \times 10^7$ erg per cal. [(a) 100·015° C. ; (b) −0·051° C.]

4. A vertical diffusion cell of height l, containing a uniform solution of concentration C, has a slow stream of pure solvent passing horizontally

[1] Birge, *Phys. Rev.*, **40**, 228, 319 (1932).

over it. Find an expression for the variation of concentration c, with distance x, above the bottom at any subsequent time t; the coefficient of diffusion being k.

$$[(4C/\pi)\{e^{\beta t} \cos \alpha x - e^{9\beta t}(\cos 3\alpha x)/3 + \ldots\}.] \qquad (\beta = -k\pi^2/4l^2 \; ; \; \alpha = \pi/2l.)$$

5. In a diffusion cell of length l the solution at the bottom is maintained at saturation concentration C, while at the top the solution is maintained at practically zero strength. If, initially, the vessel contained a saturated solution, find the concentration at any point distant x from the bottom after a time t.

$$[C - Cx/l + (8C/\pi^2)\{e^{\beta t} \sin \alpha x - e^{9\beta t}(\sin 3\alpha x)/9$$
$$+ e^{25\beta t}(\sin 5\alpha x)/25 - \ldots\}.] \quad (\alpha \text{ and } \beta \text{ as above.})$$

6. In a measurement of the osmotic pressure of a solution of sucrose, molecular weight 342·2, at 10° C., the pressure P in atmospheres and the volume V containing 1 gram-molecule of dissolved sugar were as follows :—

| P. | 2·52 | 4·93 | 9·87 | 14·98 | 20·24 | 25·92 |
| V. | 10,000 | 5000 | 2500 | 1667 | 1250 | 1000 c.c. |

Show that the relation $P(V-b)=const.$ applies to the readings, and deduce values for b and R, the gas constant per gram-molecule.

$$[b = 89 \text{ c.c.} \; ; \; R = 8·45 \times 10 .]$$

7. If the values of P and V at 60° C. for the above sugar were:

| P. | 2·74 | 5·48 | 10·96 | 16·67 | 22·52 | 28·63 |
| V. | 10,000 | 5000 | 2500 | 1667 | 1250 | 1000 |

find the value of b at this temperature, and show that $P(V-b) \propto T$.

$$[75 \text{ c.c.}]$$

8. Observations on the Brownian movement in water showed that the horizontal displacement of a given particle in eleven successive intervals of 30 sec. were 0, 5·6, $-4·7$, $-10·8$, 6·6, $-9·8$, $-11·2$, $-4·0$, 15·0, 19·1, $16·0 \times 10^{-4}$ cm. The temperature was 20° C., at which the viscosity of water is 0·0100 C.G.S., and the radius of the particle was $1·05 \times 10^{-6}$ cm. If $R = 8·32 \times 10^7$, obtain a value for the number of molecules in 1 gram-molecule. $[5·7 \times 10^{23}.]$

9. In a colloidal suspension of gamboge particles the average numbers of particles n in the field of view of a microscope at various depths h below the surface were :—

| $n =$ | 120 | 215 | 324 | 460 | 615 | 924 |
| $h =$ | 0 | 10 | 17 | 23 | 28 | 35 |

Show that these observations agree with the theoretical distribution of non-ionised particles.

10. A small oil drop is observed to drift vertically downwards with velocity v. When a vertical electrical field of intensity 6·54 E.S.U. is applied the drop is found to move upwards with the same velocity. If e is the charge carried by the drop and m is its mass, find the ratio of e/m for the drop. $[300.]$

11. The actual drift velocity in the previous question was $9·30 \times 10^{-3}$ cm. per sec. If the oil density was 0·80 gm. per c.c. and the viscosity of air 0·000181, find the value of the charge e. Is this the minimum value the charge could have ?

$$[9·53 \times 10^{-10} \text{ E.S.U.} \; ; \; \text{No, it is double.}]$$

12. When 1·065 gm. of iodine is dissolved in 30·14 gm. of ethyl ether the boiling-point is raised by 0·296° C. The atomic weight of iodine is 127, the boiling-point of ethyl ether is 34·6° C., its latent heat 81·49 cals. per gm., its density at the boiling-point is 0·6944 gm. per c.c. Show that the molecule of iodine is diatomic.

CHAPTER XI

THE PRODUCTION AND MEASUREMENT OF LOW PRESSURES

171. The Speed of a Vacuum Pump.—High-vacuum technique is a dominant factor in the modern laboratory, especially in the realms of modern radio and X-ray equipment, and it is destined to play an important part in certain branches of chemical industry.

In the high-vacuum pumping systems now generally adopted the pressure is first reduced from atmospheric to a small fraction of it, *e.g.* to about 0·1 mm. of mercury,[1] by means of a " backing pump " which is usually of the piston or rotary-vane oil type. Further reduction from this " fore-vacuum " or " backing-pressure," produced by the backing pump, down to some value ranging from 10^{-4} mm. to 10^{-7} mm. is achieved by means of some type of diffusion-condensation pump, or by means of a molecular pump. The backing and high-vacuum pumps are arranged in tandem, so that gas or vapour from the vessel to be exhausted is taken in at the " inlet " of the high-vacuum pump and ejected at its " outlet " into the fore-vacuum of the backing pump. From there the latter ejects it into the atmosphere.

An important property of a pump is its speed. This is measured by the relative rate at which the pressure is reduced in a given volume, and is defined thus :—

$$\frac{dP}{dt} = -\frac{S}{V}(P - P_0), \qquad . \qquad . \qquad . \qquad (312)$$

where S is the pumping speed at a pressure P, V the volume, and P_0 the limiting pressure. From this it follows that

$$S = \frac{V}{t_2 - t_1} \, \log \left(\frac{P_1 - P_0}{P_2 - P_0} \right),$$

where P_1 and P_2 are the pressures at the instants t_1 and t_2. This equation is useful in predicting the time $(t_2 - t_1)$ required for a vacuum system to recover from a surge of gas which raises the pressure to P_1, P_2 representing the working pressure required in the apparatus. If the limiting pressure is very low, we have

$$S = \frac{V}{t_2 - t_1} \, \log \frac{P_1}{P_2},$$

known as Gaede's equation.

[1] The mm. of mercury is generally used as the unit of pressure in high-vacuum technique. Throughout this chapter the unit mm. refers to mm. of mercury.

In equation (312) put $P_0=0$, then

$$S=-\frac{V}{P}\cdot\frac{dP}{dt}.$$

Let dV be the volume of gas, measured at pressure P, extracted from the volume V during the time interval dt, then

$$VP=(V+dV)(P+dP),$$

and

$$\frac{dV}{dt}=-\frac{V}{P}\cdot\frac{dP}{dt}=S.$$

Thus the speed of a pump is the rate of change of volume of the gas in an enclosure at any instant, the volume being measured at the pressure attained by the pump at that instant. From this equation it is evident that a pump has no pumping speed at the lowest attainable pressure. It is important that all pumps should be designed so that they can produce not only low pressures, but that they have as high a speed as possible at all pressures.

172. Rotary Oil Pumps.—An oil pump, *e.g.* the piston or the rotary type, is generally used as the backing pump. The piston type is convenient and durable, but it has been considerably replaced during the last few years by the rotary type which was evolved from the oil-circulating pump. Taking up very little space, silent, and having a high speed, these pumps are the most useful yet made if the backing pressure required is less than 10^{-1} mm.

There are two main types of rotary oil pumps; both embody a rotating part which, by means of vanes and an eccentric motion, compresses and ejects the gas through an oil-immersed non-return outlet valve. In the rotary-vane pump, first proposed by Gaede and illustrated in Fig. 90 (*a*), the cylindrical solid rotor revolves eccentrically inside the hollow stator. A slot is cut across the rotor diametrically and two vanes slide in this slot. They are separated by a spring which also presses them against the walls of the stator. The space between the latter and the rotor is limited by two end-plates. As the rotor revolves, gas taken in at the intake is trapped by the rotating vanes, compressed, and finally expelled through the exhaust valve. The pump is fitted with a self-sealing oil valve in order to ensure that when the pump is stationary, air is not sucked back from the pump into any exhausted vessel connected to it. The whole of the working parts are placed in an outer rectangular case, filled with oil, which gives perfect lubrication, prevents leakage of gas into the high vacuum, and assists in efficient cooling of the pump.

In the " Cenco " eccentric rotor pump, illustrated in Fig. 90 (*b*), the steel rotor rotates eccentrically about a shaft inside the steel stator, the walls of both being worked to a high degree of precision. A single vane is spring-operated by the arm and presses against the rotor. As the latter rotates, the gas entering via the intake port is trapped, and forced by the movement of the rotor into a smaller volume, being finally expelled through the exhaust valve. The whole mechanism is immersed in oil, and a special valve on the intake tube prevents oil from passing into the exhausted vessel when the pump is stopped. Two " Cenco " units can be mounted in series, side by side, on a common motor-driven shaft and by this arrangement a lower final pressure can be attained. Other commercial elaborations of this " Hyvac " are known as " Megavac " and " Hypervac," and pressures as low as 10^{-4} mm. are produced by them.

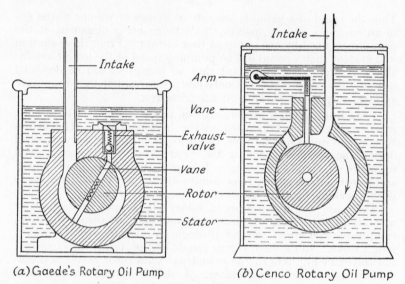

(a) Gaede's Rotary Oil Pump   (b) Cenco Rotary Oil Pump

FIG. 90.—ROTARY OIL PUMPS.

These low pressures can only be attained if the pump and oil are clean and uncontaminated by vapours—especially water vapour. Vapours are condensed to liquid on the exhaust side of the pump, contaminate the sealing oil and corrode the internal parts. To trap these vapours a bulb of phosphorus pentoxide should be placed between the pump and the vessel which is being exhausted.

173. Molecular Pumps.—All oil pumps operate between atmospheric and a comparatively low pressure, e.g. 10^{-1} mm.– 10^{-3} mm., but molecular and diffusion pumps will only work from a reduced pressure, and accordingly they must always be used in series with a backing pump.

The action of molecular pumps depends upon the fact that a dragging force, due to viscosity, is exerted on gas molecules by a rapidly rotating surface adjacent to a stationary one. The clearance between these surfaces must be very small—of the order of 0·03 mm.—so that the gas molecules make many more collisions with the walls of the annular gap than with each other. The rotation direction is such that gas is dragged from the vessel to be exhausted, by the high-speed rotor and delivered into the backing pump, the pressure difference at the inlet and outlet ports being proportional to the rotor's angular velocity. The rotor speed should be not less than 5000 revolutions per minute.

In Gaede's type [1] a set of projections from the outer stator fit into grooves in the rotor and the gas is swept along the clearance between projections and grooves. The Holweck pump [2] works on the same principle but the grooves are on the stator and there are no projections on the rotor. In this arrangement the clearance between the moving and fixed cylinders can be reduced below 0·03 mm.

Molecular pumps remove vapours as well as the more permanent gases, but traces of slowly vaporising substances, such as grease or mercury, are troublesome. In addition, the pumps are subject to considerable mechanical trouble owing to the small clearance between the stator and rotor surfaces. The final pressures attainable with these pumps depend upon the fore-vacuum pressure and the angular velocity of the rotor, e.g. a final pressure of 10^{-6} mm. can be produced with 10,000 revolutions per minute and a fore-vacuum of 2 mm.

174. Diffusion—Condensation Pumps.—The diffusion pump is the most widely used type for the production of very low pressures, and as condensation as well as diffusion plays an important part in its operation, it is often referred to as a condensation pump. It must be used in tandem with a backing pump. The pump was originated by Gaede [3] and the principle of its action is as follows :—

Consider a stream of vapour flowing along a tube in the direction from A to B (Fig. 91) (a), D representing some porous material placed near the end of a side tube C which leads to the vessel being exhausted. The vapour stream carries along with it any gas in the space AB, and as the gas pressure therein is thus reduced, gas diffuses from C into AB where it is swept along by the vapour stream. Vapour will obviously diffuse from AB into C, but if it is arranged that the small capillaries in the porous material D are of smaller dimensions than the mean free path of the vapour and gas molecules, then there will be relatively few vapour-gas molecular collisions, and this back-diffusion of vapour into C will not interfere with the gas diffusion from C to AB. Additionally, if vapour reaching C is condensed by some means, then diffusion of the gas from C into AB continues until the partial gas pressures in both spaces— C and AB—are equal. It is evident that with a gas-free vapour

[1] Gaede, *Phys. Zeits.*, **13**, 864 (1912).
[2] Holweck, *Revue d'Optique*, **1**, 274 (1922).
[3] Gaede, *Ann. d. Phys.*, **46**, 357 (1915).

stream, the diffusion process continues, theoretically, until the gas pressure at C is zero. This limit is never attained in practice, owing to gas liberated from the walls of the vessel, and there is a tendency for the gas to leak back from B to C. In addition, vapour diffuses towards C and the final pressure in the vessel being exhausted depends upon the vapour pressure, *i.e.* the temperature at C. It is obvious that no porous material is really required at D for this diffusion action, but the pump constriction must be such that vapour entering C does not prevent gas diffusion from C. The gas is swept forward to B and passes into the fore-vacuum of the backing pump,

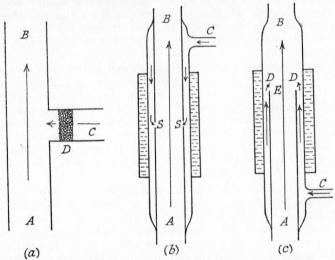

FIG. 91.—PRINCIPLE OF THE DIFFUSION-CONDENSATION PUMP.

the vapour stream along AB preventing back diffusion of the gas from B to C, provided that the gas pressure at B is sufficiently low.

Gaede originally designed a pump in which diffusion occurred across an annular slit (Fig. 91) (*b*), of width approximately equal to the mean free path of the molecules at the slit. Thus the gas molecules passing through S will not collide with the vapour molecules passing in the opposite direction and the gas therefore diffuses through S. The tube surrounding the annular slit was water-cooled, which prevented the vapour from passing to the vessel being exhausted. With low vapour pressures, *i.e.* a slowly moving vapour stream, there is some back-diffusion of the gas from B, and the pump speed is very low, being limited by the width of the slit S. The pump is interesting since it was the first one constructed, but it was never generally used, as Langmuir [1] showed that a much simpler arrangement gave better results.

[1] Langmuir, *Phys. Rev.*, 8, 48 (1916).

Langmuir prevented the vapour from passing through to C by directing the stream away, as far as possible, from the inlet to C, as shown in Fig. 91 (c). When the stream emerges from A the vapour is condensed on the walls of B by the cooling arrangement, and there is little tendency for it to diffuse through the annular gap and thence to C. If, however, the vapour pressure at the gap is high, the vapour molecules emerging from the end of A will move in all directions and some will move downwards through D to oppose the gas diffusion from C. But if the gas pressure in the fore-vacuum at B is low, the vapour pressure at E in the stream need not be

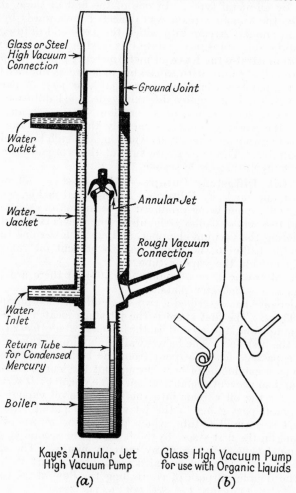

Kaye's Annular Jet
High Vacuum Pump
(a)

Glass High Vacuum Pump
for use with Organic Liquids
(b)

Fig. 92.

high to prevent the gas from diffusing back from B. Provided that this condition holds, and that the mean free path of the vapour molecules at E is greater than the width of the annular gap, the vapour molecules emerging from E will strike the cooled walls and condense without colliding with gas molecules leaving D.

From these considerations it is evident that the width of the annular gap, the pressure in the fore-vacuum of the backing pump, the vapour pressure at the gap, and the vapour condensation thereat are important factors in the successful working of any type of diffusion pump. Early models were of glass, but they have been replaced by all-metal types. In one of the first of these, made by Langmuir, the vapour stream was deflected downwards by a cowl to form an annular stream into which the gas could diffuse. Many modern diffusion pumps incorporate this cowl device. For example, Fig. 92 (a) illustrates the Kaye all-metal mercury pump. It produces a pressure of 10^{-6} mm. with a backing pressure as high as 1·5 mm. The most rapid types employ several gaps, or jets, in parallel.

Although there are many differently designed diffusion pumps, they all use either mercury, or a very low vapour-pressure organic liquid, as the working liquid. Generally the organic liquid is one of the oils known commercially as Apiezon, although butyl phthalate is also suitable. The vapour pressure of these organic compounds at room temperatures is less than 10^{-6} mm.

175. Oil Diffusion Pumps.—A single-stage all-metal oil diffusion pump made by Edwards [1] is illustrated in Fig. 93 (a), the stream of oil vapour being produced by means of an electric heater. There are two sets of baffles ; the upper one prevents the oil vapour from entering the vacuum chamber, and at the lower one the liquid oil seals the baffle to the pump wall to prevent oil vapour from ascending outside the vapour tube.

In the Metrovac Type 03 pump (Fig. 93) (b) there are two sets of baffles and a deflector plate.

Henderson [2] has described a two-stage oil-diffusion pump, shown in Fig. 93 (c). The first stage is the jet stage located near the top of the pump, and the second is the annular stage placed directly beneath the first one. The heavy-walled aluminium tube serves not only as a passage for oil vapour from the boiler to the first stage, but also as a conductor of heat throughout the length traversed by the oil, and so prevents condensation. The openings D serve as the entrance for the oil vapour into this tube, the oil vapour dividing at this point, part going to the jet stage and part to the annular stage. B is a small U-tube which permits the return of the oil, condensing in the first stage, to the boiler. The second stage is the conventional type found in many mercury pumps. The spacer C, which is of glass and which is sealed as an integral part of the pump, serves the double purpose of controlling the flow of oil vapour as

[1] Edwards, *Rev. Sci. Inst.*, 6, 145 (1935).
[2] Henderson, *ibid.*, 6, 66 (1935).

well as serving as a guide to the aluminium tube. With " Apiezon B " oil, pressures as low as 2×10^{-8} mm. have been obtained, the fore-vacuum pressure being of the order of 0·2 mm.

A simple form of glass pump designed for use with oils is shown in Fig. 92 (b).

In general, diffusion pumps designed for use with mercury are

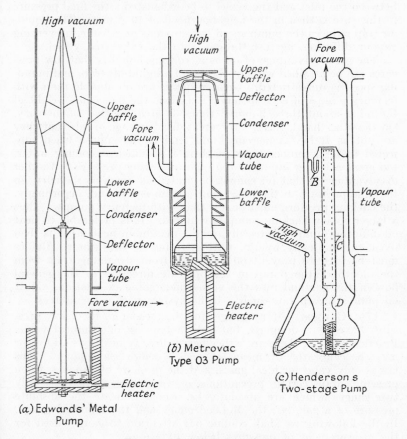

(a) Edwards' Metal Pump

(b) Metrovac Type 03 Pump

(c) Henderson's Two-stage Pump

FIG. 93.—OIL DIFFUSION PUMPS.

unsuitable with oil as the operating liquid for the following reasons : (a) the gap between the cowl and the condensing surface may be too small, and the gap may be closed by a film of oil ; (b) the cross-sectional area of the pipe supplying the vapour may be too small, so that an adequate supply of vapour to the jet may not be produced without overheating the oil ; (c) the cowl and the vapour supply pipe may become too cool, causing excessive vapour condensation.

Mercury is convenient because of its chemical stability, and reasonable temperatures are required at the jet; consequently the fore-vacuum need not be very low. The vapour pressure of mercury, however, at room temperatures is of the order 10^{-3} mm. and this represents the ultimate pressure attainable with a mercury pump. If lower pressures are required, a liquid-air trap must be placed between the inlet and the vessel to be exhausted; the final pressure in this case is then in the neighbourhood of 10^{-6} mm. The liquid-air trap reduces the pump speed but also acts as a baffle, preventing vapour diffusion, against the gas, into the exhausted vessel.

The great advantage of oil as a working liquid is that low pressures can be attained without the use of a liquid-air trap, and pumping speed is unrestricted. Greater speeds are obtainable than with mercury pumps of corresponding size since the molecular weight of the oil is about three hundred times as great as that of mercury. On the other hand, there is the great disadvantage of oils that they are not as stable as mercury, and tend to decompose when subjected to high temperatures, if there is insufficient cooling water, too great a heater input, or too high a backing pressure. Another disadvantage is that oil cannot be heated as much as mercury, so that the pressure in the oil vapour stream is less and, accordingly, the backing pressure must be less than with mercury pumps. Thus a larger rotary backing pump is required. It is preferable to heat oil diffusion pumps electrically, as the maximum heat input is then fixed automatically by the wattage-rating of the heater. Baffles must be used to prevent oil molecules from streaming back from the mouth of the pump in the opposite direction to the general flow of the gas and into the vessel undergoing evacuation. Most oil pumps incorporate such a baffle system within themselves.

176. Gauges.—Many gauges for the measurement of low pressures have been designed, but only a few are of practical value. Practically all of them are either based directly on Boyle's Law, or must be calibrated by means of such a compression gauge. This law is only valid for ideal gases, and the pressure of vapours, when present, entails certain precautions, or corrections. There are only two gauges which are absolute, *i.e.* which indicate the absolute pressure of a gas, *viz.* the McLeod gauge and the Knudsen gauge. In the following we shall confine our attention to gauges used for the measurement of pressures below 10^{-1} mm.

177. The McLeod Gauge.—The principle of the McLeod gauge consists in isolating a known volume of the gas at the unknown pressure and compressing it into a small known volume at which the pressure is measured. The gauge, illustrated in Fig. 94, consists of a closed, graduated capillary tube B sealed to a bulb A—the volume of which depends upon the pressure range to be measured. Placed very close to this capillary tube is a side capillary tube C of similar bore to eliminate surface tension errors. A scale is fixed behind these tubes and a mercury reservoir, connected by rubber tubing to the gauge, enables rising mercury when it reaches D to trap the volume of gas V contained in A and B at a pressure P, and compress it to a known volume v in B at a pressure p. Then

$$P = \frac{pv}{V}.$$

The gauge can be operated by raising the reservoir until the mercury in C is at the same horizontal level as the closed end of B. If h_1 is the difference in the mercury levels in tubes B and C, and h_2 is the length of the volume of gas trapped in B, $h_1 = h_2$ and $p = h_2$ mm. of mercury. Let k be the volume of 1 mm. length of the capillary B. Then $v = kh_2$ and

$$P = \frac{kh_2{}^2}{V} = Kh_2{}^2.$$

P is thus determined in mm. of mercury provided that K the gauge constant is known, or can be found in the usual manner. It will be noted that P is read on a quadratic scale with the zero at the upper end of B.

Many minor modifications in the McLeod gauge have been proposed from time to time. The flexible rubber tubing, which contaminates the mercury in the course of time, has been replaced by a stainless steel tube dipping into a reservoir of stainless steel, and bench types are available which reduce the overall length.

The gauge is simple, cheap, but rather unwieldly. Its range depends upon the volume of the bulb A and the bore of the capillary. In general, the latter should not be less than 1 mm. diameter, and the final volume not less than 2 cu. mm. As the principle of the instrument is based on the validity of Boyle's Law, it should only be used with the more permanent gases ; erratic and unreliable readings are obtained if condensible vapours— especially water vapour—are present. It is necessary, therefore, to eliminate all traces of such vapours before the gauge is used. The presence of mercury vapour is an undesirable feature, especially in systems incorporating

Fig. 94.—The McLeod Gauge.

oil diffusion pumps. In addition, the gauge will not register correctly pressures below that of mercury vapour pressure at room temperatures. The mercury vapour may be trapped with a liquid-air trap placed between the gauge and the rest of the system. The gauge does not give a continuous record of pressure, but must be read, an interval of a minute or so being required for the reading. If all precautions are taken, the instrument is capable of measuring pressures as low as 10^{-5} mm., but many workers consider that it is unreliable below 10^{-4} mm.

178. The Knudsen Gauge.—Although not generally accepted as a practical instrument, the Knudsen gauge possesses the outstanding advantage that, if suitably designed, it indicates very closely the absolute pressures of both gases and condensible vapours, irrespective of their nature or condensibility. The gauges can be constructed to cover a pressure range from 10^{-3} mm. to 10^{-7} mm. The principle of the instrument depends upon radiometric forces at low pressures ; Knudsen [1] calculated the repulsion produced by the molecular bombardment which is exerted between hot and cold

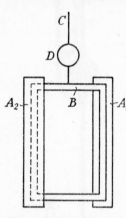

plates mounted in an exhausted vessel. If two such plates are arranged parallel, and at a distance apart small in comparison with the mean free path, there is repulsion between these plates which, over a range of pressures, is proportional to the gas pressure down to 10^{-7} mm.

To measure this effect, Knudsen set up an apparatus represented diagrammatically in Fig. 95 where A_1, A_2 are two fixed plates electrically heated, and B is the cold plate suspended by means of a quartz fibre C to which is attached a mirror D. The molecular repulsion deflects the plate B, the deflection being measured by means of a beam of light reflected from the mirror D. The calculation of the force of repulsion is an interesting example of radiometer phenomena.

FIG. 95.—THE KNUDSEN GAUGE.

Let T_1, T_2 be the temperatures of A_1 and B, respectively, N_1 the number of molecules per c.c. moving with a root mean square velocity C_1 from A_1 to B, and N_2, the number per c.c. moving with velocity C_2 from B to A_1. In the equilibrium state

$$N_1 C_1 = N_2 C_2,$$

since the number of molecular collisions per sq. cm. per second must be the same. If we consider T_2 to be the temperature of the containing vessel, and N the number of molecules per c.c. in the space outside that between A_1 and B, then

$$NC_2 = N_1 C_1 + N_2 C_2 = 2N_1 C_1 = 2N_2 C_2 \quad . \quad . \quad (313)$$

since the number of molecules flowing out from the space between A_1 and B to the rest of the enclosure must be equal to the number

[1] Knudsen, *Ann. d. Phys.*, **31**, 205 (1910).

flowing into this space. Hence the total pressure between the plates, if m is the mass of each molecule, is

$$\frac{mN_1C_1{}^2}{3}+\frac{mN_2C_2{}^2}{3},$$

while the pressure acting on that face of B removed from A_1 is $\dfrac{mNC_2{}^2}{3}$. Thus the excess pressure acting on B urging it away from A_1 is

$$\frac{mN_1C_1{}^2}{3}+\frac{mN_2C_2{}^2}{3}-\frac{mNC_2{}^2}{3},$$

and from equation (313) this is

$$\frac{mNC_2{}^2}{6}\left[\frac{C_1}{C_2}-1\right].$$

Assuming that the molecules when they strike A_1 and B take up the temperature of these surfaces,

$$\frac{C_1}{C_2}=\sqrt{\frac{T_1}{T_2}}.$$

Hence

$$\mu=\frac{P}{2}\left[\sqrt{\frac{T_1}{T_2}}-1\right],$$

where $P=\dfrac{mNC_2{}^2}{3}$ and is the pressure within the enclosure, μ being the repulsive force per sq. cm. acting on one plate. This formula is valid only if the distance between the plates is small compared with the mean free path, and if the dimensions of the plates are such that the edge effects may be neglected.

For temperature differences not exceeding 250° C. the formula may be written in the form

$$\mu=\frac{P}{4}\left[\frac{T_1-T_2}{T_2}\right]. \qquad . \qquad . \qquad . \qquad (314)$$

We see, therefore, that the force is independent of the nature of the gas, and if μ can be measured, the pressure within the enclosure can be determined.

Now if r_1 and r_2 are the distances of the vertical sides of B from the axis of suspension, L the length of the vertical side, θ the angle of deflection, and τ the constant of the fibre,

$$\tau\theta=2\int_{r_1}^{r_2}\mu Lr\,dr=\mu L(r_2{}^2-r_1{}^2)=2a\mu r, \qquad . \qquad . \qquad (315)$$

where a is the area of one vertical strip and r is its average distance from the axis of suspension. Thus from equations (314) and (315)

$$P=\frac{2\tau\theta}{ar}\cdot\frac{T_2}{T_1-T_2}.$$

If I is the moment of inertia of the suspended vanes, and t_0 the periodic time of oscillation,

$$t_0 = 2\pi \sqrt{\frac{I}{\tau}},$$

so

$$P = \frac{8\pi^2 I\theta}{t_0{}^2 ar} \cdot \frac{T_2}{T_1 - T_2}.$$

In practice the elements are placed in a chamber communicating with the vacuum to be measured. The formula is seen to be independent of the molecular weight of the gas, but the gauge will obviously cease to function correctly when the gas pressure has become so high, and the mean free path so small, that convection currents are set up, causing erratic behaviour of the vane.

The advantages of this gauge are that it involves no objectionable medium such as mercury; it gives a continuous indication of pressure; there is no filament sufficiently hot to burn out, or change the chemical constitution of vapours, or gases, whose pressures are being measured; it is very stable and insensitive to external influences, yet it is very sensitive at low pressures. Its zero point can be checked by simply turning off the current to the heater; it measures the pressure of all vapours and gases alike, quite independent of the mass of their molecules or their condensibility, and finally it is simple, easy, and cheap to construct.

179. The Quartz Fibre Gauge.—The principle of the quartz fibre gauge depends upon the fact that a vibrating system suffers decrement, due to the viscosity of the gas in which the vibrations occur, as shown in Article 119. The gauge consists of a quartz fibre about 5 cm. long and 0·1 mm.–0·4 mm. diameter, suspended from one end of a glass container, the latter being connected to the apparatus in which the gas pressure is to be measured. Oscillations may be started by a magnet acting on a small piece of iron contained in a glass pivot movable in sockets inside the container. The damping produced by the gas is nearly independent of the pressure from atmospheric pressure down to a few millimetres. At lower pressures, however, where the mean free path of the molecules becomes comparable with the dimensions of the apparatus, the gas viscosity depends upon the pressure, and so the damping of the fibre—due partly to the gas viscosity—varies with the pressure, the logarithmic decrement λ being given by

$$\lambda = a + bP\sqrt{M},$$

where M is the molecular weight of the gas in the container, P the gas pressure, a and b constants. The time for the vibration amplitude to decrease to half of its initial value is given by

$$t = \frac{T}{\lambda} . \log 2,$$

where T is the period of the system, so

$$P\sqrt{M}=\frac{A}{t}-B,$$

A and B being gauge constants. If t_0 is the damping time in an essentially perfect vacuum—below 10^{-6} mm.—$P=0$ and the ratio A/B can be determined. The values of A and B can be found from a second measurement of the time at a definite pressure. The amplitude is observed by means of a microscope, or by optical projection on a scale. The constant B depends on the fibre thickness, and A upon the elasticity of the fibre and on the temperature. In some models a bifilar arrangement is used. This causes the system to vibrate in one plane, whereas this is difficult to obtain with a single fibre, and so the observation is uncertain. A feature of the instrument is its small volume, and since it contains no metal parts, it is suitable for the measurement of the pressure of active vapours or gases. The upper limit of pressures, which can be measured with the gauge, is determined by the fact that the viscosity only depends on the gas pressure if the mean free molecular path is comparable with the dimensions of the vessel. The lower limit pressure is reached when the gas density of the molecules is so small that no frictional effects can be discerned. In general, the pressure range is 10^{-2}–10^{-4} mm.

180. The Pirani Gauge.—The gauge was introduced by Pirani [1] and depends on the cooling of a heated wire by surrounding gases. As generally used, it consists of a fine wire with a high temperature-resistance coefficient, connected in a Wheatstone bridge with three resistances of negligible temperature coefficient. A constant potential difference, sufficient to heat the manometric wire some degrees above its surroundings, is applied to the bridge and the change in resistance of the wire, due to its change of temperature with pressure of the surrounding gas, is measured. At pressures below 10^{-2} mm. the resistance change is very nearly proportional to the pressure, and a straight line is obtained for the calibration curve. At higher pressures the curve ceases to be straight, and cannot be represented by any simple formula, as it varies in a complicated manner with the gas and the temperature of its surroundings. Campbell [2] followed a suggestion by Pirani that these difficulties can be greatly lessened if, in place of measuring the resistance change of the wire when the applied potential difference is constant, the resistance—and so the temperature—of the wire is maintained constant, the applied potential difference, necessary to do this, being measured. It varies with the gas pressure.

A suitable method of using the gauge is to introduce three manganin resistances into the bridge. The gauge wire can be that in a 40-watt tungsten filament lamp, and it should be at a tempera-

[1] Pirani, *Deutsch. Phys. Gesell. Verh.*, 8, 24, 684 (1906).
[2] Campbell, *Proc. Phys. Soc.*, 33, 287 (1921).

ture of about 100° C. A voltmeter is connected to the bridge terminals, and the potential difference across the bridge is varied by means of a rheostat in the battery circuit until a balance is obtained. Then

$$\frac{V^2 - V_0{}^2}{V_0{}^2} = Cf(P),$$

where V is the potential applied to the bridge, V_0 is its value when the pressure $P = 0$, and C is a term which is constant for considerable variations in the instrument and for a considerable pressure range. Thus $\dfrac{V^2 - V_0{}^2}{V_0{}^2}$ is independent of everything except the nature and pressure of the gas, and $f(P)$ is approximately proportional to P. For several gases the calibration curves lie very close together, although for accurate work the calibration must be determined for any particular gas.

The gauge is convenient for pressures in the range 10^{-2} mm.–10^{-4} mm., and its sensitivity is proportional to the specific heat, and inversely proportional to the square root of the molecular weight of the gas, or vapour, in the gauge. Therefore, since the gauge is usually calibrated with air, or nitrogen, it will not give correct readings of the total absolute pressure if organic vapours are present. In addition, the latter " poison " the filament. With time the gauge readings bear no relation to the original calibrations with air. It is a useful gauge when readings of pressure fluctuations are required.

In a modern arrangement a pair of gauges is used, each member of which contains two filaments. One of the two gauges is pumped out and sealed off. It acts as a reference gauge. The other is connected to the vacuum to be measured. The four filaments of equal resistance are connected to the four arms of the bridge—the resistances in one and the same gauge being in opposite bridge arms. With this arrangement pressures in the range 10^{-5} mm.–10^{-6} mm. can be read, but it is very sensitive to any accidental thermal or mechanical effect.

181. The Ionisation Gauge.—If gas is present in a three-electrode valve in quantity not sufficient seriously to affect the filament activity, and if the plate voltage exceeds a value necessary to produce ionisation of the gas in the valve, it has been found that the number of ions produced is proportional both to the gas pressure and to the electron current. If a small negative potential is applied to the grid, a certain fraction of the positive ions will be drawn to it, and their number will be proportional to the current flowing in the grid circuit. The electron current is measured in the anode circuit. The equation for such a gauge may be written in the form :—

$$P = \frac{kI}{i},$$

where P is the gas pressure, I the positive ionisation current, i the electron current and k the gauge constant. This equation holds for pressures below about 10^{-3} mm. if glow discharge and saturation of the ionisation current are prevented. The gauge must be calibrated with a McLeod gauge with the kind of gas for which it is used.

A more sensitive arrangement is shown in Fig. 96 (a). Here the positive ions are collected at the anode, while the electron current is measured in the grid circuit.

In the type described by Penning,[1] and known as the " Philips gauge," the cathode is formed by two parallel plates within the tube (Fig. 96) (b). The anode is a wire frame placed between these plates, the planes of the plates and frame being parallel. A magnet is arranged so that a strong magnetic field is applied perpendicularly to the plane of the anode. The electrons thus move in a

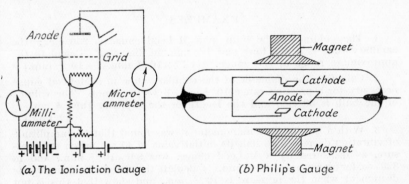

(a) The Ionisation Gauge   (b) Philip's Gauge

FIG. 96.—IONISATION GAUGES.

helical path from cathode to anode, their paths are greatly increased, and so the probability of ionisation by collision is considerably increased. Thus an appreciable current will flow even at the lowest pressures.

A great advantage of the ionisation gauge is that the valve is small, and it may therefore be placed in the immediate vicinity of the place where the pressure is to be measured. On the other hand, the manipulation of the gauge is troublesome and takes time. The sensitivity depends upon the physical dimensions and lay-out of the electrodes, together with the particular arrangement of the electrical circuit adopted.

The ionisation gauge may be used in the pressure range 10^{-3} mm.–10^{-7} mm. It is not an absolute gauge but is easy to calibrate. Organic vapours poison the filament. Generally a cold trap of carbon dioxide snow and acetone is placed between the gauge and the apparatus being tested, or a baffling arrangement is employed,

[1] Penning, *Physica*, **4**, 71 (1937).

so as to prevent back streaming of oil molecules from any oil diffusion pump being used.

In the measurement of low pressures it must be remembered that neither the pressure, nor the quality of the gases present, is the same in all parts of an exhaust system, especially if the connecting tube is narrow. A considerable time is required for equilibrium, and therefore the gauge should be as near as possible to the apparatus to be exhausted. Glasses and metals contain gases even when fused, and even if their gas content is reduced as far as possible by melting *in vacuo*, they still liberate gases after being sealed off. No vacuum measurement can claim to have an absolute value in itself. It must have a certain objective, *e.g.* the control of the pumping method, and exact values are only obtainable where permanent gases are concerned.[1]

EXAMPLES

1. The volume of the bulb in a McLeod gauge is 250 c.c. ; the capillary tube is 5 cm. long and 1·5 mm. in diameter. Calculate the approximate range of the gauge.   [$1·77 \times 10^{-2}$ mm.–7×10^{-6} mm.]

2. Calculate the diameter of the capillary tube in a McLeod gauge necessary for a pressure range 10^{-1} mm.–$6·3 \times 10^{-5}$ mm. The volume of the bulb is 50 c.c., and the length of the capillary tube 4 cm.
[2 mm.]

3. With a quartz fibre manometer it was found that the amplitude of vibration decreased to half its initial value in 45 sec. when the pressure, as measured by a McLeod gauge, was $8·6 \times 10^{-3}$ mm., and in 320 sec. for a pressure of 10^{-7} mm. Calculate the time for half-amplitude decrement when the pressure is 10^{-3} mm., and show that this is not materially affected by a 50 per cent. inaccuracy in estimating the lower pressure.   [187 sec.]

4. The amplitude of a quartz fibre gauge decreases to half value in a vacuum in 300 sec. When oxygen is admitted at a pressure 10^{-2} mm., the time for half-amplitude decrement is 100 sec. Calculate the half-amplitude decrement if hydrogen, at a pressure of 10^{-3} mm., is admitted.
[286 sec.]

5. Gas is pumped continuously from a " leaky " reservoir of 20 litres capacity. The lowest pressure reached is 1 mm. If the pump is disconnected from the reservoir, the pressure immediately rises at an initial rate of 2 mm. in 20 sec. Calculate the pump's speed.
[2 litres per sec.]

6. In a Pirani gauge bridge the resistances are 1, 1, 120 and 120 ohms, respectively, the gauge having a resistance of 120 ohms. The bridge is balanced when the gauge is exhausted and the main current is 40 milli-

[1] For further details of pumps and gauges reference may be made to the following books and papers : Newman, *The Production and Measurement of Low Pressures* ; Dunoyer, *Vacuum Practice* ; Kaye, *High Vacua* ; Strong, *Modern Physical Laboratory Practice.* Hickman, *Rev. Sci. Inst.*, **11**, 303 (1940) ; Burrows, *Journ. Sci. Inst.*, **20**, 21 (1943) ; Witty, *Journ. Sci. Inst.*, **22**, 201 (1945) ; Alexander, *Journ. Sci. Inst.*, **23**, 11, (1946).

amps. When hydrogen, at a pressure of 1.5×10^{-2} mm., is admitted to the gauge, the main current has to be increased to 60 milliamps to balance the circuit. Calculate the gauge constant. [83.]

7. The fixed metallic strips in a Knudsen gauge are maintained at 200° C. If the room temperature rises from 15° C. to 20° C., does the spot of light remain constant in position ? If not, what is the change in deflection ? [Ratio change = 185 : 180.]

CHAPTER XII

DYNAMICAL BASIS—INCLUDING VIBRATIONS

182. Introduction.—In the solution of problems in Physics, in such varied branches as Sound, Mechanics, Electricity, Heat, and Light, differential equations of special types continually recur, and it is proposed to deal here with these equations without special references to specific examples—such references being deferred to the appropriate places in the other chapters. Thus, with the exception of the symbol t to represent time, no particular interpretation is intended here of the other quantities involved in the equations, although experience may tend, probably with advantage, to suggest to readers a special case when the discussion is being studied. By the term *velocity* we shall mean a rate of change of magnitude with time, while *acceleration* denotes rate of change of velocity with time.

183. Uniformly Accelerated Motion in One Direction—No Resistance.—If a quantity x is changing so that its second differential with respect to the time t is constant, then the equation of motion is

$$\frac{d^2x}{dt^2}=a, \qquad . \qquad . \qquad . \qquad . \quad (316)$$

and integrating we have

$$\frac{dx}{dt}=at+C_1.$$

If $\frac{dx}{dt}=v_0$ when $t=0$, then $v_0=C_1$ and

$$\frac{dx}{dt}=v_0+at \qquad . \qquad . \qquad . \qquad . \quad (317)$$

Hence

$$x=v_0t+\tfrac{1}{2}at^2+C_2,$$

and if $x=A$ when $t=0$, $A=C_2$. Thus

$$x=A+v_0t+\tfrac{1}{2}at^2, \qquad . \qquad . \qquad . \quad (318)$$

and this is the direct solution to equation (316). But since

$$\frac{d^2x}{dt^2}=\frac{d}{dx}\left(\frac{dx}{dt}\right).\frac{dx}{dt},$$

equation (316) may be written, putting $v=\frac{dx}{dt}$,

$$v\frac{dv}{dx}=a, \quad \text{or} \quad vdv=adx,$$

342

and, on integrating,

$$\frac{v^2}{2}=ax+C_3 \quad \text{and} \quad \frac{v_0{}^2}{2}=aA+C_3,$$

or

$$v^2=v_0{}^2+2a(x-A) \qquad . \qquad . \qquad . \qquad (319)$$

From equations (317) and (319),

$$\frac{v^2-v_0{}^2}{v-v_0}=\frac{2a(x-A)}{at}=\frac{2(x-A)}{t},$$

and thus

$$x=A+\frac{v+v_0}{2}t \quad . \qquad . \qquad . \qquad . \qquad (320)$$

Equations (317), (318), (319), and (320) are the standard equations for uniformly accelerated motion.

184. Uniformly Accelerated Motion in One Direction— Resistance proportional to Velocity.—The equation of motion in this case is

$$\frac{d^2x}{dt^2}+k\frac{dx}{dt}=a, \quad . \qquad . \qquad . \qquad . \qquad (321)$$

where k is the resistance retardation for unit velocity and is often called the *damping factor*. Equation (321) may be rewritten

$$\frac{dv}{dt}=a-kv, \quad \text{or} \quad \frac{dv}{a-kv}=dt.$$

Integrating,

$$-\frac{1}{k}\log(a-kv)=t+C_1 \quad . \qquad . \qquad . \qquad (322)$$

If $v=0$ when $t=0$, $C_1=-\frac{1}{k}\log a$, and equation (322) becomes

$$\log\frac{a-kv}{a}=-kt, \quad \text{or} \quad v=\frac{a}{k}(1-e^{-kt}) \quad . \qquad . \qquad (323)$$

Thus $(1-e^{-kt})dt=\frac{k}{a}dx$ which, being integrated, gives

$$t+\frac{1}{k}e^{-kt}=\frac{k}{a}x+C_2,$$

and if, when $t=0$, $x=0$, $C_2=\frac{1}{k}$, so that

$$x=\frac{a}{k^2}(e^{-kt}-1+kt). \qquad . \qquad . \qquad . \qquad (324)$$

This is the value of x after any time t. From equation (323), as t becomes very large, e^{-kt} is vanishingly small and v approaches its maximum possible value under the given conditions. This value $\dfrac{a}{k}$ is called the *terminal velocity*.

185. Uniformly Accelerated Motion in One Direction—Resistance proportional to Square of Velocity.—The equation of motion in this case is

$$\frac{d^2x}{dt^2}=a-kv^2=a\left(1-\frac{k}{a}v^2\right) \qquad . \qquad . \qquad . \quad (325)$$

When $v^2=\dfrac{a}{k}$, $\dfrac{d^2x}{dt^2}=0$, and thus $\sqrt{\dfrac{a}{k}}$ is the maximum value of v, *i.e.* the terminal velocity. Putting $\sqrt{\dfrac{a}{k}}=V$, and separating the differentials we have

$$\frac{at}{V^2}=\int\frac{dv}{V^2-v^2}=\frac{1}{2V}\ \log\ \frac{V+v}{V-v}+C_1.$$

If $v=0$ at $t=0$, $C_1=0$ and

$$\frac{V+v}{V-v}=e^{\frac{2at}{V}},$$

or

$$v=V\frac{e^{\frac{at}{V}}-e^{-\frac{at}{V}}}{e^{\frac{at}{V}}+e^{-\frac{at}{V}}}=V\ tanh\left(\frac{at}{V}\right) \qquad . \qquad . \qquad . \quad (326)$$

This gives the velocity at any time, and from it

$$\int dx=V\int\ tanh\ \frac{at}{V}dt,$$

or

$$x=\frac{V^2}{a}\ \log\ cosh\ \frac{at}{V}+C_2.$$

If $x=0$ when $t=0$, $C_2=0$, and the solution to equation (325) becomes

$$x=\frac{V^2}{a}\ \log\ cosh\ \frac{at}{V} \qquad . \qquad . \qquad . \quad (327)$$

186. Simple Harmonic Motion—No Resistance.—*Definition:* If a quantity x changes so that its acceleration is always proportional, and opposite in sign, to its instantaneous value it is said to vary in a simple harmonic manner.

The equation of a simple harmonic motion may therefore be written

$$\frac{d^2x}{dt^2}=-\omega^2x \quad . \quad . \quad . \quad . \quad (328)$$

On multiplying both sides by $2\dfrac{dx}{dt}$ and integrating,

$$\left(\frac{dx}{dt}\right)^2=-\omega^2x^2+C_1,$$

while, if $x=A$ and $\dfrac{dx}{dt}=0$ at $t=0$, $C_1=A^2\omega^2$ and

$$\frac{dx}{dt}=\omega\sqrt{A^2-x^2} \quad . \quad . \quad . \quad . \quad (329)$$

This gives the velocity for any given value of x.

From equation (329)

$$\int\frac{dx}{\sqrt{A^2-x^2}}=\int\omega dt, \quad \text{or} \quad sin^{-1}\frac{x}{A}=\omega t+C_2,$$

or with the given initial conditions, $sin^{-1}\,1=C_2=\dfrac{\pi}{2}$, and thus

$$x=A\,cos\,\omega t, \quad . \quad . \quad . \quad . \quad (330)$$

while, from equation (329), $v=-A\omega\,sin\,\omega t$.

The equation (330) shows that a given value of x occurs periodically, since if t is increased by $\dfrac{2\pi}{\omega}$, x becomes

$$A\,cos\,\omega\left(t+\frac{2\pi}{\omega}\right)=A\,cos\,\omega t,$$

the same value as at time t. Thus the period t_0, or time for one complete cycle of changes in the value of x, is

$$t_0=\frac{2\pi}{\omega},$$

where ω^2 is the constant ratio of the acceleration to the instantaneous value of x.

187. Simple Harmonic Motion—Resistance proportional to Velocity.—This type of motion, which is of frequent occurrence and is generally called *damped simple harmonic motion*, may be represented by

$$\frac{d^2x}{dt^2}+k\frac{dx}{dt}+\omega^2x=0 \quad . \quad . \quad . \quad (331)$$

If we put $x=Ae^{pt}$, then, from equation (331),

$$p^2+kp+\omega^2=0,$$

or

$$p=-\frac{k}{2}\pm\sqrt{\frac{k^2}{4}-\omega^2},$$

and thus

$$x=e^{-\frac{kt}{2}}\left[Ae^{\sqrt{\frac{k^2}{4}-\omega^2}.t}+Be^{-\sqrt{\frac{k^2}{4}-\omega^2}.t}\right]. \quad . \quad (332)$$

Three cases now arise in the solution :—

(a) If $k^2 > 4\omega^2$, the indices of e are real and equation (332) may be written

$$x = e^{-\frac{kt}{2}} M \cosh \left[\sqrt{\frac{k^2}{4} - \omega^2} . t + N \right] \quad . \quad . \quad (333)$$

This represents a continuous return of x from its maximum value to zero when $t = \infty$ without alternation in sign, *i.e.* without oscillation. This type of motion is called *dead-beat motion*.

(b) If $4\omega^2 > k^2$, the indices of e are imaginary and equation (332) may be written

$$x = e^{-\frac{kt}{2}} [A e^{j\theta} + B e^{-j\theta}], \quad . \quad . \quad (334)$$

where

$$\theta = \sqrt{\omega^2 - \frac{k^2}{4}} \, t,$$

or

$$x = e^{-\frac{kt}{2}} M \cos [\theta - \gamma]. \quad . \quad . \quad (335)$$

In this case x alternates in sign and we have periodic motion, but the amplitude continually diminishes by reason of the decrement term $e^{-\frac{kt}{2}}$.

To express M and γ, the integration constants, in terms of the initial conditions, suppose that when $t = 0$, $x = x_0$, $\frac{dx}{dt} = v_0$ and $\theta = 0$. Equation (334) may be written

$$x = e^{-\frac{kt}{2}} \left[(A+B) \frac{e^{j\theta} + e^{-j\theta}}{2} + (A-B) \frac{e^{j\theta} - e^{-j\theta}}{2} \right]$$

$$= e^{-\frac{kt}{2}} [C \cos \theta + D \sin \theta].$$

Hence $C = x_0$ and

$$v_0 = -\frac{kC}{2} + D \sqrt{\omega^2 - \frac{k^2}{4}},$$

or

$$D = \frac{v_0 + \frac{k}{2} x_0}{\sqrt{\omega^2 - \frac{k^2}{4}}}.$$

Thus

$$x = \frac{e^{-\frac{kt}{2}}}{\sqrt{\omega^2 - \frac{k^2}{4}}} \left[x_0 \sqrt{\omega^2 - \frac{k^2}{4}} \cos \theta + \left(v_0 + \frac{x_0 k}{2} \right) \sin \theta \right].$$

Let

$$x_0 \sqrt{\omega^2 - \frac{k^2}{4}} = C_1,$$

$$v_0 + \frac{x_0 k}{2} = D_1.$$

Put

$$\frac{C_1}{\sqrt{C_1^2 + D_1^2}} = sin\ \beta,$$

and

$$\frac{D_1}{\sqrt{C_1^2 + D_1^2}} = cos\ \beta.$$

Then

$$x = \frac{e^{-\frac{kt}{2}}}{\sqrt{\omega^2 - \frac{k^2}{4}}} \sqrt{C_1^2 + D_1^2}\ sin\ (\theta + \beta), \quad . \quad . \quad (336)$$

where $tan\ \beta = \dfrac{C_1}{D_1}.$ This gives the value of x at any time t in terms of the constants of the motion and of the initial conditions.

Periodic Time.—By comparison with an unresisted S.H.M. we see that the period is

$$t_0 = \frac{2\pi}{\sqrt{\omega^2 - \frac{k^2}{4}}} \quad . \quad . \quad . \quad . \quad (337)$$

This indicates that the resistance exercises, on the period, an effect which is small if, as is frequently the case, ω^2 is large compared with $\dfrac{k^2}{4}.$

Logarithmic Decrement.—The values of x are maxima alternating in sign at times separated by half the period, and if these values for t are substituted in equation (336) we have, calling the successive maxima, A_1, A_2, A_3, etc.,

$$\frac{A_1}{A_2} = e^{\frac{kt_0}{4}} = \frac{A_2}{A_3} = \text{etc.}$$

The exponential index $\dfrac{kt_0}{4}$ is usually called the *logarithmic decrement* and is denoted by λ. Then

$$\lambda = \frac{kt_0}{4} = \frac{k}{4} \cdot \frac{2\pi}{\sqrt{\omega^2 - \frac{k^2}{4}}} = \frac{\pi k}{\sqrt{4\omega^2 - k^2}},$$

and from a knowledge of λ and t_0, the constants of the original motion are given by

$$k = \frac{4\lambda}{t_0},$$

and

$$\omega^2 = \frac{k^2}{4} + \frac{4\pi^2}{t_0{}^2} = \frac{4}{t_0{}^2}[\lambda^2 + \pi^2].$$

Correction for Damping.—Suppose that a system is set into motion from a position of rest, and it is required to calculate from the first observed amplitude what the value of this would be in the absence of damping forces. In these circumstances $x_0 = 0$, $v = v_0$ at $t = 0$, so that in equation (336) $D_1 = v_0$ and $C_1 = 0$. Hence $sin\ \beta = 0$ and

$$x = \frac{t_0 v_0}{2\pi} e^{-\frac{2\lambda t}{t_0}} sin\ \frac{2\pi t}{t_0}.$$

The first maximum, A_1, is obtained when $t = \frac{t_0}{4}$, or

$$A_1 = \frac{t_0 v_0}{2\pi} e^{-\frac{\lambda}{2}}.$$

If there were no friction, then the amplitude A_0 would be

$$A_0 = \frac{t_0 v_0}{2\pi},$$

where $t_0' = \frac{2\pi}{\omega}$ since $k = 0$. Thus we have

$$\frac{A_0}{A_1} = \frac{t_0'}{t_0} e^{\frac{\lambda}{2}} = \sqrt{1 - \frac{k^2}{4\omega^2}} e^{\frac{\lambda}{2}}.$$

If λ is small—and thus k^2 is small compared with $4\omega^2$—

$$A_0 = A_1\left[1 + \frac{\lambda}{2}\right]. \qquad \qquad (338)$$

To measure λ.—It is frequently convenient to observe values of x on one side of the zero only, and this is done for as many successive maxima as is possible. The observations are tabulated as follows, supposing that twelve readings are taken :—

A_1	A_3	A_5	A_7	A_9	A_{11}
A_{13}	A_{15}	A_{17}	A_{19}	A_{21}	A_{23}
$\dfrac{A_1}{A_{13}}$	$\dfrac{A_3}{A_{15}}$	$\dfrac{A_5}{A_{17}}$	$\dfrac{A_7}{A_{19}}$	$\dfrac{A_9}{A_{21}}$	$\dfrac{A_{11}}{A_{23}}$

Since

$$\frac{A_1}{A_{13}}=\frac{A_1}{A_2}\times\frac{A_2}{A_3}\times \cdots \times\frac{A_{11}}{A_{12}}\times\frac{A_{12}}{A_{13}}=e^{12\lambda},$$

while

$$\frac{A_3}{A_{15}}=\frac{A_5}{A_{17}}=etc.=e^{12\lambda},$$

which should be constant$=X$, and λ is given by

$$\lambda=\tfrac{1}{12} \log_e X.$$

(c) If $4\omega^2=k^2$ the above solution (332) ceases to hold but becomes by the rule of differential equations,

$$x=[A+Bt]e^{-\frac{kt}{2}},$$

which again represents a continuous return of x from its maximum value to zero, *i.e.* it resembles dead-beat motion. Such a case is called *critical damping*.

Many cases of damped simple harmonic motion arise in ordinary physical measurements, and the above treatment is of importance in such cases as the oscillations of material bodies in viscous media, the discharge of a condenser through a circuit containing resistance and inductance, the swing of a ballistic galvanometer, and the experiments of Angstrom on thermal conductivities.

188. Forced Simple Harmonic Vibrations—No Resistance.

—*Definition :* If a quantity x has a natural period $\dfrac{2\pi}{\omega}$ and is acted on by an additional acceleration $L \cos pt$, the resultant motion is called a *forced simple harmonic vibration*.

We may conveniently link with this case that in which the body has, alternatively, a natural acceleration ω^2x in the direction of x increasing, *i.e.* for which the equation of motion is

$$\frac{d^2x}{dt^2}-\omega^2x=L \cos pt \qquad . \qquad . \qquad . \qquad (339)$$

Using the inverse operator notation, a solution to this equation (339) is

$$x=\frac{L}{2\omega}\left[\left(\frac{d}{dt}-\omega\right)^{-1}-\left(\frac{d}{dt}+\omega\right)^{-1}\right] \cos pt.$$

But

$$\left(\frac{d}{dt}-\omega\right)^{-1} \cos pt=e^{\omega t}\int e^{-\omega t} \cos pt.dt$$

$$=\frac{e^{\omega t}}{2}\int[e^{(-\omega+jp)t}+e^{(-\omega-jp)t}]dt$$

$$=\frac{1}{\omega^2+p^2}[p \sin pt-\omega \cos pt]+A_1e^{\omega t},$$

and similarly

$$\left(\frac{d}{dt}+\omega\right)^{-1} \cos pt=\frac{1}{\omega^2+p^2}[p \sin pt+\omega \cos pt]+B_1e^{-\omega t}.$$

Hence

$$x = \frac{L}{2\omega}\left[A_1 e^{\omega t} - B_1 e^{-\omega t} - \frac{2\omega}{\omega^2+p^2} cos\ pt\right]$$

$$= \frac{L}{2\omega}\left[C_1\ cosh\ \omega t + D_1\ sinh\ \omega t - \frac{2\omega}{\omega^2+p^2} cos\ pt\right],$$

when $t=0$, $x=x_0$ and $\frac{dx}{dt}=v_0$, so $x_0=\frac{L}{2\omega}\left[C_1 - \frac{2\omega}{\omega^2+p^2}\right]$. Thus

$$C_1 = \frac{2\omega x_0}{L} + \frac{2\omega}{\omega^2+p^2},$$

and

$$D_1 = \frac{LC_1}{2}.$$

Hence

$$x = \frac{v_0}{\omega} sinh\ \omega t + \left(x_0 + \frac{L}{\omega^2+p^2}\right) cosh\ \omega t - \frac{L\ cos\ pt}{\omega^2+p^2} \quad . \quad (340)$$

If the acceleration is directed towards the equilibrium position the equation of motion is

$$\frac{d^2x}{dt^2} + \omega^2 x = L\ cos\ pt,$$

and its solution may be obtained from equation (340) by putting $j\omega$ for ω. Thus

$$x = \frac{v_0}{\omega} sin\ \omega t + \left(x_0 + \frac{L}{p^2-\omega^2}\right) cos\ \omega t - \frac{L\ cos\ pt}{p^2-\omega^2} \quad . \quad (341)$$

Hence there are two periodic motions—free and forced vibrations—where the term *cos pt* refers to the forced motion. If $p=\omega$, the last two terms become infinite and the value of x is indeterminate. In this case the solution is

$$x = \frac{v_0}{\omega} sin\ \omega t + x_0\ cos\ \omega t + \frac{Lt}{2\omega} sin\ \omega t$$

$$= \sqrt{x_0{}^2 + \left(\frac{v_0}{\omega} + \frac{Lt}{2\omega}\right)^2}\ sin\ (\omega t + \beta), \quad . \quad . \quad (342)$$

where

$$tan\ \beta = \frac{x_0}{\dfrac{v_0}{\omega} + \dfrac{Lt}{2\omega}}.$$

The amplitude and phase are no longer constant and, as t increases, the amplitude increases indefinitely. In a practical case this is not true, and the solution is inapplicable, firstly, because for large amplitudes friction is no longer negligible, and secondly, because material vibration systems are, in general, constrained and have simple harmonic motion only for comparatively small amplitudes.

A complete cycle of the motion represented by equation (342) is given by

$$(\omega t_1+\beta_1)=0 \quad \text{and} \quad (\omega t_2+\beta_2)=2\pi.$$

Thus

$$t_0=t_2-t_1=\frac{2\pi-(\beta_2-\beta_1)}{\omega},$$

so that t_0 is not constant. Also, when t is large, β is small, and the resultant motion remains in phase with the forcing acceleration. If $x_0=0$, $\beta=0$, and the period t_0 is constant. Thus we may say that a constant period is attained : (a) if at the origin of time $x_0=0$, or (b) after the applied acceleration has been acting for some time. In both cases the period is that of the forcing acceleration.

189. Forced Simple Harmonic Vibrations with Resistance proportional to Velocity.—In this case the equation of motion is

$$\frac{d^2x}{dt^2}+k\frac{dx}{dt}+\omega^2x=L \cos pt,$$

and its solution is given by

$$x=\frac{L}{\alpha_1-\alpha_2}\left[\left(\frac{d}{dt}-\alpha_1\right)^{-1}-\left(\frac{d}{dt}-\alpha_2\right)^{-1}\right] \cos pt$$

$$=\frac{L}{\alpha_1-\alpha_2}\left[\frac{1}{\alpha_1{}^2+p^2}(p \sin pt-\alpha_1 \cos pt)+A_1e^{\alpha_1t}\right.$$

$$\left.-\frac{1}{\alpha_2{}^2+p^2}(p \sin pt-\alpha_2 \cos pt)+B_1e^{\alpha_2t}\right],$$

where

$$\alpha_1+\alpha_2=-k \quad \text{and} \quad \alpha_1\alpha_2=\omega^2.$$

Hence

$$x=L\left[\frac{kp \sin pt+(\omega^2-p^2) \cos pt}{p^4+p^2(k^2-2\omega^2)+\omega^4}+\frac{1}{\sqrt{k^2-4\omega^2}}(A_1e^{\alpha_1t}+B_1e^{\alpha_2t})\right]$$

Take β such that

$$\sin \beta=\frac{kp}{\sqrt{(\omega^2-p^2)^2+k^2p^2}} ; \quad \cos \beta=\frac{\omega^2-p^2}{\sqrt{(\omega^2-p^2)^2+k^2p^2}},$$

or

$$\tan \beta=\frac{kp}{\omega^2-p^2}.$$

Then

$$x=\frac{L}{\sqrt{(\omega^2-p^2)^2+k^2p^2}} \cos (pt-\beta)$$

$$+\frac{Le^{-\frac{kt}{2}}}{\sqrt{k^2-4\omega^2}}\left[A_1e^{\sqrt{\frac{k^2}{4}-\omega^2}.t}+B_1e^{-\sqrt{\frac{k^2}{4}-\omega^2}.t}\right].$$

This equation is of great importance in the case of a periodic E.M.F. applied to a circuit containing resistance, capacity, and self-inductance, and we see that it contains two terms, the second of which refers to the free vibrations of the system. As time increases, this second term rapidly decreases while the first persists. We may thus concentrate attention on the first term, which refers to the steady state. Thus

$$x = \frac{L \sin \beta}{kp} \cos (pt - \beta), \qquad . \qquad . \qquad . \qquad (343)$$

where β represents the lag of the resultant motion behind the applied acceleration. This equation is important in the many cases of forced vibrations which are encountered in light, electricity, and sound.

From equation (343),

$$\frac{dx}{dt} = -\frac{L \sin \beta}{k} \sin (pt - \beta).$$

Thus, when the displacement is zero, all the energy is kinetic and is a maximum when $\sin (pt - \beta) = 1$, and since the maximum amount of energy is proportional to $\sin^2 \beta$, it will be obtained when $\beta = \frac{\pi}{2}$ i.e. when $\omega = p$.

If E is the energy under any conditions and E_0 its value for maximum resonance,

$$E = E_0 \sin^2 \beta,$$

and

$$\frac{\omega^2 - p^2}{kp} = \sqrt{\frac{1 - \sin^2 \beta}{\sin^2 \beta}} = \sqrt{\frac{E_0 - E}{E}}.$$

Now $(E_0 - E)$ represents the amount by which the energy falls short of the maximum. If we require this to be small for given values of p and ω, k must be large. Thus we see that the *sharpness of response* or critical tuning will be most marked when the damping is small. If k is large it is possible for p to vary widely from ω without producing a great decrease in resonance.

When we are dealing with free vibrations the energy remains constant throughout the motion, provided that friction is absent. This is not so for forced periodic vibrations, as in this case the energy supply also is periodic. The forcing agency supplies excess energy during part of the vibration and itself receives energy from the system acted on during the remainder. Thus if we write

$$x = \frac{L \sin \beta}{kp} \cos (pt - \beta) = A \cos (pt - \beta),$$

$$\frac{dx}{dt} = -Ap \sin (pt - \beta),$$

and $L \cos pt . \dfrac{dx}{dt}$—the rate at which work is being done on unit mass

—is equal to

$$-ApL \sin (pt - \beta) \cos pt = -\frac{ApL}{2} [\sin (2pt - \beta) - \sin \beta],$$

so that the rate at which energy is supplied to the system consists of two parts. The second, $\frac{1}{2}ApL \sin \beta$, is constant and represents the average rate of supply of energy, while the first, $-\frac{1}{2}ApL \sin (2pt-\beta)$, fluctuates in magnitude and alternates in sign, having a zero average over a whole period.

The above condition for resonance $\omega=p$ is the condition for maximum energy in the forced vibration, but this is not the condition for maximum amplitude. If equation (343) is differentiated with respect to p, then it will be seen that the condition for maximum amplitude is $p^2=\omega^2-k^2/2$, which indicates an applied frequency less than the natural frequency without damping, but greater than that when damping is present.

190. Symmetric and Asymmetric Vibrations.—In some cases of importance the quantity under review has a motion which, while very approximately simple harmonic for small amplitudes, diverges from this simple form for larger amplitudes. Two cases may be considered, one in which an additional acceleration bx^2 becomes appreciable and the other in which the extra acceleration may be represented by bx^3. These are called *asymmetric* and *symmetric* vibrations respectively, and in both cases it will be assumed that b is very small compared with ω.

Consider the equation

$$\frac{d^2x}{dt^2}+\omega^2x+bx^2=0 \qquad . \qquad . \qquad . \qquad (344)$$

The solution to this is most conveniently obtained by Lord Rayleigh's method of successive approximations, which consists in obtaining a first approximation to the motion by ignoring the extra term, then substituting this value in the bx^2 term and solving afresh. By continuing this method, a solution to any desired degree of approximation may be obtained.

Putting $b=0$ in equation (344) and making a convenient choice of initial conditions, the first approximation is given by equation (330), *i.e.*

$$x=A \cos \omega t,$$

and this value substituted in the bx^2 term gives

$$\frac{d^2x}{dt^2}+\omega^2x=-bA^2 \cos^2 \omega t=-\frac{bA^2}{2}(1+\cos 2\omega t). \quad . \quad (345)$$

The solution to this will be of the form

$$x=A \cos \omega t+B+C \cos 2\omega t,$$

and

$$\frac{d^2x}{dt^2}+\omega^2x=-A\omega^2 \cos \omega t-4C\omega^2 \cos 2\omega t+A\omega^2 \cos \omega t+B\omega^2$$

$$+C\omega^2 \cos 2\omega t.$$

A A

Comparing this with equation (345) we have

$$\left.\begin{array}{ll} -\dfrac{bA^2}{2}=B\omega^2, & \text{or} \quad B=-\dfrac{bA^2}{2\omega^2} \\[2mm] -\dfrac{bA^2}{2}=-3C\omega^2, & \text{or} \quad C=\dfrac{bA^2}{6\omega^2} \end{array}\right\} \qquad . \qquad (346)$$

If these values are substituted in the bx^2 term of equation (344) the first term $cos\ \omega t$ would necessitate, in the new solution, a term of the form $t\ cos\ \omega t$, indicating a steadily increasing amplitude. As this is clearly inadmissible, it is obvious that the extra term bx^2 affects also the period, and thus the second approximation should be written

$$x=A\ cos\ pt+B+C\ cos\ 2pt,$$

where the new period $\dfrac{2\pi}{p}$ is slightly different from the simple harmonic period $\dfrac{2\pi}{\omega}$. Substituting this value in the bx^2 term as before, we have

$$\frac{d^2x}{dt^2}+\omega^2x=-b[A\ cos\ pt+B+C\ cos\ 2pt]^2$$

$$=-b\left[(2AB+AC)\ cos\ pt+\left(B^2+\frac{A^2}{2}+\frac{C^2}{2}\right)\right.$$

$$\left.+\left(2BC+\frac{A^2}{2}\right)\ cos\ 2pt+AC\ cos\ 3pt+\frac{C^2}{2}\ cos\ 4pt\right], \qquad (347)$$

and the solution to this is of the form

$$x=A[cos\ pt+d+e\ cos\ 2pt+f\ cos\ 3pt+g\ cos\ 4pt].$$

Obtaining from this the value of $\dfrac{d^2x}{dt^2}+\omega^2x$ and equating to the right-hand side of equation (347),

$$-Ab(2B+C)=A(\omega^2-p^2),$$

or, from equations (346),

$$\omega^2-p^2=-b\left(-\frac{bA^2}{\omega^2}+\frac{bA^2}{6\omega^2}\right)=\frac{5b^2A^2}{6\omega^2},$$

and thus

$$\frac{p^2}{\omega^2}=1-\frac{5b^2A^2}{6\omega^4} \qquad . \qquad . \qquad . \qquad . \qquad (348)$$

This gives the effect on the period, and by equating the other coefficients and independent terms, the corresponding values may be expressed in terms of A, b, and ω.

Thus the analysis yields the following results:—

(i) The vibration is *displaced* from the previous zero by an amount Ad.

(ii) The frequency is *lowered* according to equation (348).

(iii) A full range of harmonic *overtones* is present with amplitudes decreasing rapidly with ascending frequency.

For the symmetrical vibrations the equation of motion is

$$\frac{d^2x}{dt^2}+\omega^2x+bx^3=0, \qquad . \quad . \quad . \quad (349)$$

and the solution proceeds as before,

$$x=A \cos \omega t, \quad \text{approximately.}$$

Substituting this in equation (349) we have

$$\frac{d^2x}{dt^2}+\omega^2x=-\frac{bA^3}{4}[3 \cos \omega t+\cos 3\omega t].$$

Changing ω into p to allow for an altered period, we obtain as the next approximation,

$$x=A \cos pt+N \cos 3pt,$$

where

$$\frac{p^2}{\omega^2}=1+\frac{3bA^2}{4\omega^2} \quad \text{and} \quad N=\frac{\dfrac{bA^3}{4}}{8\omega^2+\dfrac{27}{4}bA^2}.$$

Thus in this case the frequency is *raised*, there is no displacement of the zero (hence the designation *symmetric*), and the first overtone which appears is the *cos 3pt* term. Further analysis proceeds in the same way, and again the higher overtones have amplitudes which are small compared with that of the prime.

191. Asymmetric System under Double Forcing.—If an asymmetric system is under the combined action of two external forcing accelerations, the motion presents peculiarities which are of some importance particularly in the theory of Sound. The equation of motion in this case is

$$\frac{d^2x}{dt^2}+\omega^2x+bx^2=f \cos pt+g \cos (qt-\alpha).$$

Ignoring the free vibrations,

$$x=A \cos pt+B \cos (qt-\alpha), \quad \text{approximately,}$$

where $A=\dfrac{f}{\omega^2-p^2}$ and $B=\dfrac{g}{\omega^2-q^2}$ and, on substituting in the bx^2 term a solution of the form,

$$x=A \cos pt+B \cos (qt-\alpha)+C+D \cos 2pt+E \cos 2(qt-\alpha)$$
$$+F \cos (\overline{p+q}.t-\alpha)+G \cos (\overline{p-q}.t+\alpha)$$

is suggested. If we find the value of $\dfrac{d^2x}{dt^2}+\omega^2x$ from this and equate to the bx^2 term we have the following results :—

Term	Amplitude.
cos pt	$A=\dfrac{f}{\omega^2-p^2}.$
cos $(qt-\alpha)$	$B=\dfrac{g}{\omega^2-q^2}.$
Displaced zero	$C=-\dfrac{b}{2\omega^2}(A^2+B^2).$
cos 2 pt	$D=-\dfrac{bA^2}{2(\omega^2-4p^2)}.$
cos $2(qt-\alpha)$	$E=-\dfrac{bB^2}{2(\omega^2-4q^2)}.$
cos $(\overline{p+q}.t-\alpha)$	$F=-\dfrac{ABb}{[\omega^2-(p+q)^2]}.$
cos $(\overline{p-q}.t+\alpha)$	$G=-\dfrac{ABb}{[\omega^2-(p-q)^2]}.$

The system will thus have the primary and a full range of harmonic overtone vibrations for each applied forcing acceleration and, in addition, extra motions of periods equal to the *sum* and *difference* of the forcing periods. Further analysis shows the existence of a large number of these *combinational* vibrations. It will be noticed that the amplitude F of the summation vibration is less than that, G, of the difference vibration, so that, in the combination tones produced by sounding two notes simultaneously, the *summation tone* is weak and not easily heard while the *difference tone* is often obtrusively evident.

192. Two-dimensional Motion.—We have previously assumed that x varied with the time in one direction only. If, however, it is a vectorial quantity and account has to be taken of a possible variety of directions, as well as of magnitudes, then an extension of the methods already outlined is necessary. An important case is that of the uniplanar motion of a point, and this will now be considered with particular reference to the inverse square law of attraction. The use of polar co-ordinates simplifies the equations involved and, in general, the point will have both *radial* and *transverse* velocities and accelerations. By the term radial velocity is meant the rate of increase of the radius vector, while the transverse velocity refers to the velocity of the point in a direction at right angles to the radius vector.

Let P (Fig. 97) (a) be the position of a point at time t, and Q its position at time $t+\delta t$. Let $XOP=\theta$, $XOQ=\theta+\delta\theta$, $OP=r$,

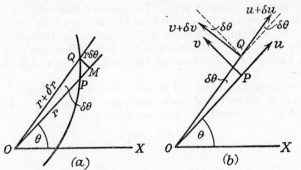

FIG. 97.—RADIAL AND TRANSVERSE VELOCITIES AND ACCELERATIONS.

$OQ=r+\delta r$. Draw QM perpendicular to OP. If u and v are the radial and transverse velocities,

$$u=Lt.\frac{MP}{\delta t}=Lt.\frac{(r+\delta r)\cos\delta\theta-r}{\delta t}$$

$$=Lt.\frac{\delta r}{\delta t}=\frac{dr}{dt} \qquad . \qquad . \qquad . \qquad . \qquad (350)$$

$$v=Lt.\frac{MQ}{\delta t}=Lt.\frac{r\delta\theta}{\delta t}=r\frac{d\theta}{dt} \qquad . \qquad . \qquad . \qquad (351)$$

The radial and transverse velocities at P, being u and v, become $u+\delta u$ and $v+\delta v$ respectively, at Q (Fig. 97) (b), so that the acceleration along OP is

$$Lt.\frac{(u+\delta u)\cos\delta\theta-(v+\delta v)\sin\delta\theta-u}{\delta t}=Lt.\frac{u+\delta u-v\delta\theta-u}{\delta t}$$

$$=\frac{du}{dt}-v\frac{d\theta}{dt}=\frac{d^2r}{dt^2}-r\left(\frac{d\theta}{dt}\right)^2 \qquad (352)$$

Also the acceleration perpendicular to OP in the direction of θ increasing is

$$Lt.\frac{(v+\delta v)\cos\delta\theta+(u+\delta u)\sin\delta\theta-v}{\delta t}=\frac{dv}{dt}+u\frac{d\theta}{dt}=\frac{d}{dt}\left(r\frac{d\theta}{dt}\right)+\frac{dr}{dt}\cdot\frac{d\theta}{dt}$$

$$=r\frac{d^2\theta}{dt^2}+2\frac{dr}{dt}\cdot\frac{d\theta}{dt}=\frac{1}{r}\frac{d}{dt}\left(r^2\frac{d\theta}{dt}\right) \qquad (353)$$

If $r=r_0$, where r_0 is a constant, the point describes a circle and, if the speed is constant and equal to $r_0\omega$, then the radial acceleration is $-r_0\omega^2$ in a direction away from the centre, while the transverse acceleration is zero.

These accelerations are of importance in connection with central orbits.

193. Central Orbits.—If a point is moving under the action of an acceleration which is always directed towards a fixed point, its path is called a *central orbit.* To consider this motion it is convenient to take the fixed point as the origin of co-ordinates, and frequently a simplification in the equation to the path may be made by an appropriate choice of the initial direction of the radius vector, *i.e.* by suitably choosing the instant from which the time is measured.

From the definition it will be seen that all central orbits will have the common property of zero transverse acceleration. Expressing this fact in the equation (353) we have

$$\frac{1}{r} \cdot \frac{d}{dt}\left(r^2\frac{d\theta}{dt}\right)=0,$$

or

$$r^2\frac{d\theta}{dt}=constant=h, \text{ say, } . \qquad . \qquad . \quad (354)$$

and if the acceleration at a point (r, θ) is equal to a and directed towards the centre, then the equation of radial accelerations (352) becomes

$$\frac{d^2r}{dt^2}-r\left(\frac{d\theta}{dt}\right)^2=-a.$$

Putting $\frac{1}{r}=u,$

$$\frac{dr}{dt}=\frac{d}{dt}\left(\frac{1}{u}\right)=\frac{d}{d\theta}\left(\frac{1}{u}\right)\cdot\frac{d\theta}{dt}=-\frac{1}{u^2}\cdot\frac{du}{d\theta}\cdot\frac{d\theta}{dt}.$$

But, from equation (354),

$$h=r^2\frac{d\theta}{dt}=\frac{1}{u^2}\cdot\frac{d\theta}{dt},$$

so that

$$\frac{dr}{dt}=-h\frac{du}{d\theta}.$$

Also

$$\frac{d^2r}{dt^2}=\frac{d}{dt}\left(-h\frac{du}{d\theta}\right)=-h\frac{d}{d\theta}\left(\frac{du}{d\theta}\right)\cdot\frac{d\theta}{dt}=-h\frac{d^2u}{d\theta^2}\cdot\frac{d\theta}{dt}=-h^2u^2\frac{d^2u}{d\theta^2}.$$

If these values are substituted in equation (352),

$$-a=-h^2u^2\frac{d^2u}{d\theta^2}-\frac{1}{u}\cdot h^2u^4,$$

or

$$\frac{a}{h^2u^2}=\left[\frac{d^2u}{d\theta^2}+u\right], \qquad . \qquad . \qquad . \quad (355)$$

which is the general differential equation to any central orbit.

Areal   Velocity.—At any point in the orbit the *areal velocity* is defined as the

$$Lt. \frac{Area\ described\ by\ the\ radius\ vector}{The\ time\ of\ description}.$$

In Fig. 97 (*a*) the area *POQ* is swept out in the time δt and thus the areal velocity is

$$Lt. \frac{Area\ POQ}{\delta t} = Lt. \frac{\frac{1}{2}r(r+\delta r)\ sin\ \delta\theta}{\delta t} = \frac{1}{2}r^2\frac{d\theta}{dt} = \frac{1}{2}h \quad . \quad (356)$$

Hence *h* represents twice the *constant areal velocity* in the orbit.

194. Motion under an Inverse Square Law of Attraction.— If the law which governs the relation between the central acceleration and the distance of the moving point from the centre is known, then, on substituting for *a*, in equation (355), the appropriate function of *r* (or *u*), the equation may be integrated to give the family of curves to which the orbit belongs. The selection of the appropriate member of the family is determined by the initial conditions. A specially important case arises if the law of acceleration is the inverse square law of distance, *i.e.* if *a* is given by

$$a = \frac{\omega^2}{r^2} = \omega^2 u^2,$$

where ω is a constant. In this case the equation of motion is

$$\omega^2 u^2 = h^2 u^2 \left[\frac{d^2u}{d\theta^2} + u \right],$$

or

$$\frac{d^2u}{d\theta^2} + u = \frac{\omega^2}{h^2}.$$

This is similar in form to equation (328) except for the constant $\frac{\omega^2}{h^2}$, and the solution is

$$\frac{1}{r} = u = M\ cos\ (\theta - \gamma) + \frac{\omega^2}{h^2},$$

or

$$\frac{\frac{h^2}{\omega^2}}{r} = 1 + \frac{Mh^2}{\omega^2}\ cos\ (\theta - \gamma), \quad . \qquad . \qquad . \qquad (357)$$

where *M* and γ are the integration constants. Comparing this with the polar equation of a conic,

$$\frac{l}{r} = 1 + \varepsilon(cos\ \theta - \gamma),$$

we see that the central orbit of a point moving under the inverse square law is a conic with one focus at the centre of acceleration.

The eccentricity, ε, of the conic is given by

$$\varepsilon = \frac{Mh^2}{\omega^2}, \qquad . \qquad . \qquad . \qquad . \qquad (358)$$

and the semi-latus rectum, l, by

$$l = \frac{h^2}{\omega^2} \qquad . \qquad . \qquad . \qquad . \qquad (359)$$

To identify any special case it is necessary to know whether the eccentricity $\dfrac{Mh^2}{\omega^2}$ is greater than, equal to, or less than unity, and this, in turn, depends on the initial conditions which determine M and γ.

For example, if a body is projected with velocity V from a point distant a from the centre of force in a direction making an angle α with the radius vector, then $h = aV \sin \alpha$ and the following initial conditions hold :—

$$\text{when } \theta = 0, \; r = a, \; \frac{dr}{dt} = V \cos \alpha, \; \frac{d\theta}{dt} = \frac{V}{a} \sin \alpha.$$

If these are substituted in equation (357), we have, after a little reduction,

$$\varepsilon^2 = \frac{M^2 h^4}{\omega^4} = 1 + \frac{a^2 V^4}{\omega^4} \sin^2 \alpha - \frac{2aV^2}{\omega^2} \sin^2 \alpha,$$

and thus the orbit is an ellipse, parabola or hyperbola, according as V^2 is less than, equal to, or greater than $\dfrac{2\omega^2}{a}$. This condition is independent of the direction of projection.

This result is of importance in connection with the movements of heavenly bodies, the motion of an electron around the positive nucleus of an atom, and the deflection of α particles shot into atoms.

The velocity v at any point distant r from the centre can be found by evaluating the radial and transverse velocities. Thus the radial velocity is

$$\frac{dr}{dt} = aV \sin \alpha . M \sin (\theta - \gamma),$$

and the transverse velocity

$$r . \frac{d\theta}{dt} = \frac{aV}{r} \sin \alpha,$$

from which, by obtaining $M \sin (\theta - \gamma)$ from (357), we have

$$v^2 = V^2 + 2\omega^2 \left(\frac{1}{r} - \frac{1}{a} \right).$$

Periodic Time in Elliptic Orbits.—For an ellipse the semi-latus rectum equals $\dfrac{b_1^2}{a_1}$, where b_1 and a_1 are the minor and major semi-axes respectively, and if we equate this value to $\dfrac{h^2}{\omega^2}$ obtained from equation (359), we have

$$h^2 = \frac{\omega^2 b_1{}^2}{a_1}.$$

Since the area of the ellipse is $\pi a_1 b_1$, the period t_0—or time for one circuit of the orbit—is given by

$$t_0{}^2 = \frac{4\pi^2 a_1{}^2 b_1{}^2}{h^2} = \frac{4\pi^2}{\omega^2} a_1{}^3,$$

or

$$t_0 = \frac{2\pi}{\omega} a_1{}^{\frac{3}{2}} \quad . \quad . \quad . \quad . \quad . \quad (360)$$

Hence the square of the period is proportional to the cube of the major axis. If the conditions of projection are as described above, then $h = aV \sin \alpha$ and the period is given by

$$t_0 = \frac{2\pi a_1 b_1}{aV \sin \alpha}.$$

But, from the properties of the ellipse,

$$\frac{b_1{}^2}{a_1} = a_1(1 - e^2) = \frac{a^2 V^2}{\omega^2} \sin^2 \alpha.$$

If a_1 and b_1 are eliminated from these equations, and the value of e^2 found above is substituted, we have

$$t_0{}^2 = \frac{4\pi^2 a^3 \omega^4}{(2\omega^2 - aV^2)^3},$$

which gives the periodic time in terms of the initial conditions and shows that it depends on the velocity of projection, but not on the initial direction.

195. Plane Motion in Cartesian Co-ordinates.—Some types of plane motion, such as projectile motions under gravity and Thomson's positive ray measurements, are more conveniently referred to cartesian co-ordinates, and in this case velocities and accelerations along the x and y axes are considered separately. This is permissible, because a force cannot affect motion in a direction at right angles to its own line of action. The results give the actual velocity and path in a parameter form—the parameter being the time—and it is not always easy to eliminate t to obtain the explicit connection between x and y. This disadvantage is merely the practical one of presenting equations in a less familiar form.

The Motion of a Projectile assuming No Friction.—The first case we shall consider is that of a particle projected from the origin with a velocity u at an angle α to the horizontal axis Ox. The motion along Ox is not accelerated, and the equation of motion in this direction is

$$\frac{dx}{dt}=u\ cos\ \alpha \qquad . \qquad . \qquad . \qquad . \qquad (361)$$

Hence, since $x=0$ when $t=0$,

$$x=ut\ cos\ \alpha \qquad . \qquad . \qquad . \qquad . \qquad (362)$$

In the vertical—or Oy—direction

$$\frac{d^2y}{dt^2}=-g,$$

and, since $\frac{dy}{dt}=u\ sin\ \alpha$ when $t=0$,

$$\frac{dy}{dt}=u\ sin\ \alpha-gt \qquad . \qquad . \qquad . \qquad (363)$$

At $y=0$, $t=0$, so

$$y=ut\ sin\ \alpha-\tfrac{1}{2}gt^2 \qquad . \qquad . \qquad . \qquad (364)$$

Eliminating t between equations (362) and (364) we have, as the equation to the trajectory,

$$y=u\ sin\ \alpha\frac{x}{u\ cos\ \alpha}-\tfrac{1}{2}\frac{gx^2}{u^2\ cos^2\ \alpha}$$

$$=x\ tan\ \alpha-\frac{gx^2}{2u^2\ cos^2\ \alpha}, \qquad . \qquad . \qquad (365)$$

which represents a parabola, and the particle describes a parabolic orbit.

To obtain the range on a plane inclined at an angle θ to the horizontal, it is necessary to find the point of intersection of the trajectory and the plane, *i.e.* to solve the equations

$$y=x\ tan\ \alpha-\frac{gx^2}{2u^2\ cos^2\ \alpha},$$

$$y=x\ tan\ \theta.$$

Thus we have

$$x=\frac{2u^2\ cos^2\ \alpha}{g}(tan\ \alpha-tan\ \theta), \qquad . \qquad . \qquad (366)$$

$$y=\frac{2u^2\ cos^2\ \alpha\ tan\ \theta}{g}(tan\ \alpha-tan\ \theta), \qquad . \qquad (367)$$

and the range R is given by

$$R^2=x^2+y^2.$$

On a horizontal plane $\theta=0$, and the horizontal range is, from equation (366),

$$R=x=\frac{2u^2\ sin\ \alpha\ cos\ \alpha}{g}=\frac{u^2\ sin\ 2\alpha}{g}.$$

The particle will reach the highest point in its path when $\frac{dy}{dt}=0$, *i.e.*

from equation (363) when $t=\dfrac{u \, sin \, \alpha}{g}$ and then, from equation (364),

$$y=\frac{u^2 \, sin^2 \, \alpha}{g}-\frac{u^2 \, sin^2 \, \alpha}{2g}=\frac{u^2 \, sin^2 \, \alpha}{2g},$$

and the x co-ordinate of the summit is

$$x=\frac{R}{2}=\frac{u^2 \, sin \, 2\alpha}{2g}.$$

At the end of a time t the particle has velocity components $\dfrac{dy}{dt}$, $\dfrac{dx}{dt}$ and the resultant velocity is given by

$$v^2=\left(\frac{dy}{dt}\right)^2+\left(\frac{dx}{dt}\right),$$

while its direction makes an angle β with the x axis, such that

$$tan \, \beta=\frac{dy}{dx}=\frac{dy}{dt}\cdot\frac{dt}{dx}.$$

From equations (361) and (363),

$$v^2=u^2 \, sin^2 \, \alpha+g^2t^2-2ugt \, sin \, \alpha+u^2 \, cos^2 \, \alpha$$
$$=u^2-2ugt \, sin \, \alpha+g^2t^2,$$

and $$tan \, \beta=\frac{u \, sin \, \alpha-gt}{u \, cos \, \alpha}=tan \, \alpha-\frac{gt}{u \, cos \, \alpha}.$$

196. The Motion of a Projectile subjected to a Resistance proportional to its Velocity.—If the particle is projected under the same conditions as those above and is subjected to a frictional resistance proportional to its velocity, the equations of motion along the x and y axes become

$$\frac{d^2x}{dt^2}=-k\frac{dx}{dt}, \qquad \text{.} \quad \text{.} \quad \text{.} \quad \text{.} \quad (368)$$

$$\frac{d^2y}{dt^2}=-k\frac{dy}{dt}-g \qquad \text{.} \quad \text{.} \quad \text{.} \quad (369)$$

Putting $\dfrac{dx}{dt}=v$,

$$\frac{dv}{dt}=-kv, \quad \text{or} \quad log \, v=-kt+C_1.$$

When $t=0$, $v=u \, cos \, \alpha$, so that $C_1=log \, (u \, cos \, \alpha)$, and thus

$$\frac{dx}{dt}=v=e^{-kt}u \, cos \, \alpha. \qquad \text{.} \quad \text{.} \quad \text{.} \quad (370)$$

Hence

$$x=-\frac{u \, cos \, \alpha}{k}e^{-kt}+C_2=-\frac{u \, cos \, \alpha}{k}e^{-kt}+\frac{u \, cos \, \alpha}{k}=\frac{u \, cos \, \alpha}{k}[1-e^{-kt}]. \quad (371)$$

Denoting the velocity along the y axis by w we have, from equation (369),

$$\frac{dw}{dt} = -kw - g,$$

or

$$\log (kw+g) = -kt + C_3 = -kt + \log (ku \sin \alpha + g).$$

Thus

$$kw + g = (ku \sin \alpha + g)e^{-kt},$$

so that

$$ky + gt = \frac{ku \sin \alpha + g}{k} e^{-kt} + C_4 = \frac{ku \sin \alpha + g}{k}[1 - e^{-kt}], \qquad (372)$$

remembering that, when $t=0$, $y=0$ and $w=u \sin \alpha$. The equation to the trajectory is given by equating the values of e^{-kt} in equations (371) and (372) and is

$$y = \frac{g}{k^2} \log \left[1 - \frac{kx}{u \cos \alpha} \right] + \frac{x}{u \cos \alpha}\left[u \sin \alpha + \frac{g}{k} \right].$$

EXAMPLES

1. A particle of mass m is projected upwards with velocity v in a medium which imposes a resistance given by mkv (k const.). Find the time taken to reach the highest point and an equation to give the time for the subsequent downward motion.
[$kt = \log (1 + kv/g)$; $-kt = \log \{(1 + kv/g) - \log (1 + kv/g) - kt\}$.]

2. If, in the previous question, the resistance factor k is small, show that its effect on the maximum height reached is appreciable before its effect on the time to reach this point is observable, supposing that measurements of heights and times to be equally sensitive.

3. The particle in question 1 above falls from rest in a medium which offers a resistance equal to mkv^2. Show that the acceleration f varies with the distance x according to the relation $\log f = \log g - 2kx$.

4. A galvanometer coil oscillates with a periodic time of 5·00 sec. and successive maximum displacements are observed to be 76, 34·2, 15·5 and 6·9 scale divisions. The moment of inertia of the suspended system is 4·86 gm.-cm.². Are these readings consistent with damping forces proportional to the velocity? If so, calculate the couple required to rotate the coil through one radian and the damping couple at unit angular velocity. [Yes ; 8·17 dyne-cm. ; 3·10 dyne-cm.]

5. What would have been the deflection of the galvanometer in the previous question in the absence of damping force? [110.]

6. A body of effective mass M has a natural simple harmonic motion of period T given by $\omega T = 2\pi$, and is acted upon by a persistent harmonic force $P \sin pt$ and a frictional force $2kMv$. Find (a) the condition for maximum amplitude in the final forced motion, and (b) the ratio of the amplitudes under the conditions $p = \omega$ and $p^2 = \omega^2 - 4k^2$.
[$p^2 = \omega^2 - 2k^2$; 1.]

7. A simple pendulum is released from a position in which it makes a small angle α with the vertical and it moves in a medium which produces a resistance mkv^2, where k is very small. Show that the time to swing across to the other side is unaffected if the square of k may be neglected, and find the angle made with the vertical when the pendulum reaches its extreme position on the other side. $[\alpha - 4\alpha^2 kl/3.]$

8. A particle, attracted towards a fixed small spherical mass M by an inverse square law force, is projected with velocity u from a point distant a from the centre of force. Show that if u is less than $\sqrt{(2GM/a)}$ the path of the particle is an ellipse, whatever the direction of projection.

9. Show that when the orbit is an ellipse the velocity v of the particle in the previous question at any distance r from the mass M is given by $v^2 = GM(2/r - 1/A)$, A being the semi-major axis of the ellipse. Hence prove that the periodic time is independent of the direction of initial projection.

10. Find the law of force towards a centre for a particle for which the polar equation to the orbit is (a) $\log r + n\theta = 0$, (b) $r = a \sin \theta$.
    $[(a)\ fr^3 = const.\ ;\quad (b)\ fr^5 = const.]$

11. A particle is projected with velocity v at right angles to the line joining it to the centre of force which is at a distance x from the point of projection. The acceleration f to the centre at a distance r is given by $fr^3 = \omega$, a constant. Find the equation to the orbit in the following cases : (a) $\omega > v^2 x^2$; (b) $\omega = v^2 x^2$; (c) $\omega < v^2 x^2$.
$[(a)\ x = r\ cosh\ \theta\ \sqrt{(\omega/v^2 x^2 - 1)}$; (b) $x = r$; (c) $x = r\ cos\ \theta\ \sqrt{(1 - \omega/v^2 x^2)}.]$

12. An anti-aircraft gun is fired at an aeroplane directly overhead. If the resistance of the air can be neglected, show that, for a hit, the elevation of the gun is independent of the height of the aeroplane, and that if the resistance is k times the velocity, the elevation is still the same, provided terms in k^2 can be neglected.

13. A shell of mass m is projected with velocity V in a medium in which the resistance is mk times the velocity. Show that for maximum range R on a horizontal plane, the elevation of the gun, α, is given by

$$A(1 + A\ sin\ \alpha) = (A + sin\ \alpha) \log (1 + A\ cosec\ \alpha)$$

where A is kV/g. Find also the value of R.
    $[R = V^2\ cos\ \alpha/g(A + sin\ \alpha).]$

14. Two particles are dropped from rest into a medium in which the resistance is proportional to the velocity, the second one a short time after the first. Show that the distance between them increases and approaches a final limiting value which is proportional to the time interval between their instants of release.

15. A point describes an ellipse with centre as the origin of coordinates and the radius vector has constant areal velocity. Show that the eccentricity of the orbit is $\left[1 - \left(\dfrac{V^1}{V} \right)^2 \right]^{\frac{1}{2}}$ where V and V^1 are the maximum and minimum velocities in the orbit.

16. A smooth horizontal tube OA of length a is movable about a vertical axis OB. A particle placed at A is projected towards O with velocity $a\omega$ while at the same time the tube revolves about OB with

angular velocity ω.   Show that the particle will have travelled half-way down the tube in time $\dfrac{\log 2}{\omega}$ and will not reach O in any finite time.

17. Two similar spheres of mass M and radius a are placed on a smooth horizontal table with their centres $4a$ apart.   Find the time for them to come into contact under their mutual attraction starting from rest.
$$\left[t\sqrt{GM} = a^{\frac{3}{2}}\left(\frac{\pi}{4} + \frac{1}{2}\right). \right]$$

CHAPTER XIII

EQUATIONS OF MOTION

197. Equation of Continuity.—Although we are concerned primarily with the properties of fluids, it is instructive to consider the motion of any entity, and by entity we mean any physical quantity such as matter, momentum, heat, electricity, *etc.* The particular properties associated with the entity considered may be introduced in the general result. We assume that the entity is continuous, so that the properties of the smallest portions into which we can conceive it to be divided are the same as those of the entity in bulk.

Let u, v, w be the components, parallel to the co-ordinate axes, of the velocity at the point (x, y, z) at the time t. As the motions which we shall have to consider are, in general, continuous, we shall assume that u, v, and w are finite and continuous functions of x, y, z, and that their space derivatives, $\dfrac{\partial u}{\partial x}$, $\dfrac{\partial v}{\partial x}$, $\dfrac{\partial w}{\partial x}$, *etc.*, are also finite.

Suppose that motion in space is opposed by obstacles, so that, if we consider an area perpendicular to the direction of motion, the space available for the passage of the entity is less than if the obstacles were absent. Let K, which may be termed *permeability*, be the ratio of the areas available in the two cases.

The increase in the mass of the entity within any closed boundary surface must be equal to the excess that flows in over that flowing out, plus any entity created within the volume. Let m be the mass created in unit volume in unit time, K_x, K_y, K_z the permeabilities, Q_x, Q_y, Q_z the entity densities parallel to the co-ordinate axes, Q being the average density at the point (x, y, z). With this point as centre construct a small parallelepiped of edges δx, δy, δz (Fig. 98). The entity flowing in across the face B in time δt is

$$\left(K_x - \frac{\partial K_x}{\partial x} \cdot \frac{\delta x}{2}\right)\left(Q_x - \frac{\partial Q_x}{\partial x} \cdot \frac{\delta x}{2}\right)\left(u - \frac{\partial u}{\partial x} \cdot \frac{\delta x}{2}\right)\delta y \delta z \delta t,$$

and the amount flowing out across the face A is

$$\left(K_x + \frac{\partial K_x}{\partial x} \cdot \frac{\delta x}{2}\right)\left(Q_x + \frac{\partial Q_x}{\partial x} \cdot \frac{\delta x}{2}\right)\left(u + \frac{\partial u}{\partial x} \cdot \frac{\delta x}{2}\right)\delta y \delta z \delta t,$$

so that the gain within the volume in time ∂t, due to flow along the x axis, is, to a first approximation,

$$-\frac{\partial}{\partial x}(K_x Q_x u)\delta x \delta y \delta z \delta t,$$

367

and the total gain in entity is

$$\left[m - \left\{ \frac{\partial}{\partial x}(K_x Q_x u) + \frac{\partial}{\partial y}(K_y Q_y v) + \frac{\partial}{\partial z}(K_z Q_z w) \right\} \right] \delta x \delta y \delta z \delta t.$$

But the original mass within the elementary volume is $Q \delta x \delta y \delta z$, and the gain in time δt is $\frac{\partial Q}{\partial t} \delta x \delta y \delta z \delta t$, so that

$$\frac{\partial Q}{\partial t} - m + \frac{\partial}{\partial x}(K_x Q_x u) + \frac{\partial}{\partial y}(K_y Q_y v) + \frac{\partial}{\partial z}(K_z Q_z w) = 0 \quad . \quad (373)$$

This is the *Equation of Continuity.*

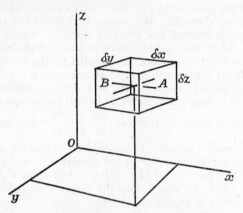

FIG. 98.—EQUATION OF CONTINUITY IN CARTESIAN CO-ORDINATES.

To express the equation in spherical polar co-ordinates, consider an elementary volume (Fig. 99) of mutually perpendicular edges δr, $r.\delta\theta$, $r \sin \theta.\delta\beta$, the components of the velocity, density, and permeability along these three edges being u, v, w; Q_1, Q_2, Q_3; K_1, K_2, K_3, respectively. Then the excess inflow at the faces *ABCD* over the outflow across *EFGH* is

$$-\frac{\partial}{\partial r}(K_1 Q_1 u r^2 \sin \theta.\delta\theta\delta\beta)\delta r.\delta t,$$

across the faces *AEFB*, *DHGC*

$$-\frac{\partial}{r.\partial\theta}(K_2 Q_2 v r \sin \theta.\delta\beta\delta r)r\delta\theta.\delta t,$$

and across *BFGC*, *AEHD*

$$-\frac{\partial}{r \sin \theta.\partial\beta}(K_3 Q_3 w r\delta\theta\delta r)r \sin \theta.\delta\beta.\delta t.$$

The entity created within the volume in time δt is

$$mr^2 \sin \theta.\delta r\delta\theta\delta\beta\delta t,$$

and the total increase within the volume may be expressed as

$$\frac{\partial}{\partial t}(Qr^2 \, sin \, \theta . \delta r \delta \theta \delta \beta)\delta t.$$

Hence

$$\frac{\partial Q}{\partial t} - m + \frac{1}{r^2} . \frac{\partial}{\partial r}(Q_1K_1ur^2) + \frac{1}{r \, sin \, \theta} . \frac{\partial}{\partial \theta}(Q_2K_2v \, sin \, \theta)$$

$$+ \frac{1}{r \, sin \, \theta} . \frac{\partial}{\partial \beta}(Q_3K_3w) = 0.$$

To transform the equation into cylindrical co-ordinates, consider

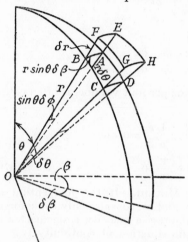

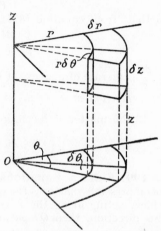

FIG. 99.—EQUATION OF CONTINUITY IN SPHERICAL CO-ORDINATES.

FIG. 100.—EQUATION OF CONTINUITY IN CYLINDRICAL CO-ORDINATES.

a small volume of which the three mutually perpendicular edges are δr, $r\delta \theta$, and δz (Fig. 100), so that δz is substituted for $r \, sin \, \theta . \delta \beta$ above. The equation of continuity thus becomes

$$\frac{\partial Q}{\partial t} - m + \frac{1}{r} \frac{\partial}{\partial r}(Q_1K_1ur) + \frac{1}{r} . \frac{\partial}{\partial \theta}(Q_2K_2v) + \frac{\partial}{\partial z}(Q_zK_zw) = 0.$$

Expressed in any form of co-ordinates, the equation of continuity takes a simplified form if the density and permeability are constant and independent of direction.

198. The Equation of Continuity applied to Matter.—As matter cannot be created or destroyed, $m=0$ and, in addition, $K_x=K_y=K_z=1$, $Q_x=Q_y=Q_z=\rho$, the density of matter, and, from equation (373),

$$\frac{\partial \rho}{\partial t} + \frac{\partial}{\partial x}(\rho u) + \frac{\partial}{\partial y}(\rho v) + \frac{\partial}{\partial z}(\rho w) = 0 \qquad . \qquad . \qquad (374)$$

This is the hydrodynamical equation of continuity.

If the density varies with time but not with distance,

$$-\frac{1}{\rho}\cdot\frac{\partial\rho}{\partial t}=\frac{\partial u}{\partial x}+\frac{\partial v}{\partial y}+\frac{\partial w}{\partial z} \qquad . \qquad . \qquad . \qquad (375)$$

Suppose we have a fixed quantity M of matter occupying a volume V. Then $M=\rho V$, and

$$\frac{dM}{dt}=0=\rho\frac{\partial V}{\partial t}+V\frac{\partial\rho}{\partial t},$$

or

$$-\frac{1}{\rho}\cdot\frac{\partial\rho}{\partial t}=\frac{1}{V}\cdot\frac{\partial V}{\partial t},$$

so that, from equation (375),

$$\frac{1}{V}\cdot\frac{\partial V}{\partial t}=\frac{\partial u}{\partial x}+\frac{\partial v}{\partial y}+\frac{\partial w}{\partial z};$$

$\frac{1}{V}\cdot\frac{\partial V}{\partial t}$, the rate of increase of volume per unit volume, is often called the *expansion at a point*.

If the matter is incompressible, $\frac{1}{\rho}\cdot\frac{\partial\rho}{\partial t}=0$ and

$$\frac{\partial u}{\partial x}+\frac{\partial v}{\partial y}+\frac{\partial w}{\partial z}=0 \qquad . \qquad . \qquad . \qquad . \qquad (376)$$

199. Euler's Equations of Motion.—If the momentum of incompressible matter is the entity and we consider only those forces which, acting along the x axis, impress a velocity u on matter in this direction, then $Q=\rho u$ and the equation of continuity is

$$\frac{\partial}{\partial t}(\rho u)+\frac{\partial}{\partial x}(\rho u^2)+\frac{\partial}{\partial y}(\rho uv)+\frac{\partial}{\partial z}(\rho uw)-m=0 \qquad . \qquad (377)$$

But for matter, ρ is independent of direction, hence, from equations (374) and (377),

$$\frac{\partial u}{\partial t}+u\frac{\partial u}{\partial x}+v\frac{\partial u}{\partial y}+w\frac{\partial u}{\partial z}-\frac{m}{\rho}=0 \qquad . \qquad . \qquad (378)$$

The momentum may be created by (*a*) an impressed force at a distance acting on the mass, or (*b*) pressure acting on the boundary surface.

Let X, Y, Z be the components of the impressed force per unit mass at the point (x, y, z), and p the pressure at this point. Then the total force acting on the elementary volume (Fig. 98) in the x direction is

$$-\frac{\partial p}{\partial x}\delta x\delta y\delta z+X\rho\cdot\delta x\delta y\delta z,$$

and the momentum created per unit volume per second is

$$m=X\rho-\frac{\partial p}{\partial x}.$$

Substituting this value of m in equation (378),

$$\frac{\partial u}{\partial t}+u\frac{\partial u}{\partial x}+v\frac{\partial u}{\partial y}+w\frac{\partial u}{\partial z}-X+\frac{1}{\rho}\cdot\frac{\partial p}{\partial x}=0 \quad . \quad . \quad (379)$$

Similarly,
$$\frac{\partial v}{\partial t}+u\frac{\partial v}{\partial x}+v\frac{\partial v}{\partial y}+w\frac{\partial v}{\partial z}-Y+\frac{1}{\rho}\cdot\frac{\partial p}{\delta y}=0, \quad . \quad . \quad (380)$$

and
$$\frac{\partial w}{\partial t}+u\frac{\partial w}{\partial x}+v\frac{\partial w}{\partial y}+w\frac{\partial w}{\partial z}-Z+\frac{1}{\rho}\cdot\frac{\partial p}{\partial z}=0 \quad . \quad . \quad (381)$$

These results are known as *Euler's equations of motion*.

200. The Boundary Surface of a Fluid.—Fluid motion depends to a large extent upon viscosity, and results obtained from considerations which ignore internal friction must be regarded as an approximation, only, to the true motion.   To avoid complications we shall regard the fluid medium as a perfect fluid incapable of exerting shearing stress, and, whether at rest or in motion, we shall assume that the pressure it exerts on any surface in contact with it is always normal to the surface.   Consequently the pressure at any point in such a fluid is the same in every direction.

If the boundary surface is fixed, the velocity of the fluid normal to the surface is zero, or

$$lu+mv+nw=0,$$

at every point on the boundary, l, m, n being the direction cosines of the boundary normal.   The co-ordinates of a point P on the surface being (x, y, z), the equation of the surface may be written

$$F(x, y, z, t)=0, \quad . \quad . \quad . \quad (382)$$

and if we consider an element of length δs perpendicular to the surface, the co-ordinates of the point P' to which the point P has moved in a time δt are $x+l.\delta s$, $y+m.\delta s$, $z+n.\delta s$, so that the point P' lies on the boundary surface after a time δt, and

$$F(x+l.\delta s, y+m.\delta s, z+n.\delta s, t+\delta t)=0 \quad . \quad (383)$$

Hence, from equations (382) and (383),

$$\frac{ds}{dt}\left(l\frac{\partial F}{\partial x}+m\frac{\partial F}{\partial y}+n\frac{\partial F}{\partial z}\right)+\frac{\partial F}{\partial t}=0,$$

but
$$l, m, n=\frac{\frac{\partial F}{\partial x},\ \frac{\partial F}{\partial y},\ \frac{\partial F}{\partial z}}{\left[\left(\frac{\partial F}{\partial x}\right)^2+\left(\frac{\partial F}{\partial y}\right)^2+\left(\frac{\partial F}{\partial z}\right)^2\right]^{\frac{1}{2}}}, \quad . \quad . \quad (384)$$

so
$$\frac{ds}{dt}=\frac{-\frac{\partial F}{\partial t}}{\left[\left(\frac{\partial F}{\partial x}\right)^2+\left(\frac{\partial F}{\partial y}\right)^2+\left(\frac{\partial F}{\partial z}\right)^2\right]^{\frac{1}{2}}} \quad . \quad . \quad (385)$$

But at every point on the boundary surface

$$\frac{ds}{dt} = lu + mv + nw, \qquad \cdot \qquad \cdot \qquad \cdot \qquad (386)$$

and thus, from equations (384), (385), and (386),

$$\frac{\partial F}{\partial t} + u \frac{\partial F}{\partial x} + v \frac{\partial F}{\partial y} + w \frac{\partial F}{\partial z} = 0 \qquad \cdot \qquad \cdot \qquad \cdot \qquad (387)$$

This is the equation to the boundary surface.

201. Velocity Potential.—In many cases the component velocities may be expressed in terms of a single function ϕ such that

$$u, v, w = -\frac{\partial \phi}{\partial x}, \quad -\frac{\partial \phi}{\partial y}, \quad -\frac{\partial \phi}{\partial z} \qquad \cdot \qquad \cdot \qquad (388)$$

This function is called a *velocity potential* and we have the relations,

$$\frac{\partial v}{\partial z} = \frac{\partial w}{\partial y}, \quad \frac{\partial w}{\partial x} = \frac{\partial u}{\partial z}, \quad \frac{\partial u}{\partial y} = \frac{\partial v}{\partial x} \qquad \cdot \qquad \cdot \qquad (389)$$

Hence Euler's equations of motion may be written

$$-\frac{\partial^2 \phi}{\partial x \partial t} + u \frac{\partial u}{\partial x} + v \frac{\partial v}{\partial y} + w \frac{\partial w}{\partial z} = -\frac{\partial \Omega}{\partial x} - \frac{1}{\rho} \cdot \frac{\partial p}{\partial x}, \qquad \cdot \qquad (390)$$

etc., where $X = -\dfrac{\partial \Omega}{\partial x}$, and Ω denotes the potential energy per unit mass at a point (x, y, z), in respect of the forces acting at a distance. Integrating equation (390),

$$\int \frac{dp}{\rho} = \frac{\partial \phi}{\partial t} - \Omega - \frac{q^2}{2} + F(t), \qquad \cdot \qquad \cdot \qquad (391)$$

where $q = (u^2 + v^2 + w^2)^{\frac{1}{2}}$ and $F(t)$ is an arbitrary function of the time. In the case of an incompressible fluid this becomes

$$\frac{p}{\rho} = \frac{\partial \phi}{\partial t} - \Omega - \frac{1}{2} q^2 + F(t). \qquad \cdot \qquad \cdot \qquad (392)$$

If p is given at some point in the fluid for all values of t, the pressure is determinate. The term $F(t)$ is without influence on the resultant pressures and is frequently omitted.

The equation of continuity (376) in terms of ϕ is

$$\frac{\partial^2 \phi}{\partial x^2} + \frac{\partial^2 \phi}{\partial y^2} + \frac{\partial^2 \phi}{\partial z^2} = 0 \qquad \cdot \qquad \cdot \qquad (393)$$

The motion of a fluid is said to be *steady* if at every point the velocity is the same in direction and magnitude at all times, or

$$\frac{\partial u}{\partial t} = 0, \qquad \frac{\partial v}{\partial t} = 0, \qquad \frac{\partial w}{\partial t} = 0,$$

so that equation (391) becomes

$$\int \frac{dp}{\rho} = -\Omega - \frac{1}{2} q^2 + constant \qquad \cdot \qquad \cdot \qquad (394)$$

202. Bernoulli's Theorem.—This law of variation of pressure along a *stream line* is known as *Bernoulli's Theorem*, a stream line being the actual path of a particle in a moving fluid. Strictly speaking, it is a curve such that, at any instant, the tangent to it at a point is the direction of the fluid motion at that point. The constant of integration may vary from one stream line to another.

Bernoulli's theorem may be deduced also from the conservation of energy principle as follows. Imagine a tube of flow in the liquid, the boundary surface of which is, of course, formed by stream lines. Let p_1 be the pressure, q_1 the velocity, and Ω_1 the potential due to the external forces at a point A where the cross-section is α_1. The values of the same quantities at another point B are represented by the suffix 2. Then, since the mass of fluid contained between the normal sections of a tube is constant, the same mass crosses every normal section in unit time, or $\alpha_1 q_1 = \alpha_2 q_2$. The work done on the mass entering A per unit time is $p_1\alpha_1 q_1$, and on the mass leaving at B, $p_2\alpha_2 q_2$. The former mass brings in energy $(\frac{1}{2}q_1{}^2 + \Omega_1)\rho q_1 \alpha_1$, and that leaving B carries off energy $(\frac{1}{2}q_2{}^2 + \Omega_2)\rho q_2 \alpha_2$. As the motion is steady, by the conservation of energy, the energy within the tube remains constant, so

$$p_1\alpha_1 q_1 + \rho q_1\alpha_1(\tfrac{1}{2}q_1{}^2 + \Omega_1) = p_2\alpha_2 q_2 + \rho q_2\alpha_2(\tfrac{1}{2}q_2{}^2 + \Omega_2),$$

or

$$\frac{p_1}{\rho} + \tfrac{1}{2}q_1{}^2 + \Omega_1 = \frac{p_2}{\rho} + \tfrac{1}{2}q_2{}^2 + \Omega_2 = C_1,$$

where C_1 is a constant.

If motion occurs under the action of gravity alone, $\Omega = gz$, where z is the vertical displacement and

$$\tfrac{1}{2}q^2 + gz + \frac{p}{\rho} = C_1 \qquad . \qquad . \qquad . \qquad (395)$$

Hence the energy consists of three parts.

(i) gz, the potential energy in a gravitational field ;

(ii) $\dfrac{p}{\rho}$, pressure energy, *i.e.* energy required to move the liquid against the pressure without imparting any velocity ;

(iii) $\tfrac{1}{2}q^2$, kinetic energy.

The theorem may be written in a slightly modified form,

$$z + \frac{p}{g\rho} + \frac{q^2}{2g} = \frac{C_1}{g} = H,$$

H being a height or vertical distance. The latter is, therefore, constant for all points in any one stream line, and its components are z the *gravitational head*, $\dfrac{p}{g\rho}$ the *pressure head*, and $\dfrac{q^2}{2g}$ the *velocity head*.

If we neglect external forces, the velocity increases as the pressure is lowered and *vice versa*. For example, if a liquid flows through a pipe having a constriction, the velocity at the constricted part is increased, and the pressure is accordingly diminished. There are several practical applications of this principle in the various jet exhaust pumps which range from the simple type of water aspirator to the more elaborate mercury vapour high-vacuum pumps.

203. Efflux of Liquids.—In the case of a liquid flowing from a reservoir, the velocity at the free surface may be neglected and, if the pressure is p_0, then, from equation (395), $C_1 = \dfrac{p_0}{\rho}$. Neglecting z,

$$p = p_0 - \frac{\rho q^2}{2}.$$

But the minimum possible value for p is zero, so that

$$q = \sqrt{\frac{2p_0}{\rho}}$$

which represents the maximum velocity with which the liquid can flow from the reservoir, *i.e.* about 45 ft. per sec. for water at atmospheric pressure.

When a liquid flows out through a small orifice in the thin base of a containing vessel, it is found that, after leaving the orifice, the cross-section of the jet contracts to a minimum value, after which it increases. This minimum cross-section is called the *contracted vein*, and the ratio of its area to that of the orifice is termed the *coefficient of contraction*. If A is the area of the orifice at which the pressure is p_1, and p_0 is the atmospheric pressure, $\dfrac{\rho q^2}{2} = p_1 - p_0$.

The pressure at the edge of the orifice just outside the vessel is p_0, but the pressure within the jet at this section is higher, so that if q is the actual velocity of the liquid at the edge of the orifice, the velocity within the jet is less and, accordingly, the rate of efflux is less than ρq. Let α be the area of the jet section where the velocity at every point in the section is parallel and uniform and the discharge rate is αq. This is less than Aq; hence α is less than A, or the coefficient of contraction is less than unity.

Momentum equal to $\rho \alpha q^2$ is carried away by the jet per second, and the resultant force is that necessary to maintain the vessel at rest. If the pressure over the whole of the base were p_1, then $(p_1 - p_0)A$ would be the force acting at the orifice which produces this change of momentum. Actually the force is $(p_1 - p_0)(A + dA)$ where dA is a small positive quantity due to the pressure over the orifice varying from p_0 to p_1. Hence

$$\rho \alpha q^2 = (p_1 - p_0)(A + dA).$$

But

$$\tfrac{1}{2}\rho q^2 = p_1 - p_0,$$

and

$$\alpha = \tfrac{1}{2}(A + dA).$$

Hence the coefficient of contraction is greater than 0·5. For circular orifices the experimental value is 0·624 approximately.

204. Torricelli's Theorem.—If A_0 be the area of the free surface of the liquid and q_0 its velocity, and if z is the depth of the orifice below the free surface—the head of liquid being maintained constant,

$$\frac{p_0}{\rho} + \tfrac{1}{2}q_0{}^2 = C_1,$$

and

$$\frac{p_0}{\rho} + \tfrac{1}{2}q^2 - gz = C_1,$$

or

$$q^2 = q_0{}^2 + 2gz.$$

But for the continuity of liquid, $A_0 q_0 = Aq$, and thus

$$q^2 = \frac{2gzA_0{}^2}{A_0{}^2 - A^2}.$$

If the orifice is small, A^2 may be neglected and

$$q^2 = 2gz \qquad . \qquad . \qquad . \qquad . \qquad (396)$$

This relation is known as *Torricelli's theorem*, and it indicates that, when the liquid particles reach the contracted vein, they have the same velocity as if they fell directly from the free surface. The theorem holds with considerable exactness if the orifice is small, and experiment shows that, for water, the efflux velocity is

$$q = 0{\cdot}97\sqrt{2gz}.$$

As the cross-sectional area of the contracted vein is cA, c being the coefficient of contraction, the volume of water issuing from the vessel in unit time is $0{\cdot}97cA\sqrt{2gz}$, $0{\cdot}97c$ being equal to $0{\cdot}62$.

To find the time in which a vessel of any form, filled with water, will be emptied through a small orifice, let A_0 be the area of the free surface at any instant. Then

$$A_0 dz = 0{\cdot}62A\sqrt{2gz} \, . \, dt,$$

or

$$t = \frac{1}{0{\cdot}62A\sqrt{2g}} \int_0^{z_0} \frac{A_0}{\sqrt{z}} dz,$$

where z_0 is the depth of the orifice below the original free surface of the liquid.

205. Efflux of Gases.—For the steady motion of a gas

$$\int \frac{dp}{\rho} + \tfrac{1}{2}q^2 + \Omega = C_1.$$

Let p_1 and ρ_1 be the pressure and density respectively, of a gas in a containing vessel, and suppose that it flows through an orifice into a gaseous atmosphere, the pressure and density of the gas when it issues being p_0 and ρ_0, respectively. Assuming that adiabatic conditions prevail, $\frac{p}{\rho}=constant$, where γ is the ratio of the specific heats of the gas. If there are no external forces,

$$\tfrac{1}{2}q^2=-\int_{p_1}^{p_0}\frac{dp}{\rho},$$

and

$$q^2=\frac{2\gamma}{\gamma-1}\cdot\frac{p_1}{\rho_1}\left[1-\left(\frac{p_0}{p_1}\right)^{\frac{\gamma-1}{\gamma}}\right].$$

Thus an increase in velocity is accompanied by a decrease in pressure. The ordinary vacuum cleaner utilises this principle.

206. Steady Flow of a Liquid past a Cylinder.—As an application of Bernoulli's theorem, consider the steady flow of an incompressible liquid parallel to the base of an infinitely long cylinder of radius R with its axis parallel to the z axis, the cylinder forming an obstacle in the path of the liquid. Suppose that the latter has a velocity U along the x axis at points far removed from the cylinder. Then, since $w=0$, from equation (393), we have

$$\frac{\partial^2\phi}{\partial x^2}+\frac{\partial^2\phi}{\partial y^2}=0,$$

or, transforming to polar co-ordinates,

$$\frac{\partial^2\phi}{\partial r^2}+\frac{1}{r}\cdot\frac{\partial\phi}{\partial r}+\frac{1}{r^2}\cdot\frac{\partial^2\phi}{\partial\theta^2}=0 \qquad . \qquad . \qquad . \qquad (397)$$

Solutions of equation (397) have the form $r^n \cos n\theta$, $r^n \sin n\theta$, and the sum of any number of such terms is itself a solution.

The flow of liquid in the x, negative, direction is given by

$$\phi=Ux=Ur \cos \theta,$$

and to this must be added a term or terms to represent the disturbance produced by the cylinder. As this disturbance vanishes when $r=\infty$, it can involve only negative values of n, so that a solution is

$$\phi=Ur \cos \theta+\frac{B \cos \theta}{r}.$$

But $\frac{\partial\phi}{\partial r}=0$ when $r=R$ is a boundary condition, and thus $B=UR^2$. Hence

$$\phi=U\left(r+\frac{R^2}{r}\right) \cos \theta=Ux\left(1+\frac{R^2}{r^2}\right).$$

Therefore

$$u=-\frac{\partial\phi}{\partial x}=-\left[U\left(1+\frac{R^2}{r^2}\right)-2\frac{Ux^2R^2}{r^4}\right],$$

and

$$v=-\frac{\partial\phi}{\partial y}=-2\frac{UR^2xy}{r^4}.$$

The resultant velocity at the surface of the cylinder is given by

$$q^2 = u^2 + v^2 = \frac{4U^2 y^2}{R^2}.$$

Substituting this value of q^2 in equation (395), the normal pressure on the cylinder becomes

$$p = \rho \left(C_1 - gz - 2\frac{U^2 y^2}{R^2} \right),$$

and is the same on that curved surface of the cylinder at which the liquid impinges as on that from which it flows away. Hence it follows that, neglecting viscosity, the cylinder is not acted upon by any resultant force due to the liquid flowing past it.

207. Green's Theorem.—Many important properties of potential not only in liquids but also in electrostatics, *etc.*, may be proved by means of Green's theorem.

Let ϕ, ϕ' be two functions of x, y, z which, with their first and second derivatives, are everywhere finite and single valued in the region considered. Consider a parallelepiped (Fig. 101), parallel to the x axis, of cross-section dy, dz, and let dS_1, dS_2 be the areas of the

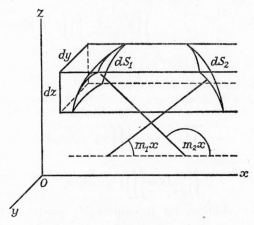

FIG. 101.—GREEN'S THEOREM.

intercepts which it makes with the boundary surface enclosing the volume throughout which the integration is to be performed. Let dn be an element of the normal, drawn into the region considered, from a point on the boundary surface, and $m_1 x$, $m_2 x$ the angles which the normals to dS_1, dS_2 make with the x axis. Then

$$dy\,dz = -dS_1 \cos m_2 x = dS_2 \cos m_1 x$$

and, integrating by parts,

$$\iiint\left(\frac{\partial\phi}{\partial x}\frac{\partial\phi'}{\partial x}\right)dxdydz=\iint\left(\phi\frac{\partial\phi'}{\partial x}\right)_1^2 dydz-\iiint\left(\phi\frac{\partial^2\phi'}{\partial x^2}\right)dxdydz$$

$$=-\iint\left(\phi_2\frac{\partial\phi'_2}{\partial x}\cos m_2 x dS_1+\phi_1\frac{\partial\phi'_1}{\partial x}\cos m_1 x dS_2\right)$$

$$-\iiint\left(\phi\frac{\partial^2\phi'}{\partial x^2}\right)dxdydz$$

$$=-\iint\phi\frac{\partial\phi'}{\partial x}\cos mxdS-\iiint\phi\frac{\partial^2\phi'}{\partial x^2}dxdydz.$$

Similarly,

$$\iiint\left(\frac{\partial\phi}{\partial y}\frac{\partial\phi'}{\partial y}\right)dxdydz=-\iint\phi\frac{\partial\phi'}{\partial y}\cos mydS-\iiint\phi\frac{\partial^2\phi'}{\partial y^2}dxdydz,$$

and

$$\iiint\left(\frac{\partial\phi}{\partial z}\frac{\partial\phi'}{\partial z}\right)dxdydz=-\iint\phi\frac{\partial\phi'}{\partial z}\cos mzdS-\iiint\phi\frac{\partial^2\phi'}{\partial z^2}dxdydz.$$

Hence

$$\iiint\left(\frac{\partial\phi}{\partial x}\frac{\partial\phi'}{\partial x}+\frac{\partial\phi}{\partial y}\frac{\partial\phi'}{\partial y}+\frac{\partial\phi}{\partial z}\frac{\partial\phi'}{\partial z}\right)dxdydz$$

$$=-\iint\phi\frac{\partial\phi'}{\partial n}dS-\iiint\phi\cdot\nabla^2\phi'dxdydz, \qquad (398)$$

where

$$\nabla^2\phi'=\frac{\partial^2\phi'}{\partial x^2}+\frac{\partial^2\phi'}{\partial y^2}+\frac{\partial^2\phi'}{\partial z^2}.$$

This result is known as *Green's theorem.*

If ϕ and ϕ' are interchanged, the left-hand side of equation (398) is the same and the right-hand side becomes

$$=-\iint\phi'\frac{\partial\phi}{\partial n}dS-\iiint\phi'\nabla^2\phi dxdydz.$$

If ϕ' is constant,

$$\iint\frac{\partial\phi}{\partial n}dS=\iiint\nabla^2\phi dxdydz,$$

and since, in addition, for incompressible matter, $\nabla^2\phi=0$ from equation (393),

$$\iint\frac{\partial\phi}{\partial n}dS=0 \qquad . \quad . \quad . \quad . \quad (399)$$

If ϕ denotes a velocity potential, this result shows that the total flow of liquid into any closed region is zero, while if $\phi=\phi'$ and both are velocity potentials,

$$\iiint\left[\left(\frac{\partial\phi}{\partial x}\right)^2+\left(\frac{\partial\phi}{\partial y}\right)^2+\left(\frac{\partial\phi}{\partial z}\right)^2\right]dxdydz=-\iint\phi\frac{\partial\phi}{\partial n}dS.$$

Multiplying both sides of this equation by $\frac{1}{2}\rho$, the left-hand side is then the kinetic energy of the liquid due to impulsive pressures exerted at the boundary surface. Denoting the kinetic energy by E, we have

$$2E = -\rho \iint \phi \frac{\partial \phi}{\partial n} dS \qquad . \qquad . \qquad . \qquad (400)$$

208. Stream Function.—If we consider two fixed points A and B in the xy plane, and suppose that the motion of a liquid takes place only in this plane, the *flux*, or quantity of liquid passing in unit time across any line joining A and B, must be the same, otherwise there would be an accumulation of fluid within the region enclosed by any two lines AB. If the point B is movable, the flux across AB is a function of the position of B and is usually denoted by ψ. If the point B moves so that the value of ψ remains constant, it will trace a curve such that no fluid crosses this curve. The latter is, therefore, a stream line. Thus the curves represented by $\psi = constant$ are stream lines, and ψ is called the *stream function*.

Let B receive a small displacement, δy, parallel to the y axis, so that the increment of ψ is $\delta \psi = -u \delta y$, *i.e.*

$$u = -\frac{\partial \psi}{\partial y}.$$

Similarly $v = \frac{\partial \psi}{\partial x}$, the flow being positive if it is from right to left as seen by an observer at A looking along AB. But in irrotational motion, *i.e.* motion without rotation, $u = -\frac{\partial \phi}{\partial x}$ and $v = -\frac{\partial \phi}{\partial y}$. Thus the velocity potential and the stream function are connected by the relations,

$$\frac{\partial \phi}{\partial x} = \frac{\partial \psi}{\partial y}; \quad \frac{\partial \phi}{\partial y} = -\frac{\partial \psi}{\partial x} \qquad . \qquad . \qquad . \qquad (401)$$

and these conditions are fulfilled if

$$\phi + j\psi = f(x + jy) \qquad . \qquad . \qquad . \qquad (402)$$

Any assumption of the form given by equation (402) represents a possible case of irrotational motion.

209. The Equation of Continuity applied to Heat.—The amount of heat per unit volume is

$$Q = Q_0 + s\rho T,$$

where s is the specific heat of the substance and T is the excess temperature above that for which $Q = Q_0$. Hence the heat passing per second across the face B (Fig. 98) is

$$Q_x K_x u \delta y \delta z = -k_x \frac{\partial T}{\partial x} \delta y \delta z,$$

where k_x is the thermal conductivity in the x direction. Thus

$Q_x K_x u = -k_x \dfrac{\partial T}{\partial x}$, together with similar expressions for the flow along the y and z axes. But

$$\frac{\partial Q}{\partial t} = s\rho \frac{\partial T}{\partial t},$$

and thus the equation of continuity (373) becomes

$$\frac{\partial T}{\partial t} - \frac{m}{s\rho} - \frac{1}{s\rho}\left[\frac{\partial}{\partial x}\left(k_x \frac{\partial T}{\partial x}\right) + \frac{\partial}{\partial y}\left(k_y \frac{\partial T}{\partial y}\right) + \frac{\partial}{\partial z}\left(k_z \frac{\partial T}{\partial z}\right)\right] = 0,$$

which is the equation for the propagation of heat in an anisotropic body. For an isotropic body $k_x = k_y = k_z = k$, and

$$\frac{\partial T}{\partial t} - \frac{m}{s\rho} - \frac{k}{s\rho}\left[\frac{\partial^2 T}{\partial x^2} + \frac{\partial^2 T}{\partial y^2} + \frac{\partial^2 T}{\partial z^2}\right] = 0, \qquad . \qquad . \qquad (403)$$

where $\dfrac{k}{s\rho}$ is termed the thermal diffusivity.

In spherical co-ordinates this equation of heat flow is

$$\frac{\partial T}{\partial t} - \frac{m}{s\rho} - \frac{k}{s\rho}\left[\frac{\partial^2 T}{\partial r^2} + \frac{2}{r}\frac{\partial T}{\partial r} + \frac{1}{r^2}\frac{\partial^2 T}{\partial \theta^2} + \frac{1}{r^2 \sin^2 \theta}\frac{\partial^2 T}{\partial \beta^2}\right.$$

$$\left. + \frac{\cot \theta}{r^2}\frac{\partial T}{\partial \theta}\right] = 0, \qquad . \qquad . \qquad (404)$$

and in cylindrical polar co-ordinates

$$\frac{\partial T}{\partial t} - \frac{m}{s\rho} - \frac{k}{s\rho}\left[\frac{\partial^2 T}{\partial r^2} + \frac{1}{r}\frac{\partial T}{\partial r} + \frac{1}{r^2}\frac{\partial^2 T}{\partial \theta^2} + \frac{\partial^2 T}{\partial z^2}\right] = 0.$$

If the flow of heat is radial, $\dfrac{\partial T}{\partial \theta} = \dfrac{\partial T}{\partial \beta} = 0$, and equation (404) reduces to

$$\frac{\partial T}{\partial t} - \frac{m}{s\rho} - \frac{k}{s\rho}\left[\frac{\partial^2 T}{\partial r^2} + \frac{2}{r}\frac{\partial T}{\partial r}\right] = 0 \qquad . \qquad . \qquad (405)$$

To illustrate the application of thermal flow, consider a sphere having an initial arbitrary symmetrical distribution of temperature, the surface radiating into surroundings at zero temperature. If ε is the emissivity, the heat flux outwards from the surface per second is $4\pi R^2 \varepsilon T$, R being the radius of the sphere. The boundary condition to be satisfied is

$$-k \frac{\partial T}{\partial r} = \varepsilon T,$$

or,

$$\frac{\partial T}{\partial r} + \frac{\varepsilon}{k}T = 0 \qquad . \qquad . \qquad . \qquad (406)$$

But $m = 0$ and, as the flow is radial, we have, from equation (405),

$$\frac{\partial T}{\partial t} = \sigma\left[\frac{\partial^2 T}{\partial r^2} + \frac{2}{r}\frac{\partial T}{\partial r}\right],$$

where σ is the diffusivity. This equation may be written

$$\frac{\partial}{\partial t}(rT)=\sigma\frac{\partial^2}{\partial r^2}(rT),$$

a solution of which is

$$rT=Fe^{bt},$$

where F is a function of r such that

$$bF=\sigma\frac{\partial^2F}{\partial r^2}.$$

Negative values of b, only, are permissible, and since σ is positive, we conclude that F is a circular function. Let

$$F=A\ cos\ nr+B\ sin\ nr,$$

so that $b=-\sigma n^2$, and we can express a particular value of T by

$$T=\frac{1}{r}e^{-\sigma n^2 t}(A\ cos\ nr+B\ sin\ nr).$$

The value of T which expresses the temperature at the centre, $r=0$, cannot be infinite, and therefore $A=0$, and substituting the value of T in the boundary condition equation (406),

$$\frac{nR}{tan\ nR}=1-\frac{\varepsilon R}{k}, \qquad . \qquad . \qquad . \quad (407)$$

of which there is an infinite number of roots which may be obtained by graphical construction. Hence the temperature at any point distant r from the centre of the sphere, after an interval of t seconds, is

$$T=\frac{1}{r}Be^{-\sigma n^2 t}sin\ nr,$$

where n satisfies the relation (407).

210. The Equation of Continuity applied to Electricity.— Considering the flow of electricity along the x axis and remembering Ohm's law,

$$Q_xK_xu\delta y\delta z=-\mu_x\frac{\partial E}{\partial x}\delta y\delta z,$$

where μ_x is the electrical conductivity along the x direction, and $\frac{\partial E}{\partial x}$ is the potential gradient. Thus the equation of continuity becomes

$$\frac{\partial Q}{\partial t}-m-\left[\frac{\partial}{\partial x}\left(\mu_x\frac{\partial E}{\partial x}\right)+\frac{\partial}{\partial y}\left(\mu_y\frac{\partial E}{\partial y}\right)+\frac{\partial}{\partial z}\left(\mu_z\frac{\partial E}{\partial z}\right)\right]=0,$$

and if the electrical conductivity is the same in all directions this reduces to

$$\frac{\partial Q}{\partial t}-m-\mu\left[\frac{\partial^2 E}{\partial x^2}+\frac{\partial^2 E}{\partial y^2}+\frac{\partial^2 E}{\partial z^2}\right]=0.$$

In free space, where there is no electricity, $m=0$ and $\dfrac{\partial Q}{\partial t}=0$, so that

$$\frac{\partial^2 E}{\partial x^2}+\frac{\partial^2 E}{\partial y^2}+\frac{\partial^2 E}{\partial z^2}=0.$$

This is often written $\nabla^2 E=0$ and is called *Laplace's equation.* The flow of electricity in spherical polar co-ordinates is

$$\frac{\partial Q}{\partial t}-m-\mu\left[\frac{\partial^2 E}{\partial r^2}+\frac{2}{r}\frac{\partial E}{\partial r}+\frac{1}{r^2}\frac{\partial^2 E}{\partial \theta^2}+\frac{1}{r^2\,sin^2\,\theta}\frac{\partial^2 E}{\partial\beta^2}+\frac{cot\,\theta}{r^2}\frac{\partial E}{\partial\theta}\right]=0,$$

and in cylindrical polar co-ordinates

$$\frac{\partial Q}{\partial t}-m-\mu\left[\frac{\partial^2 E}{\partial r^2}+\frac{1}{r}\frac{\partial E}{\partial r}+\frac{1}{r^2}\frac{\partial^2 E}{\partial\theta^2}+\frac{\partial^2 E}{\partial z^2}\right]=0.$$

211. The Equation of Continuity applied to Wave Motion. —Suppose that the particle velocity constituting the wave motion is parallel to the x axis and that there is no impressed force. The equation of continuity (374) is then

$$\frac{\partial\rho}{\partial t}+\frac{\partial}{\partial x}(\rho u)=0, \quad . \qquad . \qquad . \qquad . \qquad (408)$$

and the equation of motion (379)

$$\frac{\partial u}{\partial t}+u\frac{\partial u}{\partial x}+\frac{1}{\rho}\frac{\partial p}{\partial x}=0 \qquad . \qquad . \qquad . \qquad (409)$$

Let $p=c^2(\rho-\rho_0)$ where ρ_0 is the density at a certain standard pressure, then, from equations (409) and (408),

$$\frac{\partial u}{\partial t}+u\frac{\partial u}{\partial x}=-\frac{1}{\rho}\frac{\partial p}{\partial x}=-\frac{c^2}{\rho}\frac{\partial\rho}{\partial x},$$

and

$$\frac{\partial\rho}{\partial t}+u\frac{\partial\rho}{\partial x}=-\rho\frac{\partial u}{\partial x}.$$

Differentiating the first of these equations with respect to t, the second with respect to x, and equating

$$\frac{\partial^2 u}{\partial t^2}=c^2\frac{\partial^2 u}{\partial x^2},$$

neglecting quantities of the second order of smallness. A solution of this equation is

$$u=f_1(ct+x)+f_2(ct-x),$$

the physical interpretation of which is that $f_1(ct+x)$ represents a wave travelling with velocity c in the negative direction of the x axis, and $f_2(ct-x)$ is a wave travelling with the same velocity in the positive direction.

EXAMPLES

1. A mass of liquid rotates with angular velocity ω about a vertical axis. Find the equation of the free surface neglecting the restraining action of the supporting surfaces.

[$\omega^2(x^2+y^2)=2gz$; where z is vertical.]

2. Water is maintained at a height of 15 cm. in a vessel which has a small circular hole in its thin horizontal base. The radius of the hole is 1 mm., and the area of the free surface is 30 sq. cm. Find the rate at which the liquid leaves the vessel if the coefficient of contraction is 0·624. Would you expect the viscosity to affect the result materially?

[3·36 c.c. per sec. ; No.]

3. If the vessel in the previous question is cylindrical and the supply of water to it is stopped, find the time in which it will be emptied. Show, also, that when the depth of liquid is h the rate of fall of the upper surface is given by:—

$$dh/dt = 0{\cdot}0289\sqrt{h} \text{ cm./sec.} \qquad [4 \text{ min. } 28 \text{ sec.}]$$

4. A vessel is symmetrical about a vertical axis through a small hole in its base. Show that the radius r of cross-section of the vessel at a height h above the bottom can be expressed in the form $h=k(r^4-B)$, k and B being constants, if the surface of a liquid in the vessel descends with uniform velocity as the liquid empties itself through the hole.

5. Air at a pressure P issues through a small orifice under adiabatic conditions into a region where the pressure is p. Show that, if P exceeds $2p$, the velocity V of the air at the orifice is given by:—

$$V^2 = 2\gamma P/\rho(\gamma+1)$$

where ρ is the air density at pressure P and γ is the ratio of the specific heats of air at constant pressure and constant volume.

6. If the temperature of the air in the vessel in the previous question is $10°$ C., $\gamma=1{\cdot}41$, the air density at N.T.P. is 1·29 gm. per litre, its specific heat at constant volume is 0·172 cals. and $J=4{\cdot}18\times10^7$, find the temperature of the air at the orifice when the pressure inside the vessel is one atmosphere and the pressure outside is zero. The energy gain in a tube of flow is obtained at the expense of thermal energy of the gas. [$-3{\cdot}7°$ C.]

7. Liquid flows in streamline motion through a horizontal tapering tube of circular section, the section at the exit end having half the inlet area. If the tube length is L, inlet area A, input velocity V, pressure at entrance P, and density of liquid ρ, find (a) the velocity v at a distance x from the entrance, (b) the pressure at the same point, (c) the pressure at the exit end.

$$\left[v = \frac{2LV}{2L-x}, \quad P - \frac{\rho V^2 x}{2}\frac{(4L-x)}{(2L-x)^2}, \quad P - \frac{3}{2}\rho V^2. \right]$$

8. A liquid of density ρ flows along a uniform straight tube and loses energy due to viscosity at the rate of e units per unit volume per unit length of the tube. What must be the inclination of the tube to the horizontal if the pressure is uniform throughout the liquid?

$$\left[\tan\theta = \frac{e}{\rho g}. \right]$$

CHAPTER XIV

WAVE MOTION

212. Controlling Factors.—A wave is the continuous transfer of a particular state from one part of a medium to another. The medium itself is not transported from place to place, but the condition is propagated through it. For example, in water waves small bodies floating on the surface are not moved onwards by the waves. They appear to be carried forwards a small distance on the crest of a wave and backwards when in the trough. Thus the elevated masses are not moving bodily forwards, and, on the whole, the waves leave the floating bodies in very nearly the same positions.

When a wave moves through a liquid the characteristics of the medium which may influence its motion are :—

(a) The *depth* and other *boundary conditions* which impose limitations at the walls and base of the containing vessel.

(b) *Gravitation*, since the changed profile or contour of the surface involves work against gravity.

(c) *Surface Tension*, because the pressure under a curved surface is different from that beneath a flat surface.

(d) *Viscosity*, which is the dissipative energy agent.

In some circumstances one, or more, of these factors becomes negligible compared with the others. For example, with waves of long wave-length, or, as they are termed, *long waves*, the curvature at any point is small, and the surface tension effect may be neglected compared with the *gravity control* ; while in the opposite case of very short waves, or *ripples*, surface tension is the main controlling factor.

Although in practice no fluid is capable of perfectly frictionless motion, it is convenient in considering wave motion to ignore the effect of viscosity and to deal with an imaginary perfectly mobile liquid. Such a medium is termed a *perfect fluid*, and it is to be expected therefore that the results deduced for this hypothetical substance will, in special circumstances, be inapplicable to a practical case. In general, however, the effect of viscosity on wave motion is sufficiently small for the theoretical conclusions to be true within reasonable limits.

213. Long Waves in Canals.—If the wave-length is great compared with the wave amplitude, surface tension may be ignored, gravity and the boundary conditions being the controlling factors. Further, it will be assumed that the surface is sufficiently extensive for the wall effects to be neglected, and thus the only relevant boundary conditions will be due to the limited depth.

Let the axis of x (Fig. 102) be parallel to the length of the canal, that of y vertical and upwards, and suppose that the motion takes

place in these two directions x, y. The base of the canal is Ox,
and EF is the undisturbed level of the surface. The depth of the
liquid is h, and the ordinate of the free surface corresponding to
abscissa x at time t is denoted by $h+\eta$, where h is the ordinate in
the undisturbed state. Neglecting the vertical acceleration of the

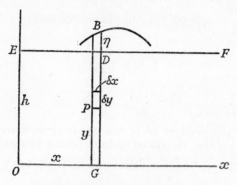

FIG. 102.—CANAL WAVES.

fluid particles, *i.e.* assuming that the pressure at any point (x, y) is
practically equal to the hydrostatic pressure due to its depth below
the free surface,

$$p-p_0=g\rho(h+\eta-y),$$

where p_0 is the pressure at the surface. Hence

$$\frac{\partial p}{\partial x}=g\rho\frac{\partial \eta}{\partial x}.$$

Thus the horizontal acceleration is the same for all particles in a plane
normal to x, and all particles which once lie in such a plane do so
always. In other words, the horizontal velocity u is a function of x
and t only, and so the equation of horizontal motion is

$$\frac{\partial u}{\partial t}+u\frac{\partial u}{\partial x}=-\frac{1}{\rho}\frac{\partial p}{\partial x}.$$

If we ignore $u\dfrac{\partial u}{\partial x}$, which is a product of small quantities,

$$\frac{\partial u}{\partial t}=-\frac{1}{\rho}\frac{\partial p}{\partial x}=-g\frac{\partial \eta}{\partial x} \qquad . \quad . \quad . \quad (410)$$

Consider the motion of the elementary volume BG, of width δx,
height $h+\eta$, and depth, perpendicular to the plane of the figure,
unity. Its original volume is $h\delta x$, but after a time t, the volume,
originally bounded by x and $x+\delta x$, is bounded by the planes at
$x+\xi$ and $x+\delta x+\xi+\dfrac{\partial \xi}{\partial x}\delta x$, where ξ is the horizontal displacement

of the particles in plane x, while the surface rises to $h+\eta$. If the liquid is incompressible, the volume is unchanged and

$$h\delta x=[h+\eta]\left[\delta x+\frac{\partial\xi}{\partial x}\delta x\right],$$

or,

$$\eta\delta x+h\frac{\partial\xi}{\partial x}\delta x=0,\quad\text{approximately.}$$

Thus

$$\eta=-h\frac{\partial\xi}{\partial x},$$

and

$$\frac{\partial\eta}{\partial x}=-h\frac{\partial^2\xi}{\partial x^2}\quad.\quad\quad.\quad\quad.\quad\quad(411)$$

Since this is independent of y, the whole strip moves together.

The force on the elementary volume acting along the x direction is $\rho h\frac{\partial^2\xi}{\partial t^2}\delta x$. But the force on the element at P, due to the pressure acting along Ox, is $-\frac{\partial p}{\partial x}\delta x\delta y$, *i.e.* from equation (410) $-\rho g\frac{\partial\eta}{\partial x}\delta x\delta y$, and the total force acting on the whole strip is $-\rho g\frac{\partial\eta}{\partial x}\delta x h$. So that $\frac{\partial^2\xi}{\partial t^2}=-g\frac{\partial\eta}{\partial x}$, and from equation (411)

$$\frac{\partial^2\xi}{\partial t^2}=gh\frac{\partial^2\xi}{\partial x^2}\quad.\quad\quad.\quad\quad.\quad\quad(412)$$

This result may also be deduced from equations (410) and (411) by substituting $\frac{\partial\xi}{\partial t}=u$.

The equation (412) is of a well-known type which occurs in several problems. The complete solution of it is

$$\xi=F(x-ct)+f(x+ct)\quad.\quad\quad.\quad\quad.\quad(413)$$

The first term represents a wave travelling along the positive direction of x with a constant velocity c, and the second term indicates a similar progressive wave moving along the negative direction of x with an equal velocity. Thus it appears that any motion whatever of the fluid, subject to the conditions stated in this article, may be regarded as composed of waves of these two kinds. From equations (412) and (413) we see that the velocity, c, of these *canal waves* is given by

$$c=\sqrt{gh}\quad.\quad\quad.\quad\quad.\quad\quad(414)$$

The motion of long waves may also be investigated [1] by making the co-ordinates refer to the individual particles of the fluid. As

---

[1] Airy, *Encyc. Metrop.*, Art. 192 (1845).

before, consider the liquid contained between two planes perpendicular to the x axis, and situated at x and $x+\delta x$. After a time t let the abscissæ of these planes be $x+\xi$ and $x+\xi+\delta x+\dfrac{\partial \xi}{\partial x}\delta x$. The mass of liquid contained between the boundary planes is $\rho A \delta x$, where A is the area of cross-section of the canal. Then

$$\rho A \frac{\partial^2 \xi}{\partial t^2}\delta x = -\frac{\partial p}{\partial x}(A+B\eta)\delta x,$$

η as before being the elevation of the free surface above the equilibrium level, and B the width of the surface, so that

$$\frac{\partial p}{\partial x}=g\rho\frac{\partial \eta}{\partial x},$$

and the equation of motion is

$$\frac{\partial^2 \xi}{\partial t^2}=-g\frac{\partial \eta}{\partial x}\left(1+\frac{B}{A}\eta\right) \qquad . \qquad . \qquad . \quad (415)$$

But in the position of equilibrium the volume of liquid between the planes is $A\delta x$, and at a time t the distance between the boundary planes is $\delta x+\dfrac{\partial \xi}{\partial x}\delta x$. As the cross-section of the liquid is $A+B\eta$,

$$(A+B\eta)\left(\delta x+\frac{\partial \xi}{x}\delta x\right)=A\delta x,$$

or,

$$\frac{B\eta}{A}=-\frac{\partial \xi}{\partial x}\left(1+\frac{\partial \xi}{\partial x}\right)^{-1} \qquad . \qquad . \qquad . \quad (416)$$

Eliminating η between equations (415) and (416),

$$\frac{\partial^2 \xi}{\partial t^2}=\frac{gA}{B}\frac{\partial^2 \xi}{\partial x^2}\left(1+\frac{\partial \xi}{\partial x}\right)^{-3}.$$

Airy has discussed the solution of this equation, and he shows that such waves cannot be propagated to infinity without change of form. If we neglect the product of small quantities,

$$\frac{\partial^2 \xi}{\partial t^2}=\frac{gA}{B}\frac{\partial^2 \xi}{\partial x^2}, \qquad . \qquad . \qquad . \qquad . \quad (417)$$

the solution of which represents *two* progressive waves travelling in opposite directions with velocity

$$c=\sqrt{\frac{gA}{B}},$$

and if the canal is of rectangular cross-section,

$$c=\sqrt{gh}.$$

214. Steady Motion.—The laws of wave propagation may also be investigated by means of the following artifice.[1] Consider a wave

[1] Rayleigh, *Phil. Mag.*, ser. 5, **1**, 257 (1876).

travelling unchanged in shape with a constant velocity c. Impress on the whole system a negative velocity c, so that it is brought to rest. The motion then becomes steady, and assuming $A=Bh$ we have, from equation (416),

$$\eta=-h\frac{\partial\xi}{\partial x}.$$

But

$$\xi=F(x-ct),$$

so

$$\frac{\partial\xi}{\partial t}=\frac{c\eta}{h},$$

and the new horizontal velocity is $\frac{c\eta}{h}-c$. Since the wave form has been reduced to rest, the horizontal vibration is independent of the time and the motion is steady to a first approximation, *i.e.* the velocity over any vertical section is the same.

The equation of continuity in the steady state is

$$ch=q(h+\eta),$$

where q is the horizontal velocity at the point where the elevation is η. Along the wave surface, which is now a *stream line*, we can apply Bernoulli's theorem,

$$\frac{p}{\rho}+\tfrac{1}{2}q^2+gy=constant,$$

or,

$$\frac{p}{\rho}=-\tfrac{1}{2}\frac{c^2h^2}{(h+\eta)^2}-g(h+\eta)+constant \quad . \quad . \quad (418)$$

The pressure at the wave surface must be constant, and c must be chosen to satisfy this condition. Expanding the relation (418)

$$\frac{p}{\rho}=-\tfrac{1}{2}c^2-gh+\frac{\eta}{h}(c^2-gh)-\tfrac{3}{2}\frac{c^2\eta^2}{h^2}+ \ . \ . \ . \ +constant.$$

But $\frac{\eta}{h}$ is supposed to be small, and therefore the pressure will be constant to a first approximation if we take $c^2=gh$, which agrees with our former result.

To obtain a more correct solution put $c^2=gh+\delta$, then

$$\frac{p}{\rho}=constant+\frac{\eta}{h}\left(\delta-\tfrac{3}{2}gh\frac{\eta}{h}\right)-\tfrac{3}{2}\frac{\eta^2\delta}{h^2}.$$

Thus p is constant if $\delta=\tfrac{3}{2}g\eta$, η being positive, and it is also constant if $\delta=-\tfrac{3}{2}g\eta$, η being negative. Hence a *wave of elevation* moves slightly *faster* than one of *depression*.

Canals of Finite Length.—Considering the solution of equation (412)

$$\xi=F(ct+x)+f(ct-x),$$

where $c^2=gh$.

If the canal has a finite length, l, then $\xi=0$ at $x=0$ and $x=l$, so that
$$f(ct)=-F(ct),$$
and
$$\xi=f(ct-x)-f(ct+x).$$
Also
$$0=f(ct-l)-f(ct+l).$$
Now if
$$f(z)=f(z+2l),$$
$f(z)$ must be a periodic function of $2l$, i.e.
$$f(z)=C \sin mz,$$
and
$$f(z+2l)=C \sin m(z+2l),$$
so that
$$2ml=2n\pi,$$
or,
$$m=\frac{\pi n}{l},$$
and
$$f(z)=C \sin\frac{\pi nz}{l}.$$

Hence
$$\xi=C\left[\sin\frac{\pi n}{l}(ct-x)-\sin\frac{\pi n}{l}(ct+x)\right]=2C \sin\frac{n\pi x}{l}\cos\frac{n\pi ct}{l}.$$

To find the profile of the surface we have $\eta=-h\frac{\partial\xi}{\partial x}$, thus
$$\eta=\frac{2\pi Cnh}{l}\cos\frac{n\pi x}{l}\cos\frac{n\pi ct}{l}.$$

If we take $n=1$ and $n=2$, we see that the time-interval between successive maximum values of η at the points of greatest disturbance is $\frac{l}{c}$. This is sometimes quoted as the time-interval between successive " *high tides.*"

Certain assumptions were made in deducing the expression for the velocity of canal waves. In the first place it was shown that the horizontal amplitude was constant throughout a vertical section, but it is probable that the ignored viscosity effect would seriously modify this result, since in the case of steady flow the layer of liquid in contact with the containing vessel is at rest. It has been shown, however, that this boundary layer is really moving over a series of *vortex filaments* which fulfil the function of roller bearings. The existence of these rotatory elements is shown by the rippled appearance of a nearly level beach when the sea recedes.

Secondly, it was assumed that the usual expression for the increase of static pressure with depth was applicable. This assumption is not strictly true, since the liquid has vertical acceleration which must be generated by the pressure, and so conditions are different from those of a liquid at rest. Thus, if we consider the vertical motion of an element at P (Fig. 102),

$$\rho\frac{\partial v}{\partial t}+\frac{\partial p}{\partial y}+g\rho=0,$$

where v is the vertical velocity along Oy. Integrating from P to the surface,

$$p=p_0+g\rho[h+\eta-y]+\int_y^{h+\eta}\rho\frac{\partial v}{\partial t}dy,$$

and the true pressure at P is equal to the static pressure approximately, if $\int_y^{h+\eta}\frac{\partial v}{\partial t}dy$ is small compared with $g\eta$, i.e. if $(h+\eta)a$ can be neglected, where a is the maximum vertical acceleration. But $a=\left(\dfrac{2\pi}{t_0}\right)^2\eta$ where t_0 is the periodic time of particle vibration, so that $h\left(\dfrac{2\pi}{t_0}\right)^2$ must be negligible compared with g, or h^2 must be very small compared with $\dfrac{\lambda^2}{4\pi^2}$, where λ is the wave-length of the canal waves.

215. Particle Motion.—Each particle in the liquid executes both horizontal and vertical oscillations about its mean position, the displacement along the x axis being ξ. But $\dfrac{\partial^2\xi}{\partial t^2}=gh\dfrac{\partial^2\xi}{\partial x^2}$, and if the vibration is simple harmonic, as it is in the simplest case,

$$\xi=A\ cos\ 2\pi\left[\frac{t}{t_0}-\frac{x}{\lambda}\right] \qquad . \qquad . \qquad . \quad (419)$$

where A is the horizontal amplitude. Hence

$$\eta=-h\frac{\partial\xi}{\partial x}=-hA\left(\frac{2\pi}{\lambda}\right)sin\ 2\pi\left[\frac{t}{t_0}-\frac{x}{\lambda}\right],$$

and if we now restrict η to mean the vertical displacement at P,

$$\eta=-yA\left(\frac{2\pi}{\lambda}\right)sin\ 2\pi\left[\frac{t}{t_0}-\frac{x}{\lambda}\right] \qquad . \qquad . \quad (420)$$

Thus, from equations (419) and (420),

$$\frac{\xi^2}{A^2}+\frac{\eta^2}{\left(\dfrac{2\pi y}{\lambda}\right)^2 A^2}=1,$$

which represents an *ellipse* of *vertical semi-axis* $\dfrac{2\pi A}{\lambda}y$ and *horizontal semi-axis* A. The vertical amplitude at the bottom of the canal is zero, and the particles execute elliptic orbits of equal horizontal displacement, the vertical displacements continually decreasing with increasing depth. This is illustrated in Fig. 103 (*a*).

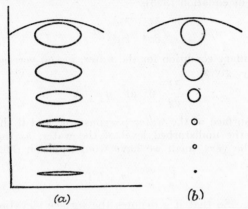

FIG. 103.—PARTICLE MOTION IN CANAL AND DEEP-WATER WAVES.

Additional Features of Canal Waves.—When a vessel travels over the surface of a canal it creates waves, and their associated energy must be obtained from the motive power driving the vessel. If the vessel's speed is greater than *c*, the velocity of the waves, new waves are being continually formed as the vessel advances into still water and there is a corresponding continuous output of energy. Again, if the speed is less than *c*, the waves formed travel away from the vessel, taking their associated energy with them and, as before, the energy drainage is maintained. The speed most economical in motive energy is the natural velocity of the canal waves, since in this case only one "*group of waves*" is formed, and this group travels along with the vessel.

As sea waves advance to the shore their depth is continually decreasing, and thus they tend to overtake those in front. The inertia effect of the crests causes them to continue at a speed greater than that of the troughs, and so the waves "*break.*" In a similar manner a line of waves advancing to the shore in an inclined direction tend to veer round into a line parallel with the shore. Those parts of the wave nearest to the land are retarded owing to the decreased depth, and thus the wave-front is refracted in a direction parallel to the shore.

216. Surface Waves.—Waves formed on relatively deep water are characterised by the agitation rapidly diminishing in amplitude as we pass downwards from the surface, and we can no longer neglect the vertical acceleration.

Consider oscillations of a horizontal sheet of water under no force but gravity, and suppose that the motion is two-dimensional, *i.e.*

the crests and troughs of the waves are all parallel to one another, one of the motions (x) being horizontal and the other (y) vertical. As the motion is generated from rest by the action of ordinary forces we have, from equation (393),

$$\frac{\partial^2 \phi}{\partial x^2} + \frac{\partial^2 \phi}{\partial y^2} = 0 \quad . \quad . \quad . \quad . \quad (421)$$

and the boundary condition for the water, *i.e.* no vertical motion at the boundary, gives

$$\frac{\partial \phi}{\partial y} = 0 \quad \text{at} \quad y = -h \quad . \quad . \quad . \quad (422)$$

At the free surface of the water p=constant, and if the origin, O, be taken at the undisturbed level of the water, as the motion is assumed to be very small we have from equation (392),

$$\frac{p}{\rho} = \frac{\partial \phi}{\partial t} - gy + F(t) \quad . \quad . \quad . \quad (423)$$

where $\Omega = gy$. So that if η denotes the surface elevation at time t above the point (x, 0),

$$\eta = \frac{1}{g} \left(\frac{\partial \phi}{\partial t} \right)_{y=\eta} , \quad . \quad . \quad . \quad . \quad (424)$$

assuming that $F(t)$ and $\dfrac{p}{\rho}$ are merged into the value $\dfrac{\partial \phi}{\partial t}$.

The boundary surface equation may be written $y - \eta = 0$ and is equivalent to the expression (387) for the boundary surface. Hence, since $p =$ constant represents the free surface, we have, from equation (387),

$$\frac{\partial p}{\partial t} + u \frac{\partial p}{\partial x} + v \frac{\partial p}{\partial y} = 0 \quad . \quad . \quad . \quad (425)$$

Differentiating equation (423) with respect to t and substituting in equation (425)

$$\rho \frac{\partial^2 \phi}{\partial t^2} - g\rho \frac{\partial y}{\partial t} - \frac{\partial \phi}{\partial x} \left[\rho \frac{\partial^2 \phi}{\partial x \partial t} - g\rho \frac{\partial y}{\partial x} \right] - \frac{\partial \phi}{\partial y} \left[\rho \frac{\partial^2 \phi}{\partial y \partial t} - g\rho \frac{\partial y}{\partial x} \right] = 0,$$

or,

$$\frac{\partial^2 \phi}{\partial t^2} - \frac{\partial \phi}{\partial x} \cdot \frac{\partial^2 \phi}{\partial x \partial t} - \frac{\partial \phi}{\partial y} \left(\frac{\partial^2 \phi}{\partial x \partial t} - g \right) = 0,$$

remembering that $u = -\dfrac{\partial \phi}{\partial x}$ and $v = -\dfrac{\partial \phi}{\partial y}$. Neglecting terms of the second order of smallness,

$$\frac{\partial^2 \phi}{\partial t^2} + g \frac{\partial \phi}{\partial y} = 0, \quad . \quad . \quad . \quad . \quad (426)$$

which must be satisfied at $y = 0$.

Assuming that we are dealing with simple harmonic waves, ϕ is a simple harmonic function of x and t, or

$$\phi = f \cos 2\pi \left(\frac{t}{t_0} - \frac{x}{\lambda} \right),$$

which may be written

$$\phi = f \cos (kx - \omega t),$$

where f is a function of y. Substituting in equation (421)

$$\frac{d^2 f}{dy^2} - k^2 f = 0,$$

a general solution of which is

$$f = Pe^{ky} + Qe^{-ky},$$

so that

$$\phi = (Pe^{ky} + Qe^{-ky}) \cos (kx - \omega t). \qquad . \qquad . \qquad (427)$$

If the water is of depth h and is unlimited in extent, or is contained in a canal with parallel sides at right angles to the crests and troughs,

$$\frac{\partial \phi}{\partial y} = 0 \quad \text{at} \quad y = -h.$$

Thus, from equation (427),

$$Pe^{kh} = Qe^{-kh} = \frac{C}{2}, \text{ say,}$$

and

$$\phi = C \cosh k(y+h) \cos (kx - \omega t). \qquad . \qquad . \qquad (428)$$

Substituting this value of ϕ in equation (426) and putting $y = 0$,

$$\omega^2 = gk \tanh kh \qquad . \qquad . \qquad . \qquad (429)$$

But the period of the waves is $\frac{2\pi}{\omega}$ and their wave-length $\frac{2\pi}{k}$, so that

their velocity is given by $\frac{\omega}{k} = c$, say. Hence

$$c^2 = \frac{g}{k} \tanh kh.$$

From equations (428) and (424)

$$\eta = \frac{\omega}{g} C \cosh kh \sin (kx - \omega t) = A \sin (kx - \omega t), \qquad . \qquad (430)$$

where

$$A = \frac{\omega C \cosh kh}{g}, \qquad . \qquad . \qquad . \qquad (431)$$

and is the amplitude of the waves.

When the wave-length is very small compared with the depth, i.e. for *deep water waves*, kh is large and $\tanh kh = 1$, so that

$$\omega^2 = gk,$$

and the velocity of deep water waves is given by

$$c^2 = \frac{g}{k} = \frac{g\lambda}{2\pi}.$$

In the case of long waves in shallow water $\frac{h}{\lambda}$ is small, $tanh \; kh = kh$
and $$c^2 = gh,$$
which is the expression for the velocity of canal waves obtained previously.

From equations (428), (429), and (431)

$$\phi = \frac{A\omega}{k} \cdot \frac{cosh \; k(y+h)}{sinh \; kh} \; cos \; (kx - \omega t), \qquad . \qquad . \qquad (432)$$

and

$$\phi = \frac{Ag}{\omega} \cdot \frac{cosh \; k(y+h)}{cosh \; kh} \; cos \; (kx - \omega t), \qquad . \qquad . \qquad (433)$$

But

$$\frac{dx}{dt} = -\frac{\partial \phi}{\partial x} = \frac{kAg}{\omega} \cdot \frac{cosh \; k(y+h)}{cosh \; kh} \; sin \; (kx - \omega t),$$

$$\frac{dy}{dt} = -\frac{\partial \phi}{\partial y} = -\frac{kAg}{\omega} \cdot \frac{sinh \; k(y+h)}{cosh \; kh} \; cos \; (kx - \omega t),$$

i.e.

$$x = \frac{kAg}{\omega^2} \cdot \frac{cosh \; k(y+h)}{cosh \; kh} \; cos \; (kx - \omega t),$$

$$y = \frac{kAg}{\omega^2} \cdot \frac{sinh \; k(y+h)}{cosh \; kh} \; sin \; (kx - \omega t).$$

Squaring, adding, and remembering that $\omega^2 = gk \; tanh \; kh$,

$$\frac{x^2}{cosh^2 \; k(y+h)} + \frac{y^2}{sinh^2 \; k(y+h)} = \frac{A^2}{sinh^2 \; kh},$$

and each particle describes an *ellipse* about its mean position, the semi-axes, horizontal and vertical, of the elliptic orbits being

$$\frac{A \; cosh \; k(y+h)}{sinh \; kh}, \qquad \frac{A \; sinh \; k(y+h)}{sinh \; kh},$$

respectively. Both these values diminish from the surface to the bottom $(y = -h)$ where the second one vanishes. Passing from the surface to the bottom, the horizontal amplitude decreases in the ratio $cosh \; kh : 1$, and the vertical amplitude diminishes from A to zero. Comparing these expressions for x and y with equation (430), a surface particle on a crest moves in the direction of wave propagation, but a particle at a trough moves in the opposite direction.

When h becomes large, e^{-kh} is very small and may be neglected so that under these conditions

$$x = Ae^{ky} \; cos \; (kx - \omega t), \qquad y = Ae^{ky} \; sin \; (kx - \omega t),$$

since $$\frac{\omega^2}{kg \; cosh \; kh} = \frac{1}{sinh \; kh}.$$

Each particle therefore describes a circle of radius Ae^{ky} and the radii of the circles diminish rapidly as h increases. These circular orbits occur, practically, for values of h greater than half a wave-length (Fig. 103) (b).

217. Energy of Progressive Waves.—The potential energy of a system of waves due to the elevation and depression of the fluid above and below the level of the undisturbed surface is, per unit width, given by

$$g\rho \int\int y\,dx\,dy,$$

where the integration limits are for y, o and η, and for x, over the whole length of the waves, so that the potential energy is

$$\tfrac{1}{2}g\rho \int \eta^2 dx.$$

Consider a train of progressive waves at the surface of water of depth h. Representing the wave profile by

$$\eta = A \ sin \ (kx - \omega t),$$

and remembering that

$$\phi = \frac{Ag}{\omega} \frac{cosh \ k(y+h)}{cosh \ kh} \ cos \ (kx - \omega t),$$

the potential energy of the liquid, per wave-length, between two vertical planes unit distance apart, the planes being parallel to the propagation direction, is

$$\int_0^\lambda \frac{g\rho\eta^2}{2} dx = \frac{g\rho A^2 \lambda}{4}.$$

But from equation (400) the kinetic energy of this mass of liquid is

$$\tfrac{1}{2}\rho \int_0^h \int_0^\lambda \left\{ \left(\frac{\partial\phi}{\partial x}\right)^2 + \left(\frac{\partial\phi}{\partial y}\right)^2 \right\} dx\,dy,$$

and by Green's theorem this is equal to

$$\tfrac{1}{2}\rho \int \phi \frac{\partial\phi}{\partial n} ds,$$

where the integral is taken along the profile and dn is measured normal to the surface of the liquid. For very small values of n this may be written

$$\tfrac{1}{2}\rho \int_0^\lambda \phi \left(\frac{\partial\phi}{\partial y}\right)_{y=0} dx = \tfrac{1}{2}g\rho A^2 \int_0^\lambda cos^2 \ (kx - \omega t) \ dx = \tfrac{1}{4}g\rho A^2\lambda,$$

so that the total energy per wave-length is $\tfrac{1}{2}g\rho A^2\lambda$, and half of it is kinetic and half potential.

218. Stationary Waves.—If two simple harmonic progressive waves of the same amplitude, wave-length, and period travel in opposite directions, the resultant disturbance in a medium through which the waves travel may be represented by

$$y = A \sin (kx - \omega t) + A \sin (kx + \omega t),$$

i.e. by

$$y = A_1 \sin kx \cos \omega t.$$

This represents a system of "*stationary*" or "*standing*" *waves* of wave-length $\lambda = \dfrac{2\pi}{k}$ and vertical amplitude A_1. At any instant the profile is a sine curve, but the amplitude—$A_1 \cos \omega t$—varies continuously. The velocity potential for such a system can be deduced, therefore, by regarding the system as the result of superposing two such trains of waves, and as ϕ must satisfy the conditions in equations (421), (422),

$$\phi = \frac{A_1 g}{\omega} \frac{\cosh k(y+h)}{\cosh kh} \sin kx \sin \omega t.$$

To find the paths of the particles of liquid,

$$\frac{dy}{dt} = -\frac{\partial \phi}{\partial y} = -\frac{A_1 gk}{\omega} \frac{\sinh k(y+h)}{\cosh kh} \sin kx \sin \omega t,$$

$$\frac{dx}{dt} = -\frac{\partial \phi}{\partial x} = -\frac{A_1 gk}{\omega} \frac{\cosh k(y+h)}{\cosh kh} \cos kx \sin \omega t,$$

and

$$x = \frac{A_1 gk}{\omega^2} \frac{\cosh k(y+h)}{\cosh kh} \cos kx \cos \omega t,$$

$$y = \frac{A_1 gk}{\omega^2} \frac{\sinh k(y+h)}{\cosh kh} \sin kx \cos \omega t,$$

so that

$$\frac{y}{x} = \tanh k(y+h) \tan kx.$$

This motion is independent of t, and each particle therefore executes a simple harmonic linear movement varying from a vertical movement beneath the crests and troughs—$kx = (n + \frac{1}{2})\pi$—to a horizontal one beneath the nodes—$kx = n\pi$. Since $\omega^2 = gk \tanh kh$ we have

$$x = A_1 \frac{\cosh k(y+h)}{\sinh kh} \cos kx \cos \omega t,$$

and

$$y = A_1 \frac{\sinh k(y+h)}{\sinh kh} \sin kx \cos \omega t.$$

As we pass downwards from the surface of the liquid to the bottom, the amplitude of the vertical motion varies from A_1 to zero, and the horizontal motion diminishes in the ratio $\cosh kh : 1$.

If the wave-length is small compared with h, then kh is large and $tanh\ kh=1$, so that the displacements may be written

$$x=A_1e^{ky}\ cos\ kx\ cos\ \omega t,$$
$$y=A_1e^{ky}\ sin\ kx\ cos\ \omega t,$$

y being given negative values in the indices as it is measured below the surface, *i.e.* in the negative direction. Thus for a decrease in vertical distance of λ, the amplitude diminishes in the ratio $1:\varepsilon^{-k\lambda}$, *i.e.* $1:e^{-2\pi}$.

If we superpose two systems of stationary waves such that the crests and troughs of one component system coincide with the nodes of the other, the amplitudes are equal in magnitude but differ in phase by a quarter-period. Thus

$$\eta=\eta_1\mp\eta_2,$$

where

$$\eta_1=A\ sin\ kx\ cos\ \omega t,\qquad \eta_2=A\ cos\ kx\ sin\ \omega t,$$

and

$$\eta=A\ sin\ (kx\mp\omega t),$$

which represents an infinite train of *progressive waves*, travelling in the positive or negative direction of x, with a velocity c given by

$$c^2=\frac{\omega^2}{k^2}=\frac{g}{k}\ tanh\ kh.$$

219. Energy of Stationary Waves.—For a system of stationary waves

$$\eta=A\ sin\ kx\ cos\ \omega t,$$

and

$$\phi=\frac{Ag}{\omega}\ \frac{cosh\ k(y+h)}{cosh\ kh}\ sin\ kx\ sin\ \omega t.$$

Hence the potential energy of the liquid, for a length λ, contained between two planes parallel to the x axis and situated unit distance apart is

$$\tfrac{1}{2}g\rho\int_0^\lambda \eta^2 dx=\frac{g\rho A^2\lambda}{4}\ cos^2\ \omega t,$$

and the kinetic energy of the same mass is as shown in the expression (400),

$$\tfrac{1}{2}\rho\int_0^\lambda \left(\phi\frac{\partial\phi}{\partial y}\right)dx,$$

i.e.

$$\frac{g\rho A^2\lambda}{4}\ sin^2\ \omega t.$$

Thus the two energies change with time, the total remaining constant and equal to

$$\frac{g\rho A^2\lambda}{4}$$

per unit width per wave-length.

220. Capillary Waves.—Surface tension modifies the surface conditions. The pressure is no longer constant, the difference of pressure, δp, on opposite sides of the surface being

$$\delta p = S\left(\frac{1}{R_1} - \frac{1}{R_2}\right),$$

where S is the surface tension and R_1 and R_2 are the principal radii of curvature of the surface.

Consider a strip of surface of length δl and unit width. The force acting on it along the direction y due to the pressure difference is $\delta p\, dx$ approximately, and that due to surface tension is $\delta\left(S\dfrac{\partial\eta}{\partial x}\right)\delta x$ along the same direction, so that

$$\delta p + S\frac{\partial^2\eta}{\partial x^2} = 0,$$

which must be satisfied at $y=0$.

It has been shown in Article 214 that if in any case of waves travelling in one direction only, without change of form, we impress on the whole mass of liquid a velocity equal and opposite to that of propagation, c, the motion becomes steady, while the forces acting on any particle remain the same as before.

As in Article 208, assume that

$$\frac{\phi+j\psi}{c} = -(x+jy) + jPe^{jk(x+jy)} + jQe^{-jk(x+jy)},$$

so that

$$\frac{\phi}{c} = -x - (Pe^{-ky} - Qe^{ky})\sin kx, \qquad . \qquad . \quad (434)$$

and

$$\frac{\psi}{c} = -y + (Pe^{-ky} + Qe^{ky})\cos kx \qquad . \qquad . \quad (435)$$

These expressions satisfy Laplace's equation (Article 210), and represent a motion which is periodic in respect to x, superimposed on a uniform velocity c.

The surface must be a stream line, i.e. $\psi=0$, and from equation (435) the form of the surface is given by

$$y = (P+Q)\cos kx,$$

if k is small, and since the bottom, $y=-h$, is a *stream line*, i.e. $\psi=constant$, from equation (435),

$$Pe^{kh} + Qe^{-kh} = 0,$$

so that equations (434) and (435) become

$$\frac{\phi}{c} = -x + C\cosh k(y+h)\sin kx,$$

$$\frac{\psi}{c} = -y + C\sinh k(y+h)\cos kx, \qquad . \qquad . \quad (436)$$

where $\tfrac{1}{2}C = -Pe^{kh} = Qe^{-kh}.$

But Bernoulli's theorem may be written

$$\frac{\delta p}{\rho}+gy+\tfrac{1}{2}\left[\left(\frac{\partial\phi}{\partial x}\right)^2+\left(\frac{\partial\phi}{\partial y}\right)^2\right]=constant,$$

i.e.

$$-\frac{S}{\rho}\frac{\partial^2\eta}{\partial x^2}+gy+\tfrac{1}{2}\left[\left(\frac{\partial\phi}{\partial x}\right)^2+\left(\frac{\partial\phi}{\partial y}\right)^2\right]=constant, \quad . \quad (437)$$

and since at the free surface $\psi=0$, from equation (436),

$$y=\eta=+C\ sinh\ kh\ cos\ kx.$$

Substituting this value in equation (437) and neglecting k^2,

$$-\frac{Sk^2C}{\rho}\ sinh\ kh\ cos\ kx-gC\ sinh\ kh\ cos\ kx-\frac{c}{2}\{1-2kC\ cosh\ kh\ cos\ kx\}$$
$$=constant.$$

Equating to zero, the coefficient of $cos\ kx$,

$$\frac{Sk^2}{\rho}+g=c^2k\ coth\ kh,$$

or,

$$c^2=\left(\frac{Sk}{\rho}+\frac{g}{k}\right)tanh\ kh,$$

i.e.

$$c^2=\left(\frac{2\pi S}{\rho\lambda}+\frac{g\lambda}{2\pi}\right)tanh\ kh.$$

If h is large compared with λ,

$$c^2=\frac{2\pi S}{\rho\lambda}+\frac{g\lambda}{2\pi} \quad . \quad . \quad . \quad . \quad (438)$$

For sufficiently large values of λ the second term in this expression is large compared with the first, the force governing the motion of the waves being mainly that of gravity. Thus the velocity of " gravity " waves is given by

$$c^2=\frac{g\lambda}{2\pi}.$$

In the case of ocean rollers, for example, at no part of the wave is the curvature sufficiently rapid to produce an appreciable surface tension effect, and gravity is the only considerable controlling factor.

If, on the other hand, λ is very small, the first term preponderates, and the motion is mainly governed by *capillarity*. In this case

$$c^2=\frac{2\pi S}{\rho\lambda}.$$

It will be noted that as the wave-length diminishes from ∞ to 0, the wave velocity, as given in the expression (438), after falling to a certain minimum begins to increase again. This minimum value occurs at the wave-length λ_m, where

$$-\frac{2\pi S}{\rho \lambda_m{}^2}+\frac{g}{2\pi}=0,$$

or when

$$\lambda_m{}^2=\frac{4\pi^2 S}{\rho g},$$

and Kelvin has suggested that those waves of wave-length less than $2\pi\sqrt{\dfrac{S}{\rho g}}$ should be called *ripples*. They may be seen in front of any solid moving horizontally through the surface of a liquid. As Kelvin [1] has stated, ripples may be produced by " a sailing vessel, a fishing line kept approximately vertical by a lead weight hanging down below the water and carried along at about half a mile per hour by a becalmed vessel, or a pole held vertically and carried horizontally."

221. Group Velocity.—Although the examples of wave motion quoted above relate to a special type, *i.e.* those waves in which the profile is simple harmonic and the train extends to infinity, with the help of Fourier's theorem we may, by superposition, build up a solution which represents the effect of any arbitrary initial conditions. The motion is, in general, composed of systems of waves of all wave-lengths travelling in both directions, each with its own velocity corresponding to its own wave-length. As a result of this motion the form of the free surface continually alters. When, however, the wave-lengths are large compared with the depth of liquid, the velocity of propagation is independent of the wave-length, and in this case if the waves travel in one direction only, the wave profile remains unchanged as the system advances.

In general, if waves are started by a local disturbance such as, for example, the dropping of a stone into a pond, or the motion of a boat through water, the successive waves have different lengths and are propagated with different velocities. In studying wave motion practically, the observed velocity, wave-length, and period are those of the resultant disturbance caused by the interaction of the constituent waves. The velocity of the *group* as a whole is less than that of the individual waves composing it, and if attention be fixed on a particular wave, it is seen to advance through the group, gradually dying out as it approaches the front, while its former place in the group is occupied in succession by other waves which have come forward from the rear.

From these considerations we may introduce the important conception of *group velocity*,[2] which has application, notably to water

[1] Kelvin, *Math. and Phys. Papers*, **4**, 76.

[2] Lamb, *Proc. Lond. Math. Soc.*, (2), **1**, 473 (1904) ; Green, *Proc. Roy. Soc. Edin.*, **29**, 445 (1909).

waves, but also to every case of wave motion, where the velocity of propagation of a simple harmonic train varies with the wave-length.

Consider a group obtained by the superposition of two systems of waves of the same amplitude and of nearly the same wave-length. The equation of the surface is

$$\eta = A[\cos(\omega_1 t - k_1 x + \xi_1) + \cos(\omega_2 t - k_2 x + \xi_2)],$$

where $k = \dfrac{2\pi}{\lambda}$, $k_1 - k_2$ is small, and $\omega = f(k)$, so that

$$\eta = 2A \cos\left(\frac{\omega_1+\omega_2}{2}t - \frac{k_1+k_2}{2}x + \frac{\xi_1+\xi_2}{2}\right)\cos\left(\frac{\omega_1-\omega_2}{2}t - \frac{k_1-k_2}{2}x + \frac{\xi_1-\xi_2}{2}\right).$$

If we consider any particular instant, then for a considerable range of values of x the last factor is approximately constant, and the wave surface for a large range of x given by

$$\eta = B \cos\left(\omega t - kx + \frac{\xi_1+\xi_2}{2}\right).$$

The surface presents the appearance of a series of groups of waves separated at equal intervals by bands of nearly smooth water, and the motion of each group is sensibly independent of the presence of others. The group velocity, U, is

$$U = \frac{\omega_1-\omega_2}{k_1-k_2} = \frac{d\omega}{dk}.$$

But the wave velocity is

$$c = \frac{\omega}{k}.$$

Hence

$$U = \frac{d}{dk}(ck) = c + k\frac{dc}{dk}, \qquad . \qquad . \qquad . \quad (439)$$

and since

$$k = \frac{2\pi}{\lambda},$$

$$U = c - \lambda\frac{dc}{d\lambda}.$$

This result is true for any waves travelling through a uniform medium.

The velocity of surface waves is given by

$$c^2 = \left(kS + \frac{g}{k}\right) \tanh kh,$$

and in the case of deep water $\tanh kh = 1$, so that from equation (439)

$$cU = c^2 + \frac{k}{2}\frac{d}{dk}(c^2) = \left(kS + \frac{g}{k}\right) + \frac{k}{2}\left(S - \frac{g}{k^2}\right) = \frac{3kS}{2} + \frac{g}{2k}.$$

Hence

$$\frac{U}{c} = \frac{\dfrac{3kS}{2} + \dfrac{g}{2k}}{kS + \dfrac{g}{k}}.$$

For gravity waves

$$U = \tfrac{1}{2}c.$$

For capillary waves or ripples

$$U = \tfrac{3}{2}c,$$

so that a group of ripples travels *faster* than one of the individual waves.

If we consider gravity waves at any depth,

$$c^2 = \frac{g}{k} \tanh kh,$$

and

$$cU = c^2 + \tfrac{1}{2}k\left[\frac{gh}{k} \operatorname{sech}^2 kh - \frac{g}{k^2} \tanh kh\right] = \tfrac{1}{2}[c^2 + gh \operatorname{sech}^2 kh].$$

Thus [1]

$$U = \frac{c}{2}\left[1 + \frac{2kh}{\sinh 2kh}\right] \qquad . \qquad . \qquad . \quad (440$$

As kh approaches zero value, $\dfrac{2kh}{\sinh 2kh}$ increases to the value unity,

so that the group velocity continually increases from $\dfrac{c}{2}$, its value

when h is very large, to c, when the depth is small.

222. Transmission of Energy in Simple Harmonic Surface Waves.—In a progressive wave the wave form advances with a definite velocity. The particles of the liquid possess energy which they transfer, but there is no reason to suppose that the rate at which this energy is handed on is equal to the velocity of the waves. In fact, energy is transmitted at a smaller rate.

Consider a vertical section of the liquid taken at right angles to the direction of propagation. The rate of energy transmission is the rate at which the pressure on one side of this section is doing work on the liquid at the other side. If the liquid depth is h, we have, equation (433),

$$\phi = \frac{Ag}{\omega} \frac{\cosh k(y+h)}{\cosh kh} \cos (kx - \omega t),$$

and from equation (432) the variable part of the pressure is given by

$$\rho \frac{\partial \phi}{\partial t},$$

[1] Stokes, *Papers*, **5**, 362; Rayleigh, *Papers*, **1**, 540.

approximately, so that as the horizontal velocity is $-\dfrac{\partial\phi}{\partial x}$, the work done in unit time, or the energy carried across unit width of the section, is

$$-\int_{-h}^{0}\delta p\frac{\partial\phi}{\partial x}dy,$$

i.e.

$$\int_{-h}^{0}\frac{\rho kA^{2}g^{2}}{\omega}\frac{\cosh^{2}k(y+h)}{\cosh^{2}kh}\sin^{2}(kx-\omega t)dy,$$

or,

$$\frac{\rho kg^{2}A^{2}}{\omega\cosh^{2}kh}\sin^{2}(kx-\omega t)\left[\frac{\sinh 2kh}{4k}+\frac{h}{2}\right].$$

But, from equation (429), $\omega^{2}=gk\tanh kh$, so that the energy transmitted per unit time is

$$\frac{\rho g\omega A^{2}}{2k}\sin^{2}(kx-\omega t)[1+2kh\ cosech\ 2kh].$$

The average value of this expression taken over an interval of time, long compared with the periodic time, is [1]

$$\frac{\rho g\omega A^{2}}{4k}[1+2kh\ cosech\ 2kh],$$

and as $\dfrac{\omega}{k}=c$, the energy is transmitted at an average rate equal to

$$\frac{\rho gA^{2}}{2}\times group\ velocity,$$

since the group velocity is

$$\frac{c}{2}[1+2kh\ cosech\ 2kh].$$

But it has been shown in Article 217 that $\dfrac{\rho gA^{2}}{2}$ is the total energy at any instant, per unit length of waves, so that the average rate of energy transmission is the same as the group velocity.

223. Echelon Waves.—Let a pressure point move with velocity v along a line QO, and suppose at the moment considered it has reached the position O. The disturbance at any point P at that instant may be considered as produced by the resultant of a series of impulses, applied at uniformly spaced short intervals, at points along QO. Of the wave systems thus generated only those will combine to have an additive effect which have their origin in the neighbourhood of a point Q, such that the phase at P is stationary for variations in the position of Q. If the angle OQP is θ, and we

---

[1] Rayleigh, *Proc. Lond. Math. Soc.*, **9**, 21 (1877).

regard Q as fixed, the velocity of the disturbance along QP is $v \cos \theta$ and, for deep-water waves,

$$v^2 \cos^2 \theta = \frac{g\lambda}{2\pi},$$

so that if the point P is at a crest, PQ must be a multiple of λ, and therefore

$$QP = p, \text{ say, } = k \cos^2 \theta, \quad . \quad . \quad . \quad (441)$$

where

$$k = \frac{2\pi n v^2}{g}, \text{ n being an integer.}$$

Points in the immediate neighbourhood of P for which the resultant phase is the same as at P will lie on a line perpendicular to QP, and a locus of uniform phase will be the envelope of such lines. The equation to a line perpendicular to QP is

$$p = x \cos \theta + y \sin \theta, \quad . \quad . \quad . \quad (442)$$

and the adjacent line is given by

$$p + \delta p = x \cos (\theta + \delta\theta) + y \sin (\theta + \delta\theta).$$

By subtraction

$$\frac{\delta p}{\delta \theta} = \frac{dp}{d\theta} = -x \sin \theta + y \cos \theta \quad . \quad . \quad (443)$$

A point on the envelope must satisfy equations (442) and (443), *i.e.*

$$x = p \cos \theta - \frac{dp}{d\theta} \sin \theta, \qquad y = p \sin \theta + \frac{dp}{d\theta} \cos \theta,$$

and from equation (441)

$$x = k \cos^3 \theta + 2k \cos \theta \sin^2 \theta = \frac{k}{4}(5 \cos \theta - \cos 3\theta), \quad . \quad (444)$$

$$y = k \cos^2 \theta \sin \theta - 2k \cos^2 \theta \sin \theta = -\frac{k}{4}(\sin \theta + \sin 3\theta) \quad (445)$$

From these equations the curves defined by equation (441) may be traced.

If $\dfrac{dx}{d\theta} = \dfrac{dy}{d\theta} = 0$ we obtain *singular points*. Both of these differentials are zero if

$$\cos^2 \theta = \tfrac{2}{3} \quad . \quad . \quad . \quad . \quad (446)$$

Two curves defined by equations (444) and (445) pass through any assigned point P, and as the singular points are given by equations (444), (445), and (446),

$$x = \tfrac{4}{3} k \cos \theta, \qquad y = -\tfrac{2}{3} k \sin \theta,$$

$$\frac{y}{x} = -\tfrac{1}{2} \tan \theta = \pm \frac{1}{2\sqrt{2}},$$

and a series of *cusps* is situated on these lines.[1] Waves of this type

[1] Havelock, *Proc. Roy. Soc.*, A, **81**, 398 (1908).

are produced by the action of the bows of a ship, two systems of transverse and lateral waves being observed. The two systems coalesce at the cusps, producing the well-defined *echelon waves.* They are generated also at the stern of a ship and are exhibited when a duck swims across a pond.

224. Compression Waves in a Liquid.—When a portion of a liquid is locally compressed, the state of strain is communicated to other parts of the liquid at a rate which gives the velocity of compressional waves, *e.g.* sound waves, in the medium. Suppose the wave motion to be along the Ox direction. Each particle of the medium vibrates parallel to Ox about its mean position, and, if the amplitude is small, this motion will be simple harmonic. Let A and B be two planes, at the equilibrium positions x and $x+\delta x$, each of area α.

At a time t let the displacement at A, along Ox, be e, then that at B is $e+\dfrac{de}{dx}.\delta x$. Thus the distance δx between the planes is increased to $\delta x\left(1+\dfrac{de}{dx}\right)$, or the linear strain along Ox is $\dfrac{de}{dx}$. As there is no displacement at right angles to Ox, this is also the dilational strain. Thus the pressure at A, due to the disturbance, is $-P=-K\dfrac{de}{dx}$, where K is the adiabatic value of the bulk modulus, while that at B is $-P-\dfrac{dP}{dx}.\delta x$. There is thus a resultant force $\alpha\dfrac{dP}{dx}\delta x=K\alpha\dfrac{d^2e}{dx^2}.\delta x$ acting on the medium between A and B along the Ox direction. If the density of the medium in the equilibrium position is ρ, then the constant mass of liquid between the planes is $\rho\alpha\delta x$, and the acceleration is

$$\frac{K}{\rho}\frac{d^2e}{dx^2}=\frac{d^2e}{dt^2}.$$

The velocity of propagation, c, is given by

$$c^2=\frac{K}{\rho}.$$

225. Compression Waves in an Extended Solid.—The foregoing principles apply also to this case, but the pressure over the edges of the slab AB will not be $-P$, but, owing to the absence of displacement at right angles to Ox, will be $-\dfrac{\sigma P}{1-\sigma}$, where $-P=-\chi\alpha\dfrac{de}{dx}$, χ being the axial modulus. Thus in this case,

$$c^2=\frac{\chi}{\rho}=\frac{3K+4n}{3\rho}.$$

Seismic Prospecting for minerals under the earth's surface is based on the capacity of the material of the earth to transmit longitudinal low-frequency vibrations, set up by explosions, with this velocity, the time of transmission from the origin of the disturbance to a measuring site depending upon the material traversed by the wave.

In addition to the air-borne and transverse waves two distinct longitudinal waves exist, the first of which is assumed to travel just under the earth's surface with a speed characteristic of the surface medium, while the second wave travels downwards from the explosion point, and is reflected from an underlying stratum. From records of the times of arrival of these waves at a series of observation stations, deductions as to the nature and position of the intervening media can be made. The seismometers employed are distinguished according to the dynamical function of the tremor to which they react, e.g. displacement, velocity, and acceleration types. The first are usually mechanical in nature, the second are electromagnetic induction seismometers in which the original displacement of the ground is transformed by means of electromagnetic induction into a variation of current proportional to the velocity of the motion. The third type depends upon the principle that a variable force is proportional to the acceleration of the motion related to it, and the displacement of the ground is made to vary a pressure exerted on an electrical device such as a microphone, the current in which then varies in a manner proportional to the acceleration of the original ground movement.

226. Compressional Waves in a Rod.—If longitudinal elastic displacements are propagated along a rod, the conditions of strain are different from those of the previous article, because of the removal of the side constraints imposed by the surrounding medium. If the length of the rod is great compared with its lateral dimensions, the strain is a simple Young's modulus extension or contraction, and the tensile force at A, acting along Ox is $-Y\dfrac{de}{dx}$, where Y is the adiabatic value of Young's Modulus for the material of the rod. Thus we have

$$c^2 = \frac{Y}{\rho}.$$

227. Transverse Waves in a Stretched String.—Let the undisplaced length of the string lie along Ox and let the displacement at A be y, while that at B is $y + \delta x \cdot \dfrac{dy}{dx}$, each of these being assumed small. Thus the element δx of the string is inclined at a small angle $\dfrac{dy}{dx}$ to Ox and, if F is the tension, the resolved part of this, acting at A, along Oy is approximately $-F\dfrac{dy}{dx}$. The force at B along Oy is

$$F\frac{dy}{dx} + F\frac{d^2y}{dx^2}\delta x,$$

if the tension is the same throughout the string. Thus the resultant force along Oy is $F\dfrac{d^2y}{dx^2}\delta x$, and the mass of the element is $m\delta x$, where m is the mass per unit length of the string. Therefore the acceleration along Oy is $\dfrac{F}{m}\cdot\dfrac{d^2y}{dx^2}$, and thus

$$c^2=\frac{F}{m}.$$

This result, which has been deduced on the assumptions (a) that the amplitude is small compared with the wave-length, (b) that the tension, in the displaced position, is unaltered, and (c) that the string is perfectly flexible will apply with considerable accuracy to long, thin metal or gut strings vibrating with small intensity, but will not be accurate for shorter, thicker specimens or more intense vibrations.

228. Compressional Waves in a Gas.—Let the pressure of the gas be p and its density ρ when undisturbed. Then if at time t the displacement at A is e, that at B is $e+\dfrac{de}{dx}.\delta x$, and the new volume of gas between A and B is $\alpha\delta x\left(1+\dfrac{de}{dx}\right)\cdot$ Since the change of volume occurs under adiabatic conditions,

$$p=P\left(1+\frac{de}{dx}\right)^{\gamma},$$

where P is the pressure at A at time t. If the particle displacement is small compared with the wave-length, we have

$$P=p\left(1-\gamma\frac{de}{dx}\right).$$

Hence the force at A acting along Ox is $P\alpha$, while that at B is $-P\alpha-\alpha\dfrac{dP}{dx}.\delta x$, and thus the excess force along Ox is

$$-\alpha\frac{dP}{dx}\delta x=\alpha\delta x\gamma p\frac{d^2e}{dx^2},$$

and

$$c^2=\frac{\gamma p}{\rho}.$$

It should be noticed, however, that if the amplitude is not very small c^2 will exceed $\dfrac{\gamma p}{\rho}.$ This has been verified experimentally.

EXAMPLES

1. Show that the formula for long, deep liquid waves of length λ is correct within 1 per cent. if the depth of the liquid exceeds $0\cdot43\lambda$ and viscosity effects are negligible.

2. If the depth of the liquid in the previous question is $\lambda/4$, find the equation to the orbit of a surface particle, the vertical amplitude being A. $[0\cdot887x^2+y^2=A^2.]$

3. What would be the equation of particle motion at the bottom of a liquid of depth $\lambda/4$, surface amplitude A, and negligible viscosity ?
$$[x=0\cdot435A \; sin \; (75\cdot3t/\sqrt{\lambda}).]$$

4. Find the velocity of long waves for a liquid whose depth is $\lambda/4$ and compare it with (a) the velocity for a similar wave-length λ in a deep liquid and (b) that for canal waves. $[12\sqrt{\lambda} \; ; \; 12\cdot5\sqrt{\lambda} \; ; \; 15\cdot7\sqrt{\lambda}.]$

5. Find the maximum depth of liquid for which the formula $V^2=gh$ represents the velocity of waves of length λ to within 1 per cent.
$$[0\cdot028\lambda.]$$

6. Compare the minimum velocities of surface waves at 10° C. for mercury and water if the surface tensions are 544 and 74 respectively, and the specific gravity of mercury is 13·56. $[0\cdot858 : 1.]$

7. In an experiment to measure the surface tension of water by the ripple method, the waves were created by a tuning fork of frequency 100, and the mean wave-length was 3·66 mm.   Calculate the surface tension of water.   [74·7 dynes per cm.]

8. For what wave-length will the group velocity of surface waves in a liquid of surface tension S and density d be a minimum ?
$$[16\sqrt{(S/gd)}.]$$

9. Taking the surface tension of water as 75 dynes per cm., its density as 1 gm. per c.c., find the wave-lengths of surface waves on water with a velocity of 30 cm. per sec.   Which of these would it be preferable to use in determining the surface tension by means of ripples ?
[5·18 and 0·583 cm. ;   the latter.]

10. Taking for the material of the earth the following elastic constants $K=2\times10^{11}$ and $n=1\cdot2\times10^{11}$ dynes per sq. cm., compare the velocities of transverse and longitudinal waves.   [0·573.]

CHAPTER XV

UNITS AND DIMENSIONS

229. Units.—The quantitative measure of anything is a number which expresses the ratio of the magnitude of the entity to the magnitude of some other amount of the same kind. In order that the number expressing the measure may be intelligible, the magnitude of the thing used for comparison must be known. This leads to the conventional choice of certain magnitudes as units of measurement, and any other magnitude is then simply expressed by a number which tells how many magnitudes, equal to the unit of the same kind of magnitude, it contains. For example, if we say that a rod is 12 ft. long, we imply that the rod is measured in terms of the foot, which is the unit in this particular case, and that the ratio of the rod's length to the unit of length is 12. Every different type of physical quantity requires a separate unit, but these units are not necessarily independent of one another, and it is desirable that as few different kinds of unit quantities as possible should be introduced into our measurements. They must be definite, not subject to secular change, and easily comparable experimentally with the quantities in which they are expressed. In addition, they must be such that they are easily copied.

There are certain relations which exist between different types of physical magnitudes, and by utilising these relations it is possible to select the units in a limited number of cases, and thus to fix the magnitude of the remainder. The units chosen as the basis for this system are called *fundamental units*, and the others, which are determined by the relation existing between them and the fundamental units, are called *derived units*. Such a system is described as *absolute* —a term first introduced by Gauss in 1832 in connection with his measurements on the strength of the earth's magnetic field at Göttingen.

There are several absolute systems of units possible according to the fundamental units chosen, and the physical relation employed in obtaining the derived units, *etc.*, but by far the most widely used one, is that referred to as the *C.G.S.* (*centimetre, gram, second*) system. Another, often called the *English system*, employs the *foot, pound,* and *second* as the fundamental units.

A third system, closely allied to the C.G.S. system, is that called the *M.K.S.*, which makes the metre, the kilogram, and the second the fundamental units. This selection is most useful in electrical theory as it makes the so-called practical units absolute values. In mechanical engineering practice the unit of force becomes more basically valuable, and is defined gravitationally as the weight of

409

a pound. This necessitates a re-definition of the unit mass which, under the name *slug*, becomes the mass to which the unit force, 1 pound weight, gives unit acceleration. Thus one slug contains *g* pounds and is therefore strictly a local unit.

230. Fundamental Units.—The fundamental units which have been chosen are those of *mass*, *length*, and *time*, and most physical units may be explicitly defined in terms of these three.

In the metric system the standard of length is defined as the distance between the ends of a certain platinum bar when the whole bar is at the temperature 0° C. A line standard *metre* has been constructed by the International Bureau of Weights and Measures and is known as the International Prototype Metre. A number of standard-metre bars which have been carefully compared with the International Prototype have been made by the International Bureau of Weights and Measures and furnished to the various governments. The *British yard* is defined as the straight line or distance (at 62° F.) between the transverse lines in the two gold plugs in the bronze bar deposited in the office of the Exchequer.

The unit of time in both the systems here referred to is the *mean solar second*, or the 86,400th part of the mean solar day. The unit of time is thus founded on the average time required for the earth to make one revolution on its axis relatively to the sun as a fixed point of reference. Strictly, the solar day is the interval between two successive transits of the first point of Aries across any selected meridian. This point is that one of the two nodes of intersection of the ecliptic and the celestial equator where the sun, moving in the ecliptic, crosses the equator from south to north at about 21st March, the ecliptic being the apparent yearly track of the sun in the great circle on the celestial sphere.

The French, or metric, standard of mass, the *kilogram*, is the mass of a piece of platinum made by Borda in accordance with a decree from the French Republic. It was connected with the standard of length by being made as nearly as possible of the same mass as that of a cubic decimetre of distilled water at the temperature of 4° C., or nearly the temperature of maximum density. The British standard of mass is the *pound avoirdupois*, and is the mass of a piece of platinum marked " P.S. 1844, 1 lb.," preserved in the Exchequer office.

231. Derived Units.—Units of quantities depending on powers greater than unity of the fundamental length, mass, and time units, or on combinations of different powers of these units, are called *derived units*. Thus the unit of area and of volume are, respectively, the area of a square whose side is the unit of length and the volume of a cube whose edge is the unit of length. A *velocity* is expressed by the ratio of the number representing a length to that representing an interval of time, or $\frac{L}{T}$; an *acceleration* by a velocity number divided by an interval of time number, or $\dfrac{L}{T^2}$, etc. Equations of this form given for velocity and acceleration, which show the dimensions of the quantity in terms of the fundamental units, are called *dimensional equations.* Thus

$$E = ML^2T^{-2}$$

is the *dimensional equation* for *energy* and ML^2T^{-2} is the *dimensional formula* for *energy.*

The dimensional equation for any physical quantity may be deduced or formed from the definition of that quantity. For example, *momentum* is quantity of motion in the Newtonian sense and is, at any instant, measured by the product of the mass number and the velocity number for the body. Thus the dimensional formula is MV or MLT^{-1}, so that the dimensions of momentum are 1 in mass, 1 in length, and -1 in time.

The dimensional formulæ for various physical quantities are given in Table XIX.

TABLE XIX.—DIMENSIONAL FORMULÆ FOR VARIOUS PHYSICAL
QUANTITIES

Quantity.	Dimensional formulæ.	Quantity.	Dimensional formulæ.
Length . . .	L	Moment of inertia .	ML^2
Time . . .	T	Force . . .	MLT^{-2}
Mass . . .	M	Energy. Work . .	ML^2T^{-2}
Linear speed . .	LT^{-1}	Torque . . .	ML^2T^{-2}
Angular speed . .	T^{-1}	Surface tension . .	MT^{-2}
Linear acceleration .	LT^{-2}	Strain . . .	0
Angular acceleration .	T^{-2}	Stress . . .	$ML^{-1}T^{-2}$
Density . . .	ML^{-3}	Modulus of elasticity .	$ML^{-1}T^{-2}$
Moment of momentum	ML^2T^{-1}	Viscosity . . .	$ML^{-1}T^{-1}$

It must be remembered that units other than mass, length, and time may be chosen as the fundamental units, and the physical quantities expressed in terms of the new fundamental units. For example, suppose we take length, time, and force, F, as fundamental units. Then, since $F = MLT^{-2}$,

$$M = FL^{-1}T^2,$$

and the dimensional formula for viscosity is $FL^{-2}T$.

232. Homogeneity of Dimensions in a Physical Equation. —Dimensional equations may be used to convert the magnitude of any physical quantity expressed in terms of the units belonging to one system into those of another system. They also form a check on the accuracy of the reasoning whereby an equation between various physical quantities has been obtained. Thus, suppose we consider the expression for the velocity, v, generated by a uniform acceleration, a, acting over a specified distance, s,

$$v^2 = 2as.$$

The dimensional formula for the left-hand side of the equation is $[LT^{-1}]^2$, and for the right-hand side, $LT^{-2}L$, so that the dimensional formulæ are identical, and the original equation is possible. All terms in any such equation having a physical significance must necessarily have identical dimensional formulæ. This principle is known as *homogeneity of dimensional formulæ*.

Suppose that it is required to convert a surface tension, S_0, expressed in terms of dynes per centimetre, into pounds weight per foot. Representing the fundamental units in the C.G.S. and British systems by L_0 and L_1, and the derived units of force by F_0 and F_1 in the two systems, and remembering that the actual value of the surface tension remains the same whatever the units employed,

$$S_0[F_0L_0^{-1}] = S_1[F_1L_1^{-1}],$$

or

$$S_1 = S_0\left[\frac{F_0L_1}{F_1L_0}\right] = \left[\frac{M_0}{M_1}\right]S_0,$$

where S_1 is the number which expresses the surface tension in pounds weight per foot. The ratio, $\dfrac{M_0}{M_1}$, *i.e.* the gram to the pound, is termed the *conversion factor*.

233. Homogeneity in Preliminary Analysis of Problems. —The principle of homogeneity of dimensions provides information regarding the form which relations between physical quantities should take, and in many problems a preliminary analysis may be made in this way. In using this method practically, there are two important points to be considered. First, a numerical coefficient cannot be determined from this principle alone. It must be found by calculation or experiment. Secondly, it is necessary to specify all the quantities on which the desired result may reasonably be supposed to depend, and afterwards it may be shown that one or more of these may be omitted. For example, the velocity with which a disturbance travels along a stretched string might be a function of the stretching force F, the mass of the string m, and its length l, *i.e.*

$$v = \phi(F,\ m,\ l),$$

where ϕ is the function to be determined. Hence

$$v = CF^x m^y l^z,$$

C being a constant, or transforming to the dimensional equation

$$[LT^{-1}] = [MLT^{-2}]^x[M]^y[L]^z.$$

Hence

$$x + y = 0, \qquad x + z = 1, \qquad 2x = 1,$$

or

$$x = \tfrac{1}{2}, \qquad y = -\tfrac{1}{2}, \qquad z = \tfrac{1}{2},$$

and
$$v=C\sqrt{\frac{Fl}{m}}=C\sqrt{\frac{F}{m_0}},$$

where m_0 is the mass per unit length, and one experiment suffices to determine the value of C.

The time taken by a simple pendulum to swing through an angle θ might depend upon the mass, m, of the bob, the length, l, of the suspension, and g, the acceleration due to gravity, or

$$t_0=Cm^xl^yg^z,$$

i.e.

$$T=[M]^x[L]^y[LT^{-2}]^z,$$

so

$$y+z=0, \qquad 2z=-1, \qquad x=0,$$

and

$$z=-\tfrac{1}{2}, \qquad y=\tfrac{1}{2},$$

$$t_0=C\sqrt{\frac{l}{g}}.$$

Thus t_0 is independent of the bob's mass. It will be noted that $t_0\sqrt{\frac{g}{l}}$ has no dimensions.

If two pendulums are situated at different places on the earth's surface, where the values of the acceleration due to gravity are g_1 and g_2, the lengths of the pendulums being l_1 and l_2 respectively, and if t_1 and t_2 are the times taken by the bobs to swing over equal arcs, then

$$t_1\sqrt{\frac{g_1}{l_1}}=t_2\sqrt{\frac{g_2}{l_2}},$$

and the pendulums pass through identical phases for equal values of the non-dimensional expression $t\sqrt{\frac{g}{l}}$. Such moving systems are said to possess *dynamical similarity*.

234. Non-dimensional Variables.—From the examples quoted above it is evident that not more than three equations can be obtained by equating the dimensions of mass, length, and time. Sometimes one of the fundamental units is missing as in the pendulum formula, but there may be more than three quantities upon which the physical relation depends. Thus, if there are n quantities, the indices of three of them may be expressed in terms of the remainder, and there will remain a relation between $n-3$ non-dimensional groups of terms. For example, the velocity, c, of capillary waves depends upon the wave-length, λ, the acceleration due to gravity, g, the surface tension, S, and the density, ρ, so that

$$c=C\lambda^xg^yS^z\rho^p,$$

and

$$[LT^{-1}]=[L]^x[LT^{-2}]^y[MT^{-2}]^z[ML^{-3}]^p,$$

hence
$$z=-p, \qquad y=p+\tfrac{1}{2}, \qquad x=2p+\tfrac{1}{2},$$
or
$$c=C\sqrt{\lambda g}\left(\frac{\rho\lambda^2 g}{S}\right)^p,$$

three of the variables being expressed in terms of the fourth. This result may also be written

$$c=C\sqrt{g\lambda}\phi\left(\frac{\rho\lambda^2 g}{S}\right),$$

where ϕ represents an undetermined function.

In a similar manner it may be shown that the mass, m, of a drop of liquid, density ρ, delivered from a tube of external radius r is given by

$$m=\frac{Sr}{g}\phi\left(\frac{S}{g\rho r^2}\right),$$

S being the surface tension and ϕ an arbitrary function which varies little from 3·8.

235. Application to Particle Dynamics.—If a particle is projected with an initial velocity u into a gravitational field so that it is subjected to an acceleration a, the distance, s, travelled during an interval of time, t, after the particle has been projected is given by

$$s=Cu^x a^y t^z,$$
or
$$[L]=[LT^{-1}]^x[LT^{-2}]^y[T]^z,$$
and
$$x=1-y, \qquad z=1+y,$$
$$s=Cu^{1-y}a^y t^{1+y}=ut\phi\left(\frac{at}{u}\right).$$

Thus we have the two non-dimensional groups of terms,

$$\frac{s}{ut} \quad \text{and} \quad \frac{at}{u}.$$

But for linear accelerated motion

$$s=ut+\tfrac{1}{2}at^2=ut\left(1+\tfrac{1}{2}\frac{at}{u}\right),$$

which is of the same form as that deduced above.

Another interesting example in mechanics is the motion of a small mass m about a massive nucleus of mass W. We have shown that the resultant path taken by the small mass is a conic, which, under special conditions, is an ellipse. Since the force of attraction between the two masses is given by $F=\dfrac{GWm}{r^2}$, where r is the distance between the masses and G the Newtonian constant, we see that the dimensional formula for G is $L^3 T^{-2} M^{-1}$. Now the periodic time for the small mass to revolve round about the nucleus depends upon m, W, R, and G, where R is the major axis of the elliptical orbit, and

$$t_0 = Cm^x W^y R\, G^p,$$

or

$$[T] = [M]^x [M]^y [L]^z [L^3 T^{-2} M^{-1}]^p,$$

so

$$p = -\tfrac{1}{2}, \qquad z = +\tfrac{3}{2}, \qquad x = -y - \tfrac{1}{2},$$

and

$$t_0 = \frac{R^{\frac{3}{2}}}{\sqrt{Gm}} \phi\!\left(\frac{W}{m}\right),$$

the square of the periodic time being proportional to the cube of the major axis of the orbit.

236. Application to Surface Tension.—Owing to capillary forces, a drop or bubble that is deformed from a spherical shape, and then left to itself, will execute periodic vibrations about its figure of equilibrium. This phenomenon, which is seen when a liquid issues from a circular orifice, has been studied by Rayleigh,[1] and may be used to measure the value of the surface tension of the liquid. The frequency, ν, of vibration is a function of S the surface tension, ρ the density, and d the diameter of the drop, so that

$$\nu = CS^x \rho^y d^z,$$
$$[T^{-1}] = [MT^{-2}]^x [ML^{-3}]^y L^z,$$

and

$$\nu = C\sqrt{\frac{S}{\rho d^3}}.$$

237. Application to Viscosity.—The motion of a fluid changes at a certain critical velocity from orderly to turbulent motion, and a simple formula for this critical velocity, v_c, may be deduced from dimensional formulæ. The factors which determine its value are the coefficient of viscosity, η, of the liquid, the density ρ, and the radius, r, of the tube along which the liquid flows. Thus

$$v_c = C\eta^x \rho^y r^z,$$
$$[LT^{-1}] = [ML^{-1}T^{-1}]^x [ML^{-3}]^y [L]^z,$$

and

$$v_c = C\frac{\eta}{\rho r}.$$

A body moving through a viscous medium is subjected to a retarding force, F, which depends upon the velocity, v, with which it moves, relative to a point in the fluid far removed from the body, the size of the body, say its length l, and the coefficient of viscosity, η, of the medium, so that

$$F = C_0 v^x \eta^y l^z,$$

and using the dimensional formulæ,

$$F = C_0 v\eta l.$$

[1] Rayleigh, *Proc. Roy. Soc.*, A, **29**, 71 (1879); **34**, 130 (1882); **47**, 281 (1890).

This formula is true, provided that the resultant liquid motion is not turbulent, *i.e.* the velocity of the body must be less than the *critical velocity* associated with the liquid through which the body moves. Stokes [1] has shown that a sphere moving through a viscous medium is subjected to a viscous drag equal to $6\pi r \eta v$, where r is the radius of the sphere.

The liquid itself will be disturbed, and assuming that the slope of the stream line at a point is given by

$$\theta = \phi(l,\ \eta,\ v,\ \rho),$$

it can be shown that

$$\theta = \phi\left(\frac{\eta}{lv\rho}\right),$$

so that the group $\dfrac{\eta}{lv\rho}$ is *non-dimensional*, its value depending upon the geometrical conditions. If these conditions are fixed, then θ is constant, and the stream lines in liquids through which bodies of the same shape, *i.e.* geometrical conditions fixed but of different sizes, move are similar if $\dfrac{\eta}{lv\rho}$ is constant. This is a very important deduction and is widely utilised in naval and aerodynamic problems, since it provides a method of analysing and studying problems connected with machines by means of tests on miniature models constructed to scale.

When the relative motion of a body through a liquid becomes great, eddies are formed and turbulent motion results. If F is the retarding force acting on a body of dimension l as it moves with a velocity v through a liquid of density ρ, viscosity η,

$$F = \phi(v,\ \eta,\ l,\ \rho),$$

and by means of dimensional formulæ

$$F = \rho v^2 l^2 \phi\left(\frac{vl\rho}{\eta}\right),$$

the *non-dimensional number* $\dfrac{vl\rho}{\eta}$ being known as *Reynolds' number.*

It is obvious that the resistance of a body of given shape, moving in a fluid of density and viscosity ρ_1, η_1 at a speed v_1, may be predicted from the measured resistance of a scale model moving in a fluid of density and viscosity ρ_2, η_2, at a speed v_2, provided that

$$\frac{v_2 l_2 \rho_2}{\eta_2} = \frac{v_1 l_1 \rho_1}{\eta_1},$$

for then

$$F_1 = \frac{\rho_1 v_1^2 l_1^2}{\rho_2 v_2^2 l_2^2} F_2,$$

and F_1 can be determined, since all the terms on the right-hand side are known, or can be measured. This suggests that the resistance

---

[1] Stokes, *Collected Papers*, 3, 1.

which any body experiences in moving through a medium may be estimated by measuring the resistance acting on a small scale model of it. In practice the use of this method is limited by the fact that the necessary conditions, $\dfrac{v_2 l_2 \rho_2}{\eta_2} = \dfrac{v_1 l_1 \rho_1}{\eta_1}$, to be fulfilled in the test on the model are nearly always impossible to realise. For example, if a model to a scale $\frac{1}{10}$ is available, it would be necessary to move it ten times faster than the object in the same medium to fulfil the necessary conditions, a speed which is not easily realised in the laboratory. Thus, if it is required to predict the resistance acting on a boat 500 ft. long moving at 20 ft. per sec., and a model of the boat to a scale $\frac{1}{20}$ is used, the test being made in water, it would be necessary to move the model at 400 ft. per sec. By studying the manner in which $\dfrac{R}{\rho v^2}$ varies at different velocities, useful information is afforded, however, concerning the probable variation of this quantity outside the velocity range available for the model.

This retarding force is of the greatest importance in the case of ships moving through the water. It may be regarded as consisting of that due to (a) the friction of the liquid against the immersed surface, (b) eddy-making and the formation of waves. The component arising from wave formation cannot be estimated by the application of the law $\dfrac{vl\rho}{\eta} = constant$, but a law of comparison for both friction and wave-making may be derived by noting that in addition to velocity, density, and viscosity of the fluid, and the linear dimensions of the body, the acceleration due to gravity must also be taken into account. Then it may be shown that

$$F = \rho v^2 l^2 \phi\left(\frac{gl}{v^2}, \frac{vl\rho}{\eta}\right),$$

and in order to predict the total resistance of a ship, from experiments with a small scale model, the following relations must hold :

$$(a)\ \frac{gl_0}{v_0{}^2} = \frac{gl_1}{v_1{}^2},$$

$$(b)\ \frac{v_0 l_0 \rho_0}{\eta_0} = \frac{v_1 l_1 \rho_1}{\eta_1},$$

where the suffix 0 refers to the ship and the suffix 1 to the model. Hence

$$\frac{\eta_1}{\eta_0} = \frac{v_1 l_1 \rho_1}{v_0 l_0 \rho_0} = \frac{l_1{}^{\frac{3}{2}} \rho_1}{l_0{}^{\frac{3}{2}} \rho_0}.$$

In practice it is usual to separate the wave-making resistance from the frictional resistance. If we denote the former by F_w, then

$$F_w = \rho v_0{}^2 l_0{}^2 \phi\left(\frac{gl}{v^2}\right)_0,$$

and if f_w is the *wave-making resistance* of the model under the conditions $\dfrac{l_0}{v_0{}^2} = \dfrac{l_1}{v_1{}^2}$,

$$\frac{F_w}{f_w} = \frac{v_0{}^2 l_0{}^2}{v_1{}^2 l_1{}^2} = \frac{l_0{}^3}{l_1{}^3}.$$

Experiments are made with the model in a tank, and f is measured at a velocity given by $v_1{}^2 = \dfrac{v_0{}^2 l_1}{l_0}$, where f is the total resistance for the model. The *frictional resistance*, f_f, is then calculated, and f_w deduced from

$$f_w = f - f_f.$$

For a full-sized ship the wave-making resistance is given by $F_w = f_w \dfrac{l_0{}^3}{l_1{}^3}$.

Summarising these results we may say that the resistances experienced by similarly shaped ships are in the ratio of the cubes of their dimensions, when their speeds are in the ratio of the square root of their dimensions. This is known as *Froude's Law*.

EXAMPLES

1. Express (a) the surface tension of water, 75 dynes per cm.; (b) the standard atmospheric pressure, 1.013×10^6 dynes per sq. cm.; (c) the viscosity of air, 0.000170 C.G.S. units, in terms of corresponding F.P.S. units if 1 lb. $= 453.6$ gm. and 1 foot $= 30.48$ cm.

[(a) 0.165 pdl. per ft.; (b) 6.806×10^4 pdl. per sq. ft.;
(c) 1.142×10^{-5}.]

2. Experiment suggests that the velocity of a sphere allowed to fall from rest in a viscous medium varies with the time according to the law :—

$$\log [1 - kv/g] = -kt$$

where k is a constant for the given sphere and medium. Examine this suggested law for dimensional homogeneity and express k in terms of the radius r and mass M of the sphere, and η the viscosity of the medium.

[$k = A\eta r/M$; A being a numeric.]

3. If the velocity of light c, the Newtonian constant of gravitation G and Planck's constant of action h are chosen as the fundamental units, find the dimensions of the ordinary units of mass, length, and time in the new system.   [$M^2 = hcG^{-1}$; $L^2 = c^{-3}hG$; $T^2 = hGc^{-5}$.]

4. In the new unitary system suggested in the previous question, c, h, and G are all of unit value. Find the value of the gram, centimetre, and second in terms of the new units of mass, length, and time respectively, given that, in C.G.S. units, $c = 3 \times 10^{10}$, $G = 6.7 \times 10^{-8}$, $h = 6.6 \times 10^{-77}$.   [1.84×10^4; 2.47×10^{32}; 7.41×10^{42}.]

5. The frequency n of transverse vibration of a stretched string depends upon its length l, its tensional stress F, and its density ρ. Find the form of relationship existing between them and show that it reduces to the familiar form.   [$ln = k\sqrt{(F/\rho)}$.]

6. In a rotating cylinder method of measuring the viscosity of a liquid there is a critical angular velocity ω above which turbulence occurs. Find how ω is related to the viscosity η, the separation distance x between the cylinders, and the density ρ of the liquid.

$$[\omega = k\eta/\rho x^2.]$$

7. The range R of a body projected *in vacuo* at a given angle to the horizontal depends only on the velocity of projection V and on the acceleration of gravity g. Find the form of the necessary relationship.

$$[Rg = kV^2.]$$

8. It has been suggested that for liquids $S^3\beta^4 = k$, a constant, S being the surface tension and β the compressibility. Show that the quantity k cannot be a mere numeric.

9. If the resistance experienced by a body when moving through a liquid with velocity v is proportional to the square of the velocity, show that it is independent of the viscosity.

10. The viscosity η of a gas is determined by its density ρ, its average molecular velocity c, and its mean free path L. Show that $\eta = k\rho cL$.

11. Investigate dimensionally the connection between the reverberation period of a room t, its volume V, its surface area A, and the velocity of sound c.

$$\left[t = \frac{k}{c}\left(\frac{V^2}{A^3}\right)^\alpha V^{\frac{1}{3}}. \right]$$

INDEX

[*References are to pages. Names of persons in italics.*]